The Walnut Lane Bridge in Philadelphia, Pennsylvania. Completed early in 1951, it was the first engineered construction of a prestressed concrete bridge undertaken in the United States.

Basic
Reinforced Concrete
Design:

Elastic and Creep

GEORGE ELWYN LARGE

Professor of Structural Engineering
and Past Chairman
Department of Civil Engineering
The Ohio State University

SECOND EDITION

THE RONALD PRESS COMPANY · NEW YORK

PREFACE

This textbook has been planned for use by students who are acquiring their basic understanding of reinforced concrete design. The problems method of instruction which it offers is a development arising from some twenty-five years' experience in teaching undergraduate students of civil engineering and architecture. The author believes that the study and discussion of numerical examples, followed by problem work, best develops the student's understanding of basic principles.

In order to make topics clear within a limited time, the instructor needs certain instructional material. He needs a backlog of dependable Examples. These lessen the need for making large blackboard demonstration sketches and thus increase the time available for class discussion. He will also require blackboard drill Problems; and individualized home or laboratory Problems are also necessary. The lists of individualized Problems in this book are large enough to take care of a class of twenty-five, or more by appropriate interpolations. Furthermore, discussion or quiz Questions will be needed. All these day-to-day materials have been incorporated in the present volume. In addition, a helpful Summary is included at the end of each chapter.

For a five-hour basic course, a coverage of Chapters 2 through 6 is all that should be attempted. These chapters include the rock-bottom fundamentals: beam bending, beam shear, columns, and practical continuity. The student needs to concentrate upon these topics until he has the understanding which develops principally from his experiences in attacking a well-chosen group of problems, rather than from listening to formal lectures or reading textbook explanations.

Most practicing engineers and many professors tend to forget how little they themselves really knew about this subject at the age of twenty-one years. Keeping this limited background of the student in mind, the author has begun each topic at an elementary level, leading the student to work simply from his fundamental mechanics until he can develop algebraic expressions. The first three weeks of instruction can be a period of discipline during which only the transformed section–internal couple method is used. Thus none of the trusty old concrete beam formulas are to be found in Chapter 2 on bending! For convenient later use in constructing design charts, they may be found in Appendix A. A new topic is introduced by means of an instructional Example which

iii

has been solved part by part by applying methods which, though somewhat lengthy, are already familiar. Next, the student practices on similar Problems. Finally, the example may be retraced, substituting algebraic symbols, and a formula evolved, or possibly a chart.

The author believes that in Chapter 3, shear, diagonal tension, and anchorage have been treated in such fashion as to make these topics more easily grasped. In the past, they have been the least understood. The term "shear" has been largely avoided, as its use leads to inaccurate concepts of the internal action, which is actually tensile in a diagonal direction.

This text employs the ascending order of drawing the family of five beam curves; namely, load, shear, moment, slope, and deflection. This will seem odd to those unused to that technique. It is, however, a feature of the problems method of teaching begun almost forty years ago by Professors C. C. More and W. E. Duckering and used with notable success by them and many others.

The problems method of instruction offers an opportunity to develop in the student the orderliness in computations which he will later find so desirable in professional practice. This skill is taught in engineering problems courses at a number of institutions. Throughout the laboratory or home computation work, the importance of maintaining a high standard of paper neatness can hardly be overestimated. If the instructor will set the example in his own lecture and demonstration work by ruling off sections of the blackboard and setting down headings, subheadings, and references, the student will respond accordingly and later make a good impression during his very first day on the job.

Since too few textbooks present designing procedures, or even distinguish designing from analysis, the author considers the presentation of sound practical design methods to be of paramount importance. The full-page calculation sheets, begun in Chapter 6, develop in the young engineer the necessary sense of organization and completeness.

All students of design need practice in interpreting a code and following it. Many illuminating discussions arise from such experience. In the design problems of this book, the 1956 American Concrete Institute Building Code has been followed with but few exceptions. The treatment of some topics upon which the Code is silent reflects the author's own ideas, as, for example, in the detailed locating of bent-up bars. The obscure clauses of the Code have been explained and reconciled with fundamental theory.

The added retaining walls chapter follows the new 1953 AREA specifications and modern soil mechanics findings generally.

Developments since the first edition was published in 1950 have suggested the desirability of a continuation sequence covering creep, shrinkage, ultimate strength, and prestressed concrete. These added chapters have been prepared in the familiar extended manner suitable for undergraduate students. A sustained effort has been made to reduce the corresponding findings of contemporary research to everyday methods by means of numerical examples. So far as is known, this is the first American textbook to illustrate how to take concrete creep into account in predicting the stresses and long-time deflections of beams, using everyday methods of a fundamental nature. It also includes ultimate strength methods and the only detailed fundamental evaluation of the losses of prestress. Professor J. R. Shank's findings on creep are the basis for the method of predicting long-time creep deflection from 24-hour data. Consequently, it is considered that the book now provides the material for continuation courses. Column design methods are now well onto a creep and ultimate strength basis. Beam design may be expected to follow soon.

It is believed that the student should know something about the great contributions that outstanding investigators have made to the subject of concrete design. Hence, the book includes photographs and biographical sketches of more than a dozen such prominent individuals. It should be mentioned, however, that, as Professor Frank E. Richart said, modern research is a teamwork effort, and in many cases the director acts partly as a steward of the honors merited by unidentified individuals of a group or organization.

The author wishes to express his appreciation to Professors J. R. Shank and the late C. C. More for stimulating his early interest in the subject. He is also indebted to Professor L. E. Vandegrift and Lecturer R. F. Baker of The Ohio State University, Professor Phil M. Ferguson of the University of Texas, and to Dr. Paul W. Abeles of London, England, for recent inspiration and advice. To Mrs. Edward H. Tinsley go his thanks for her patience in typing and checking, to Professor R. W. Parkinson for delineating the new illustrations, and to his wife and family his appreciation of their forbearance during the months of preoccupation in preparing this second edition.

G. E. Large

Columbus, Ohio
    January, 1957

CONTENTS

mum Length of Flexural Bars. Anchorage. The Moment Dia-
gram Method of Spacing Diagonal Tension Reinforcement.
Anchorage of Diagonal Tension Steel. Anchorage of Bottom
Flexural Steel. Maximum Spacings of Web Reinforcement. De-
sign of Combined Web Reinforcement. *Continuous and Restrained
Beams:* Web and Tie Reinforcement for Continuous and Re-
strained Beams and Frames Having No Slab Construction Integral
Therewith. Summary of Bond, Shear, Diagonal Tension, and
Anchorage.

Introduction. Column Reinforcement. Spiral Versus Tied Col-
umns. Performance of Columns to Ultimate Failure. Column
Safe Axial Load by the ACI (Creep) Method. *Axially Loaded
Columns:* Design of an Axially Loaded Round (Spiral) Column by
the ACI Creep Method. Design of an Axially Loaded Rectan-
gular (Tied) Column by the ACI Creep Method. Column Econ-
omy. The Elastic Method of Column Design. *Rectangular (Tied)
Columns with Bending.* Homogeneous Column Elastic Theory.
Investigation by the ACI Interaction Approximation Recognizing
Creep. Discussion of the Interaction Method. Designing by the
ACI Interaction Method. The Design of Rectangular (Tied) Col-
umns Under Ordinary Bending — by the ACI Interaction Method.
Investigation of Columns Subject to Heavy Bending by the Elastic
Method. Discussion of the Two Investigation Methods for Col-
umns with Bending. Columns Subject to Biaxial Bending. The
Design of Rectangular Tied Columns and Combined Stress Mem-
bers Subject to Heavy Bending — by the Elastic Method. Check
upon Column Elastic Designing by $Mc/I + N/A$ of Its Cracked
Section. *Round (Spiral) Columns with Bending:* Introduction.
The Designing of Spiral Columns Under Ordinary Bending by the
ACI Interaction Method. The Designing of Round (Spiral) Col-
umns Subject to Heavy Bending. Final Comments on Reinforced
Concrete Columns.

Introduction. The Relationship of Beam Curves. Signs Convention for Beam Curves. The Laws of Related Beam Curves.
Fixed End Moments. Continuity in Reinforced Concrete. Continuity Methods. Continuity Analysis by the Moment Distribution Method. Continuity Shear and Moment Diagrams. (Check)
Continuous Beam Analysis by the Moment-Area Method. Translational Moment Distribution. (Check) Rigid Frame Analysis by

forcement, Section 707. *Eccentric Shrinkage (Warpage):* Effect of Concrete Shrinkage upon the Stress in the Tensile Reinforcement of Beams and Slabs. Contraction and Expansion Joints. Summary of Shrinkage and Temperature Change.

Introduction. Failure of Reinforced Concrete Beams. Methods of Predicting the Ultimate Strength of Reinforced Concrete Beams. Whitney's Stress Block Method. *Singly Reinforced Beams:* Whitney's Balanced Beam Designing. The Balanced Beam Steel Ratios of Whitney and the ACI. Failure Action of Under-Reinforced Beams. The Under-Reinforced Beam Formula. Ultimate Strength T-Beams and Otherwise. Load Factors for Ultimate Strength Design. Whitney's Versus Other Methods. Economy of Ultimate Strength Beams. *Doubly Reinforced Beams:* Whitney's Doubly Reinforced Beams. Ultimate Diagonal Tension and Bond Strengths. *Combined Stress Members:* Designing for Bending plus Axial Load. Ultimate Strength Designing of Symmetrical Reinforcement for Columns with Bending. Combined Stress Member Investigations. *Axially Loaded Columns:* Ultimate Strength of Axially Loaded Columns. Summary of Ultimate Strength Design.

Introduction. Concept of a Prestressed Beam. The Basic Mechanics of Prestressing. Discussion of the Prestressed Slab Designing. Further Study of the Pre-tensioned Slab Design. Types of Prestressed Beams. Prestressed Concrete Codes. The Loading Stages of Prestressed Beams. *The Losses of Pretension:* Introduction. The Loss Due to Shrinkage of the Concrete. The Loss Due to the Elasticity of the Concrete. The Loss Due to the Creep of the Concrete. Total Losses. The Loss Due to the Creep of the Steel. The Nature of the Losses of Pre-tensioning. *Pre-tensioned Girder Designing:* The Proportioning (Designing) of the Girder. *Pre-tensioned Girder Investigation:* The Detailed Flexural Investigation. Check upon the Girder Flexural Designing by the "Prestress Formulas." Refined Prediction of the Ultimate Strength. Resistance to Initial Cracking. The Prediction of the Deflection of the Bonded, Pre-tensioned, Prestressed Girder. The Web Reinforcement of the Pre-tensioned Girder. Stirrup Designing. Final Design Sketch of the Pre-tensioned Girder. Bond and Anchorage of Pre-tensioned Reinforcement. Post-tensioning Versus Pretensioning. Mechanical End Anchorages. Summary of Prestressing Principles.

APPENDIX

Basic
Reinforced Concrete
Design:

Elastic and Creep

CHAPTER 1

INTRODUCTION

Part I. The Making of Concrete

1-1. Concrete. Concrete is artificial stone made from *portland cement* and inert filler materials called *aggregates* which are mixed with water to a plastic consistency and placed in forms to harden and gain strength.

Greater firesafety is possible with concrete than with almost any other building material. It is relatively economical, easy to place, and highly weather resistant when properly made.

Franklin R. McMillan, for over twenty years Director of Research, The Portland Cement Association, Chicago. Author or co-author of a number of research papers on concrete. Recipient of the Wason Medal of the American Concrete Institute for his booklet *Concrete Primer*. Past president and Honorary Member of the Institute.

Those responsible for concrete construction work should realize that they are manufacturers as well as constructors. Such is not the case with steel structures, the material for which is all made in a permanent plant under strict and continuous control. Some concrete is still made on the job site, sometimes under adverse weather conditions, and complete control of the process is usually not quite possible. Furthermore, the class of labor ordinarily available leaves much to be desired, though everyone *thinks* he knows how to make concrete. Continuous supervision is imperative if the reliable material contemplated in the chapters of this text is to be created.

1–2. Portland Cement. The cementing material now known as *portland cement* was first made in England about 130 years ago.[A] Since it will set and gain strength under water, an invaluable property in connection with the construction of river and harbor works, it is classed as a *hydraulic*[1] cement.

In 1926 The American Society for Testing Materials adopted the following definition:[2]

Portland cement is the product obtained by finely pulverizing clinker produced by calcining to incipient fusion an intimate and properly proportioned mixture of argillaceous and calcareous materials, with no additions subsequent to calcination excepting water and calcined or uncalcined gypsum.

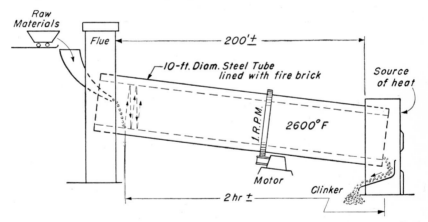

Fig. 1–1.   Schematic view of a continuous rotary kiln used in making portland cement.

Briefly,[E] the manufacturing process consists typically in quarrying limestone and shale, crushing and milling them separately until very fine, proportioning quite carefully and charging them into the upper end of a rotary kiln, shown schematically in Fig. 1–1. As the kiln rotates, the raw materials move toward the lower, and hotter, end where

A The superscript letters refer to items of the Bibliography at the end of each chapter.

1 For a detailed discussion of other well-known cementing materials both old and new see any standard text on materials of construction or plain concrete.

2 The 1938 definition is less descriptive.

new compounds are formed at incipient fusion, and emerge as red hot portland cement in clinker form.   After being cooled the clinkers are ground in ball and tube mills to extreme fineness, small amounts of plaster of paris or gypsum having been added in the meantime to slow the setting time of the cement to that desired for construction work. The ground cement is next conveyed to large bins and silos, from which it is drawn to be bagged and shipped, or shipped in bulk.

The principal active compounds in portland cement have different rates of reaction with water, as shown in the accompanying Table 1–1.

TABLE 1–1

COMPARISON OF PORTLAND CEMENT COMPOUNDS

Principal Constituent Compounds	Rate of Chemical Reaction and Heat Generation	Most Active Period	Contribution to Final Strength
Tricalcium aluminate	Fast	First day	Small
Tricalcium silicate	Moderate	Second to seventh day	Large
Dicalcium silicate	Slow	From seventh day onward	Moderate

This *hydration* is accompanied by an evolution of heat which, in massive structures, is difficult to dissipate, and causes a rise in temperature. The subsequent cooling, together with the evaporation of water, is responsible for the shrinkage of the mass commonly observed.   The sum total of chemical reactions is quite complex.   It continues for years, albeit at a greatly decreasing rate, which accounts for the continued increase in strength over long periods partially depicted in Fig. 1–2.

1–3. High Early Strength Portland Cements. In response to the demand for shorter construction periods, premium brands of portland cement, compounded to develop a greater percentage of the final strength during the first several days, began to appear in the late 1920's.   They are called *high early strength portland cements* to distinguish them from (standard) portland cement.   Figure 1–2 shows the extent to which high early strength portlands outdo standard portlands at early ages.   The final strength of high early strength portland cement concrete should be assumed to be about the same as that made from standard portlands. They may be used whenever their extra cost is offset by the value of the earlier use of the structure.   The use of additional standard portland cement in a mix gives high early (and later) strengths, but the practice has the disadvantage of causing greater shrinkage of the mass in curing, with the attendant dislocations and danger of cracking.

1–4. Concrete Aggregates. Aggregates are the so-called *inert* materials, both fine and coarse, which are used with the cement paste to increase greatly the bulk of a mix. Their presence also prevents excessive shrinkage of the mass.

Care in the selection of aggregates is of the utmost importance. The stone must be hard, tough, strong, sound, clean, graded, and free of organic impurities. A poor aggregate is likely to deteriorate, or expand under severe weather conditions, causing disintegration of the concrete.

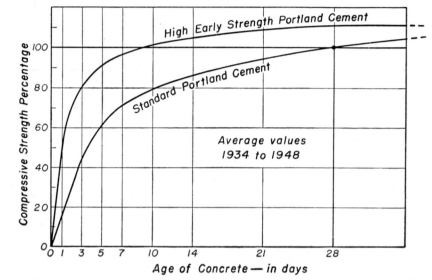

Fig. 1–2. Test strength of concrete at early ages relative to the design standard 28-day strength. (Courtesy the Ohio State Highway Testing and Research Laboratory.)

Some aggregates can react adversely with the cement, also causing disintegration. Siliceous sands and gravels and igneous rock sources are generally excellent, while soft materials such as shale should never be tolerated for structural concrete. The ASTM standard tests should always be performed upon strange or doubtful aggregates.

Cement is the most expensive ingredient of a concrete mix, so aggregates are used to extend a sack of cement to as many cubic feet of concrete as possible; but there is a practical limit to the aggregate content of a mix. The amount of water required to make a mix plastic is roughly proportional to the amount of aggregate to be moistened. The cement-water paste may be thought of as a liquid glue whose true function is to coat the aggregate particles. If the aggregate content is doubled, approximately twice as much water will be needed. This means that the glue will be correspondingly diluted, thus halving the concrete strength.

1–5. Aggregate Size and Grading. Since a cubic foot of 2-in. gravel has only one-fourth as much surface area to be moistened as a cubic foot of one-inch gravel, one should use as large a coarse aggregate as possible. A maximum size up to one-fourth of the least dimension of the member may be used. The aggregate should contain appreciable amounts of a variety of particle sizes smaller than the maximum size so that all void spaces will thereby be filled with smaller sizes, including those of the smallest particles of sand. These smaller particles contribute

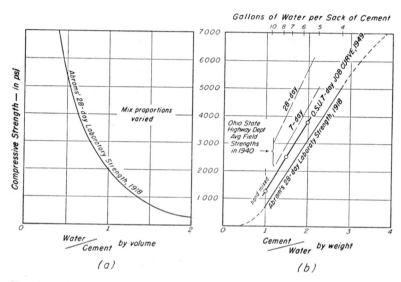

Fig. 1–3. Effect of cement and water content upon the compressive strength of standard portland cement concrete. (After Abrams.)

smoothness, or **workability** to the mix. However, an *excess* of sand increases void space, and demands additional moistening water. A practical balance must be struck between the use of proportionately more gravel to make more concrete from a given amount of cement, and proportionally more sand to improve workability.

1–6. Abrams' Strength Law. In 1918, Professor Duff A. Abrams, of the Lewis Institute, announced important findings[B] from the results of a comprehensive series of compression tests on cylindrical concrete specimens. He had found that *the compressive strength of workable mixes varied inversely with the water/cement ratio, regardless of the proportions of the mixes*, as shown in Fig. 1–3(a). The ramifications of this discovery were quite far-reaching, and it continues to be the most important one ever made in concrete technology.

In Fig. 1–3(b) the reversed curve shows Abrams' findings replotted on a cement/water basis. This latter arrangement has some advantages, especially since the curve is a straight line between the 1000 and 5000 psi strengths, which is the practical range of most concretes. The new strength ratio is shown on a weight basis in conformity with the present trend in stating concrete proportions.

Abrams' strength law may be restated as follows:

With given materials and conditions of test, the compressive strength of concrete varies directly with the cement/water ratio, provided the mix is of a workable consistency.

1–7. The Trial Mix Method of Concrete Proportioning. Textbooks on plain concrete all present several methods for proportioning the four ingredients of a concrete mix, namely cement, fine aggregate, coarse aggregate, and water. Only the very practical Trial Mix method will be described here.[3]

Aggregates vary so widely in size, grading, particle shape, absorption and surface smoothness that it is best not to entertain any preconceived idea of the aggregate content of a mix, but to let it work out in the process of making *trial mixes* of the materials to be used later in the job itself. For these mixes the aggregates should be dry.

In starting to design a mix by the trial mix method, decide upon the concrete consistency demanded by the job itself and be sure to make all trial mixes to that consistency, or "slump."

Referring to Fig. 1–3(b), consider that three c/w ratios, say 1.0, 1.5 and 2.0, by weight, will yield enough data to define your *job curve*. Take 7 lb. of water[4] and 7 lb. of cement, make the cement/water paste, then from weighed piles add sand and coarse aggregate alternately until the mix has the desired workability as judged by troweling and by making slump tests. Then tamp into two 6 in. by 12 in. cylinder molds in the standard manner.

Next, make two other such mixes, to the same c/w ratio, but varying the ratio of sand to coarse aggregate from that used in the first mix. Record the improvement or worsening in workability.

Repeat the above procedure with mixes having the other two c/w ratios. Because of the familiarity developed in the first series of three mixes, two mixes for each of these latter ratios will probably be enough, say a total of seven mixes.

---

[3] The Talbot-Richart method, involving the "cement-space ratio" and "basic water content" is the most scientific and best method, but requires more laboratory work than can be justified for moderate sized jobs. See Bauer's *Plain Concrete*, 3d ed., p. 108.

[4] If three 6 by 12 in. cylinders are desired from each mix take 10 lb. of water and the corresponding weight of cement.

In curing the cylinders, simulate the same relative exposure of their surfaces to the ground and/or atmosphere that the structure itself will undergo. See that both ends of each cylinder have been made *plane* by capping before testing. Plot the job curve of the results as in Fig. 1–3(b), and deduce the desired mix by interpolation, utilizing the strength and workability data.

1–8. Mix Design from a Seven-Day Job Curve.

EXAMPLE 1–1

Given the mix data and the 7-day job curve of Fig. 1–3(b).

Required to deduce the proportions of the mix for 4000-lb. standard portland cement concrete at the 28-day age to which reinforced concrete specifications are referred.

Solution: Referring to Fig. 1–2 we must have 0.7(4000) = a 2800-lb. strength at 7 days. From Fig. 1–3(b) this strength will be attained by using a c/w of about 1.6.

Interpolating between the quantities (not shown) of aggregates used in the most workable of the 1.5 and 2.0 c/w mixes:

c   s   c.a.

Use 1 : 1.9 : 2.8 by weight, 7 gal. of water per sack of cement.

Make a final adjustment of aggregate content on the job. *If the aggregates get wet during the course of the work decrease the water added at the mixer until the slump is restored.*

1–9. Concrete-making Fundamentals.

To close this brief treatment[E] on concrete-making, the factors affecting strength are, in the order of their importance:

1) The cement/water ratio of the concrete,
2) The extent to which the chemical reactions of the cement have progressed, as influenced by:
   a) keeping the mass warm
   b) keeping the surfaces wet
   c) allowing plenty of curing time
3) The age of the cement since ground, and the particular brand involved,
4) The particular aggregates used.

To make concrete which is dense, impermeable and highly resistant to severe weather, as well as strong:

1) Use a high cement/water ratio,
2) Employ a well-graded aggregate combination,
3) Mix thoroughly, for uniform distribution of the ingredients,

4) Place carefully to avoid honeycombed areas, but do not over-trowel exposed surfaces,

5) Wet-cure for an extended period.

1–10. The Absolute Volumes Method of Estimating Quantities of Material for Concrete. It is highly important to be able to compute quickly the amounts of concrete materials to "order out" to a job of known size, or yardage. Such facility is second in importance only to a clear understanding of Abrams' findings.

Let us first consider how much concrete will result from mixing known quantities of the ingredients, as indicated by the proportions of the mix. **The absolute (or solid) volumes method assumes that there will be no voids whatever in the concrete as placed, and that the sum of the "solid" volumes of the cement, sand, coarse aggregate, and water will be the amount of concrete made.** For these purposes it is necessary to remember that the absolute, or solid, unit weights of cement and good aggregate stone are about 195 and 165 lb. per cu. ft., respectively, that a sack of cement weighs 94 lb., and that $7\frac{1}{2}$ gal. of water make a cubic foot. If a mix is stated *by volume* it is necessary also to know the bulk weights of the aggregates per cubic foot, which vary from about 90 to 110 lb. for good natural stone aggregates.

EXAMPLE 1–2

A mix was designed 1 : 1.9 : 2.8 by weight, 7 gal. of water per sack of cement, as in Art. 1–8.

Required:

a) to predict the yield[5] of the mix by the Method of Absolute Volumes, and

b) to prepare an order for enough materials to make 30 cu. yd. of this concrete.

Solution:

a) Yield

Material	Proportions	Quantity	Calculations	Absolute Volume
Cement	1.0	94 lb.	94/195	0.48 cu. ft.
Aggregate	1.9			
	2.8			
Total	4.7	442 lb.	442/165	2.68
Water		7 gal.	7/7.5	0.93
			Yield =	4.09 cu. ft. per sack

---

[5] *Yield* is the number of cubic feet of concrete made from one sack of cement.

b) Quantities for 30 cu. yd. of concrete

$$\text{Required number of 1-sack batches} = \frac{30(27)}{4.09} = 198.$$

Order:

198   sacks of cement

$$\frac{198(1.9)(94)}{2000} = \quad 17.7 \text{ tons of sand}$$

$$\frac{198(2.8)(94)}{2000} = \quad 26.0 \text{ tons of coarse aggregate}$$

$$198(7) = 1390 \quad \text{gal. of water}$$

1–11. Weight of Concrete. Concrete structures must first be capable of carrying their own dead weight, which is relatively large and can never be neglected in designing.

An examination of the table in the preceding Example 1–2 will reveal that 594 lb. of material were used to make 4.09 cu. ft. of concrete. This is 145 lb. per cu. ft., which is the figure usually used for the weight of (plain) stone concrete. The use of reinforcing steel adds about 5 lb., so 150 lb. per cu. ft. is used for the weight of reinforced stone concrete.

The weight of concretes made from lighter aggregates, and of standard concrete block in place, should be taken as given in the following table for the different types of mix:

Light weight structural concretes	Lb. per cu. ft. unreinforced
Slag concrete	130–140
Haydite (burned clay) concrete .	95–100
Vermiculite (expanded mica) concrete	35–40

8 in. × 16 in. concrete blocks	Lb. per sq. ft. of wall, including mortar
Stone aggregate	
12 in. wall	78
8 in.	54
Haydite aggregate	
8 in. partition or wall	35
4 in.	24

Part II. Strength Properties of Concrete

1–12. Relative Strengths. In discussing the several strength properties of concrete or mortar, it is customary to compare them to the

TABLE 1–2

Relative Concrete Strengths and Factors of Safety

Type of Strength	Avg. Ultimate Strength		ACI Code Design Allowable Stress psi	Corresponding Ultimate Factor of Safety	Remarks
	Avg. Percentage of Compressive	In psi			
Compressive, uniform axial	100	**3000**	675†	4.4	†For spiral columns.
Tensile, beam diagonal	10	300	90*	3.3	*with A-305 bars
Bending, extreme fiber compressive	100	3000	1350‡	2.2‡	‡if creep is disregarded
tensile, unreinforced footing	15§	450§	90	5.0	§by Mc/I
Bond, to A-305 deformed bars	25	750	300‖	2.5‖	‖to bottom bars
Shear, pure	20 min.	600 min.	240¶	2.5 min.	¶A.R.E.A. '54 ruling

For a complete table of allowable stresses see Appendix J.

ultimate compressive strength of 6 in. by 12 in. cylinders, f'_c, as a standard. The percentages shown in the accompanying table for 3000-lb. concrete apply as well to ordinary concretes of other strengths.

Tensile Strength is such a small percentage of the compressive strength that it is ignored entirely in reinforced concrete beam calculations. Instead, tensile resistance is provided by longitudinal steel bars well embedded in the tension side, namely *reinforced* concrete construction. Plain concrete tension members are never permitted, though a safe bending tensile strength of $0.03f'_c$ is relied upon in the design of unreinforced footings.

The most common reliance upon concrete tensile strength is to provide a portion, usually $0.03f'_c$, of the tensile resistance needed to resist the combination of horizontal and vertical shear in the tension side of beams which results in **diagonal tension** at about 45° to the horizontal. This matter is taken up in detail in Chapter 3 in connection with the design of *stirrups*.

Shear Strength, as revealed by the *punching shear* resistance to pushing a cylindrical slug out of a steel plate, is never observed in concrete since the underside of a concrete slab subjected to a downward concentrated load always suffers an enlarged conical breakout due to the flexural diagonal tensile weakness. Consequently the pure shear strength of concrete can seldom be utilized except across keys at construction joints.

Bond Strength is the resistance developed by concrete to the pulling out of a steel bar embedded therein. The whole philosophy of reinforced concrete beam design is based upon the assumption that a bond exists between the steel and concrete which prevents relative movement between them as load is applied. The amount of bond strength that can be developed depends largely upon the **area of contact** between the two materials. Tests show that it exists first as a limited adhesion between the two materials, and later as a frictional resistance to sliding after the adhesion is destroyed by a very small slippage, and very importantly as shear and bearing resistance against any projecting irregularities on the surface of the bar. Due to their superior bond value, bars manufactured with a very rough outside surface, called **deformed bars,** have entirely replaced plain bars. For an illustration of several types of deformed bars see Fig. 1–9.

The Bending Strength of plain concrete beams is limited by their very low tensile strength in relation to the compressive. However, the bending tensile strength of an extreme fiber at failure, or tensile **modulus of rupture,** as computed from the fundamental formula $f_t = Mc/I$, using the applied bending moment at failure, has an average value of about 15 per cent of the compressive strength of ordinary concretes, which is about 1.5 times the direct axial, or the beam diagonal, *tensile strength* of the concrete. This is because the actual bending stress distribution at failure is not linear, due to several causes, among which are creep, the rise of water after placing, and possibly nonuniform shrinkage. See Fig. 1–6.

1–13. Modulus of Elasticity. The ratio of unit axial stress to unit axial deformation, the slope of the stress/strain line, is called the **modulus of elasticity**. It has a fixed value of about 30,000,000 psi for all steels, regardless of such factors as ultimate strengths, heat treatment, or method of rolling. For concrete in compression, its value, E_c, depends largely upon the ultimate strength, f'_c. Standard specifications direct the use of 1000 times the compressive strength, namely 3,000,000 psi for 3000-lb. concrete, for all reinforced concrete designing. On the other hand, some authorities have insisted that concrete can have no definite modulus of elasticity because they find the stress/strain line curved over its full length. Others advocate the use of the **initial modulus** computed from the tangent at the origin of the graph, or the **secant modulus** obtained by using the total strain up to the working stress contemplated.

It has been found that if a test specimen is preloaded a few times to about two-thirds of the failure strength, the disturbing effect of shrinkage stresses and possibly other factors will be eliminated. A rapidly conducted test will then reveal a straight-line performance throughout the working range, from which the **instantaneous modulus** may be computed.

1–14. Creep of Concrete. The tendency for loaded concrete to deform with lapse of time is known as **creep,** or plastic flow.[C] Of course, steel and many other materials become plastic and deform without increase in load at stresses above the elastic limit, but concrete tends to exhibit this continuing deformation over the whole stress range. Fig. 1–4

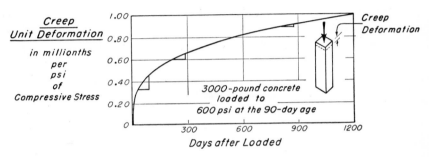

FIG. 1–4. A typical creep-time curve.

illustrates a typical creep-time graph. Note that the creep takes place rapidly at first, then much more slowly, becoming small or negligible after a year or two, but that the total is quite appreciable in comparison with the corresponding *elastic* deformation of 0.33 millionths per psi (not shown).

Curve *OBX* of Fig. 1–5 illustrates the curved line type of stress-strain data obtained by early investigators in leisurely conducted cylinder tests, and accounts for their contention that concrete has no well-defined modulus of elasticity. On the other hand, if the specimen is (1) preworked as mentioned in Art. 1–13, and (2) the time element is decreased to a minimum during data-taking, the performance will be found to be along the "Instantaneous" straight line *OA*. Such a test is typical of many conducted at Ohio State University by taking all strain readings during about 30 sec. of continuous load application. The E_c computed therefrom compares very favorably with the $1000f'_c$ figure recommended by standard design specifications.

There is a strong presumption that well-designed reinforced concrete structures have their disturbing initial strains removed during the first few service loadings, and thereafter perform elastically as long as they are not overloaded.

In reinforced concrete beams the effect of creep and inelasticity is to cause a curved line stress distribution at overloading, such as in Fig. 1–6, instead of the commonly assumed straight-line variation. The shape of

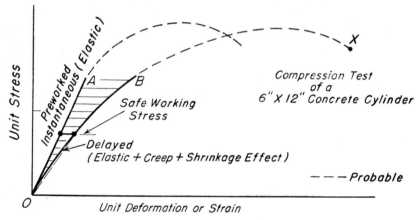

FIG. 1–5. Instantaneous and delayed action stress-strain relations of concrete.

the curve is similar to the stress-strain curves of Fig. 1–5 when viewed from the left side of the page. Thus the high compressive stress value, f_c max., computable from the conventional straight-line relation, is probably never realized. Consequently the allowable compressive stress, $f_c = 0.45f'_c$, for designing reinforced concrete beams has been set rather high in anticipation of the expected redistribution.

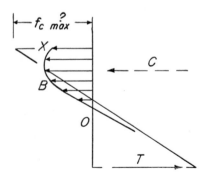

FIG. 1–6. Compressive stress distribution in reinforced concrete beams at overload.

Because of creep the deflection of concrete structures cannot be predicted by the common deflection formulas with a satisfactory degree of accuracy. Nevertheless no failures have been traced to creep, since in well-proportioned structures the phenomenon ceases before deflections become excessive.

Part III. The Reinforcing of Concrete

1–15. Beam Reinforcement. As previously stated, concrete is strong in compression but relatively weak in tension. For slender steel bars exactly the reverse is true. Thus when the two materials are used together each makes up for the deficiency of the other.

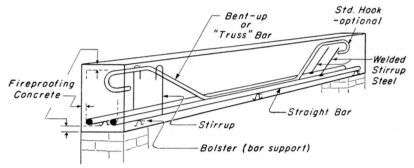

FIG. 1–7. Types of beam reinforcing steel.

Figure 1–7 shows the four common types of beam reinforcement. Both the straight and bentup **principal reinforcing** bars are relied upon to resist the heavy bending tension in the bottom over the central portion of the span. Toward the ends of the span, where the bending moment is small, fewer bottom bars are necessary, so some may be "bentup" so that their inclined portion may be utilized to resist the diagonal tension resulting from beam shear. In continuous beam construction their horizontal upper portions are continued across the supports to resist the tension in the top in that locality. Refer to the illustrations of Chapter 6.

There are seldom enough bent bars available for resisting all the diagonal tension, so additional small U-shaped bars, called **stirrups,** are usually necessary. Since they become stressed in tension they must must pass underneath the bottom steel and be perpendicular thereto to prevent lateral slippage. In recent years *welded stirrups* have appeared. They may be placed at any desired angle, as shown.

In first-class construction the horizontal reinforcement is supported on gadgets called **bolsters,** or **chairs,** which hold it in place during construction operations. They come in a variety of heights to suit any situation.

Since steel is not firesafe, the bars carrying computed stress must be kept from one to two inches within the outside surface of the member or structure at all points. This outer shell, shown in the figure, is called **fireproofing concrete,** though some of it is also relied upon for strength.

1–16. Column Reinforcement. Examples of column reinforcement will be found in the illustrations of Chapter 4. In them the **vertical reinforcement** is the principal reinforcement. It shares the compressive load with the concrete. The whole is confined by **lateral reinforcement** which surrounds the column horizontally and consists of individual **ties** or a continuous **spiral,** all as shown in Fig. 4–1.

1–17. Shrinkage and Temperature Reinforcement. Slabs and walls must not only be reinforced by *principal reinforcement* against the applied loads to which they are subjected, but also in the lateral direction perpendicular thereto to resist the effects of shrinkage and temperature change.

In drying, following the wet curing period, concrete shrinks a maximum of about 0.0005 of its length. To whatever extent the adjacent construction interferes with this movement the concrete tends to become stressed in tension; so a small percentage of steel must be used to resist it. The action is largely reversible upon complete re-wetting.

Similarly, concrete must be allowed to contract with a lowering of temperature about 0.000006 of its length per degree Fahrenheit.[6] Thus a fall in temperature of 83 degrees causes as much movement as drying shrinkage. A *rise* in temperature above that prevalent during curing is attended by a corresponding expansion, for which provision must be made.

The amount of *"shrinkage and temperature" reinforcement* usually provided is approximately ⅕ of 1 per cent, as required by specifications. There are indications that more should be used, and that the percentage to be provided in each case should be computed from fundamental mechanics. The effect of longitudinal shrinkage upon the relatively large percentage of principal reinforcement in a member is to cause compressive stresses therein which are usually disregarded.

1–18. Grades of Reinforcing Steel. Concrete reinforcing steel is available in ten bar sizes ranging from ¼ in. round to about $1\frac{13}{32}$ in. round, as wire for column spirals, and wire mesh for shrinkage and temperature reinforcement of slabs and walls. Metallurgically it comes in three grades, namely structural, medium, and hard. The minimum yield points, ultimate strengths and the relative unit deformations thereof are shown in Fig. 1–8.

For practical purposes **the yield point is the limit of useful strength of reinforcing bars,** since higher stresses cause permanent deformation,

---

[6] For steel the coefficient is 0.0000065, or almost the same.

which means that the bar does not return to its original length when
the load is removed. Note in the figure that the American Concrete
Institute allowable stresses contemplate a factor of safety of from 1.8
to 2.5 against yielding, and that the structural grade steel is penalized
on account of its low yield point.

The wire mesh is cold drawn from hard-grade steel and has a higher
yield point than that pictured.

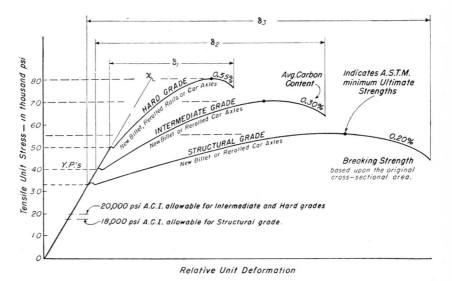

Fig. 1–8. Stress-strain curves of concrete reinforcing steels.

**1–19. Effect of Steel Ductility upon the Performance of Reinforced
Concrete Members.** A steel that would break at the point x in Fig. 1–8
would have no ductility. Reinforced concrete beams made therefrom
would fail without any warning and actually fall apart if the tensile
strength of the steel were reached. All the steels used to manufacture
concrete reinforcing bars are ductile, having a considerable range of
inelastic deformation between the yield point and the actual breaking
point, as indicated by the δ's in the figure. Consequently the failure of
reinforced concrete beams in a testing machine is seldom sudden. When
the yield point stress in the tensile steel in the bottom of a beam is
reached, small cracks which have developed in the adjacent concrete
begin to "open up," giving ample warning of overload.[7] With a very
ductile steel these cracks will continue to open until the beam sags

---

[7] If the loads applied are dead weights, as many are in service (as distinguished
from testing machine loading), the bars stretch rapidly, concrete crushes, and ultimate
failure ensues much more quickly.

ridiculously, but the steel will not actually break nor will the beam come apart. The amount of ductility needed in any particular member is a matter of judgment, with a majority favoring the intermediate grade of steel.

Reinforcing steel should also preferably be ductile enough that *hooks* of relatively small radius, shown in Fig. 1–7, can be cold-formed on the job without breakage. However, the importance of this preference is disappearing because the newer shaped bars seldom require hooking. The minimum radius of bend (measured to the axis of the bar) permitted by the ACI Code is $3d'$, where d' is the diameter of the bar. The student should calculate how much of a range of inelastic unit deformation, δ, is necessary to permit such bending.

1–20. Reinforcing Bar Shapes, Sizes, and Designations. Figure 1–9 shows, from right to left, the development of some typical concrete reinforcing bar shapes. In the lower photograph each bar has been rotated through 90° to reveal the longitudinal rib, when present. Bars (e), (f) and (g) are representative of recent developments.

Reinforcing bars originally were plain round rods, such as at (a), which had relatively poor resistance to slippage through the concrete. For a number of years slow progress was made through types (b), (c) and then to (d). Well-organized research therein was pursued through the 1930's and into the 1940's. Recent tests[D] have shown that bars such as (e), (f) and (g), having *closely spaced transverse projections*, called **deformations,** which conform to the ASTM Specification A 305 for deformed-bar cross sections, are so superior in bond value that hooking their ends adds very little strength. Such bars are sometimes referred to as the *improved deformed bars* or *high-bond bars.* Bars which do not meet the ASTM requirements are no longer rolled for concrete reinforcement.

Two of the most important dimensional requirements of ASTM Specification A 305 are that the maximum spacing of the deformations must not exceed seven-tenths of the nominal diameter of the bar, and that their minimum height must not be less than 4 per cent thereof in the smaller sizes, and 5 per cent in the larger sizes.

The *nominal diameter* of a deformed bar equals the diameter of a plain round bar of the same weight per foot. Due to the volume of metal in the transverse deformations the effective, or root, area of a bar is now about 91 per cent of the nominal one used in design calculations. Therefore a computed stress of 20,000 psi in the reinforcement actually means about 21,900 psi.

Bar Sizes and Designations. The selection of steel for concrete reinforcement must always be limited to the ten round standard bars whose areas are shown in Table 1–3. Although the first seven of them represent

rounds of exactly ⅛-in. increment diameters, the bars are now known
by their *numbers*, namely, the number of whole eighths of an inch included
in the nominal diameter of the bar. On today's drawings, 3-#4 @ 6″
means 3-½″ φ @ 6″ as formerly stated.

Fig. 1–9. Typical reinforcing bar shapes.
(g) HI–BOND bar of Inland Steel Company.
(f) BETHLEHEM bar of Bethlehem Steel Company.
(e) CRESCENT bar of Sheffield Steel Corporation.
(d) DIAMOND bar of Jones & Laughlin Steel Corporation.
(c) MULTI–RIB bar of Laclede Steel Company.
(b) CARNEGIE bar of Carnegie-Illinois Steel Corporation.
(a) The plain (round) bar.

Note in Table 1–3 that the perimeter per unit of cross-sectional area,
the measure of bar *bond* efficiency, varies widely, being greatest for the
smallest sized bar.

In selecting bars, use the largest suitable size, since the bars less than ¾ in. in diameter not only cost more per pound but also require much more setting labor (per pound).

TABLE 1–3

STANDARD CONCRETE REINFORCING BAR SIZES

Std. Bar Designations	Std. (Nominal) Bar Areas, in sq. in.	Nominal Dimensions, in inches		
		Diameter	Perimeter	Perimeter per sq. in. of Area
#2‡	0.05	0.25	0.79	16.0
#3	0.11	0.375	1.18	10.7
#4	0.20	0.50	1.57	8.0
#5	0.31	0.625	1.96	6.4
#6	0.44	0.75	2.36	5.4
#7	0.60	0.875	2.75	4.6
#8	0.79	1.00	3.14	4.0
#9	1.00*	1.13	3.54	3.54
#10	1.27*	1.27	3.99	3.14
#11	1.56*	1.41	4.43	2.84

*These areas are those of the former 1-in., 1⅛-in., and 1¼-in. square bars re-formed into the round shape.
‡Bar #2 comes in plain rounds only.

1–21. Standard Specifications for Designing Reinforced Concrete Structures. Although this text deals principally with the mechanics of reinforced concrete, its application to the common problems of design has been influenced greatly by the *practical experience* of countless structural engineers and by the results of *tests* conducted at the universities and elsewhere. One learns from them that some variables are relatively unimportant, while others must receive close attention. As a result, certain everyday rules and methods, possibly 97 per cent correct, have been developed, standardized, and published for the benefit of all, and are called *standard specifications*. When making any practical design, engineers always make reference to one such "book of rules" even though it may not be followed in its entirety.

At present the best American practice is represented by two well-known specifications, namely the *1940 Joint Committee Report on "Recommended Practice and Standard Specifications for Concrete and Reinforced Concrete,"* and the *1956 American Concrete Institute, "Building Code Requirements for Reinforced Concrete."* The former was first promulgated in 1916 and was revised in 1924. The present (1940) edition was prepared by a joint committee consisting of well-known representatives of six national engineering societies, including architecture. It is very complete and authoritative and is commonly referred to as "The 1940 Joint Committee Specifications."

In 1928 the American Concrete Institute adopted the above-mentioned similar set of specifications (Requirements) particularly applicable to building design. It was revised in 1941 and again in 1947, 1951,

TABLE 1–4

CONDENSED TABLE OF 1956 ACI BEAM ALLOWABLE STRESSES

For the *Concrete* of Reinforced Concrete Beams Containing ASTM Spec. A-305 Deformed Bars	Symbol	Allowable Unit Stresses in psi	
		For 3,000-lb. concrete $f'_c = 3,000$	For concrete of any compressive strength, f'_c, as established by tests
Bending—on extreme fibers in compression	f_c	1,350	$0.45f'_c$
Diagonal Tension—in localities: where no diag. tension reinforcement is used	v_c	90	$0.03f'_c$, maximum 90 psi
where diag. tension reinforcement is used	v_c	240	$0.08f'_c$,* maximum 240 psi
Bond for ASTM Spec. A-305 deformed bars: top bars	u	210	$0.07f'_c$ but not over 245 psi
bottom bars	u	300	$0.10f'_c$ but not over 350 psi
Modulus of Elasticity	E_c	3,000,000	$1000f'_c$
For the *Steel* of Reinforced Concrete Beams			
Tension in bending or diag. tension reinforcement for intermediate and hard grades	f_s, f_v	20,000 psi	
for structural grade steel	f_s, f_v	18,000	

*More under certain conditions.

and 1956. It differs from the Joint Committee specifications only in minor respects. Copies are readily available in all Portland Cement Association district offices. It has been followed in most of the design examples of this text, being referred to as "The ACI Code." All the clauses referred to herein will be found in Appendix J. The accompanying brief table of allowable stresses has been excerpted from Secs. 305

and 306 thereof for the convenience of the beginner in dealing with the early beam problems.

1–22. The ACI Manual of Standard Practice. In 1951 the American Concrete Institute, in cooperation with the Concrete Reinforcing Steel Institute, published the above-mentioned 9 by 11 in. looseleaf manual "for detailing reinforced concrete structures." This book consists principally of fold-in drawings of typical reinforced concrete structures and of the members thereof, together with detailed information on bar bending, hooks, column ties, bolsters, and other accessories. Since there is usually little time for making complete drawings in courses in reinforced concrete, the *Manual* fills a long-felt need by bridging the gap between theory and practice. It should be purchased ($3.00) by everyone entering the field.

BIBLIOGRAPHY

A) Bauer, Edward E. *Plain Concrete.* 3d ed. New York McGraw-Hill Book Co., Inc., 1949.
B) Abrams, D. A. *Design of Concrete Mixtures, Bulletin* No. 1. Structural Materials Research Laboratory, Lewis Institute, Chicago.
C) Shank, J. R. The Mechanics of Plastic Flow of Concrete, *Proc. American Concrete Institute,* 1936, Vol. 32, p. 149.
D) Clark, Arthur P. Bond of Concrete Reinforcing Bars, *Proc. American Concrete Institute,* 1950, Vol. 46, p. 161.
E) Portland Cement Assn. 16 mm sound color films obtainable on loan. "The Drama of Portland Cement," 30 min., "How to Make Quality Concrete," 33 min.

CHAPTER 2

BEAM FLEXURE

2-1. Introduction. In structural engineering one deals repeatedly with three types of members, namely, tension members, compression members, and bending members called **beams.** Of the three, beams

Dean Emeritus F. E. Turneaure, 1866–1951, College of Engineering, University of Wisconsin. He directed much of the early experimentation in reinforced concrete and was co-author of one of the earliest textbooks: *Principles of Reinforced Concrete Construction.* In it he proposed the use of a parabolic distribution of concrete compressive stress in beams, thus anticipating by many years a concept only presently beginning to be used generally to predict the ultimate strengths thereof.

require the most study. This is because bending stress varies over the cross section, instead of being uniformly distributed, as in the other two types of members. Furthermore, taking the beam pictured in Fig. 2–1 as an illustration, the bending effect of the loads, called the **bending** moment, usually varies along the span, and it is necessary to find the "dangerous section" where it has its greatest value in order to check the safety of the member.[1] Finally, beams are also subject to transverse stress called **beam shear,** which is due to the crosswise manner in which the loads are applied.

Beams composed of the same material throughout, such as steel or timber beams, are said to be **homogeneous.** The theory of **straight line variation of stress** from maximum compression at the top fiber to maximum tension at the bottom fiber applies to them directly. The level where the bending stress is zero is called the **neutral axis.** In homogeneous beams it is at the **center of gravity** of the cross section, which may be found by taking **moments of areas** about some convenient horizontal line. The familiar $s = Mc/I$ formula for bending unit stress is the algebraic expression of the above relationships.

Unfortunately, reinforced concrete beams are not homogeneous, since they consist of two materials, steel and concrete. For designing them the $s = Mc/I$ formula is not directly applicable. A different method of approach, called the **internal couple method,** must be used, and thoroughly mastered.

2-2. Homogeneous Beam Stress Analysis by the Internal Couple Method. Since the $s = Mc/I$ formula is unsuitable for designing reinforced concrete beams, let us try to get along without it in the simpler case of finding the maximum unit stress in a homogeneous beam.

EXAMPLE 2–1

Given an 8 by 20 in. timber beam carrying a uniformly distributed load of 0.7 kip[2] per lin. ft. (klf) over its 20-ft. span, and a concentrated load of 7.0 kips at 4 ft. from the left end. Refer to Fig. 2–1(a) and (e). It is required to find the maximum bending unit stress, in pounds per square inch, by the internal couple method.

Solution: As in all beam problems, first find each *reaction* by making a summation of the moments of loads and reactions about the other *reaction point.* Clockwise moments are taken as positive:

$$\Sigma M \text{ about } q \equiv 0$$
$$20R_L - 0.7(20)[10] - 7.0[16] = 0$$
$$R_L = 12.6 \text{ kips}$$

Similarly, by moments about p, $R_R = 8.4$ kips.

---

[1] Students for whom this discussion is not an adequate review will need to restudy "Beams" in their strength of materials text during the first week of the course.

[2] A *kip* equals 1000 lb., a convenient structural unit.

Check by ΣV:

$$+12.6 + 8.4 - 7.0 - 0.7(20) = 0$$

The shear diagram, Fig. 2–1(b), is next constructed (1) to locate the span-wise point of maximum bending moment and (2) to evaluate the maximum bending moment by computing the area of the shear diagram (either end):

$$M_{max} = \frac{8.4}{2}(12) = 50.4 \text{ kip-ft.}$$

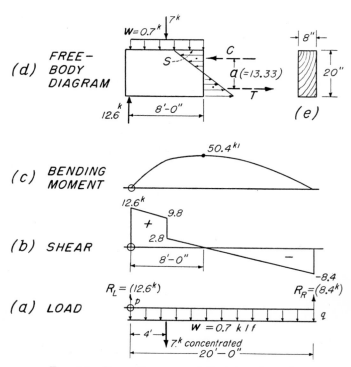

FIG. 2–1. Beam diagrams and the internal couple.

To find the maximum unit stress, remove at (d) one end of the beam as a *free body in equilibrium* under its loads, reaction, and the resultant internal forces, C and T. Noting that each of the latter must act at the centroid of the stress distribution triangle, the arm, a, of the *internal couple $Ca = Ta$* is found to be 13.33 in.

At the cut section, the **moment of the internal couple** (*resisting moment*) must equal the **external bending moment** of the reaction and loads:

$$Ca = M$$
$$13.33C = 50.4(12)(1000)$$
$$C = 45{,}350 \text{ lb.}$$

Let s, Fig. 2–1(d), be the maximum unit stress. By definition, C is the summation of all compressive unit stresses; namely, the volume of the "wedge" of stress:

$$\frac{s}{2}(10)(8) = C = 45,350$$

$$s = 1134 \text{ psi.} \qquad\qquad Ans.$$

This beam is safe if the timber allowable stress is greater than 1134 psi.

Check by formula:

$$s = \frac{Mc}{I}, \qquad c = 10 \text{ in.}, \qquad I = \frac{bd^3}{12} = \frac{(8)(20)^3}{12} = 5333 \text{ in.}^4$$

$$s = \frac{50.4(12)(1000)(10)}{5333} = 1134 \text{ psi.}$$

2–3. Reinforced Concrete Beams. When steel is embedded in concrete in a manner which assists it in carrying imposed loads, the combination is known as *reinforced concrete.* Since, as shown in Table 1–2 of Chapter 1, the tensile strength of concrete is only about 10 per cent of the compressive, it is obvious that beam strength can be increased tremendously by the use of steel in the tension side. In fact it is customary to ignore the relatively small tensile strength of the concrete in computing the bending strength of reinforced concrete beams, and to rely entirely upon the tensile steel.

Figure 3–1(a) of Chapter 3 illustrates typical beam cracking at failure in test. In the central portion of the span, where the bending moment was greatest, the tension cracks are approximately normal to the bending reinforcement. *Reinforced concrete designing consists principally in predicting the position and direction of* **potential tension cracks** *in concrete, and in forestalling the cracking by locating sufficient steel across them.*

In the *transformed section method* of calculation used throughout this text, the flexure steel is conceived to be replaced by a larger area of imaginary concrete which can take tension. This creates a homogeneous **transformed section** of concrete to which ordinary beam mechanics may be applied.

The basis for the transformation is an elastic one, maintaining the original bending strain, and recognizing that concrete is several times as soft as steel. Taking E as the modulus of elasticity, let $E_c = 3,000,000$, and $E_s = 30,000,000$ psi. A 1-in. cube of steel will deform axially 0.001 in. under a load of 30,000 lb., but if we substitute concrete for steel there will have to be $E_s/E_c = 10$ one-inch cubes, each carrying 3000 lb., if we are to have the same 0.001 in. deformation or strain.

Consider now the use of a firesafe concrete beam of the same outside dimensions as the timber beam of Example 2–1.

EXAMPLE 2-2

Figure 2-2(a) shows the cross section of a reinforced concrete beam. It carries a bending moment of 50.4 kip-ft. What are the maximum unit stresses in steel and concrete? Take 3000-lb. concrete, $E_c = 3,000,000$ psi, $E_s = 30,000,000$ psi.

Solution: Draw the transformed section, (b), by first discarding all tensile concrete (considered of no value in bending). Next, conceive the steel* to be replaced by an elastically equivalent area of ideal concrete which can take tension, equal to $E_s/E_c = n$ times the steel area. From mechanics, **the neutral axis for bending will be at the center of gravity of this equivalent homogeneous section.**

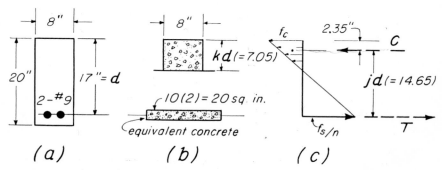

FIG. 2-2. Beam investigation by the Transformed Section Method.

To find the neutral axis, *take the sum of the moments, ΣM, of the transformed* areas **about the unknown neutral axis,** distant kd inches from the top of the beam:

$$8(kd)\,\frac{kd}{2} = 10(2)[17 - kd]$$

$$(kd)^2 + 5.0kd = 85.0$$

Note system of solution by completing the square:

$$(kd)^2 + 5.0kd + (2.5)^2 = 91.25$$

$$
\begin{array}{ll}
kd + 2.5 = +9.55 & \text{or} \quad -9.55 \\
\qquad\quad\; -2.50 & \qquad\quad -2.50 \\
\hline
kd = \quad 7.05 \text{ in.} &
\end{array}
$$

$$\frac{kd}{3} = 2.35 \text{ in.}$$

Then jd, the lever arm of the internal couple $= 14.65$ in.

----

* Refer to Table 1-3 near the end of Chapter 1 for bar sizes and areas.

Next, *equate the moment of the internal couple to the external bending moment:*

$$Tjd = Cjd = M, \qquad T = C = \frac{M}{jd}$$

$$T = C = \frac{50.4(12)(1000)}{14.65} = 41,300 \text{ lb.}$$

To find the steel unit stress, f_s, reconvert to the 2 sq. in. of steel:

$$f_s = \frac{41,300}{2} = 20,650 \text{ psi.} \qquad\qquad\qquad Ans.$$

The concrete unit stress, f_c, is obtained by recognizing that C *equals the volume of the wedge of compressive unit stress:*

$$C = \frac{f_c}{2}(7.05)(8) = 41,300$$

$$f_c = 1470 \text{ psi.} \qquad\qquad\qquad Ans.$$

EXAMPLE 2–3

What is the maximum safe bending moment that the beam of Example 2–2 can carry if the allowable unit stresses in steel and concrete are 20,000 and 1350 psi, respectively? $E_s/E_c = 10$, as before.

Solution: Since the cross section of the beam is unchanged, jd, the arm of the internal couple will be 14.65 in., as before.

Determine which side of the beam is the weaker, by calculating:

Max. safe $T = (2)(20,000) = 40,000$ lb.

Max. safe $C = \dfrac{1350}{2}(7.05)(8) = 38,100$ lb.

Therefore the strength of this beam is limited by the concrete. The safe internal **resisting moment** of the section $= \dfrac{38,100(14.65)}{12,000} = 46.5$ kip-ft., equals the maximum safe bending moment. $\qquad Ans.$

2–4. Student Problem Work. This text is based upon the idea that one learns principally from personal attempts made after having watched another's performance. The **EXAMPLES** are followed by lists of **Problems,** the solution of which will develop the thorough understanding of the subject which comes with practice.

The importance of being systematic about such calculations is very great. Poorly arranged, slovenly, and unclear figures lead to arithmetical errors which obscure the learning process. A well-organized sheet, similar to Fig. 2–3, is familiar to students of *engineering problems* courses and should be emulated by all. In engineering offices,

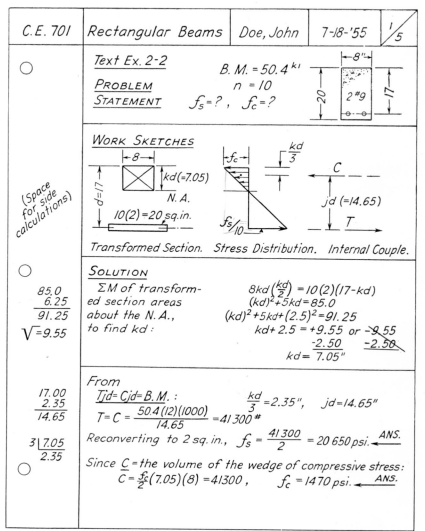

FIG. 2–3. Approved arrangement of calculation sheets.

lasting first impressions often are formed from the manner in which the novice *arranges* his first calculations.

PRACTICE PROBLEMS

Always take the weight of reinforced concrete[3] at 150 lb. per cu. ft.

Problem 2–1. A timber beam, of the built-up section shown in Fig. 2–4(a) has a simple span of 14 ft. It carries a uniform dead plus live load of 0.8 kip

[3] For dense natural stone concrete. Refer to Art. 1–11.

per lin. ft., and a concentrated load of
4 kips at 4 ft. from the right end.

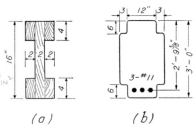

(a) Find the maximum bending
unit stress, using the internal
couple method. Recognize the
variation in beam width. $1.45\,k/in^2$

(b) Check (a) by the $s = Mc/I$
formula.

(c) Evaluate C, the total compressive force, in pounds. $81.2\,k$

(a)   *(b)*

Fig. 2-4.

★
Problem 2-2. (a) A rectangular reinforced concrete beam is 10 in. wide by
22 in. deep to the center of its two #11 bars. The total bending moment to be
carried is 90 kip-ft. $E_s/E_c = n = 12$. Find the unit stresses f_s and f_c.

Ans. *N.A. at 9.64 in., $f_s = 18,400$, $f_c = 1190$ psi.*

(b) How much bending moment can the beam carry safely if the allowable
steel and concrete stresses are 20,000 and 1000 psi, respectively?

(c) Suppose the allowable stresses are 16,000 and 1050 psi. Find the maximum safe bending moment.

Problem 2-3. (a) Find the maximum safe bending moment for the beam
shown in Fig. 2-4(b) if the allowable stresses are 20,000 and 1000 psi, and
$n = 12$.

(b) Taking a span of 24 ft., how much uniformly distributed live load can
the beam carry safely if the weight of reinforced concrete is 150 lb. per cu. ft.?

★
Problem 2-4. A cantilever rectangular beam 8 ft. long carries a concentrated load of 19 kips at its outer end. It is 14 in. wide by 30 in. total depth,
and has four #9 bars centered 3 in. from the top. Report upon its safety,
taking the ACI specification 20,000–1350–10 (f_s, f_c and n).

2-5. Investigation Versus Design. All reinforced concrete beam
problems are of two types, namely, *investigational* or *designing* problems.
It is very important that the student early learn to distinguish between
them, since the methods of attack are quite different in the two cases.

I. *Investigation Problems.* These problems call for a strength *investiga-
tion*, or analysis, of an existing (or proposed) beam, all the dimensions of
the concrete and steel being given, together with the class of the concrete.
   Required:
   A. With the applied bending moment given, to find the unit
      stresses, or
   B. With the allowable unit stresses given, to find the maximum
      safe bending moment, or load that the beam can carry.

II. *Design Problems.* Designing is deciding upon dimensions. In
these problems the applied bending moment, the allowable stresses,
and the class of the concrete are given.

Required:

To find all or some of the dimensions of the beam cross section, including that of the steel reinforcement.

There are several cases of these problems, the most important of which follow.

In attacking any beam problem, first determine whether it is a *design* or an *investigation*, since in the two types of problems the neutral axis is located by entirely different methods. Its correct position is of critical importance in the succeeding work. The preceding Examples 2–2 and 2–3 and Problems 2–2, 2–3, and 2–4 are *investigations*. The following examples are *design* problems. Notice how the neutral axis is found, and that there are always some dimensions to be decided upon.

EXAMPLE 2–4

Balanced Beam Design. **Given a total bending moment of 50.4 kip-ft. and the specification 20,000–1350–10. It is required to design a beam to suit.[4]** (**Note that the cross section taken in the preceding examples was not strong enough.**)

Solution: The work consists of (1) predetermining a neutral axis location such that both steel and concrete will work economically at their allowable stresses (balanced); and (2) providing adequate steel and concrete areas consistent therewith:

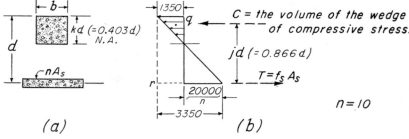

FIG. 2–5. The design of a balanced beam.

Considering the similar right triangles of Fig. 2–5(b), cornering at q and r:

$$\frac{kd}{d} = \frac{1350}{1350 + 2000}, \qquad kd = 0.403d, \qquad jd = 0.866d$$

Next, take the very useful fundamental expression: $Cjd = M$.

$$\frac{1350}{2}(b)(0.403d)[0.866d] = 50.4(12,000)$$

$$bd^2 = 2570$$

---

[4] Refer to Table 1–4 at the end of Chapter 1, or to Art. 305 of the American Concrete Institute *Building Code*, Appendix J, at the back of the book.

Obviously there are many combinations of b and d that will yield a correct design. To make a convenient comparison with other examples, suppose we choose $b = 8$ in., corresponding $d = 17.90$ in.

b	d	$C = T$	A_s
8''	17.9''	39,000 lb.	1.95 sq. in.
( )	( )	( )	( )

To get the correct steel area, A_s, substitute back, evaluating C:

$$C = 675(8)(0.403)(17.90) = 39,000 \text{ lb.}$$

or, evaluating T:

$$T = \frac{M}{jd} = \frac{50.4(12,000)}{0.866(17.90)} = 39,000 \text{ lb.}$$

$$Req'd. \quad A_s = \frac{39,000}{20,000} = 1.95 \ sq. \ in.$$

EXAMPLE 2–5

The Beam Made Arbitrarily Deeper. **Suppose that architectural considerations dictate that d of Example 2–4 be made 20 in., with b still 8 in. How much steel will be required?**

Solution: First consider in a *qualitative* manner what change takes place in the internal couple if the beam of Fig. 2–5 and 2–6(a) is replaced by a deeper one, as at (b). The greater depth means a longer arm, called $jd+$, but since

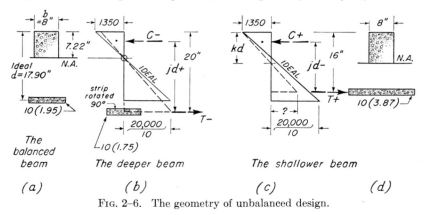

FIG. 2–6. The geometry of unbalanced design.

the bending moment is unchanged, the internal forces become $C-$ and $T-$, both less than in the balanced beam. We can still work the steel to 20,000 psi by using less of it. However, the beam is now an unbalanced one, since bd^2 no longer equals 2570 as in the preceding (balanced design) Example 2–4. Therefore the concrete must be the material which is stressed to less than its 1350 psi allowable, the steel being at 20,000 psi. Knowing this, it is possible to write $Cjd = M$, utilizing the known steel stress, similar stress triangles, and the volume of the wedge of compressive stress, all in terms of the unknown kd. (The student should be prepared to do this.) Unfortunately, the equation proves to be a cubic, and is not readily solved.

   Ans.: $kd = 7.38$ *in.,* $jd = 17.54$ *in.,* $f_c = 1170$ *psi,* $A_s = 1.73$ *sq. in.*

Approximate Method (Use). Noting that the value of kd just found differs little from the 7.22-in. one of the ideal *balanced beam*, the following statement will be found helpful:

   The neutral axis distance kd, in inches, is not appreciably affected by small percentage-wise changes in depth, d, accompanied by corresponding inverse changes in steel area, A_s.

This is tantamount to saying that the level of C and $C-$ are about the same, and suggests that we may get the steel area from the 1.95 sq. in. balanced beam steel area by taking a proportion upon the arms of the couples. Instead, designers conveniently use the ratio of the beam depths:

$$\text{Req'd. } A_s = \frac{17.9}{20.0}(1.95) = 1.75 \text{ sq. in.}$$

✶ *Query.* Why are such beams said to be "under-reinforced"?

EXAMPLE 2–6

The Beam Made Arbitrarily Shallower. **What steel area will be required if d is made 16 in., with b still 8 in.? B.M. = 50.4 kip-ft., Spec. 20,000–1350–10.**

Solution: The situation is shown *qualitatively* by Fig. 2–6(c) and (d) which has been drawn with the top of the beam in projection with that of the *balanced beam* at (a). In this case the lesser depth means a shorter arm, $jd-$, and a correspondingly greater internal compressive force, $C+$. Therefore the concrete area resisting the compression must be increased somehow, in order to keep f_c down to 1350 psi. Referring to the indented statement in the preceding example, one sees that the necessary increase in kd cannot be obtained by using more steel in inverse proportion to the depths. A much greater amount of steel will be needed to pull the neutral axis down. Again writing $Cjd = M$:

$$\frac{1350}{2}(8)(kd)\left[16 - \frac{kd}{3}\right] = 50.4(12{,}000)$$

$$kd = 8.51 \text{ in.,} \quad jd = 13.16 \text{ in.,} \quad C = T = 45{,}900 \text{ lb.}$$

From the figure, by similar triangles **this steel does not work at the allowable stress** but at:

$$\frac{16.0 - 8.51}{8.51}(1350)(10) = 11{,}870 \text{ psi}$$

$$A_s = \frac{T}{f_s} = \frac{45{,}900}{11{,}870} = 3.87 \text{ sq. in.} \qquad\qquad Ans.$$

Check. By ΣM of transformed areas about the neutral axis:

$$A_s(10)[7.49] = 8(8.51)[4.26]$$
$$A_s = 3.87 \text{ sq. in.} \hspace{3cm} Ans.$$

Such beams are "over-reinforced," uneconomical of steel, and to be avoided. When the available depth is less than about 90 per cent of the ideal depth, steel should be provided in both the upper and lower portions of beams, as in the following Example 2–7. Such beams are said to be *doubly reinforced.*

BEAM DESIGN PROBLEMS

Unless otherwise noted, take 2500-lb. concrete, ACI Specification 20,000–1125–12.

★
Problem 2–5. (a) Find the theoretical d and A_s for a singly reinforced beam 14 in. wide. The total bending moment is 300 kip-ft.

$$Ans. \quad d = 36.20 \text{ in., } A_s = 5.72 \text{ sq. in.}$$

(b) Find b and A_s for a singly reinforced beam 30 in. deep to center of steel. The total B.M. is 240 kip-ft.   16.3   5.55

★
Problem 2–6. (a) Find the theoretical A_s for Problem 2–5(a) if d is arbitrarily made 40 in.   *Ans.* $A_s = 5.17$ sq. in.

(b) Find the theoretical A_s for Problem 2–5(a) if d is arbitrarily made 33 in.   *Ans.* N.A. $= 16.66$ in., $A_s = 9.91$ sq. in.

★
Problem 2–7. Calculate the required steel area for a singly reinforced beam 20 in. wide by 50 in. deep to center of steel, to resist a total bending moment of 900 kip-ft.

Hint. Make a preliminary study to find whether the given space is larger or smaller than it should be.

★
Problem 2–8. The total bending moment is 60 kip-ft. Compute b and d for a singly reinforced beam to use 2—#9 bars from stock.

Problem 2–9. Formulate a rule governing the use of the allowable stresses to find the neutral axis in design problems.

Problem 2–10. Calculate the required b, d, and A_s of a beam if the total B.M. is 263 kip-ft., and b must be 0.6d. Is the beam a balanced one?

$b = 17.9$
$d = 29.9$
$A_s = 6.1$
YES

★
Problem 2–11. (Individual) It is desired to completely design a reinforced concrete slab for the loading platform shown in Fig. 2–7. Assume a one-foot strip of slab for study, estimate the dead load at 150 lb. per cu. ft., and adjust as found necessary.

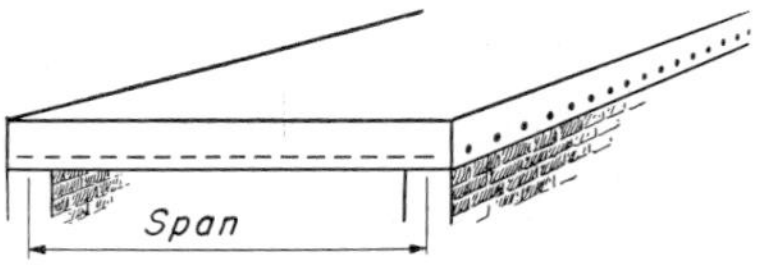

Span

Fig. 2–7.

Do not initially assume a value of d. Let it work out algebraically.

Design total slab thickness to *nearest* half-inch and use only standard reinforcing bars, all one size, spaced from 3 to 6 in. center to center, by half-inches. Provide exactly one inch of fireproofing concrete. As always, make a final design sketch (Art. 2–7).

Use the thinnest slab consistent with the above instructions.

Cases	Specification	Live Load in psf	Span in ft.
Series A 29 assignable combinations	18,000–1000–12 *18,000–1200–10 18,000–1000–10	300 *250	10 *11 12 13 14
Series B 30 combinations	1947 ACI Specs. 20,000–1125–12 20,000–1688–8 20,000–1800–7½	300 250	10 11 12 13 14

Sample Ans. Make slab 6 in. thick and use #5 bars spaced 3½ in. c. to c.

EXAMPLE 2–7

The Design of Double Reinforcement. **Given a bending moment of 50.4 kip-ft., a specification of 20,000–1350–10, and a space $b = 8$ in., by $d = 16$ in. Calculate double reinforcement, the upper steel to be centered 2½ in. from the top, as in Fig. 2–8.**

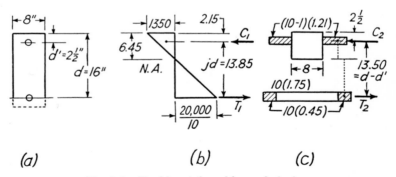

(a)   (b)   (c)

Fig. 2–8. Doubly reinforced beam designing.

Method: Determine to have the neutral axis in the *balanced beam* location, and provide both bottom and top reinforcement consistent therewith.

Solution: (1) First find how much of the given bending moment can be resisted by designing *balanced single reinforcement* for the section:

$$\frac{kd}{16} = \frac{1350}{3350}, \qquad kd = 6.45 \text{ in.}, \qquad jd = 13.85 \text{ in.}$$

Balanced $C_1 = T_1 = 675(8)(6.45) = 34,900$ lb.,

$$A_{s_1} = \frac{34,900}{20,000} = 1.75 \text{ sq. in.}$$

Corresponding safe $B.M. = \dfrac{34,900(13.85)}{12,000} = 40.3$ kip-ft. $= M_1$

(2) Allocate the remaining bending moment, M_2, to a supplementary steel couple, $T_2(d - d')$, and calculate the additional tensile steel needed:

$$M_2 = 50.4 - 40.3 = 10.1 \text{ kip-ft.}$$

$$A_{s_2} = \frac{M_2}{f_s(d - d')} = \frac{10.1(12,000)}{20,000(13.5)} = 0.45 \text{ sq. in.}$$

From Step 1, $A_{s_1} = \underline{1.75}$
Total bottom steel area $= 2.20$ sq. in. $= A_s$

(3) Calculate the compression steel area by taking moments of the steel couple transformed areas[5] about the neutral axis:

$$9(A'_s)[6.45 - 2.5] = 10(0.45)[9.55]$$

Top steel, $A'_s = 1.21$ sq. in.

Query. In what other manner can the upper steel area be obtained?   It should check perfectly.

Problem 2–12. Calculate the required areas of double reinforcement for a beam 14 in. wide by 2 ft. 6 in. total depth, if the $DL + LL$ bending moment is 250 kip-ft.   Conveniently assume that all steel can be centered $2\frac{1}{2}$ in. from the top or bottom surfaces.   Specification: 20,000–1125–12.

Ans. Bottom steel = 6.21, top steel = 3.85 sq. in.

Problem 2–13. (Individual) Design double reinforcement for the case assigned.   Specification: 20,000–1200–10.   Fireproof the steel 2 in. all around. Observe a minimum clear horizontal spacing of one bar diam., but not less than one and one-third times the 1-in. aggregate maximum size.   Use two layers in the bottom, all one size, spaced at one inch clear, vertically.   Use one layer in the top, all one size, not necessarily the same as the bottom bar size.

Investigate your design, working from your final design sketch, after studying Example 2–8.   The maximum safe bending moment of an economical design should not be over 3 per cent greater than the design bending moment. Show results clearly and completely.

---

[5] The multiplier $n - 1$, equal to 9 in this case, is used on the compression side of beams to allow for the area of compression concrete displaced by the steel.

Student's Name	Case	Width b in.	Total depth h, in.	B. M. DL + LL, kip-ft.
	a	12	38	297
	b	15	40	414
	c	14	34	287
	d	14	38	344
	e	14	33	266
	f	16	43	530
	g	19	40	550
	h	18	34	368
	i	13	43	430
	j	16	47	613
	k	17	58	977
	l	20	37	476
	m	14	49	560
	n	14	36	330
	o	18	41	555
	p	21	46	805
	q	16	45	571
	r	18	38	461
	s	21	44	770
	t	14	35	308
	u	20	36	450
	v	15	38	370
	w	18	32	330
	x	22	46	870
	y	20	40	575
	z	15	36	340

2–6. Practical Design Considerations. The designer's choice of steel must be limited to the ten concrete reinforcing bar sizes shown in Table 1–3 near the end of Chapter 1.

The ACI Code[6] Secs. 505 and 507 govern the spacing and covering of bars. The minimum clear vertical space between beam bars is 1 in. *Horizontally*, the minimum clear distance is the nominal diameter of the bar, but must never be less than 1 in.,[7] nor less than one and one-third times the maximum size of the coarse aggregate. The outer surface of all beam steel must be covered with a minimum of $1\frac{1}{2}$ in. of concrete all around to serve as fireproofing (f'p'f'g).

It is customary to round off the beam width, b and the total depth, h, to a whole number of inches. The standard heights of the reinforcing bar supports, called *bolsters*, are also an influence.[8] See Fig. 2–9(a).

---

[6] All clauses of the American Concrete Institute *Building Code Requirements for Reinforced Concrete* referred to in this text will be found in Appendix J.

[7] The intention of Committee 318 was not clearly stated in Sec. 505.

[8] Refer to pp. 22 and 23 of the ACI *Manual of Standard Practice for Detailing R/C Structures* for illustrations and standard heights of bolsters and chairs.

In the accompanying Table 2–1, bar sizes and total beam depths have been determined for the beams of the preceding examples. Note that the "shallow beam" did not prove so in the end, after the bar

TABLE 2–1

SUMMARY OF RECTANGULAR BEAM DESIGNS

Design safe B. M. = 50.4 kip-ft., Spec.: 20,000–1350–10, 1½ in. f'p'f'g. All concrete dimensions shown below are in inches.

Example	Case	b	d	Req'd. A_s	Selection Bars	h	Remarks
2–4	Balanced beam	8	17.9	1.95	2–#9	20	Ideal.
2–5	Deep beam	8	20	1.73 or 1.75	{1–#9 1–#8	22	Enough head room?
2–6	Shallow beam	8	16	3.87	4–#9	19	Wastes steel. Two bar layers mean extra concrete.
2–7	Doubly reinf. shallow beam	8	16	Top 1.21 Bot. 2.20 Tot. 3.41	2–#7 {1–#10 1–#9	18	Bar selections need checking.

arrangement had been worked out. Sometimes there is more steel but less depth, d, than planned, so the safety of a design can be proven only by a final *investigation*.

Query. Do all the beams of Table 2–1 have the same live-load carrying capacity? Explain.

2–7. The Design Sketch. The designer's decisions are summarized in final *design sketches* of the member, such as Fig. 2–9(a). They are made principally to save the time of supervisors and draftsmen who must read "the answer" at a glance. They must always be made to scale (same scale vertically as horizontally), with the scale stated. The outside dimensions of the concrete are clearly shown. The number of bars, their location, spacing, the bar size number and the concrete coverage thereof must be included. The dimensions most useful to the construction man are presented, e.g., the total beam depth, and the bolster height, not d. No decimal measurements are to appear.

A *complete* design sketch shows all the dimensions necessary for planning the forms and detailing the steel, without straining the eyes or exercising mental arithmetic. Incomplete ones are not tolerated. Design sketches are required of students at the completion of all design problems.

EXAMPLE 2-8

Investigation of a Doubly Reinforced Beam. Draw the final design sketch of the *cross section* of the doubly reinforced beam designed in Example 2-7 and investigate it to find the stresses under the design bending moment of 50.4 kip-ft. Specification: 20,000–1350–10.

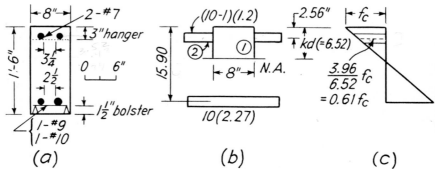

Fig. 2-9. Doubly reinforced beam investigation.

Solution: Referring to the design sketch, Fig. 2-9(a), the centroid of the bottom bar group may be found by taking moments of bar areas about the center of the smaller bar:

$$\frac{1.27(0.07)}{1.00 + 1.27} = 0.04 \text{ in.}$$

$$0.56 = \#9 \text{ radius}$$
$$1.50 = \text{bolster}$$

So centroid is 2.10 in. from the bottom.

Therefore $d = 15.90$ in.

ΣM of areas to find the neutral axis of the transformed section at (b):

$$4(kd)^2 + 9(1.2)[kd - 2.56] = 10(2.27)[15.90 - kd]$$
$$kd = 6.52 \text{ in.}$$

Due to the presence of compression steel, C *does not act at kd/3 in. from the top,* but must be located by taking **moments of stress volumes,** preferably about the top of the beam.

Always use the tabular form:

Pc. No.	Stress Volume	Arm to Top, in.	Moment
1	$\frac{f_c}{2}(8)(6.52) = 26.08f_c$	2.17	$56.60f_c$
2	$0.61f_c(10.8) = 6.60f_c$	2.56	$16.87f_c$
	$C = 32.68f_c$		$73.47f_c$

$$z = \frac{73.47}{32.68} = 2.24 \text{ in.}$$

$$jd = 13.66 \text{ in.}$$

$$C = T = \frac{M}{jd} = \frac{50.4(12,000)}{13.66} = 44,200 \text{ lb.}$$

$$f_c = \frac{44,200}{32.68} = \dots\dots\dots\dots\dots 1350$$

Top $f_s = n(0.61f_c) = 10(0.61)(1350) = 8230$

Bot. $f_s = \dfrac{44,200}{2.27} = \dots\dots\dots\dots\dots 19,500$

Ans. in psi. The design is satisfactory.

Problem 2–14. A doubly reinforced rectangular beam is 16 in. wide by 3 ft. 4 in. deep to the centroid of the tensile steel bar group consisting of 8–#11 bars. There are also 4–#11 bars centered $2\frac{1}{2}$ in. from the top.

Find the maximum safe bending moment for the beam. Specification: 20,000–1500–8.   *Ans. kd = 15.37 in., safe B.M. = 709 kip-ft.*

2–8. T-Beams. Wide beams with concrete missing from the tension side are called **T-**beams. The undercut portion of Fig. 2–10(b) shows how a great deal of concrete may be saved thereby. Furthermore, the resulting **T**-beam can then carry more superimposed load, equal to the weight of the concrete removed. Thus the removal of *this* material from the section makes it stronger!

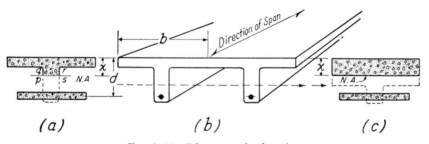

(a)   (b)   (c)

FIG. 2–10. T-beams and otherwise.

Technically, a **T**-beam is one consisting of a horizontal compression flange, or **slab,** and a vertical web, or **stem,** so proportioned that the neutral axis falls below the slab, as at Fig. 2–10(a). If the recess extends upward some lesser distance, as shown dotted in (b) and (c), the neutral axis may fall within the slab, in which case rectangular beam calculations apply in spite of appearances to the contrary.

T-beam problems are also of two types, *investigation* and *design,* depending respectively upon whether the dimensions of the beam cross section are known or to be found, as in rectangular beams. Four cases of T-beams will be taken up, two investigation and two design. The student should note the parallelism of the T-beam cases with those of rectangular beams.

In T-beam calculations it is customary to omit the stem concrete area, *pqrs*, of Fig. 2-10(a), which makes a negligible error in most cases.

EXAMPLE 2-9

(a) **Given the T-shaped section of Fig. 2–11(a), with a slab thickness,** $t = 6$ **in., a bending moment of 70 kip-ft., and** $n = 10$**. It is required to find** f_c **and** f_s**.**

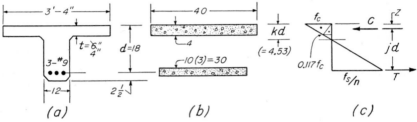

Fig. 2–11. T-beam investigation.

Solution: First, take a summation of moments of transformed areas about the bottom of the slab to find if it is really a T-beam:

$$40(6)[3] > 10(3)[12].$$

Therefore the neutral axis is within the slab, making it a rectangular beam calculation similar to Example 2–2.

(b) **Same as (a) above, except that the slab thickness,** *t*, **has been decreased to 4 in.**

Solution: A quick mental calculation having indicated that the neutral axis is below the slab, the transformed section, Fig. 2-11(b), is drawn and the neutral axis found:

$$40(4)[kd - 2] = 10(3)[18 - kd], \quad 190\ kd = 860$$

$$kd = 4.53 \text{ in.}$$

The centroid distance, *z*, at (c) may be found conveniently by dividing the trapezoidal stress prism into two triangular ones, and **taking moments of stress volumes,** using a one-inch width of slab:

Pc.	Stress Volume Per Inch of Slab Width	Arm to Top, in.	Moment
Upper	$\dfrac{f_c}{2}(4) = 2.00 f_c$	1.33	$2.67 f_c$
Lower	$\dfrac{0.117}{2} f_c(4) = \underline{0.23 f_c}$	2.67	$\underline{0.62 f_c}$
	$C/40 = 2.23 f_c$		$3.29 f_c$

$$z = 3.29 \div 2.23 = 1.47 \text{ in.}$$

$$jd = 16.53 \text{ in.}$$

$$T = C = \frac{\text{B.M.}}{jd} = \frac{70(12,000)}{16.53} = 50,800 \text{ lb.}$$

$$f_s = \frac{50,800}{3} = 16,900,$$

$$f_c = \frac{50,800}{40(2.23)} = 568 \text{ psi.} \qquad Ans.$$

Due to the relatively great width of T-beam compression flanges, the concrete stress is usually well below the allowable.

EXAMPLE 2–10

(a) **Find the maximum safe bending moment for the section, Fig. 2–11(a) of the preceding example, with $t = 4$ in., according to the ACI Specification: 20,000–1350–10.**

Solution: From the preceding example:

$$\frac{20,000}{16,900} < \frac{1350}{568},$$

so the strength is limited by the steel.

$$\text{Max. safe B.M.} = \frac{20,000}{16,900}(70) = 82.8 \text{ kip-ft.} \qquad Ans.$$

(b) **What is the maximum safe live load per square foot of floor over a simple span of 20 ft.?**

Solution:

$$M = \frac{wL^2}{8},$$

$$w = \frac{8M}{L^2} = \frac{8(82.8)(1000)}{(20)^2} = 1656 \text{ plf}$$

The dead load, $\dfrac{[(40)(4) + 16.5(12)]}{144}(150) = \dfrac{373}{1283}$

$$\frac{1283(12)}{40} = 384 \text{ lb.} = \text{safe live load per sq. ft. of floor.} \qquad Ans.$$

T–BEAM INVESTIGATION PROBLEMS

Unless otherwise noted, take 2500-lb. concrete, ACI Specification: 20,000–1125–12, and make all investigations by the internal couple method.

★ **Problem 2–15.** A T-beam has a slab portion 30 in. wide by 3 in. thick. Its depth to the center of 2–#10 bars is 16 in. Is it safe under a total bending moment of 60 kip-ft.?

Ans. Yes, N.A. $= 5.16$ *in., jd* $= 14.71$ *in., f_s* $= 19,200, f_c = 770$ *psi*

★ **Problem 2–16.** Find the maximum safe bending moment for a T-beam having a slab portion 30 in. wide by 3 in. thick, and a depth of 18 in. to the center of 2–#11 bars.

✓ **Problem 2–17.** Find the maximum safe total bending moment that the box girder section of Fig. 2–12 can carry.

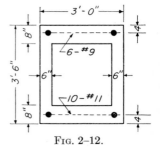

Fig. 2–12.

2–9. T-Beam Design. T-beam design theory involves one more variable than in rectangular beams, namely the slab thickness, t. Nevertheless, by conveniently assuming a slab thickness as some fraction of d, *balanced* T-beams can be evolved by a straightforward procedure, as in the following example.

EXAMPLE 2–11

Given a bending moment of 30.2 kip-ft. and the specification 20,000–1350–10. It is required to design a balanced T-beam.

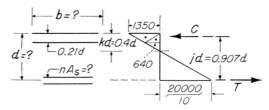

Fig. 2–13. **T-beam design, t/d assumed.**

Solution: Since no dimensions are initially set, the neutral axis can be put in the ideal balanced location of $0.40d$, defined by the allowable stresses, as shown in Fig. 2–13.

Assuming a slab thickness of $0.21d$, and a unit width of slab, take moments of stress volumes to find the centroid for C:

Pc.	Stress Volume Per Inch of Slab Width	Arm to Top	Moment
Upper	$675(0.21d) = 141.8d$	$0.07d$	$9.93d^2$
Lower	$320(0.21d) = 67.2d$	$0.14d$	$9.41d^2$
	$C/b = 209.0d$		$19.34d^2$

$$z = \frac{19.34d^2}{209.0d} = 0.093d, \qquad \text{so } jd = 0.907d$$

Now $\qquad$ $C = T = 209.0bd$

And $\qquad$ $Cjd = $ B.M., so $209.0\ bd[0.907d] = 30.2(12,000)$

Therefore $\quad bd^2 = 1910$, from which to prepare a table of values.

The corresponding

$$A_s = \frac{T}{20,000} = \frac{209.0\ bd}{20,000} = 0.01045\ bd$$

b	d	t ($=0.21d$)	A_s	Remarks
12.0 ( )	12.62 ( )	2.65 ( )	1.58 ( )	2–#8

The table of values shows the resulting dimensions if a steel area corresponding to an exact bar size is initially chosen.

Balanced T-beams are seldom achieved in practice because T-beams are usually units of a repeating construction having the stems so widely spaced to save dead load that the slab width, b, is greater than necessary for concrete strength. Tests have shown that there is a limit to the width of slab that may be relied upon to *act with the stem* as a beam. The ACI Code, Sec. 705(a), wisely limits b to (1) one-fourth of the T-beam span, (2) the center-to-center distance between stems, or (3) the stem thickness plus 16 times the slab thickness, whichever is the smaller. Stem and slab must be poured monolithically.

The required stem thickness, b', is dictated by the beam shear, and is taken up in Chapter 3.

A continuing floor slab with stems only a very few feet apart, as in Fig. 2–10(b), is called *concrete joist* construction.

2–10. "Pan System" T-Beam Forms. Figure 2–15 illustrates how T-beam construction is facilitated by employing removable metal forms, called "pans," which are used repeatedly on a rental basis. The most common pan width is 20 in., the soffit plank being 5 in., making the b of the slab 25 in. The standardized depths of pans available are 6, 8, 10, 12, and 14 in. The pans of some systems are devised for early removal and reuse, while the soffit and shoring remain until the concrete has attained full strength. A conservative minimum slab thickness is $2\frac{1}{2}$ in.

In pan T-beam *designing*, the dimensions of the slab are usually predetermined, leaving only the pan depth and steel area to be found.[9]

---

[9] Sometimes the slab thickness and slab width also are to be chosen.

One procedure is to try two or three pans, computing the necessary steel, and then to decide which is the most suitable and economical. The deeper pans require less steel but more concrete, have greater dead weight, and sometimes interfere with head room.

EXAMPLE 2–12

Given the specification 20,000–1350–10, and a 2½-in. slab thickness. It is required to design a pan T-beam section for a live load of 200 psf over a 19 ft. 8 in. simple span. Provide one inch of fireproofing. Assume, for a start, that the bars will be of 1-in. dimension.

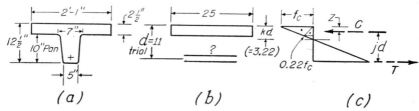

FIG. 2–14.   Design of pan T-beam steel.

Solution: (Trial of a 10-in. pan illustrated in Fig. 2–14.)
Loads

$$\text{L.L.} = 200(\tfrac{25}{12}) \qquad\qquad = 417$$

$$\text{D.L.} = \frac{[25(2.5) + 6(10)]150}{144} = 128$$

$$\text{Total} = 545 \text{ plf}$$

$$\text{Bending moment} = \frac{wL^2}{8} = \frac{545(19.67)^2}{8} = 26{,}300 \text{ lb. ft.}$$

The neutral axis can neither be gotten by moments of transformed areas nor from a diagram of allowable stresses. (Why not?)

It is permissible **in this one case** to (1) assume a trial value of *jd*, usually 0.9*d*, from which an approximate steel content can be quickly calculated; then (2) to *investigate* the section to find an improved value of *jd* for use in correcting the steel area:

Trial

$$jd = 0.9d = 9.90 \text{ in.}$$

$$\text{Approx. } A_s = \frac{M}{f_s jd} = \frac{26{,}300(12)}{20{,}000(9.90)} = 1.59 \text{ sq. in.}$$

Investigation

ΣM of transformed areas:

$$25(2.5)[kd - 1.25] = 10(1.59)[11 - kd],$$
$$kd = 3.22 \text{ in.}$$

Referring to Fig. 2–14(c) it is possible *in* T-*beams* to circumvent the summation of moments of stress volumes to find the distance z to the centroid for C. The desired centroid will be on a straight line between those pictured for the individual triangular prisms. Upon examining the moment-taking of Example 2–11 it will be evident[10] that the desired point will be nearer to the centroid of the larger triangle in inverse proportion to the areas, or the horizontal dimensions, of the triangles:

$$\frac{0.72}{3.22}(f_c) = 0.22f_c$$

The *vertical* distance between the centroids of the triangles is $\dfrac{2.50}{3} = 0.83$ in.

Then
$$z = \frac{0.22}{1.0 + 0.22}(0.83) + 0.83 = 0.98 \text{ in.}$$

$$\text{Improved } jd = 10.02.$$

Redesign

$$\text{Corrected } A_s = \frac{9.90}{10.02}(1.59) = 1.57 \text{ sq. in.}$$

Use 2–#8 bars. Actual $d = 11.00$ in.

Check on f_c:

$$f_c = \frac{3.22}{7.78}\left(\frac{20,000}{10}\right) = 827 \pm \text{psi,} \qquad < 1350, \text{ therefore satisfactory.}$$

Comment: When a true T-beam is being made either deeper or *shallower,* the required bottom steel area may be calculated by an inverse proportion upon the depths, d, involved, subject only to a later check upon the actual f_c value.

This procedure is possible when such beams are being made shallower because the compression concrete area does not abut the neutral axis, as it does in rectangular beams; and because T-beam f_c values are *usually* well below the allowable anyway.

NOTE TO THE INSTRUCTOR: Since Example 2–12 is the last of the basic examples of flexural computation by the transformed section method, the corresponding twelve examples of Appendix A, illustrating the time-saving use of the *beam charts,* may well be taken up at this point.

T–BEAM DESIGN PROBLEMS

Take 2500-lb. concrete, ACI Specification: 20,000–1125–12, unless otherwise noted.
★
Problem 2–18. Calculate the steel area and slab width required for a T-beam having a slab thickness of 5 in. and a depth to center of steel of 20 in.

---

[10] If this shortcut is not fully understood, avoid it by taking moments of stress volumes, as formerly, such as in Example 2–11.

The beam is to carry 5 kips D.L. + L.L. per lin. ft. over a 20-ft. simple span. The beam stem is 14 in. wide. Ref.: ACI Code, Sec. 705(a).

Can the design be managed so that the neutral axis will be in the ideal location? Explain.

★
Problem 2–19. The total bending moment is 61 kip-ft. Calculate the exact amount of steel required for a **T**-beam 17 in. deep to center of steel if the slab is 30 by 3½ in. *Ans. $A_s = 2.35$ sq. in.*

★
Problem 2–20. *Design of a Pan-Construction* **T**-*Beam Floor (Concrete Joist).* Refer to Fig. 2–15 for dimensions of available forms. The minimum slab thickness, t, is 2 in. Provide exactly 1-in. fireproofing, vertically and laterally.

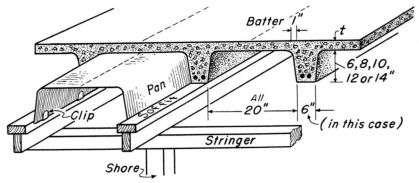

Fig. 2–15. Pan system forms for a concrete joist floor.

Allow a minimum clear distance of one diam. between bars, but never less than 1 in. Refer to Art. 2–6. Use only one size of bar in a design. The (simple) span is 20 ft. center to center of supports.

Indiv. Case	Live Load (lb. per sq. ft. of floor)	Specification f_s f_c n	Class of Concrete f'_c
a	200	20,000–1000–12	2500
b	125	20,000–1200–10	3000
c	100	20,000–1688–8	3750
d	150	20,000–1000–12	2500
e	150	20,000–1200–10	3000
f	150	20,000–1500–8	3750
g	75	20,000–1000–12	2500
h	100	24,000–1350–10	3000
i	80	24,000–1125–12	2500
j	125	24,000–1688–8	3750
k	175	20,000–900–12	2500
l			
m			
n			
o			

Required (for the case assigned):

(a) To evolve the first design by assuming only t/d and the dead load at one-third to one-half of the live load. Solve algebraically for the required d and choose the corresponding pan, having meantime corrected the dead load.

(b) Make a second design, assuming a different pan depth at the outset and striving for better *steel economy*.

(c) Study *over-all economy* by taking the steel at 9 cents per lb. in place, and concrete (including form costs) at \$45 per cu. yd. Report which of your two designs is best. Steel weighs 490 lb. per cu. ft.

If uncertainties develop, *investigate* designs after choosing standard bars but before making the two final design sketches. Refer to Art. 2–7.

2–11. Beam Investigation by the Moment of Inertia Method. It is possible to *investigate* any reinforced concrete beam by computing the moment of inertia of the transformed section and using the traditional Mc/I expression to find the stresses. Irregular sections, especially, are most easily handled by this method, since it sidesteps the necessity for the determination of the location of the centroid of the compressive force, C.

EXAMPLE 2–13

Reinvestigate the double reinforced beam of Example 2–8 by the Mc/I method. Refer to Fig. 2–9.

Solution: The neutral axis is found by the usual method to be 6.52 in. down. (Example 2–8.)

Moment of inertia of the transformed section about the neutral axis:

$$\text{Concrete,} \quad \frac{bd^3}{3} = \frac{8(6.52)^3}{3} \qquad\qquad = \quad 741$$

$$\text{Transf. steel,} \ (n-1)Ay^2 = 9(1.2)[3.96]^2 = \quad 169$$
$$n(Ay^2) = 10(2.27)[9.38]^2 = 1997$$
$$I = 2907 \text{ in.}^4$$

$$f_c = \frac{Mc}{I} = \frac{50.4(12,000)(6.52)}{2907} \qquad = 1356 \text{ psi}$$

$$f_{sc} = \frac{nMc}{I} = \frac{10(50.4)(12,000)(3.96)}{2907} = 8230$$

$$f_{st} = \frac{nMc}{I} = \frac{10(50.4)(12,000)(9.38)}{2907} = 19,500 \qquad\qquad Ans.$$

Obviously this method would be cumbersome for *designing* beams. The *internal couple method*, $Ca = Ta = M$, illustrated repeatedly throughout this chapter, is useful both in investigating and designing.

2–12. Doubly Reinforced Beam Investigation by the 2n Approxima-tion to Creep Effect. As mentioned in Art. 1–14 of Chapter 1, concrete is not truly elastic. It **creeps** with lapse of time even under small loads. This phenomenon, formerly called *plastic flow*, practically ceases after a few years. In the meantime a redistribution of stress takes place in members such as columns and double reinforced beams wherein concrete and steel *share* a compressive stress. The creeping concrete gradually relieves itself of part of its stress by unloading it upon the unyielded compression steel. The **2n creep method** of beam investigation recognizes that such steel may be stressed to fully twice the corresponding elastic value by applying a factor of 2 in neutral axis, moment of inertia, and steel stress calculations. (See ACI Code, Sec. 706(b), of Appendix J.)

EXAMPLE 2–14

Reinvestigate the doubly reinforced beam of Example 2–8 by the 2n creep method and compare the results with those of Example 2–13.

Solution: Referring to Fig. 2–9, the neutral axis will be given by:

$$4(kd)^2 + [2(10) - 1](1.2)[kd - 2.56] = 10(2.27)[15.90 - kd]$$

$$kd = 6.03 \text{ in.}$$

The moment of inertia of the transformed section will be:

$$\text{Concrete, } \frac{bd^3}{3} = \frac{8(6.03)^3}{3} \qquad\qquad = \quad 585.$$

$$\text{Comp. steel, } \quad 2Ay^2 = [2(10) - 1](1.2)[3.47]^2 = \quad 274.$$

$$\text{Tens. steel, } \quad Ay^2 = 10(2.27)[9.87]^2 \qquad\quad = 2214.$$

$$\overline{\qquad\qquad 3073. \text{ in.}^4}$$

Now

$$M/I = \frac{50.4(12,000)}{3073} = 196.7$$

So,

	2n Creep	Elastic
$f_c = \dfrac{Mc}{I} = 196.7(6.03) \qquad = 1{,}088$ psi		1,356
$f_{sc} = 2n \dfrac{Mc}{I} = 20(196.7)(3.47) = 13{,}680$		8,230
$f_{st} = n \dfrac{Mc}{I} = 10(196.7)(9.87) \quad = 19{,}420$		19,500

Note the much greater stress in the compression reinforcement when creep is recognized.

Alternate Procedure: A simpler and better method is first to compute the increased n value from $E_s/\tfrac{1}{2}E_c$, and then to perform the calculations in every respect as formerly, as in Example 2–8 or 2–13. By so recalculating Example 2–14 the following results will be obtained:

$$kd = 7.84 \text{ in.,} \qquad f_c = 972, \qquad f_{sc} = 13{,}100, \qquad f_{st} = 20{,}000 \text{ psi}$$

Note that the resulting creep (later) value of f_c is only about $\tfrac{7}{10}$ of the elastic value, as it should be. Refer to Art. 1–14 and Fig. 1–6 in Chapter 1.

This method has general application, such as to the investigation of the *final* value of f_c in both *singly*[11] and doubly reinforced beams; and to *designing* which recognizes creep, once a decreased allowable f_c and a greatly increased n value have been agreed upon. Refer to the *Comments* at the end of Example 10–3 in Chapter 10.

Mc/I METHOD AND CREEP PROBLEMS

Take 2500-lb. concrete, ACI Specification: 20,000–1125–12.

Problem 2–21. Find the maximum safe bending moment for the precast reinforced concrete joist of Fig. 2–16(a) by the Mc/I elastic method.

Note. When the slab width of a T-beam is so narrow in comparison with the stem thickness, the compression concrete in the stem should be included in strength calculations.

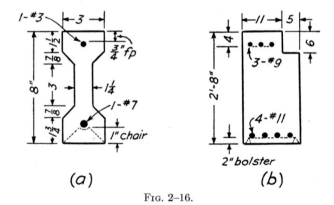

(a)   (b)

FIG. 2–16.

Problem 2–22. Find the maximum safe bending moment for the irregular doubly-reinforced beam of Fig. 2–16(b) by the Mc/I method, (a) considering concrete elastic, and (b) considering concrete creep, following the ACI Code.

Problem 2–23. Recalculate the stresses in the beam of Example 2–14 recognizing creep, following the $\tfrac{1}{2}E_c$ *Alternate Procedure* outlined therein. Also tabulate a comparison of the stresses found by all three methods, and comment upon the trends thereof.

---

[11] The *pn diagram*, Plate V of Appendix A, gives k for all values of n.

Skidmore, Owings and Merrell, Architects

PLATE 2–1. Construction photograph of pan construction T-beam floor with curved top pans in place, ready for the setting of the steel. Note that all end pans are tapered to give greater stem width near the supports, where shear and diagonal tension stresses tend to be high.

The wall in the foreground has been waterproofed below the final grade line.

2–13. General Summary of Reinforced Concrete Beam Flexure. In calculating the bending strength of reinforced concrete beams, the relatively small tensile strength of the concrete is ignored and the steel is relied upon to take all the tensile stress.

By conceiving the steel to be transformed into an elastically equivalent amount of imaginary concrete, a homogeneous section is created, to which ordinary mechanics principles may be applied.

It is quite necessary to distinguish clearly between situations involving the *investigation* of a section of known dimensions and those of a *design* nature wherein dimensions must be solved for, since the methods of attack in the two cases differ widely.

To design intelligently it is necessary to visualize the internal couple, equate it to the applied external bending moment, and provide enough concrete and steel to safely resist the compressive and tensile forces, respectively.

Beams are said to be "balanced" when both the steel and concrete allowable bending stresses are realized simultaneously.

For any given bending moment and allowable stresses, there are many combinations of beam breadth and depth which will produce balanced designs.

In *designing* singly reinforced beams, determine the neutral axis from the diagram of allowable stresses when not more than one of the following dimensions is already set, namely: b, d, and A_s. *Less freedom makes a balanced beam an impossibility.*

To save steel, beams that are decidedly shallower than required for balance should be doubly reinforced.

To design a doubly reinforced beam, first find how much of the applied bending moment can be safely resisted if only balanced single reinforcement is provided. Then take care of the remaining bending moment by additional steel in the bottom and some in the top.

Due to the time-dependent creep property of concrete, the compressive reinforcement of a beam becomes more highly stressed than the common elastic theory indicates. Such steel must be well tied in place.

The effect of loading and creep upon beam stresses may be approximated by taking an n value of two times the common figure (at early ages, four times after one year) and calculating steel and concrete stresses in the usual manner.

QUESTIONS

1. Define the terms bending moment, beam shear, centroid, internal couple, transformed section, free-body diagram, reinforced concrete, and balanced beam.

2. Distinguish clearly between the design and investigation types of beam problems.

3. Why not use the ratio of the two allowable stresses to transform the steel of a beam? Explain.

4. In singly reinforced rectangular beam design, give, qualitatively, the reasoning behind the method of designing (a) a beam deeper than necessary, and (b) a beam shallower than it should be. What is an "over-reinforced" beam?

5. Tell in detail how to design a uniformly loaded simple span solid slab.

6. Are all doubly reinforced beams balanced beams? Explain.

7. State what should be included in a final design sketch.

8. Are all T-shaped beams truly T-beams? Explain.

9. Tell in detail how to design a doubly reinforced beam.

10. Tell in detail how to find the centroid of compressive forces for a doubly reinforced T-beam.

11. In what single situation may the arm of the internal couple be assumed? How is the value later corrected?

12. What are the advantages of the moment of inertia method (a) for investigations, (b) for designing?

13. Tell how to design an economical pan-construction T-beam floor.

14. Formulate a general rule governing the use of the allowable stresses to find the neutral axis in the design of rectangular beams, T-beams, and doubly reinforced beams.

REVIEW PROBLEMS

Take ACI 2500-lb concrete and specification: 20,000–1125–12, unless otherwise noted.

Problem 2–24. Calculate the maximum safe D.L. + L.L. bending moment for this column section of Fig. 2–17 if used as a beam.

Note. Treat the two layers of tension steel separately.

Problem 2–25. Calculate the required amount of single reinforcement for a rectangular cantilever beam 14 in. wide by 30 in. total depth which carries a uniformly distributed live load of 6.1 kips per ft. over its 8-ft. length. The required cover for steel is 2 in.

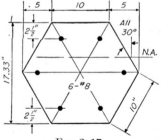

Fig. 2–17.

Problem 2–26. Same as Problem 2–19, except that the slab is 15 in. by 3½ in.   *Ans. $A_s = 3.50$ sq. in.*

What new situation was encountered?

Problem 2–27. Determine how much stronger the beam designed in Example 2–7 would be if an additional 0.6 sq. in. of steel content were added (a) at the bottom, (b) at the top, (c) at both bottom and top (elastic method).

Problem 2–28. Redesign the double reinforcement for the beam of Example 2–7, recognizing creep. Check by an investigation, as in Example 2–14. Take the same class of concrete as originally used.

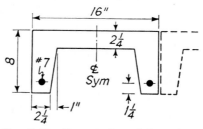

FIG. 2–18. Precast channel floor slab.

Ans. Decrease the top steel to one #7 bar. The investigation will then show:

$$kd = 6.51 \ in., \quad f_c = 1330 \ psi,$$
$$f_{sc} = 16,400, \quad f_{st} = 19,400.$$

Problem 2–29. Calculate the maximum safe bending moment.

Take ACI 3750-lb. concrete and specification.

Problem 2–30. A 16 by 32 in. rectangular beam has 3–#9 bars centered 3 in. from the top. The bottom reinforcement consists of 5–#9 bars centered 3 in. from the bottom, plus 2–#9 in a second layer centered $2\frac{1}{2}$ in. higher up. Find the maximum safe bending moment.

Problem 2–31. Conservatively compute balanced single reinforcement for

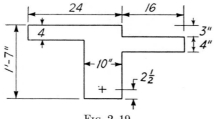

FIG. 2–19.

this beam, and report the corresponding maximum safe bending moment.

Problem 2–32. Accurately calculate the maximum safe bending moment,

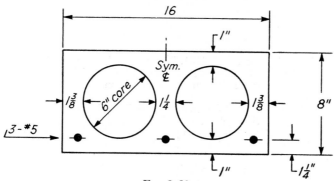

FIG. 2–20.

for this Flexicore-type of section by the Mc/I method. Refer to Plate XI of Appendix A.

Take ACI $n = 8$ concrete and specification.

CHAPTER 3

BOND, SHEAR, DIAGONAL TENSION, AND ANCHORAGE

3–0. Introduction.* Although the concrete in the tension side of a reinforced concrete beam is considered of no value in bending, its *bond* strength is indispensable for preventing bar slippage.   In addition,

Professor Willis A. Slater, 1878–1931, Research Professor of Engineering Materials and Director of the Fritz Engineering Laboratory, Lehigh University. A careful and indefatigable investigator, well known for his findings on concrete flexure and diagonal tension.

Chairman of the Reinforced Concrete Column Investigation Committee, his most notable work was with The Arch Dam Investigation of the Engineering Foundation, 1925–1927. His World War I paper upon the feasibility of constructing ships of concrete won him the Wason Medal of The American Concrete Institute.

such concrete is relied upon to help resist certain *diagonal tension* forces that result from beam shear. This chapter is devoted entirely to problems illustrating these two functions.

---

* Preferably the use of the beam flexure formulas and charts of Appendix A should be mastered before taking up Chapter 3.

EXAMPLE 3-1(a)

Consider the beam of Fig. 3-0(a) and (g) weightless, and carrying only the 18-kip load. It is required to compute the bond, shear, and diagonal tension unit stresses in the concrete at a section $24\frac{1}{2}$ in. from the left reaction, and to report upon safety. Take ACI 3000-lb. concrete and specification. The allowable stresses will be found in Table 1-4 of Chapter 1, or in Sec. 305 of Appendix J.

✳ **3-1. Calculation of the Concrete Stresses Related to Beam Shear by the Unit Slice Method.** The shear and moment diagrams for the beam were drawn at (b) and (c), and a 1-in. **unit slice** taken out at the section in question, for study as a *free body*, as at (d). The values of C and T on each side of the slice were obtained from the bending moments, using $\frac{7}{8}d$ as the arm of the internal couples, as is customary in bond, shear, and diagonal tension calculations.[1] A check was made by a summation of moments about the point p:

$$(12)(1) - (21.43 - 20.57)(14) = 0$$

Bond Unit Stress. At the bottom of the beam, the inequality of the two tensile forces, T_{24} and T_{25}, on each side of the unit slice, is made up by a horizontal force of adhesion between the steel and the concrete which is called *bond*. The bond unit stress, u, is the unit shear in an imaginary glue between the two materials and is an indication of the tendency for the bars to slip through the concrete.

In the case at hand, dividing the difference of the T's by the contact area:

$$u = \frac{(21.43 - 20.57)1000}{2(1.13)(\pi)} = 121 \text{ psi.}$$

For 3000-lb. concrete, the ACI Code, Sec. 305, allows u to be 300 psi, assuming deformed bars. Therefore the beam is safe in bond at the section taken.

Horizontal Shear Unit Stress. The forces on the slice may be simplified, as indicated at (e), from which one sees that **all horizontal planes below the neutral axis are subject to a horizontal shearing force equal to ΔT, the difference of the T's over the span distance taken.**

Let v be the horizontal shear unit stress in the concrete below the neutral axis. Then in the example:

$$v = \frac{(21.43 - 20.57)1000}{6} = 143 \text{ psi. See Fig. 3-0(f).}$$

---

[1] For T-beams use $0.9d$. In most shear-related calculations the rounded values give sufficient precision.

Vertical Shear Unit Stress. Consider at (h) the forces on a 1-in. cube of concrete taken from the tension side of the slice at (d). The horizontal shearing forces, v, 1 in. apart, form a counterclockwise couple which is balanced by a clockwise couple consisting of corresponding *vertical* forces, v. Therefore the **unit vertical shear equals the unit horizontal shear,**[2] and is 143 psi in this case.

Diagonal[3] *Tension Unit Stress.* Materials finally fail by direct stress or shear, whichever is the weaker. Concrete has a unit compressive strength of over three times the shear strength,[A,B] but the tensile strength is less than one-half of the shear strength. If the cube's four shear forces, v, are progressively increased, they combine into resultant forces acting in the particular diagonal direction indicated, producing *diagonal tension* in the cube, and early failure by tensile cracking perpendicular to the resultant forces, long before the shear failure strength of the cube is reached. Refer to Table 1–2 of Chapter 1.

Returning to (h) of the figure, the resultant diagonal tensile force of $1.41v$ lb. acts on a fracture area of 1.41 sq. in., so the diagonal tension unit stress equals v psi, the same as the shear unit stress. Therefore:

In the tension side of reinforced concrete beams, the unit horizontal shear, vertical shear, and diagonal tension stresses are equal at any given point.

Allowable Diagonal Tension Unit Stress. For 3000-lb. concrete, the ACI Code allows a unit diagonal tension stress of only 90 psi. Since our beam has a v of 143 psi, it is unsafe in shear and diagonal tension at the section studied.

Query. Show the forces upon a unit cube from the compression side of the beam. Will diagonal tension cracks develop there? Explain.

Generalization: From the preceding development and discussion:

$$M_{n+1} - M_n = V \qquad \text{(from fundamental mechanics)}$$

Therefore:

$$(T_{n+1} - T_n)jd = V$$

$$T_{\text{diff.}} = \Delta T = \frac{V}{jd} \tag{3-1}$$

From which:

$$\text{Bond unit stress, } u = \frac{V}{\Sigma_o jd} \tag{3-2}$$

---

[2] This important principle of mechanics should be reviewed.

[3] Throughout this discussion, 45° diagonal directions are meant.

[A] The superscript letters refer to items of the Bibliography at the end of each chapter.

wherein Σ_o is total bar perimeter.   Therefore it is evident that:

$$\text{Diagonal tension unit stress, } v = \frac{V}{bjd} \qquad (3\text{-}3)$$

Part I. Simply Supported and Cantilever Beams

3–2. Diagonal Tension Reinforcement. Numerous tests[C] have shown that the type of ultimate failure pictured in Fig. 3–1(a) may be expected if the diagonal tension unit stress in the concrete at the design load is appreciably greater than $0.03f'_c$, or 90 psi for 3000-lb. concrete.   In the central part of the span, where the bending moment was large, the vertical cracks attest to the weakness of the concrete in bending tension;

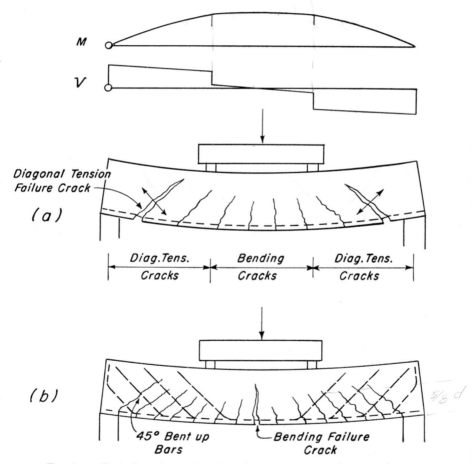

FIG. 3–1. Typical cracking of reinforced concrete beams when tested.

but since the beam as a whole failed elsewhere, the bottom steel obviously was adequate for bending. In the outer portions of the span, where the beam shear was great, the cracks took the general 45° direction shown; and since additional steel was not placed across the direction of these diagonal tension cracks, some opened widely and caused failure of the beam.

In the beam of Fig. 3–1(b), 45° reinforcement was used in the outer portions, in the direction of the diagonal tension. Instead of a few large diagonal cracks, numerous small ones developed but did not open. This beam proved appreciably stronger than the beam at (a), and finally failed, due to the yielding of the bottom steel, as indicated by the open crack near midspan.

Diagonal tension reinforcement is used as insurance against the development of noticeable diagonal tension cracks. It is often called *web reinforcement* to distinguish it from the flange, or flexural, reinforcement used in the tension side.

To be effective, the 45° diagonal tension reinforcement should be firmly attached to the flexural steel, as by the welding pictured in Fig. 3–0(i); or be integral with it, as when bottom bars are quite commonly *bent up* for this purpose. Otherwise, it will tend to slip horizontally when the load is applied.

SHEAR, BOND, AND DIAGONAL TENSION PRACTICE PROBLEMS

For these two problems, take 2500-lb. concrete, specification: 20,000–1125-12, $f_v = 20{,}000$, $v = 50$ and $u = 100$ psi (plain bars).

Problem 3–1. A singly reinforced beam carries a uniform dead load plus live load of 2.3 kips per lin. ft. over a simple span of 16 ft., center to center of 12-in. walls, and two concentrated loads of 12 kips each symmetrically located 3 ft. each side of the center line of span. The beam is 16 in. by 25 in., ($b \times d$), and has three #10 plain bars.

(a) Investigate the beam for both horizontal shear and bond unit stresses at the following three sections:

> 2 ft. 6 in. from center of span
> 5 ft. from center of span
> at the inside face of wall.

(a′) Alternately work individually at three sections s, $s + 28$ in. and $s + 56$ in. from the center of span, as assigned by the instructor.

Work from fundamental principles, taking unit slices.

Make for each section a free body sketch of the slice taken, showing *all* forces (there are more than five of them) exactly as applied, with their *values* as computed. The summations $H \equiv 0$, $V \equiv 0$, and $M \equiv 0$ must be satisfied on each sketch.

(b) Check by the formulas.

(c) Make a graph from the findings, plotting V, v, and u vertically against span distance horizontally. Plot also the allowable values of v and u and *report* upon the safety of the beam in these respects.

Problem 3–2. In the sections pictured in Fig. 3–2, the steel indicates the tension side and the neutral axes are at the levels shown.

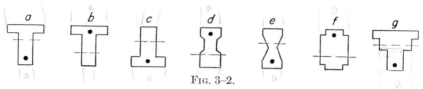

Fig. 3–2.

(a) Show clearly for each case what width to use in calculations for maximum diagonal tension unit stress.

(b) Formulate a rule defining the width to take in computing unit diagonal tension for any section.

(c) Show clearly, for each case pictured, the width to take in calculating p, the steel ratio, for use with the bending stress charts, where applicable. (Appendix A.)

EXAMPLE 3–1(b)

45-Degree Web Reinforcement. **Taking the beam of Fig. 3–0, find the unit stress in the 45° diagonal tension reinforcement at the section shown if, in (i), the spacing s is 10 in. and the bars are #4 size.**

Solution: As found previously in Example 3–1(a), a unit diagonal tension of 143 psi exists over the whole $(1.41)(\frac{5}{8})d$ length of the potential 45° crack pictured. Here we are concerned only with the diagonal tension which is tributary to the 45° bar crossing the section, as pictured.

Tests have shown that it is safe to rely upon the tensile strength of concrete to help the steel resist *diagonal* tension. Ordinarily,[4] the Code permits a maximum of $0.03f'_c$ to be assigned to the concrete. Subtracting 90 from 143 leaves 53 psi to be taken care of by the steel. This remainder, or *excess*, is called v'.

In studying diagonal tension reinforcement, the key thought is that the tension in a 45° diagonal bar, in pounds, equals the excess diagonal tension tributary to it which the concrete cannot assume.

Considering the middle 45° bar of Fig. 3–0(i), and the region tributary to it, the tension[5] therein will be, in pounds:

$$0.20(f_v) = 53(6)(0.707)(10)$$

---

[4] The particular continuous beams which cannot be so assigned as much as $0.03 f'_c$ are taken up in Art. 3–17.

[5] Current experimental researches are revealing that resistance to diagonal tension failure also is affected by the percentage of flexure reinforcement, the proximity of concentrated loads and probably other factors. Until these findings have led to recodification, the relatively *simple* diagonal tension hypothesis presented herein amply serves to justify the established code formulas for stirrup and bentup bar content.

Then

$$f_v = 11{,}250 \text{ psi}, \quad < 20{,}000, \text{ safe but wasteful.}$$

Algebraically:

$$T_v = A_v f_v = v'b(0.707)s$$

or

$$f_v = \frac{0.707sbv'}{A_v}$$

EXAMPLE 3–1(c)

Find the *correct* spacing, s, for the 45° #4 bars.

Solution: Set f_v equal to 20,000 psi and state the *bar tension* expression in terms of s:

$$0.20(20{,}000) = 53(6)(0.707)s$$
$$s = 17.8 \text{ in.}$$

Algebraically:

$$T_v = A_v f_v = v'b(0.707)s$$

But $v' = \dfrac{V'}{bjd}$, where V' is the portion of the whole beam shear at the

section which is taken care of by the steel.

Therefore:

$$s = \frac{A_v f_v jd}{0.707V'} . \qquad \text{Memorize.[6]} \quad (3\text{–}4)$$

for 45° diagonal tension reinforcement.

3–3. Stirrups. Although the ideal arrangement of diagonal tension reinforcement is in the direction of that tension, namely at 45°, practical considerations often dictate that vertical steel be used instead, as in Fig. 3–0(j). Fig. 3–4(a) also illustrates the widely used U-shaped *stirrups*. To be effective, stirrups must extend around the flexural reinforcement and be normal[7] thereto so that they will not slide along the flexural steel as tension develops. Refer to ACI Sec. 904(c).

EXAMPLE 3–1(d)

Vertical Web Reinforcement. **Again taking the beam of Fig. 3–0, find the unit stress in the #4 bar welded *vertical* reinforcement, as at (j), if the spacing, s is 10 in.**

---

[6] The reason for eliminating v' in favor of V' will become apparent in a succeeding example.

[7] Throughout this textbook the stirrups discussed are vertical and are unwelded to the flexure reinforcement.

Solution: Referring to the preceding example, (b), **equate the *component* of bar tension *in the diagonal tension direction,*** in pounds, to the **excess diagonal tension in the concrete:**

$$0.707 A_v f_v = 0.707(0.20)f_v = 53(6)(0.707)(10) \qquad \text{[Fig. 3-0(j).]}$$

Canceling coefficients and solving:

$$f_v = 15,900 \text{ psi}$$

EXAMPLE 3–1(e)

Find the *correct* spacing for the vertical #4 bars.

Solution: Set f_v equal to 20,000 psi and state the 45° *component of bar tension* in terms of s:

$$0.707(0.20)(20,000) = 53(6)(0.707)s$$
$$s = 12.6 \text{ in.}$$

(But see ACI Code, Sec. 806.)

Comparing the results of Examples 3–1(c) and (e), it is obvious that vertical steel is only 0.707 times as effective as 45° steel, since the bars must be spaced correspondingly closer together.

Algebraically:

$$0.707(A_v f_v) = v'b(0.707)s$$

But

$$v' = \frac{V'}{bjd}$$

Therefore:

$$s = \frac{A_v f_v jd}{V'}$$

Memorize.   (3–5)
for (vertical) stirrups.

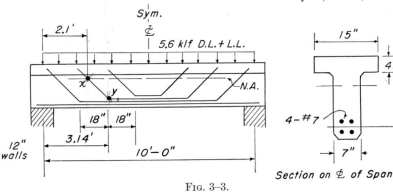

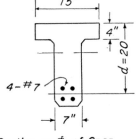

Section on ℄ of Span

Fɪɢ. 3–3.

DIAGONAL TENSION STEEL DRILL PROBLEM

Problem 3–3. Given the beam and loading of Fig. 3–3. Take ACI 2500-lb. concrete and specification: 20,000–1125–12, $f_v = 20,000$, $v = 75$ psi without diagonal tension steel.

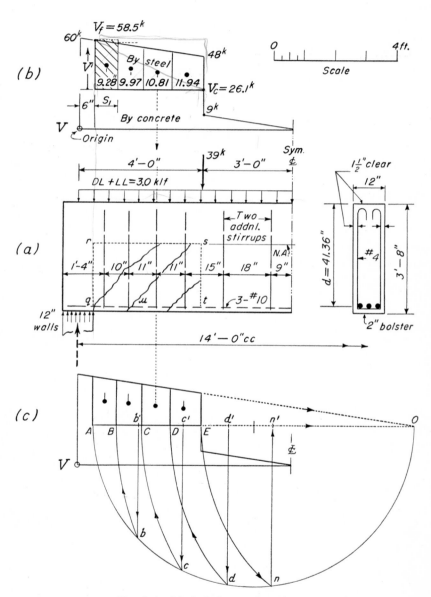

Fig. 3–4. Methods for spacing stirrups.

Required:

(a) If flexure steel is bent up at 45° as shown, compute $f_v =$ in the middle bar at x, and also at y.   *Ans.* _____ *and* _____ *psi.* $Kd = 7.5''$

(b) If no bars are bent up, but #5 bar stirrups (having almost exactly the same useful cross section) are used at the same 18-in. spacing, find f_v at the same section 2.1 ft. inward.   *Ans.* _____ *psi.*

(c) Same as (b), except that the stirrups are spaced 13 in. center to center.   *Ans.* _____ *psi.*

(d) Compare and discuss the three results.

EXAMPLE 3–2

The Design of Stirrup Reinforcement. **Given the beam and loading of Fig. 3–4(a). The concrete is 2000-lb., ACI Specification: 20,000–900–15, allowable stress in diagonal tension reinforcement, f_v, = 20,000. The allowable unit diagonal tension, v, is 60 psi upon the concrete where stirrups are absent, 160 psi where stirrups (vertical) are present. The allowable bond stress, u, is 200 psi.**

Required:[8]

(a) To check the beam for safe bond stress.

(b) To demonstrate that diagonal tension reinforcement is needed, and to state where.

(c) To determine the maximum suitable stirrup *size*.

(d) To calculate the theoretically required *number* of stirrups needed.

(e) To *space* the above stirrups correctly.

(f) To provide the additional empirically required stirrups.

Procedure: Since bond stress and diagonal tension are proportional to the beam shear, *always begin by drawing the shear diagram, V, as at (b) of the figure,* preferably to scale.

Solution of (a):

$$ v = \frac{V}{b j d} $$

$$ \text{Max. } u = \frac{V_f}{\Sigma_o j d} = \frac{58,500}{3(1.27)(\pi)(\%)(41.36)} = 135 \text{ psi.} $$

$$ \Delta \vdash $$
$$ b \, (1) $$

Ans.(a). <200, ∴ O.K.

Solution of (b): The maximum unit diagonal tension occurs at the *inside face* of the wall, since the opening of cracks farther out is prevented by the upward pressure of the end reaction, as shown at (a) of Fig. 3–4.

$$ v_{max} = \frac{V_f}{b j d} = \frac{58,500}{12(\%)(41.36)} = 135 \text{ psi} $$

Ans. (b). > 60, < 160, use stirrups.

---

[8] An investigation will reveal that the beam is safe in bending.

Theoretically, diagonal tension steel is not needed in the central part of the span where v is less than 60 psi:

$$V_c = vbjd = \frac{60(12)(\frac{7}{8})(41.36)}{1000} = 26.1 \text{ kips, the limiting shear.}$$

Figure 3–4(a) shows that the region *qrst* must have diagonal tension reinforcement.

3–4. Choice of Stirrup Size. Stirrups must be small and numerous enough that every potential diagonal tension crack is crossed by at least one of them. In Fig. 3–4(a), the crack beginning at *u* would have been uncovered if the stirrup spacing had been about 0.6*d* or greater. Referring to Sec. 806 of the ACI Code, one sees that 0.5*d* is the maximum spacing permitted in this case.[9]

To find the largest stirrup that can be used economically, consider the spacing to have the maximum permissible value at the point of minimum V' value:

Solution of (c) of Example 3–2: Rearranging Formula 3–5:

$$\text{Max } A_v = \frac{V's}{f_v jd} = \frac{21,900(0.5)(41.36)}{20,000(\frac{7}{8})(41.36)}$$

$$= 0.63 \text{ sq. in.}$$

Since all stirrups consist of two bar areas:

        Ans.(c). The #5 stirrup is the max. size. Conveniently use #4 size.

Stirrups also must be far enough apart that the coarse aggregate stones will not wedge between them. The ACI Code, Sec. 505(a), requires that the clear distance between stirrups shall not be less than $1\frac{1}{3}$ times the maximum size of the coarse aggregate, and never less than one inch. Any infringement upon this requirement is discoverable after computing the width of the first (outermost) stirrup region.

3–5. The Theoretical Number of Stirrups Needed. If Formula 3–5 is rewritten in the form:

$$sV' = A_v f_v jd$$

the left-hand side expresses geometrically the area on the shear diagram which one stirrup can take care of.

Then the theoretically required number of stirrups needed in one end of a beam between the V_f and the V_c ordinates will be the whole sV' area of the shear diagram divided by the sV' formula value for one stirrup.

---

[9] ACI Sec. 806 sets a limit of 0.25*d* if *total v* values are high.

Solution of (d) of Example 3–2: Referring to Fig. 3–4(b), the *theoretically* required number of stirrups will be:

$$N = \frac{\Sigma s V'}{s V'} = \frac{0.5(32.4 + 21.9)(42)}{2(0.2)(20)(\frac{7}{8})(41.36)} = \frac{1140.^{k''}}{290.^{k''}} = 3.9$$

This means four stirrups in each end of this beam.

STIRRUP PRACTICE PROBLEMS

Problem 3–4. (a) For the beam of Fig. 3–5, show clearly on a sketch the portions of the span needing diagonal tension reinforcement. Take ACI 2000-lb. concrete and specification, including $f_v = 20,000$, $v = 60$ and 160, $u = 200$ psi (deformed bars).

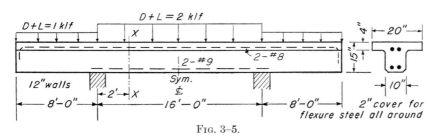

FIG. 3–5.

(b) Calculate the theoretical total number of #9 wire stirrups needed for the beam.

(c) Find how far apart stirrups should be at Section X–X.

(d) Calculate the maximum bond stress in the beam.

Problem 3–5. Investigate the diagonal tension in the pan T-beam designed in Example 2–12 of Chapter 2, assuming 12-in. walls, and compute the size and number of stirrups needed, if any. Take ACI 3000-lb. concrete and specification. Refer to Table 1–4 at the end of Chapter 1, or Art. 305 of the ACI Code for allowable stresses.

Problem 3–6. Examine the beam of Problem 3–3, Fig. 3–3, for maximum bending, bond, and diagonal tension unit stress, and state whether or not it can be made safe if no flexure steel is bent up, but stirrups provided. Take ACI $n = 12$ concrete and specification. Deformed bars.

Partial Answer: No.

3–6. The Step Method of Stirrup Spacing. Again refer to Fig. 3–4(b). Since V' decreases toward the *center* of the span while the sV' for one stirrup remains constant, the width of the regions, s, increases; so the stirrups become farther and farther apart, though not in a true linear relation.

In the Step Method a start is made by dividing the sV' shear area for one stirrup by the V' at the inside face of the wall, as in the first line of the accompanying Table 3–1. This gives a slightly approximate value of s_1, the width of the first *stirrup region*, near the middle of which the first stirrup finally will be located.

TABLE 3–1

SOLUTION OF EXAMPLE 3–2(e)—THE SPACING OF STIRRUPS

Region	Approx. Region Widths, s	Subsequent V'	Corrected Region Widths, s
1	$290/32.4 = 8.95''$	30.16^k	$9.28''$
2	$290/30.16 = 9.61''$	27.76	$9.97''$
3	$290/27.76 = 10.43''$	25.15	$10.81''$
4	$290/25.15 = 11.52''$	—	$11.94''$
	$\overline{\quad\quad\quad 40.51''}$		$\overline{42.00''}$
			check

$$\frac{42.00}{40.51} = 1.036 = \text{correction factor to apply}$$

In the third column, the stepped down value of V' at the right side of the first region (30.16^k) is calculated and used to find the width of the second region, and so on.

When the approximate widths of N regions have been so found, a correction factor, 1.036 in this case, is computed and used to expand the region widths to fit the spanwise distance needing stirrups.

The center of each region is judged *visually* and the stirrups drawn in. Finally, *the stirrup spacings are scaled to the nearest whole inch,* including the measurement to the end of the beam, and put on the drawing, as in Fig. 3–4(a).

3–7. The Graphic Method of Stirrup Spacing. Figure 3–4(c) illustrates an alternate method of spacing stirrups, originator unknown, which is applicable also when the V' portion of the shear diagram is a triangle, as it is in single-span beams carrying only uniform load. This method can be proved to be exact.

Procedure:
1. Draw the V' portion of the shear diagram accurately to scale.
2. Calculate N, the *number* of stirrups needed, as formerly.
3. Prolong the upper and lower straight-line boundaries of the V'area to an intersection at O.
4. With A at the outer lower corner of the V' area, draw a semicircle with diameter AO.
5. From E, the inner lower corner of the V' area, describe an arc about O as a center, and intersecting the semicircle at n.
6. Project n vertically to n' on the diameter, and subdivide An' equally at b', c', and d' (etc.) into N parts.

7. Project b', c', and d' vertically to intersect the semicircle at b, c, and d, respectively.

8. With O as a center, describe arcs from b, c, and d, intersecting AE at B, C, and D, the desired interior boundaries of the stirrup regions.

9. Draw the stirrups from the centers of the regions.

It will be found that the Graphic Method is better suited to cases in which the V' *area* is triangular, or nearly so. When the area approaches the rectangular, the Step Method excels.

3–8. Additional Web Reinforcement Empirically Required. The common assumption of uniformly distributed loadings, or concentrated loads in fixed off-center locations, is sometimes unjustifiable for designing web reinforcement, since it results in beam shear diagrams having very small ordinates in the central portion of a span. In the past some codes have required that the shear diagram be arbitrarily elevated at midspan as much as one-fourth the end shear value before its being used for designing stirrups or bent-up bars.

In 1956 the ACI revised Sec. 801(d) to require that all flexural members must have some web reinforcement *additional* to that required by the common theory thus far presented.

For simply supported and cantilever beams the web reinforcement must now be continued a distance d beyond the theoretically computed V_c limiting point. When uniformly distributed loading only is involved, the V' ordinate of the shear diagram becomes zero at the V_c point, so the $d/2$ Code limitation on stirrup spacing will normally rule on both sides of the V_c point. Usually, *two additional stirrups* spaced at $d/2$ in. will be sufficient.

For a case of the combination of uniform and concentrated loads:

Solution of (f) of Example 3–2: Refer to Fig. 3–4(a) and (b). The remaining 3-ft. distance between the V_c point and midspan is less than d. Furthermore, if the first additional stirrup is conservatively assigned *all* the 9-kip maximum remaining shear, the calculated permissible spacing becomes, by Art. 3–5, $290/9 = 32$ in., or more,[10] which is greater than the $d/2$ limiting spacing of 20.7 in. Therefore:

> *Ans.* (*f*). *Center two additional stirrups,* 18 *in. apart,*[10] *in the* 3-*ft. central space, making a total of* 6–#4 *stirrups in each half of the beam, or* 12 *in all.*

Problem 3–7. Redesign the stirrups for the beam of Example 3–2, Fig. 3–4, taking 2500-lb. concrete. Use the Step Method and check by the Graphic Method.

---

[10] Attention is directed to another requirement for minimum size of web reinforcement, namely, ACI (new) Sec. 807, which demands that not less than $0.0015sb$ sq. in. be used. In the case at hand, $0.0015(18)(12) = 0.32$ sq. in. is required per stirrup space, versus the 0.40 sq. in. adequately provided.

Problem 3–8. It is desired to design a singly reinforced wall beam with stirrups, for ACI 2500-lb. concrete and specification:

$$f_s = f_v = 20,000, \qquad f_c = 1125, \qquad n = 12.$$

The v allowed for concrete $= 75$ psi, 150 with stirrups, spaced not over $d/2$. Allowable $u = 250$ psi (deformed bars). The aggregate maximum size is 1 in.

The beam is to be 13 in. wide. It is supported on 12-in. walls, and has a total length of 11 ft., 0 in., making the span for loading and bending calculations 10 ft., 0 in.

There is a central concentrated load of 85 kips, a uniformly distributed live load of 1.5 kips per lin. ft., and the dead load of the beam at 150 lb. per cu. ft.

Completely design both flexural steel and stirrups. Use not more than three bars for flexure, all in one layer, observing the minimum bar spacing and fireproofing clauses of the Code, Secs. 505(a) and 507(b), respectively. Design the total depth to some whole inch. See that maximum diagonal tension and bond stresses are not exceeded. Use deformed bars.

On a single $8\frac{1}{2}$ x 11 in. sheet of *good* graph paper, draw to the scale 1 in. = 10 in. a side view and a cross-sectional view of the beam, together with the shear diagram, *all in projection with each other*. Show all steel to scale.

Include on the shear diagram the corrected widths of the (tributary) stirrup regions.

The stirrup spacings are finally to be scaled to the nearest inch and so dimensioned. Completely dimension the concrete and the rest of the steel as for all final design sketches. Show standard hooks on the stirrups, per ACI Sec. 906.

✳ 3–9. Concrete Economy.

In Chapter 2, which covers bending stresses in beams, the economy of flexural steel was emphasized. At least two other factors affect over-all economy, namely, the amount of concrete and of formwork. The deepest possible beam requires the least steel, but tends to have an excessive amount of concrete which must not only be paid for but also carried as dead load. In the next example attention is directed toward using a minimum amount of concrete. The topic of over-all economy must await our further advances.

EXAMPLE 3–3

Given the cantilever beam and loading of Fig. 3–6, and 3000-lb. concrete, specification 20,000–1350–10, $f_v = 20,000$, $v = 90$ and 240, $u = 210$ psi (top bars). Required to proportion the beam for economy of concrete,[11] using stirrups for diagonal tension. Refer to ACI Sec. 803(c).

---

[11] To simplify the presentation of the fundamental principles involved, the stated load has been assumed to include an accurate estimate of the dead load.

Solution: For maximum economy, the concrete must work at the allowable, both in (a) diagonal tension and (b) bending.

For diagonal tension economy:[12]

$$v = \frac{V}{bjd}, \qquad \text{so} \qquad bd = \frac{V_f}{jv} = \frac{60{,}500}{(0.866)(240)} = 291 \qquad \text{(A)}$$

For bending economy:[13] $Ca = M = 1/2 f_c bkd[jd]$

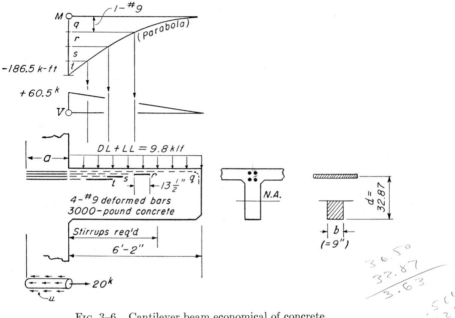

FIG. 3–6. Cantilever beam economical of concrete.

Therefore:

$$bd^2 = \frac{M}{1/2(f_c kj)} = \frac{186.5(12{,}000)}{675(0.403)(0.866)} = 9510 \qquad \text{(B)}$$

Solving Eqs. (A) and (B) simultaneously:

$$d_{\text{econ.}} = 32.70 \qquad b = 8.90 \text{ in.}, \qquad A_s = \frac{C}{f_s} = 3.96 \text{ sq. in.}$$

---

[12] The exact value of j is used here, so as to be consistent with the subsequent bending equation.

[13] Beginning at this point in this text the student is presumed to be familiar with the beam design charts, Plates I to IX of Appendix A. The author introduces them with the flexure formulas immediately after the students have completed their work in Chapter 2.

Try 4–#9 bars:

$$u = \frac{V}{\Sigma_o jd} = \frac{60,500}{4(1.13)(\pi)(0.866)(32.70)} = 150 \text{ psi.}$$

$$< 210, \quad \text{therefore satisfactory.}$$

Make total depth, $h = 36.50$, $d = 32.87$, $b = 9$ in.; use 4–#9 bars in two tiers. Stirrups are needed also.

Remark. Refer to Example 2–4 of Chapter 2 wherein the form of the above Eq. (B) was developed for the flexural design of a balanced beam. Note that while there are numerous sets of values of b and d which will satisfy Eq. (B), there is only one which satisfies both the diagonal tension and bending expressions, Eqs. (A) and (B).

CONCRETE ECONOMY PRACTICE PROBLEMS

—— **Problem 3–9.** Determine the theoretical b, d, and A_s for an economical rectangular cantilever beam 8 ft. long, and carrying 12 kips per lin. ft. D.L. + L.L. Take ACI 3000-lb. concrete and specification, 20,000–1350–10, $v = 90$, and 240 psi.

(a) If stirrup diagonal tension steel is to be used.

(b) If no diagonal tension steel is to be used.

$\qquad$ *Answers:* (a) $b = 10.92$, $\quad d = 42.24$ *in.,* $\quad A_s = 6.28$ *sq. in.*
$\qquad\qquad\quad$ (b) $b = 77.60$, $\quad d = 15.87$ *in.,* $\quad A_s = 16.72$ *sq. in.*

Problem 3–10. Derive a single expression for economy of concrete in reinforced concrete beams.

(a) For rectangular beams.

(b) For T-beams.

Problem 3–11. Redesign the cantilever beam of Example 3–3, Fig. 3–6, for economy of concrete, using no diagonal tension reinforcement. Correct for the increased dead load. Keep the 3000-lb. concrete and specification of the example. Comment.

Determine the anchorages, as in Example 3–4, and draw boldly to scale.

3–10. Theoretical Minimum Length of Flexural Bars. The amount of reinforcement needed for bending at every section of a beam is closely proportional to the bending moment. In Fig. 3–6 the moment diagram has been subdivided to indicate also the number of bars required at any section. The lines projecting vertically downward mark the permissible *theoretical* cut-off points for bars r, s, and t. These points are usually called *bend-up limits*, since instead of being cut off, the bars are often *bent* at such points and extended diagonally across the beam at an angle to serve as diagonal tension reinforcement.

3–11. Anchorage. Anchorage is the *extension*, a, of a reinforcing bar beyond its permissible theoretical end-point in order to prevent structural failure by bar slippage.

For every stressed point along a bar there must be enough bar length on *each* side thereof to resist safely by bond at a safe value u_a the pounds of direct force existing therein.

The most dependable anchorage is achieved within a region of compressed concrete, because such concrete will seize the bars more tightly as their stress is increased by the loading. When bars *must* be anchored in tensile concrete, a longer extension should be provided.

The ACI Code, Sec. 305(a), recognizes also that the adhesion of the concrete will be poor along the under side of a horizontal bar below which more than a 12-in. depth of concrete has been placed, because it settles from underneath thereof. The corresponding specified safe u_a value thereat (top bars) is only 70 per cent of the normal $0.10f'_c$ allowable.

Since the occasional failure of a concrete structure has usually been traced to inadequate anchorage, the importance of the topic can hardly be overemphasized. The ACI Code, Sec. 902(a), should be consulted in connection with the following example.

EXAMPLE 3–4

Anchorage of Top Flexural Steel. **Given the 3000-lb. concrete beam and specification of Example 3–3 and Fig. 3–6. Required to determine the endings of all four bars.**

Solution: At the support, where the bending moment is greatest, each #9 bar is presumed to be stressed to 20 kips, as shown. Taking one bar, and a, as the required length of embedment for anchorage, equate the required safe bond resistance, in pounds, to the tension in the bar, using the $0.07f'_c$ bond allowable: $\Sigma_o(a)u = A_s f_s$

$$1.13(\pi)(210)(a) = 20(1000)$$

Req'd. $a = 26.8$ in., almost 24 bar diameters.

Algebraically, letting d' be the bar diameter:

$$u_a(\pi d')(a) = f_s \frac{\pi}{4}(d')^2$$

$$a = \frac{f_s}{4u_a}(d') \qquad\qquad (3\text{–}6)$$

Thus for deformed bars in 3000-lb concrete, the ACI Code requires about 24 bar diameters[14] of embedment for *full anchorage* of top bars.

In Fig. 3-6, obviously all bars must also extend from the face of the wall *into the beam* at least 24 diameters. The extension of bar t to meet this requirement is shown boldly.

---

[14] More embedment is necessary if a poorer class of concrete is used.

Furthermore, Sec. 902(a) of the Code states that *within* any cantilever beam span every (flexural) reinforcing bar shall be extended at least 12 diam. beyond the theoretical cut-off point. Therefore bars q, r, and s have been so extended. Such bar extensions serve as insurance against a lack of uniformity in the loading distribution and in the quality of the concrete. They also provide anchorage for the bit of tension in the last few inches of the bar, and are sometimes referred to as *partial anchorage*.

Bond versus Anchorage. It is necessary to distinguish clearly between beam bond and anchorage. Fundamentally, *bond stress per inch*, $\Sigma_o u = V/jd$, is the *rate*, ΔT, in pounds per inch of span at which beam flexural stress gets into the reinforcement, at points *along* the clear span. Refer to Fig. 3–0(d) and (e).

Anchorage is a bar extension dictated by the *whole value of T*. Typically, it is developed *outside* the clear span, in both top and bottom bars. In Fig. 3–6 the anchorage distance a must be sufficiently large to resist the summation of all the ΔT's over the full length of the beam, namely T.

For the computation of the required anchorage of bottom bars, bent-up bars, and stirrups, see the succeeding Arts. 3–13 and 14.

BOND AND ANCHORAGE PRACTICE PROBLEMS

—— **Problem 3–12.** A cantilever rectangular beam 9 in. wide by 14 in. deep to center of steel needs two #8 and one #5 bars for flexure at the face of the wall, where the beam shear is 13.5 kips. Take 2500-lb. concrete and specification. Deformed bars.

(a) Calculate from fundamental principles the bond unit stress in each size of bar, at the wall.

Ans.: 146 *psi in the large bars, and* 92 *psi in the small one.*

(b) Calculate the required anchorage in the wall for each bar.

Problem 3–13. Derive a formula for the required anchorage distance, a, for square bars, and similar to Formula 3–6.

3–12. The Moment Diagram Method of Spacing Diagonal Tension Reinforcement.

When flexural steel is bent up from the tension side of a simple beam to serve as 45° diagonal tension reinforcement, its spacing is dictated by the demands of diagonal tension (Formula 3–4), but limited by the flexural steel requirement at the section in question, since the bars bent up are lost so far as resistance to bending moment is concerned.

Fortunately, the bending moment diagram can be used to determine bent-up bar spacings that meet both the diagonal tension and the flexural requirements. Its use is a necessity when bars are bent up, though it can be used to space stirrups also. Instead of dealing with sV' *areas* on the shear diagram, one lays off sV' *ordinates* on the moment diagram,[15] as illustrated in the following example.

EXAMPLE 3-5

Design of a Singly Reinforced Rectangular Beam with Bars Bent Up for Diagonal Tension Reinforcement, Using the Moment Diagram ($v < 0.08f'_c$). Given a live load of 17.79 kips per lin. ft. to be carried on a span of 17.40 ft., center to center of 12-in. walls. It is required to design a beam having the least amount of concrete, with bent-up bars and stirrups spaced by the Moment Diagram Method. Use 3000-lb. concrete, ACI Specification: 20,000–1350–10, f_v = 20,000, v allowed on concrete alone is 90 psi, 240 psi (or $0.08f'_c$) total with the bent-up bar spacing not exceeding $\frac{3}{8}d$, 180 psi ($0.06f'_c$) where the bent-up bar spacing does not exceed $\frac{3}{4}d$. Allowable u = 300 and 210 psi. Assume a 1-in. maximum aggregate size.

Design the outside dimensions in whole inches. Observe ACI fireproofing and bar spacing requirements, Secs. 507(b) and 505(a), respectively. Meet anchorage requirements, Sec. 902(c). Use an economical amount of flexure reinforcement, arranged in two layers.

Solution:

Second Trial Designing

Estimating the dead load at 0.84 klf, trial total w = 18.63 kips.
Bending:

$$\text{Trial bending moment} = \frac{18.63(17.40)^2}{8} = 706 \text{ kip-ft.}$$

For bending economy:

$$bd^2 = \frac{M}{\frac{1}{2}f_c kj}$$

$$= \frac{706(12,000)}{675(0.403)(0.866)} = 36,000. \qquad (A)$$

Shear and D. T.:
Trial V_f = 18.63(8.20) = 153 kips
For diagonal tension economy,

$$bd = \frac{V_f}{vj} = \frac{153(1000)}{240(0.866)} = 735. \qquad (B)$$

---

[15] Recall these fundamental relationships from engineering problems and strength of materials courses:
 1. The ordinate at any point on a shear diagram equals the slope of the moment diagram at the same point.
 2. The area of a shear diagram between any two points equals the change in moment ordinate between the same two points.

Solving (A) and (B):

Required $d = 49.0$, $b = 15.0$ in.,

$$A_s = \frac{C}{f_s} = \frac{675(15.0)(0.403)(49.0)}{20,000} = 10.0 \text{ sq. in.}$$

Required bar perimeter at inside face of wall:

$$\Sigma_o = \frac{V_f}{ujd} = \frac{153(1000)}{300(0.866)(49.0)} = 12.0 \text{ in.}$$

ACI Code Sec. 902(c) requires that at least $\frac{1}{3}A_s$ be left in the bottom of the beam for end anchorage.

$$\text{Req'd. } \frac{\text{perimeter}}{\text{area}} = \frac{12}{3.33} = 3.6$$

From Table 1–3 of Chapter 1, we *must use #9 bars or smaller.*

FINAL DESIGN

Taking 10–#9 *bars*, 5 in each layer:

Req'd. b to cover $= 5(1.13) + 4(1.33) + 2(0.50) + 2(1.50)$
$= 14.98$ in., assuming a few #4 stirrups needed.

$$\text{Req'd. } h = 49.0 + \frac{1.00}{2} + 1.13 + 0.50 + 1.50 = 52.63 \text{ in.}$$

> *Make*[16] $b = 15$ *in.*, $h = 4$ *ft.* 5 *in.*
> *Use* 10–#9 *bars, d now* 49.37 *in.*
> *Six bars may be bent up.*

FINAL INVESTIGATION

Corrected loading $= 17.79 + \dfrac{15(53)}{144}(0.15) = 18.62$ klf.

Final bending moment $= 705$ kip-ft.
Corresp. $R = 232$, $p = 1.35\%$, $f_c = 1330$, $f_s = 19,800$ psi.
Final $V_f = 18.62(8.2) = 152.8$ kips.

Final $v_f = \dfrac{152,800}{15(0.866)(49.37)} = 238$ psi, < 240 ∴ $O.K.$

Max. final $u_f = \dfrac{152,800}{4(1.13)(\pi)(0.866)(49.37)} = 252$ psi, < 300 ∴ $O.K.$

The design is satisfactory.

---

[16] Seeking better concrete economy, a section 14 in. by 4 ft. 6 in., having less concrete area, was tried. The 10–#9 bars then required could not be spaced within the 14-in. width; and the total v_f proved to be 250 psi, exceeding the 240 psi allowable.

Spacing of Bent-up Bars

Figure 3-7 shows scale drawings of the beam, together with the moment diagram (parabolic)[17] accurately drawn. The shear diagram is not necessary, but has been included in this case to facilitate explanation.

Concrete:

$$V_c = vbjd = \frac{90(15)(0.866)(49.37)}{1000} = 57.8 \text{ kips}$$

Diagonal tension reinforcement is needed, beginning at $57.8/18.62 = 3.10$ ft. from the center of the span and extending 5.10 ft. to the inside face of the wall. Even in this region the concrete can take care of a total of $57.8(5.10) = 295$ kip-ft. of *shear area*, as indicated by the division of the shear diagram.

The corresponding division of the moment diagram, indicated in the figure, is in accordance with the fundamental relationship of shear and moment diagrams previously recalled.[15] The inclined dividing line becomes a base line for subsequent projections parallel thereto.

In elevation, the portion of the beam theoretically requiring diagonal tension reinforcement is the region *efgh*. We shall begin at *he* and endeavor to cover *efgh* with 45° parallelogram areas, each of which represents the tributary region that one bent-up bar can take care of.

Due to its inclination, the upper portion of each bent-up bar is subject to larger beam shears, V', than the lower. Therefore if the bars are spaced to be safely stressed at the level of the neutral axis, *ef*, the stresses will be less at lower points thereon. The spacing is worked out along the neutral axis by erecting sV' ordinates on the moment diagram and projecting to the moment curve. For one #9 bar bent up at 45°:

$$sV' = \frac{A_v f_v jd}{0.707} = \frac{20,000(0.866)(49.37)}{0.707(12,000)} = 101 \text{ kip-ft.}$$

Unfortunately the vertical plane at the face of the wall, represented by the line *he*, must first be made safe against diagonal tension before proceeding along the neutral axis plane. To produce a safe design in the vicinity of the wall it is necessary to project the sV' ordinates to *an inclined straight line vw which is tangent to the moment diagram at v*, the face of the wall. The slope of this line is V_f, or 152.8 in this case.[15]

By projecting vertically downward from *c* to *i*, the region *hij* was defined, and bar #1 was centered within it. An investigation of the stress,

---

[17] Construct parabolic moment diagrams by offsets from the horizontal tangent at the high point. The offsets vary as the square of the distance from the point of tangency.

f_v, therein ($V'_{max} = 95^k$, $s_1 = 12.7$ in.) will reveal a maximum of 20,000 psi, as planned.

The intercept, jk, was made safe by bending up bar #2 into a similar region defined by the same projection line ci, *since the sV' ordinate erected at v is at the left-hand side of this region also.*

The region tributary to bar #3 is partly defined by the vertical intercept ke, but mostly by the horizontal neutral axis distance en. It was specially determined by erecting an sV' ordinate at a *horizontal* distance of ek' to the *left* of the face of the wall, and projecting to m on the moment curve itself (for the first time), then vertically downward to n.

Beginning at n, the sV' ordinates are projected to the curve of the moment diagram as originally outlined. In all cases, whether traversing the vertical plane he, or the horizontal plane ef, observe the following:

Rule: From the outermost point on the unreinforced region project vertically to the moment diagram and erect upon it the sV' ordinate corresponding to the amount of steel bent up. The projection of its top point parallel to the inclined base line to an intersection with the moment diagram (or initially with the tangent to the moment diagram at the wall) gives s, the horizontal width of the inclined region, in the middle of which the bent-up steel is to be located.

By projecting upward from n, the region for bar #4 made the situation safe as far as the line op. Upon again erecting an sV' ordinate opposite the point o, the inclined projection line overshot the moment diagram. This meant a very wide region for bar #5, and that its bend-up point might be too close to the centerline of span to permit the removal of that steel area from the A_s quantity needed for flexure at midspan.

Flexural Bend-up Limits

At the right side of the moment diagram, the total bar area was laid off and fitted into the height thereof, as was done in the cantilever example, Fig. 3–6. By projecting each bar area horizontally to the curve, beginning at the top, a diagram of *bar bend-up limits* was evolved along the base of the moment diagram.

Considering now the locating of bar #5, one sees that it cannot be bent upward to the right of point s, in view of flexure. Therefore bar #5 was bent upward at point s and will take care of the region extending from line op to a line qr, which was located a tributary distance ahead equal to half the $\frac{3}{4}d$ maximum permissible spacing.

A similar examination of the bending up of the first four bars will reveal that they already are in safe positions with respect to flexure.

It is now apparent that the sixth bar, the last one available for bending up, cannot be so utilized in this case, in view of the demands of flexure.

Stirrups

The remaining region, *qfr*, 0.7 ft. in width, was reinforced with stirrup *a*, the required size of which is best computed from the shear diagram.[18]

For the additional stirrups empirically required in the remaining 37-in. distance, use of the formula $A_v = 0.0015sb$, previously illustrated in footnote 10 to Art. 3–8, justified the provision of #4 stirrups *b* and *c* at 17 in. spacing. This left 3 in. adjacent to the triangle *qfr* to be included in the region that stirrup *a*, of the same size, could take care of.

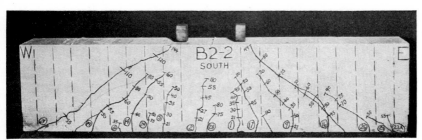

American Iron and Steel Institute

PLATE 3–1. Typical cracking of stirruped beams which failed in diagonal tension. From a series of tests reported by Mr. Arthur P. Clark in 1951.

3–13. Anchorage of Diagonal Tension Steel. All diagonal tension reinforcement should be extended far enough into the uncracked concrete of the compression side of a beam to secure *full anchorage*, measured preferably from the neutral axis. In Fig. 3–7, the required 24-diam. anchorage required by the $0.07f'_c$ allowable bond stress was achieved in two cases by continuing the bent-up bars along the compression face. [Ref.: ACI Code, Sec. 904(e).]

To avoid crushing the concrete at a bend, the radius should preferably be 4 diam. or more, as in the case of bar #3, Fig. 3–7, which was bent through 135° and continued until 24 diam. total anchorage had been secured.

---

[18] The statement is sometimes made that if enough bent-up bars and/or stirrups are used to make a beam safe in diagonal tension at the level of the flexural steel one need not be concerned if the computed stress is higher elsewhere, say just below the neutral axis.

The above philosophy is based upon the idea that diagonal tension cracks always tend to start at the bottom (of simple beams) and progress upward. It is argued that if they are not permitted to start at the bottom there will not be any.

The author disagrees because tests have shown that diagonal tension cracks often start at about one-third the way up from the bottom of a beam, and progress both upward and downward therefrom as the load is increased. On this account stirrup *a* was used in Fig. 3–7. Also bars #1, #2 and #3 were conservatively located in a special manner to ensure that *fv* would not exceed 20,000 psi anywhere along their effective lengths.

For bars which cross the vertical plane *he*, anchorage begins thereat, since the wall reaction puts the whole beam end into compression.

It is customary to extend stirrups to within fireproofing distance of the top of beams, and to hook the ends, whether or not the added length is needed from an anchorage standpoint. For the particular hooking thereof see ACI new Sec. 906(a)(3).

3–14. Anchorage of Bottom Flexural Steel. The ACI Code requires that at least one-third of the flexural steel shall remain in the bottom of simple beams and be extended 6 in. into the support. [Sec. 902(c).] The necessity for such a clause may be roughly checked by computing T_f, the flexural tension at the inside face of the wall, and computing the embedment length required beyond that point for anchorage.

BENT–UP BEAM PROBLEMS

Problem 3–14. The same as Example 3–5 except that the live load is 19 kips per ft. over a 22-ft. span, center to center of 16-in. walls. Take an 8½ in. by 11 in. sheet of *good* graph paper, and do the drawing work carefully. Arrange it as in Fig. 3–7.

Problem 3–15. (Large dividers needed.)

(a) Investigate the bent-up bars and stirrups of the beam designed in Example 3–5 for the maximum f_v in each, and report upon their safety. Compute your V' values from the shear diagram, after scaling the necessary spanwise distances.

(b) Investigate f_c and f_s just to the left of the bend-up points of bars #2, 3, 4, and 5, using the beam chart, and report upon safety.

(c) Calculate the unit bond stress, u, in the bottom reinforcement just to the left of the bend-up points for bars #2, 3, 4, and 5, and report upon safety.

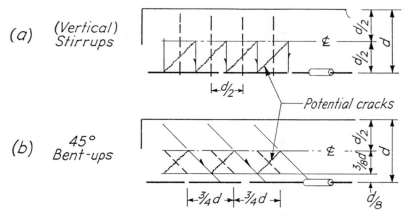

Fig. 3–8. ACI maximum spacings of web reinforcement when the total diagonal tension is less than $0.06f'_c$.

(d) Calculate the anchorage stress, u_a, in the bottom steel outside the face of the support by first calculating T at the face, and report.

3–15. Maximum Spacings of Web Reinforcement. Figure 3–8 illustrates the application of ACI Sec. 806 regarding potential 45° cracks to the determination of the maximum (vertical) stirrup, and 45° bent-up bar spacing when the total unit diagonal tension, v, does not exceed 0.06 times f'_c, the ultimate compressive strength of the concrete.

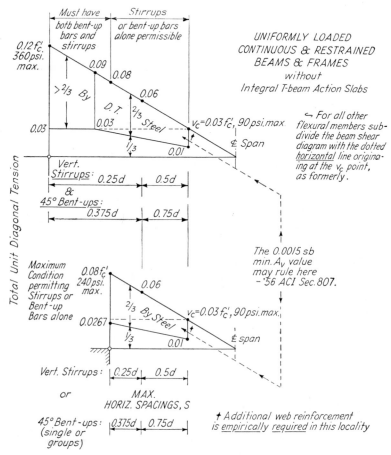

Fig. 3–9. The $1/3 : 2/3$ division of the shear diagram for the designing of the *theoretically required* web reinforcement of continuous and restrained beams and frames having no integral slab providing T-beam action. [ACI Sec. 801(e).] The maximum web reinforcement spacings shown apply to *all* flexural members (Art. 3–13).

Note in the case of bent-up bars that the construction is made also with reference to ACI Sec. 804(a), which considers that the lower $1/8 d$ portion of a bent-up bar is not "effective."

Having in mind our concept of the necessity for reinforcing the parallelogram-shaped regions of diagonal tension all the way down to the flexure steel, your author applies the effective depth idea only to the determination of *maximum spacings* of bent-up bars.[19]

Wherever total v is greater than 0.06 f'_c, the permissible maximum spacings of web reinforcement are only half the values pictured in Fig. 3–8. Figure 3–9 includes such information, arranged for ready reference in connection with Art. 3–17 matters. The closer spacing is interpreted to be required only in the portion of the span where total v is greater than 0.06 f'_c, and not throughout the whole locality needing web reinforcement.

3–16. Design of Combined Web Reinforcement. Wherever the total v is between $0.09f'_c$ and $0.12f'_c$, the portion of the whole diagonal tension which is to be resisted by the web reinforcement varies between two-thirds and three-fourths, as shown in the upper diagram of Fig. 3–9.

Furthermore, wherever the total v exceeds $0.08f'_c$, separate overlapping reinforcement systems consisting of (a) bent-up bars and (b) stirrups should be provided, with neither of them assigned more than two-thirds of the V' value, but bent-ups to carry a minimum of $0.04f'_c$. Refer to ACI Secs. 305 and 805.

Part II. Continuous and Restrained Beams

NOTE: This part should be preceded by the work of Chapters 5 and 6.

3–17. Web and Tie Reinforcement for Continuous and Restrained Beams and Frames Having No Slab Construction Integral Therewith. Those continuous beam and frame members which lack the benefit of an integral T-beam-action slab for providing lateral stability and resistance to possible longitudinal tensions due to shrinkage and/or temperature change are required by ACI Sec. 801(e) to have increased *diagonal tension resistance* which

1) Is not only much greater at each section than is required in other flexural members, but
2) Must also usually extend over a larger portion of the span.

To compute the corresponding *theoretically required* amount of web reinforcement needed outside the familiar V_c point, refer to Fig. 3–9. Note the greater beam shear ordinates assigned to the steel by the ⅓ : ⅔

---

[19] Those who consider the lower ⅛d portion of bent-ups ineffective for resisting diagonal tension must either provide a duplicating system of stirrups to take care of the lower ⅛d portion of the diagonal tension regions or rely upon the excess strength of the adjacent flexural reinforcement to provide a *horizontal stirrup* type of diagonal tension resistance.[D]

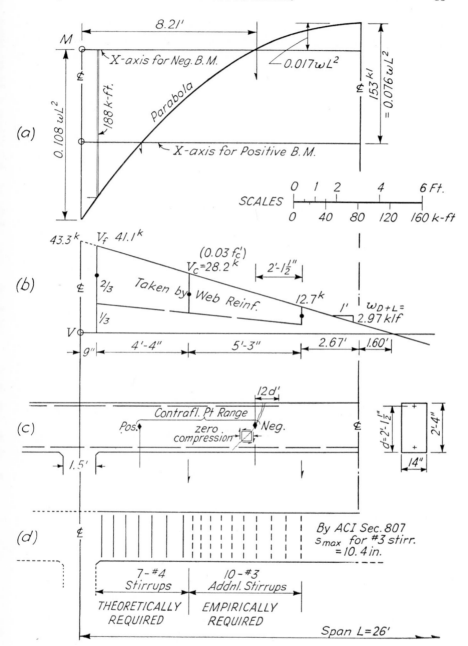

FIG. 3–10. The determination of the region of the *empirically required* additional web reinforcement in the case of continuous and restrained beams and frames having no integral slab providing T-beam action.

demand.   In the case of the continuous girder of Fig. 3–10, the left
portions of views (b) and (d) define such a seven-stirrup region.

The additional *empirically required* web reinforcement content is
also greater than in the simple span cases heretofore worked out.   This
may be seen from the central portion of Fig. 3–10(b), the length of which
is largely dictated by the position of the maximum negative bending
moment contraflexure point.

The situation taken is that of a typical interior *span* and *support* of a uniformly loaded continuous girder of rectangular cross section.   The dual moment diagram at (a) shows design maximum positive and negative bending
moments taken from the lower portion of Fig. 6–3 and adjacent Calc. Sheet
5/11.   The shear diagram at (b) is also in its extreme position dictated by the
loading criterion for the maximum negative bending moment.

The two contraflexure points shown in Fig. 3–10(c) were projected from
the moment diagram.   At the right is the *extreme* (negative) *position* referred
to in ACI Sec. 801(e).   It requires that the web reinforcement be continued
beyond such point an amount d, or $L/16$, whichever is the greater.   *This is to
ensure relatively great diagonal tension resistance at all possible contraflexure
point localities; where the beneficial effect of flexural compression in preventing
diagonal tension cracking through the full depth of a beam is largely absent.*
Refer to the unit cube pictured in Fig. 3–10(c).   An even more severe condition exists when some of the flexural compressive stress turns tensile due to
longitudinal shrinkage of the concrete, temperature drop, or the absence of
contraction joints.

In the case at hand, since $d = 2$ ft. $1\frac{1}{2}$ in., the region to be additionally
reinforced proved to be 5 ft. 3 in. long, and required 10–#3 stirrups, as shown
at (d).

Still more conservatively, it has been recommended that some of the top
flexural steel extend throughout the full length of all such members, and that
in regions of small bending moment the web reinforcement be designed for the
entire[E] beam shear.

The reader is reminded that when there is a slab providing an effective
T-beam cross section, the less stringent ACI Sec. 801(d) applies.[20]   Also that
Sec. 706(a) requires *in every case of compression reinforcement* the inclusion of
enveloping stirrups or *ties* throughout the distance where such flexural reinforcement is required.

----

[20] The 1956 practice (presented throughout this chapter) for providing diagonal
tension reinforcement may be expected to change considerably within the next several
years as a result of current experimental research.[D]

It has been found already that the amount of flexural reinforcement at a section
and the shear span/beam depth ratio (in the case of concentrated loads) have an
important influence upon the shear strength of beams.   Greater attention is also
likely to be given to the effect of the redistribution of internal stresses following initial
diagonal tension cracking.   Diagonal tension reinforcement possibly will be designed
for the whole diagonal tension at a section, the concrete being relied upon only in
localities of low beam shear where no stirrups are involved, as in some European codes.

3–18. Summary of Bond, Shear, Diagonal Tension, and Anchorage.
In a reinforced concrete beam the difference of the bending moments at
any two chosen sections causes a corresponding difference in the flexural
steel tensions, which results in a tendency for bar slippage, called *bond
stress*. Unit bond stress, u, varies directly with the beam shear, but
inversely as the effective depth of the beam and the perimeter of the
bars. Shallow beam subject to heavy shear, and having only a few
large bars, tend to have prohibitively high bond stresses.

The difference of the flexural steel tensions also causes a *horizontal
shear* in the concrete, which has a uniform value below the neutral axis
but decreases parabolically to zero at the extreme compressive fiber.
Along the span, unit horizontal shear, v, varies with the beam shear.
From the mechanics of shearing forces on a unit cube, the unit vertical
shear equals the unit horizontal shear at every point in the beam. Both
vary inversely with the beam width and its effective depth. Beams of
small cross-sectional area, and subject to heavy external shear, tend to
have high unit shearing stresses.

The distinct tensile weakness of concrete invites the particular combination of unit vertical and horizontal shearing stresses which results
in a unit *diagonal tension* at 45° to the horizontal, also of an intensity, v,
over sections normal thereto. Beams are prevented from failing in
diagonal tension by providing *web reinforcement*, preferably normal to
the direction of the diagonal tension.

In well-designed beams, diagonal tensile cracking near the supports
does not develop until considerably more than the design safe working
load has been applied, so the concrete is relied upon to resist a portion
of the diagonal tension. On the other hand, *flexural* cracks usually
occur in the region of high bending moment *before* all the design safe
load has been applied, so the tensile strength of *that* concrete is thereby
destroyed.

The total unit diagonal tension, v, is controlled in designing by providing sufficient beam depth and minimum width, b', on the tensile side.
Diagonal tension reinforcement is usually needed near the supports of
short beams, where the beam shear is great, but may be unnecessary in
the longer spans.

The ACI Code now requires that all flexural members have an empirically determined amount of web reinforcement *additional* to that
demanded by the accepted theory. Typically, it calls for providing two
additional stirrups beyond the V_c point. A minimum percentage for
web reinforcement content has also been established.

Every section of a reinforcing bar must be *anchored* by enough embedded length on both sides thereof to resist at a safe unit bond stress
the pounds of computed tension (or compression) there existing. A

curved embedded length is considered to provide no better anchorage value than a straight one, and none at all if bent so sharply as to cause crushing of the concrete. The specified allowable unit bond stresses apply to anchorages achieved in a region where the concrete stress is zero or compressive, and must be lowered for less desirable localities.

Due to the tendency for concrete to settle away from the under side of horizontal bars, their allowable bond stress is now taken at only 70 per cent of the normal value if the depth of concrete placed beneath them is more than 1 ft.

With the advent of the high-bond type of deformed bar, the *standard hook* is no longer required by the Code, except on plain bars. The former are sometimes referred to as "the bars with the built-in hooks."

BIBLIOGRAPHY

A) SMITH AND BROWN. The Shearing Strength of Cement Mortars, *University of Washington Engineering Experiment Station Bulletin* No. 106, 1941. Also in *Civil Engineering*, June, 1941, p. 362.
B) RICHART, BRANTZAEG, AND BROWN. Failure of Concrete under Combined Compressive Stresses, *Univ. of Illinois Engineering Experiment Station Bulletin* No. 183, 1928.
C) RICHART AND LARSON. Investigation of Web Stresses in Reinforced Concrete Beams, *University of Illinois Engineering Experiment Station Bulletin* Nos. 166 and 175, 1927–28.
D) MOODY, VIEST, ELSTNER, AND HOGNESTAD. "Shear Strength of Reinforced Concrete Beams" (in four parts), *Proc. American Concrete Institute*, 1955, Vol. 51.
E) Warehouse Failures Pinpointed, *Engineering News-Record*, Jan. 12, 1956, p. 21.

QUESTIONS

1. At a given section of a reinforced concrete beam, how does horizontal shear vary (a) below the neutral axis, (b) above the neutral axis?

2. Is bond stress a form of shear? Explain.

3. Derive the expression for unit diagonal tension in reinforced concrete beams.

4. Demonstrate by Mohr's Circle (combined stress) construction how to find the theoretical maximum unit shearing stress in reinforced concrete beams, (a) below the neutral axis, (b) above the neutral axis.

5. Sketch the typical diagonal tension cracks for a fixed-end reinforced concrete beam. Be sure they are correct in position and direction.

6. Write the expression for the maximum value of unit horizontal shear in (a) a timber beam, (b) a reinforced concrete beam, and (c) a structural steel beam. Explain your notation.

7. Is there any connection between the need for diagonal tension reinforcement in reinforced concrete beams and the use of stiffeners on the webs of steel beams? Make your answer clear with a sketch of the stresses involved.

8. Derive expressions for the theoretical maximum spacing of (a) 45° bent-up bars, (b) vertical stirrups, (c) bars bent at 30° to the horizontal, and (d) at 60° with the horizontal.

9. Comparing bent-up bars and stirrups: Which is the more efficient? Convenient? Expensive?

10. Should stirrups be placed inverted (a) in cantilever beams, (b) near the ends of continuous beams? Why?

11. Is there any regulation which sets a minimum cross-sectional area for reinforced concrete beams? Explain.

12. Distinguish clearly between bond stress and anchorage. Is it possible to have one without the other? What circumstances demand increased anchorage?

13. How are the maximum and minimum possible *sizes* of stirrup steel determined for any given beam? How find the maximum and minimum *spacing* thereof?

14. Show how economy of concrete is achieved in reinforced concrete beams.

15. It has been said that "bond stress is always computed between supports, while anchorage is calculated within them." If true, are there exceptions?

16. Under exactly what circumstances is $0.07f'_c$ to be considered the allowable unit bond stress?

CONTINUATION PROBLEMS

Unless otherwise noted in the individual problem, take 2500-lb. concrete, specification: 20,000–1125–12, $f_v = 20,000$, $v = 75$ and 200, $u = 250$ psi (for deformed bars). Make complete final sketch of designs evolved.

Problem 3–16. Given the cantilever beam of Fig. 3–11.

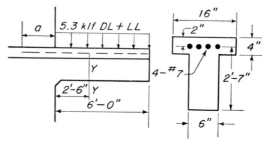

Fig. 3–11.

(a) Sketch typical diagonal tension cracks.
(b) Dimension the region of theoretically required diagonal tension steel.
(c) Calculate the theoretically required number of #3 stirrups needed.
(d) Calculate the stirrup spacing at Sec. Y–Y.

(e) Find the maximum unit diagonal tension, also bond stress.

(f) Calculate the required anchorage distance a.

(g) Calculate the theoretical point along the span where one top bar may be discontinued.

Problem 3–17. Derive a formula for spacing diagonal tension reinforcement inclined at any angle to the horizontal.

Problem 3–18. Re-perform the bent-up bar and stirrup designing of Example 3–5 if only four bars are to be bent up. Lay tracing paper over Fig. 3–7 and show all construction neatly.

Problem 3–19. Design the stirrup steel for the beam of Example 3–3, Fig. 3–6, by the Moment Diagram method. Construct and subdivide the moment diagram accurately.

Problem 3–20. Redesign the beam of Example 3–5, assuming that the live load has been changed to a concentrated one of 265 kips, which may be anywhere on the span. What difference in required flexural and diagonal tension steel do you find?

Problem 3–21. Calculate the maximum safe beam shear, in kips, for the Flexicore-type section of Problem 2–32 at the end of Chapter 2, if:

(a) No web reinforcement is used,

(b) Stirrups alone are used,

(c) Both stirrups and bent-up bars are used.

Problem 3–22. Check the shear and diagonal tension work of Fig. 3–10, and especially the stirrup designing of Fig. 3–10(d).

CHAPTER 4

COLUMNS

4–1. Introduction. A slender vertical member which carries a super-imposed load is called a **column.** Concrete columns are always required to be reinforced with steel, unless the height is less than three times the

Prof. Frank E. Richart, 1892–1951, Research Professor of Engineering Materials, University of Illinois. Prominent in numerous investigations of concrete, he, in collaboration with Prof. W. A. Slater and Prof. Inge Lyse, of Lehigh University, conducted the A.C.I. Reinforced Concrete Column Investigation which resulted in design methods which recognize the creep of concrete.

least lateral dimension, in which case the member is called a **pier** or **pedestal.** When the height is between three and ten times the least lateral dimension a normal working load is permitted, and the member is known as a **short column.** More slender columns, called **long columns,** are limited to lighter loads and are encountered infrequently. The majority of concrete columns are also subjected to bending, and must be designed accordingly.

4–2. Column Reinforcement. When a concrete column is loaded, it shortens vertically and expands laterally, as exaggeratedly pictured in Fig. 4–1. To restrain the expansion, some kind of hooping, called

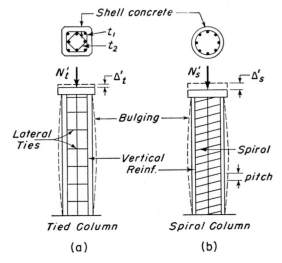

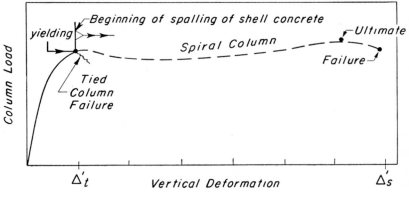

(C) Typical Column Test Data

Fig. 4-1. Performance of reinforced concrete columns.

lateral reinforcement, is always used. It may consist of a number of individual lateral **ties,** as at (a), the principal value of which is in providing intermediate lateral support for the **vertical,** or longitudinal, reinforcement. Such columns are called **tied columns.**

When there is a continuous **spiral** winding, as in (b), the concrete also is well confined thereby, and the member is known as a **spiral column.**

The longitudinal, or vertical, reinforcement helps to carry the direct axial load as the column shortens an amount Δ. It is held in place by attachment to the lateral reinforcement such as the ties, t_1. These vertical bars are always located around the periphery of a column where they are very effective for resisting possible bending. Each acts somewhat like an individual column, tending to buckle in the direction of least opposition, which is outward. Therefore every such bar should be securely held against outward lateral movement at close vertical intervals. The second system of ties, t_2 of Fig. 4–1(a), is necessary to confine the four intermediate vertical bars. If such ties are omitted, the eight-bar group tends to come into a slightly circular configuration when load is applied, and the attendant bulging leads to destructive cracking of the concrete **shell** and early failure of the column. Obviously a round column has a distinct advantage in this respect.

4–3. Spiral Versus Tied Columns. Numerous tests have shown that a *spiral column*, pictured in Fig. 4–1(b), is tougher than a *tied column*. This is due in large part to the continuity of the spiral reinforcement, as distinguished from the many imperfect anchorages of the ends of individual lateral ties in the other type of column. Furthermore, the *pitch* of the spiral reinforcement can be made quite small at comparatively low expense. Such steps provide effective lateral support.

The performance of the two types of column is shown in Fig. 4–1(c). A tied column is characterized by a sudden or "brittle" failure, accompanied by violent breakouts of the concrete and outward buckling of the vertical reinforcement between the ties. A spiral column continues to accept a small load increase and exhibits toughness long after excessive deformation, cracking, and spalling of the outer concrete shell have given adequate warning of impending failure. Such warning enables the engineer to relieve the load on a structure and prevent a disaster.

4–4. Performance of Columns to Ultimate Failure. As previously mentioned in Art. 1–14 of Chapter 1, concrete yields or "creeps" with lapse of time, even at low loads. Drying shrinkage produces a similar effect. In columns the concrete thereby gradually relieves itself of part of the load originally accepted, by unloading it upon the steel.[A] This "buck-passing" characteristic may, without serious error, be thought of as a gradual decrease in E_c, or an increase in n. Many years ago investigators found surprisingly high stresses in column reinforcement, known now to have been due to concrete shrinkage and creep. Since column design had for many years been on an elastic basis which considered n as the fixed ratio of the steel to concrete unit stresses (f_s/f_c), a comprehensive series of column tests was conducted at Lehigh University and the University of Illinois, principally during the decade 1930–1940, which is usually referred to as the *ACI Reinforced Concrete Column Investigation*. The results[B] showed that the ultimate strength of axially loaded tied columns, and the yield point of all columns, may be predicted by the formula:[1]

$$N' = 0.85f'_c(A_g - A_s) + f_y A_s$$

---

[1] The coefficient 0.85 is principally a size and slenderness factor used to relate the indicated ultimate strength of standard 6 × 12 in. test cylinders, f'_c, to that of full-sized columns.

wherein A_g is the gross concrete area of the column as defined by its outside dimensions, and f_y is the yield point strength of the vertical reinforcement.

The action of a column under test loads slowly increasing to failure will be discussed, taking one consisting of 3000-lb. concrete and 40,000-psi yield point steel. It may be considered to take place in four stages:

1) At very low loads the f_s/f_c ratio would be approximately 10, the elastic modular ratio.

2) With increased load and lapse of time, creep and shrinkage cause the concrete to relieve itself[2] of part of its initial share of the load, thereby increasing that upon the reinforcement. During this safe load stage the f_s/f_c ratio may reach 25 or more, the steel becoming stressed to fully twice its original ratio to the concrete.

3) With continued increase in test load the steel reaches its yield point stress and *remains at that value*. Thereafter, the concrete is *forced* to accept all further increase in load, so the f_s/f_c ratio begins to decrease.

4) Further increases in load having forced the concrete stress to its failure level, and the steel being already at its useful limit stress, namely, the yield point, the column itself fails. At that time the f_s/f_c ratio[3] will have decreased to about $40,000/0.85(3000) = 16$, in this case of 3000-lb. concrete and intermediate grade steel.

4–5. Column Safe Axial Load by the ACI (Creep) Method. The engineers who prepared the 1941 ACI Code, and succeeding editions thereof, applied factors of safety to the results of the *Column Investigation* and presented a new type of expression for the maximum safe axial load, P:

For *spiral columns*:

$$N_{safe} = P = A_g(0.225f'_c + 0.4f_y p_g) \qquad (4\text{-}1)$$

For *tied columns*, as discussed in Art. 4–3, and below:

$$P = 0.8A_g(0.225f'_c + 0.4f_y p_g) \qquad (4\text{-}2)$$

wherein A_g = the gross concrete area of the column as defined by its outside dimensions.

p_g = the vertical steel area per unit of gross concrete area. It must not be less than 1 per cent in any case, nor more than 4 per cent for tied columns, 8 per cent for spiral.

f_y = the minimum yield point strength of the vertical reinforcement.

---

[2] As at any chosen point in any member in which concrete and steel *share* a load or force for an appreciable length of time.

[3] The reader is advised that the f_s/f_c ratios mentioned herein are not intended for use in calculations, but are used only to give an idea of the relative variability of the ratio.

Note that n is conspicuously absent from the above Formulas 4–1 and 4–2, but that for 3000-lb. concrete and 40,000-psi yield point steel the f_s/f_c ratio at maximum safe load turns out about 24, approximately as in Stage 2 of Art. 4–4.

Regarding the 20 per cent smaller safe load assigned to *tied columns*, the ACI committee considered the ultimate strengths of the two types of columns to be about the same, as in Fig. 4–1(c), but required a greater factor of safety for the tied column because of its *sudden* type of failure.

Limitations of the P-formulas. Formulas 4–1 and 4–2 give (a) the safe axial load for a given column, or (b) the concrete and steel areas required to carry a given load.

They must not be used to investigate for unit stresses because, as shown in Art. 4–4, the f_s/f_c ratio varies for different levels of loading. At half the safe load the unit stresses are not half the formula values.

Strictly speaking, the P-formulas give the relation between *safe load* and the *failing strengths* of the materials—nothing more.

Part I.   Axially Loaded Columns

4–6. Design of an Axially Loaded Round (Spiral) Column by the ACI Creep Method. Since very little mechanics[4] is needed to design axially loaded columns, the work consists principally in familiarizing oneself with the particular specification being followed, with respect to permissible maximum and minimum steel contents, bar spacing requirements, fireproofing, and the spiral cage.   An even number of vertical bars should be taken.

EXAMPLE 4–1

Given an axial load of 400 kips, 3000-lb. concrete, 40,000 psi yield point steel, and 1-in. maximum size aggregate.   Required to design a round spiral column of not over 4 per cent longitudinal steel content,

---

[4] The philosophy behind the current specifications for spiral column design has been well stated in the Joint Committee Report of 1940, Sec. 851(b):

"The formula for spiral columns is based upon recognition of the fact that the strength (contributed) by spirals (comes into action with the) spalling of the column shell and excessive column shortening; hence the spiral is utilized only as a toughening element or an insurance against a sudden and complete collapse of the column. With spiral reinforcement provided, which is somewhat stronger than the protective shell,[*] these two elements of strength (which cannot act simultaneously) become interchangeable, and justify the formula which uses gross area of column and omits any reference to the (strength of the) spiral.   The formulas for tied and spiral columns are thus . . . identical, except that the latter is allowed 25% greater load-carrying capacity because of the presence of adequate spiral reinforcement to carry part of the load if the outer shell should spall."

[*] Normally $1\frac{1}{2}$ to $2\frac{1}{4}$ in. minimum thickness, depending upon the maximum size of the aggregate.

by the ACI Code. Recognize the necessity for splicing when spacing bars.

Solution: From Code, Sec. 1103:

$$\text{Concrete area, } A_g, \text{ required } = \frac{P}{0.225f'_c + 0.4f_y p_g}$$

$$= \frac{400,000}{0.225(3000) + 0.4(40,000)(0.04)}$$

$$= 304 \text{ sq. in. (req'd. } d = 19.7 \text{ in.)}$$

Make outside diameter 20 in.

This concrete will carry $314(0.675) = \dfrac{400 \text{ kips}}{212}$

Remaining for the steel $= 188$

Required $A_s = 11.75$ sq. in.

To select bars, refer to ACI Sec. 1103(b). *Use 12-#9 bars.*

Since 1½ in. (net) fireproofing cover is required, the core diameter, A_c, which is measured out to out of spiral steel, equals 17 in.

Spiral Reinforcement. ACI Code, Sec. 1103(d), includes the complete notation for the empirical formula:

$$p' = 0.45 \left(\frac{A_g}{A_c} - 1 \right) \frac{f'_c}{f'_s}$$

It gives the required *volumetric* percentage, p', of spiral reinforcement, which is based upon the *core* volume of the column. When hot rolled steel is used, f'_s is the yield point strength, previously designated as f_y.

Minimum spiral steel content:

$$p' = 0.45 \left[\frac{(20)^2}{(17)^2} - 1 \right] \frac{3000}{40,000}$$

$$= 0.013 = 1.3\%$$

This calls for $0.013(17)^2(\pi/4) = 2.95$ cu. in. per in. of column height.

Code on spiral pitch, h'.

[ACI Sec. 1103(d)]

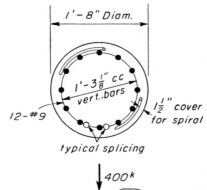

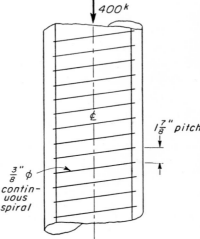

FIG. 4-2. Axially loaded spiral column design.

Max. center to center spacing $= 17/6 = 2.83$ in.
Clear spacing, min. $= 1.50$ in., max. $= 3$ in.

Spiral rod[5] selection:
The first trial $\frac{1}{2}$-in. rounds proved too large, since they exceeded the 2.83 in. maximum center to center spacing.
Trial of $\frac{3}{8}$-in. rounds: $2.95h' = 0.11(16.63)\pi$, $h' = 1.95$ in., max.

Use $\frac{3}{8}$-in. rod, spaced at $1\frac{7}{8}$ in. center to center.

Location of vertical steel:
The center to center spacing of the vertical steel must now be on a $15\frac{1}{8}$ in. diameter. This makes the center to center spacing of bars 3.96 in., which leaves 1.70 in. clear spacing at splices, and which is 0.20 in. more than the specified clear minimum of $1\frac{1}{2}$ in.

Comment: To investigate the strength of a given column, following the ACI creep philosophy, do not attempt to compute actual unit stresses under a proposed load. Do use the *P*-formula above to calculate the maximum safe load for the column and compare it with the proposed load. Also check the adequacy of the spiral steel content.

SPIRAL COLUMN PRACTICE PROBLEMS

Unless otherwise noted, take 3750-lb. concrete of $1\frac{1}{2}$-in. aggregate maximum size and 50,000 psi yield point reinforcement. Recognize the necessity for splicing vertical reinforcement. Follow the ACI Code.

Problem 4-1. Design a column and its spiral for 1400 kips, with not over 3 per cent of vertical steel, to the smallest whole inch of diameter.

Problem 4-2. Find the maximum safe load for a spiral column 28 in. in diameter, having 10-#11 vertical bars, a $23\frac{1}{2}$-in. core diameter and a $\frac{1}{2}$-in. spiral of $2\frac{1}{4}$-in. pitch.   *Ans.* 831 *kips.*

Problem 4-3. Find the maximum safe load for a column 22 in. square, containing a $\frac{1}{2}$-in. spiral at a 3-in. pitch on an $18\frac{1}{2}$-in. core diameter. There are 8-#10 vertical bars. Consult the Code.   *Ans.* 524 *kips.*

4-7. Design of an Axially Loaded Rectangular (Tied) Column by the ACI Creep Method. Tied columns are typically rectangular or square. Their sectional dimensions should be in whole inches. Their average cross dimension will be closely the same as the diameter of the corresponding spiral column of equivalent strength. (Why?) The number of vertical bars in a square column should, for convenience, be some multiple of four, though an even number will serve well.

EXAMPLE 4-2

Alternately redesign the column of Example **4-1** as a rectangular tied column. Take the same **400-kip load, 3000-lb. concrete strength, 1-in.**

[5] Available in $\frac{1}{4}$-in., $\frac{3}{8}$-in., $\frac{1}{2}$-in., and $\frac{5}{8}$-in. rounds.

max. aggregate size, and not over 4 per cent of 40,000 yield point vertical
steel.

Solution: From ACI Code, Sec. 1104:

$$\text{Required } A_g = \frac{P}{0.8[0.225f'_c + 0.4f_y p_g]}$$

$$= \frac{400,000}{0.8[0.225(3000) + 16,000(0.04)]}$$

$$= 380 \text{ sq. in.}, \qquad \textit{Make column } 19 \textit{ by } 20 \textit{ in.}$$

Corresponding required steel area $= 0.04(380) = 15.2$ sq. in.

To select bars, refer to ACI Sec. 1104(a). *Use* 12–#10 *bars.*

Lateral Ties. Section 1104(c) of the ACI Code requires that the ties must
"be at least $\frac{1}{4}$ in. in diameter and ... spaced not over 16 (vertical) bar
diameters, 48 tie diameters, or the least dimension of the column."

Three groups of *ties*, t_1, t_2, and t_3 in Fig. 4–3, must be provided, since every
vertical bar must have the lateral support of a 90° (or smaller) corner of a tie.

A common rule (not ACI) for *size* of tie requires
its area to be at least 2 per cent of the area of all
the longitudinal bars confined by it, e.g.,

$$0.02(4.0)(1.27) = 0.10 \text{ sq. in.} \qquad \textit{Use } \frac{3}{8}\textit{-in. ties.}$$

Space ties at 18 *in. center to center. Keep them* $1\frac{1}{2}$ *in.*
clear from the outside faces, per ACI Code, Sec. 507(b).

4–8. Column Economy. Had a smaller steel
content of 2 per cent been taken in the preceding
Example 4–2 of tied column designing, the result
would have been a 21 by 24 in. column with 10–#9
bars. Thus, by providing 129 sq. in. more concrete
(net), a saving of 5.2 sq. in. of steel would be realized. Since steel is about 100 times as expensive
as concrete, volume for volume, a net saving in
material costs would result. Theoretically, one
square inch of steel can support approximately 24
times as much column load as a square inch of
this concrete, so it is evident that, insofar as column
load-carrying capacity is concerned, steel is about 4
times as expensive as concrete. Columns with minimum steel content are most economical of ma-

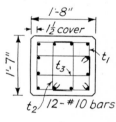

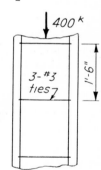

Fig. 4–3. Axially
loaded, tied-column de-
sign.

terials, but they have large outside dimensions which often encroach
upon valuable rentable space, obstruct light, increase the dead load, and
are sometimes unsightly. In such cases they are seldom favored either
by technical advisers or owners. However, the square or rectangular
shape has distinct advantage over the round in resisting bending be-

PLATE 4–1.   The Lake Washington Bridge at Seattle, Washington.   It is, in effect, a 1.3-mile floating highway.   Closed reinforced concrete pontoons, securely anchored to the lake bottom, support the pavement.   In the distance there is a 200-ft. pontoon drawspan, which retracts to allow large ships to pass.

cause it has greater moment of inertia; therefore, tied columns will no doubt continue to be used where heavy bending is involved.

Round columns are unsuited to some interior architectural treatments, so spiral columns are sometimes "squared" by using additional concrete. In fact, a column of almost any shape may contain a perfectly good continuous spiral reinforcement, or possibly two!

The use of concretes up to 5000-psi ultimate strength in columns is a real economy since such higher strength mixes do not cost proportionately more. They do require closer supervision of proportioning, delivery, and testing, mostly because they are still a bit unusual and are subject to greater shrinkage. In multistory construction, the saving in dead load is also quite appreciable.

4–9. The Elastic Method of Column Design. This older, classical method states that the ratio of steel to concrete stresses, f_s/f_c, is equal to n, the elastic modular ratio still used in beam designing. By this non-ACI column method, the safe axial load may be said to be:

$$P = A_g f_c [1 + (n - 1)p_g]$$

and the low n ratio of f_s to f_c is considered constant for all levels of loading. Correspondingly, f_c may be calculated to be:

$$f_c = \frac{N}{A_g[1 + (n - 1)p_g]}$$

Although this elastic method contemplates steel stresses that are roughly half the values now known to exist, it still is used in conjunction with the elastic bending formula Mc/I to design or investigate columns subject to large amounts of bending, as will be seen.

TIED COLUMN PRACTICE PROBLEMS

Unless otherwise noted take 3750-lb. concrete of 1½-in. aggregate maximum size, 50,000-psi yield point reinforcement, and the ACI Code.

Problem 4–4. Completely design a square tied column for 975 kips, with not over 3 per cent of vertical reinforcement, to the smallest whole inch of dimension.

Problem 4–5. An 18 by 24 in. tied column 12 ft. high has 12–#10 vertical bars and adequate lateral ties. Find the maximum safe load.

Ans. 536 kips.

√**Problem 4–6.** Find the safe load for the column of Problem 4–5 by the elastic method. Take $n = 8$, and the corresponding former allowable f_c of 750 psi. *Ans. 404 kips.*

If only 202 kips are applied to the column what then will the unit stresses be by the elastic method? *Ans. $f_c = 375$; $f_s = 3000$ psi.*

Part II.   Rectangular (Tied) Columns with Bending

4–10. Homogeneous Column Elastic Theory. Figure 4–4 shows an eccentrically loaded plain concrete pier with the load, N, located as far to the right as possible without causing tension on the left side, as indicated by the triangular diagram of combined stress at the lower part of the figure. This position of the load is known as the **kern limit** and, for rectangular sections, is at the *edge of the middle third* of the depth t, making $e = t/6$.

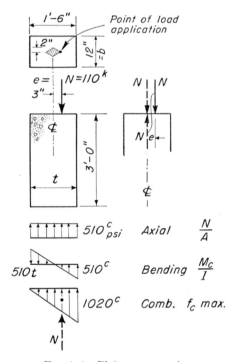

Fig. 4–4.   Plain concrete pier.

The maximum combined compressive stress, $f_{c\,max}$, may be computed by employing the device shown at the right to separate in one's mind the axial force N and the bending moment Ne. The unit stress distributions due to each are shown, with stress values. Their geometrical sum gives the combined stress values.

If unfamiliar, this topic of strength of materials should be reviewed.[c]

In reinforced concrete columns, the position of the kern limit differs somewhat from the value mentioned above, due to the presence of the reinforcement. If the load acts somewhat outside the **kern,** shown shaded in Fig. 4–4, some tensile cracking of the concrete may be expected.

Part II(A).   Rectangular Columns under Ordinary Bending
$(e < \frac{2}{3}t)$

4–11. Investigation by the ACI Interaction Approximation Recognizing Creep. Although the elastic modular ratio, $n = E_s/E_c$, has disappeared from axially loaded column computations, it still is used to

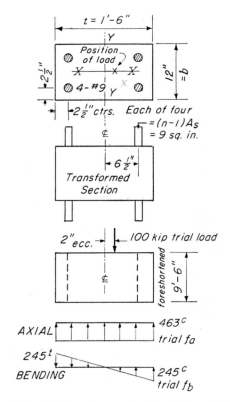

Fig. 4–5.   Reinforced concrete column investigation.

calculate column *bending* stresses.   This is because reinforced concrete beam bending calculations continue to be on the elastic basis.   Consequently, in dealing with columns subject to bending we now have the somewhat inconsistent practice of computing bending stresses from the *elastic* transformed section, but of determining a *nominal* axial stress *inelastically* from the gross concrete area, A_g, of the axially loaded column (Formula 4–1 or 4–2), as will be seen from the accompanying examples.

EXAMPLE 4–3

Tied Column Safe Load Investigation ($e < \frac{2}{3}t$). **Given the reinforced concrete column of Fig. 4–5, consisting of 3000-lb. concrete and 50,000-psi yield point steel. It is required to find the maximum safe load to act at 2 in. from its central axis, assuming that adequate lateral ties will be provided. Follow the ACI Code.**

Solution: Taking a 100-kip convenient trial load, refer to ACI Secs. 1109(a) and 1100.

$$\text{Nominal axial unit stress} = \frac{100,000}{12(18)}$$

$$= 463 \text{ psi} = f_a$$

Bending stress:

First get I: $\dfrac{12(18)^3}{12} = 5830 \text{ in.}^4$

$$4(9)(6.5)^2 = 1520$$
$$I = 7350 \text{ in.}^4$$
$$\frac{Mc}{I} = \frac{100,000(2)(9)}{7350} = 245 = f_b$$

ACI Sec. 1109(a) states in part:

"Members subject to an axial load and bending in one principal plane, but with the ratio of eccentricity to depth, e/t, no greater than $\frac{2}{3}$, shall be so proportioned that:

$$\frac{f_a}{F_a} + \frac{f_b}{F_b} \quad \text{does not exceed unity} \quad \text{[ACI Formula (18)]}$$
$$\textit{The Interaction Formula}$$

wherein f_a = nominal axial unit stress = axial load divided by A_g, the area defined by the outside dimensions of the section.

    F_a = nominal allowable axial unit stress ($0.225f'_c + 0.4f_yp_g$ for spiral columns, and 0.8 of this value for tied columns). See Example 4–2.

    f_b = actual bending unit stress = bending moment divided by the section modulus of the transformed section (assumed uncracked).

    F_b = allowable bending unit stress that would be permitted if bending stress only existed.

It is noted that axial and bending unit stresses are not themselves combined in the Interaction Formula, but that if, for example, the axial stress be, say, 70 per cent of the column allowable, and the actual bending stress 30 per cent of the beam allowable, the column is considered safe.

Now $p_g = \dfrac{A_s}{bt} = \dfrac{4}{12(18)} = 0.0185$

And from Formula 4–2:

$$F_a = \frac{P}{A_g} = 0.8[0.225f'_c + 0.4f_y p_g]$$

So $F_a = 0.8[0.225(3000) + 0.4(50,000)(0.0185)] = 836$ psi

$F_b = 1350$ psi, from Chapter 2.

The trial $\dfrac{f_a}{F_a} + \dfrac{f_b}{F_b} = \dfrac{463}{836} + \dfrac{245}{1350} = 0.735$

Therefore, at 2-in. eccentricity,

$$\text{Max. safe load } N = \frac{100}{0.735} = 136 \text{ kips} \qquad\qquad Ans.$$

COLUMN BENDING PRACTICE PROBLEMS

Problem 4–7. A 15 by 20 in. rectangular tied column has 4–#9 bars in the corners, and one more at the midpoint of each of the longer sides. All six bars are centered $2\frac{1}{2}$ in. from the outside faces. The load is 3 in. eccentric in the 20-in. direction. Taking ACI 2500-lb. concrete and specifications, and 50,000 psi yield point steel, calculate the maximum safe load.

Ans. 155 kips.

Problem 4–8. Compute the maximum safe load for the column of Example 4–3 if it acts $1\frac{3}{4}$ in. from the Y-axis, and $\frac{3}{4}$ in. from the X-axis. Consult Code Section 1109(b).   *Ans. 121.5 kips.*

4–12. Discussion of the Interaction Method. The components f_a, F_a and f_a/F_a are axial load conveniences exclusively for studying columns subject to bending. They are not to be used with columns carrying axial load only, since the unit stress situation therein is variable, as explained in Art. 4–4.

For calculating unit bending stress, an uncracked (transformed) section is to be assumed throughout the range of cases from $e = 0$ to $e = \frac{2}{3}t$, even though over most of it the columns actually will be tensile cracked, and the remaining effective section will have a much smaller I and greater bending stress therein when computed elastically. However, the lesser stress found by using the uncracked section approximates that existing in the column after creep of the concrete and, incidentally, is more easily obtained.

The following example illustrates the $e = \frac{2}{3}t$ limiting case for which tensile cracking may be so disregarded. Columns with greater eccentricity of the resultant force are required to be computed elastically, using n throughout, and considering their sections as cracked.

EXAMPLE 4–4

ACI Interaction Safe Load Investigation for the $e = \frac{2}{3}t$ Limiting Case. Given the same situation as in the preceding Example 4–3 and Fig. 4–5, except that e is now 12 in., causing the resultant position of the load to be

3 in. outside the face of the column. It is required to find the correspond-ing maximum safe load.

Solution: Taking a 100-kip convenient trial load, as before:

Nominal axial stress = (as before) 463 psi

$$\text{Bending stress} = \frac{Mc}{I} = \frac{100,000(12)(9)}{7350} = 1470$$

$$(I = 7350 \text{ as before})$$

Since F_a and F_b are unchanged:

Trial
$$\frac{f_a}{F_a} + \frac{f_b}{F_a} = \frac{463}{836} + \frac{1470}{1350} = 1.64$$

At 12-in. eccentricity

$$\text{Max. safe load } N = \frac{100}{1.64} = 61.0 \text{ kips} \qquad\qquad Ans.$$

4–13. Designing by the ACI Interaction Method. Figure 4–6 shows a few common cases of reinforced concrete columns subject to bending as well as to direct axial load. Before any designing is attempted, all such

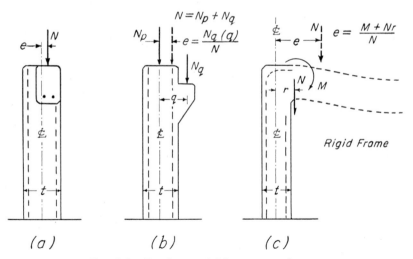

$$N = N_p + N_q$$

$$e = \frac{N_q(q)}{N}$$

$$e = \frac{M + Nr}{N}$$

Rigid Frame

(a)   (b)   (c)

FIG. 4–6. Resultant axial force upon columns.

forces should be reduced to a single resultant axial force N (shown dashed), acting eccentrically a calculated distance, e, measured from the axis of the column.

The ACI Code recognizes that elastically computed bending stresses in columns are relieved by creep. Accordingly, Sec. 1109(a) now *re-*

quires that when e/t is less than $\frac{2}{3}$, the uncracked transformed section shall be used in the flexural computation. Actually, cracking will usually have occurred. However, such a procedure results in lowered computed concrete stresses which are close to those obtained by creep methods.

4–14. The Design of Rectangular (Tied) Columns Under Ordinary Bending ($e < \frac{2}{3}t$)—by the ACI Interaction Method. The method of attack is (a) to proportion a trial section for an increased *equivalent axial load* only, (b) to verify it by the interaction method, and (c) to adjust if necessary.

In this connection, ACI revised Sec. 1109(c) states that for designing a column subject to both axial load and bending, the preliminary selection of the column may be made for an equivalent axial load, as given by:

$$P_{\text{equiv.}} = N\left(1 + \frac{Be}{t}\right) \qquad \text{[ACI Formula (20)]}$$

In trial computations B values are taken as follows:

> For rectangular tied columns, 3.0 to 3.5 for p_g values of 1 per cent to 4 per cent, respectively.
> For round spiral columns, 5.0 to 6.0 for the same range of p_g values.

Let us examine this formula by referring to Fig. 4–4, the plain concrete pier with a load at the $\frac{1}{6}t$ kern limit. In that case the maximum unit stress would be the same if an *axial* load of $2N$ were substituted, so B should be 6.

In rectangular *reinforced* concrete columns, B has smaller values principally because:

a) The allowable axial stress, F_a, is considerably less than the allowable bending, F_b,

b) The ratio of F_a to F_b differs with change in the percentage of reinforcement, and

c) The actual axial stress, f_a, is based upon a smaller section than the one used to calculate the actual bending stress $f_b = Mc/I$.

As an illustration, let us calculate B for a 20 by 20 in. tied column of 3000-lb. concrete, with 2 per cent of 50,000-psi yield point reinforcement. Conveniently take a trial load of 100 kips at any eccentricity, say, $0.3t$:

Then $\qquad \dfrac{f_a}{F_a} = \dfrac{100{,}000/400}{0.8[675 + 20{,}000(0.02)]} = 0.29$

Also $\qquad \dfrac{f_b}{F_b} = \dfrac{\dfrac{100{,}000(6)(10)}{16{,}370}}{1350} = 0.27$

$\qquad\qquad\qquad\qquad\qquad\qquad\qquad\qquad \overline{0.56}$

wherein 16,370 is the moment of inertia, including 8-#9 peripheral bars centered $2\frac{1}{2}$ in. from the four faces.

$$\text{Safe eccentric load} = \frac{100}{0.56} = 178 \text{ kips}$$

According to the formula:

$$P_{eq.} = 178\left[1 + \frac{B(6)}{20}\right] \equiv 0.8[675 + 20,000(0.02)](20)^2 = 344 \text{ kips}$$

from which $B = 3.1$, for this 2 per cent column.

EXAMPLE 4–5

Interaction Design of a Tied Column under Ordinary Bending $(e < \frac{2}{3}t)$. **Given an axial load of 120 kips, a corresponding moment of 75 kip-ft. and the specification** $f'_c = 3000$, $n = 10$, **and steel** $f_y = 50,000$ **psi. It is desired to design a tied column 18 in. deep with about 2 per cent of reinforcement centered** $2\frac{1}{2}$ **in. from the two bending faces.**

Solution:

$$e = \frac{M}{N} = \frac{75(12)}{120} = 7.5 \text{ in.,} \qquad \frac{e}{t} = \frac{7.5}{18.0} = 0.417$$

Trial Design: For a 2 per cent column take $B = 3.17$, by interpolation.

Then $\qquad P_{eq.} = N\left(1 + \frac{Be}{t}\right) = 120[1 + 3.17(0.417)] = 278. \text{ kips}$

Req'd. $\qquad A_g = \dfrac{278,000.}{0.8[675 + 0.4(50,000)(0.02)]} = 323. \text{ sq. in.}$

Trying an 18 by 18-in. section:

Its concrete can carry $\qquad 0.8(0.675)(18)^2 = 175.$

So the steel must carry $\qquad\qquad\qquad\qquad 103. \text{ kips}$

$$\text{Req'd. } A_s = \frac{103,000}{0.8(0.4)(50,000)} = 6.43 \text{ sq. in.}$$

$$\text{Corresp. } p_g = \frac{6.43}{(18)^2} = 1.98\%, \text{ near } 2\%, \text{ O.K.}$$

Try 6–#9 centered at 2½ in. as in Fig. 4–7.

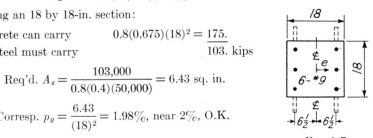

FIG. 4–7.

Investigation thereof:

$$\text{Actual } p = \frac{6}{18(18)} = 1.85\%$$

Axial $\qquad \dfrac{f_a}{F_a} = \dfrac{\dfrac{120,000}{18(18)}}{0.8[0.225(3000) + 0.4(50,000)(0.0185)]} = 0.443$

Bending

$$I = \frac{18(18)^3}{12} + 2(3)(9)(6.5)^2 = 11,030.$$

$$\frac{f_b}{F_b} = \frac{\dfrac{120,000(7.5)(9)}{11,030}}{1350} = \frac{0.543}{0.986}$$

Total $$\frac{f_a}{F_a} + \frac{f_b}{F_b} = 0.443 + 0.543 = 0.986, \; <1.00, \; \therefore \; O.K.$$

Use an 18 × 18-*in. column with* 6–#9 *bars.*

Comment: When the reinforcing bar group first tried proves inadequate or wasteful, try another. This method is permitted for eccentricities up to ⅔ of *t*.

COLUMN DESIGN PROBLEM

Problem 4–9. (*Individual*) *Interaction Design of a Rectangular Tied Column Subject to Bending Tension.* Given 3000-lb. concrete, $n = 10$, 40,000-psi yield point (intermediate grade) steel, and the bar center lines shown in Fig. 4–8. Required:

(a) To design standard bar reinforcement, symmetrically, along two sides only. Conveniently assume that bar centers 2½ in. from the outside surface will provide satisfactory cover for the bars. Provide about 2 per cent of reinforcement, based upon the *bt* area. Observe the minimum bar spacing re-

Case	t in inches	N in kips	e in inches
a	20	103	5½
b	24	150	6¾
c	26	177	7¼
d	28	206	7¾
e	31	250	8½
f	32	270	9
g	35	320	9¾
h	37	360	10¼
i	22	125	6
j	27	190	7½
k	29	220	8
l	23	140	6½
m	33	280	9¼
n	36	340	10
o	34	300	9½
p	25	165	7
q	19	100	6
r	21	115	6½
s	30	230	9
t	20	103	6
u	22	125	5½
v	24	150	6
w	26	177	7¾
x	28	206	7¼
y	30	230	8
z	32	270	8½

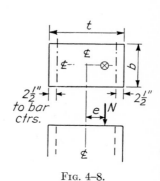

Fig. 4–8.

quirements of ACI Secs. 1104(a) and 1103(b). Consider the maximum size of the aggregate to be $1\frac{1}{4}$ in. Finally choose b in whole inches, and use only one size of bars.

No Make and present the calculation for an alternate design to demonstrate the economy of the one selected. Make final design sketch, as always, after designing the ties per Example 4–2.

Part II(B).   Rectangular Columns Under Heavy Bending

$$(e > \tfrac{2}{3}t)$$

4–15. Investigation of Columns Subject to Heavy Bending by the Elastic Method. When the eccentricity, e, is greater than $\frac{2}{3}$ of the depth of a column it must be investigated for *maximum combined unit stress* by the well-recognized elastic theory which assumed that concrete cannot resist any tension, namely, the cracked-section method. Refer to ACI Sec. 1109(d), which requires that for safety the corresponding maximum *combined* unit stress in the concrete shall not exceed $0.45f'_c$, the beam allowable. Such a member *is* more a beam than a column. Also note that the use of $2n$ is *required* in calculating the stress in the compression steel, instead of being *permitted*, as in Sec. 706(b) for beams.

EXAMPLE 4–6

Tied Column Elastic Cracked Section Investigation $(e > \tfrac{2}{3}t)$. Given the 12 by 18-in. column section of the preceding examples, but with e, the ratio M/N at the geometric centerline of the column, equal to 12 in., as in Fig. 4–9. It is required to find the maximum safe eccentric load for this (border line) case. The concrete is 3000-lb., $n = 10$, ACI allowable maximum combined $f_c = 1350$, $f_s = 0.4(50,000) = 20,000$ psi.

Solution: Since the load is far outside the kern, the tensile stresses on the left side are considered to have cracked the concrete open in that region, rendering it useless, as indicated by the transformed section sketch at (b). The principal problem is to find kt, the distance to the combined stress axis, sometimes called the *column neutral axis*, or the axis of zero *combined* stress; as shown at (c). The variation in the concrete combined unit stress is shown at the bottom of the figure. The steel stresses are also derived therefrom.

Taking a trial N of 100 kips, the sum of the moments of all forces on the free-body, about the point q must equal zero:

$$12kt\left(\frac{f_c}{2}\right)\left[\frac{kt}{3} + 3\right] + 38\left(\frac{kt - 2.5}{kt}\right)(f_c)[5.5] - 20\left(\frac{15.5 - kt}{kt}\right)(f_c)[18.5] \equiv 0$$

From which:

$$(kt)^3 + 9(kt)^2 + 289.kt = 3131.2; \qquad kt = 7.56 \text{ in.}$$

Next write the sum of all vertical forces by eliminating the bracketed *arm* items from the original equation, revising signs and inserting the load term:

$$\Sigma V = 6(7.56)f_c + \frac{38(7.56 - 2.50)}{7.56}f_c - \frac{20(15.50 - 7.56)}{7.56}f_c - 100,000. = 0.$$

Stresses:

$f_{c \max} = 2006.$ psi,   corresponding $f_{st} = 21,050.$ t, $f_{sc} = 26,860.$ c

(2n *used.*)

all of which are due to the 100-kip trial load.

By inspection, the concrete stress governs:

$$\text{Max. safe load} = \frac{1350}{2006}(100) = 67.2 \text{ kips} \qquad\qquad Ans.$$

The corresponding safe load steel stresses are 14,200 psi tensile, and 18,100 psi compressive.

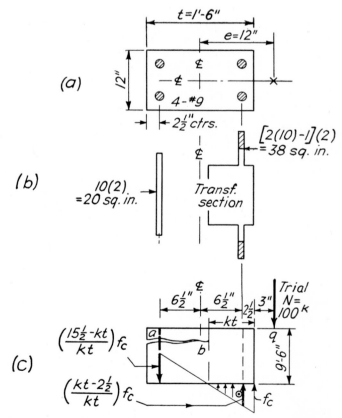

FIG. 4–9. Elastic investigation of a column subject to tension on one side.

Comments: The above procedure can also be adapted to the *designing* of columns with $e > \frac{2}{3}t$. Your author first investigates a trial section of fixed depth and steel percentage (but with a trial b) under the design loading, for kt and trial unit stresses, as above. He then "slices" the section to the *required* width, maintaining the original steel percentage by correspondingly changing the steel area. This is known as the *Slicing Method.*

For example, the column above can be made safe for the 100-kip load by increasing b to $(100./67.2)(12) = 17.9$ in., and using 5.95 sq. in. of steel. Refer to ACI Sec. 1109 (d).

4–16. Discussion of the Two Investigation Methods for Columns with Bending. The safe loads computed for the columns of three preceding examples are compared in the accompanying Table 4–1. When the resultant position of the load is within the approximate $t/6$ kern limit, as in Example 4–3, the two methods give about the same result,

TABLE 4–1

COMPARISON OF COLUMN BENDING CALCULATION METHODS

3,000-LB. CONCRETE AND 50,000-PSI YIELD POINT STEEL

Case	e	Actual Condition of the Column Section	Calculated Maximum Safe Load in kips, for Varying Eccentricities		12 by 18 in. Column with 4–#9 bars
			By the ACI Creep & Interaction Method	By the Elastic Method throughout	Remarks
Ex. 4–3	$0.11t$	uncracked	136.0	134.0*	*Using '51 ACI allowable combined stress f_p, from Plate X of Appendix A.
—	$0.50t$	cracked	73.0	75.1†	†Using 1350 psi allowable combined stress, and n, throughout.
Ex. 4–4 etc.	$0.67t$	cracked	61.0	56.9†	
Ex. 4–6 etc.	$0.67t$	cracked	61.0	67.2‡	‡1350 psi allowable, $2n$ for compression. ACI Sec. 1109 (d).

(Note: In the "By the ACI Creep & Interaction Method" column for the lower three rows is marked "cracking disregarded"; in the "By the Elastic Method throughout" column is marked "cracking recognized".)

since the whole cross section is relied upon in both. When the resultant is at the edge of the section, $(e = 0.50t)$, a good deal of the concrete area has been lost by cracking; but the disregarding of it in conjunction with the use of the interaction formula gives about the same result as the elastic calculation recognizing cracking, with the *beam* allowable stress used as the allowable combined stress.

This is partly because, as in Fig. 4–9, the neutral axis for the bending of the cracked transformed section is then considerably to the right of the geometric (centerline) axis of the column, thus *decreasing the effective eccentricity of the load!* This topic is taken up later in Art. 4–19, in some detail.

When, as in Examples 4–4 and 4–6, *e* becomes $\frac{2}{3}t$, the table shows that the purely elastic method is relatively more conservative. One reason is that the interaction method takes advantage of the fact that the actual f_c at the extreme compressive fiber after creep is less than the theoretical elastic value, as pictured in Fig. 1–6 of Chapter 1. The inequality of such computable safe loads increases as *e* becomes greater than $\frac{2}{3}t$; so the use of the interaction method is then not permitted.

The last line of Table 4–1 shows a reversal of the trend when $2n$ is used for the compression steel, at least for this $e = \frac{2}{3}t$ border-line case. Somewhat greater eccentricities should also be explored.

CRACKED SECTION PRACTICE PROBLEMS

Problem 4–10. For the 12 by 18-in. column of the preceding examples, calculate the maximum safe load *N* to act at the extreme edge of the section, 9 in. from the center of the column: (a) by the interaction formula, (b) by the elastic method, and so check the corresponding items of Table 4–1.

Partial answer, kt = 8.94 in.

Problem 4–11. A 15 by 20-in. rectangular tied column has 4–#9 bars in the corners, and one more at the midpoint of each of the longer sides. All six bars are centered $2\frac{1}{2}$ in. from the outside faces. The load is 18 in. from the centerline of the column, in the 20-in. direction. Taking ACI 3750-lb. concrete and specifications, and 50,000-psi yield point steel, calculate the maximum safe load. Refer to Sec. 1109(d).

4–17. Columns Subject to Biaxial Bending. Attention is directed to ACI Sec. 1109(b) which is applicable when the resultant position of the load is eccentric to both coordinate (principal) axes of the section. This is the case of corner columns in buildings. Note that a three-term interaction formula (19) is applicable when *e* does not exceed $\frac{2}{3}t$ in either principal direction.

The elastic cracked section (cubic) method must be used when the eccentricities are greater. For *square columns*, Andersen[F] has shown that when the unequal moments delivered by the two spandrel girders cause the plane of resultant bending to be at an angle other than 45° the neutral axis for bending still will be closely perpendicular to it. The concrete compressive stress volume of Fig. 4–9 then often becomes a simple tetrahedron, having its centroid at the position $kt/2$.

4–18. The Design of Rectangular Tied Columns and Combined Stress Members Subject to Heavy Bending—by the Elastic Method

($e > \frac{2}{3}t$). When the resultant eccentricity of the load approaches t, the depth of the member, *bending is the predominant factor* and unequal[6] areas of reinforcement are usually called for on the two sides of the section. It is required that such a member be designed elastically. By transferring the axial force to the tensile steel location, and computing the corresponding bending moment, the member may be designed essentially as a doubly reinforced beam (Example 2–7). The ACI new Sec. 1109(d) permits an allowable combined compressive stress of $0.45f'_c$.

EXAMPLE 4–7

Elastic Design of Combined Stress Member Reinforcement ($e > \frac{2}{3}t$). Given a load of 78.5 kips acting 2 ft. 6 in. from the central axis of a 16 by 30-in. column or arch ring, as in Fig. 4–10. Take 3000-lb. concrete, $n = 10$, and 50,000-psi yield point steel. It is required to design the longitudinal reinforcement, with 2-in. cover for the tensile steel.

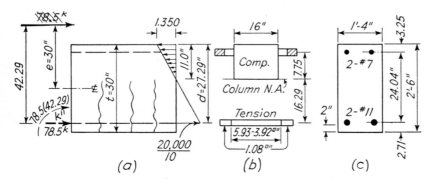

Fɪɢ. 4–10. Elastic designing of a compression member subject to heavy bending.

Solution: From mechanics, the 78.5-kip direct force may be transferred to the tensile steel location, provided that an offsetting moment of 42.29(78.5) = 3323 kip-in. is also applied [both shown dashed in (a)].

Proceed to design beam double reinforcement. The singly reinforced balanced beam neutral axis will be at $\dfrac{1350}{1350 + 2000}$ (27.29) = 11.00 in. "down," assuming that #11 bars will finally be used in the tension side, as shown at (c).

The corresponding couple arm = $27.29 - \dfrac{11.00}{3}$ = 23.62 in.

---

[6] When e has a value between $\frac{2}{3}t$ and t, columns may be economically designed elastically by the *slicing* *method* to have symmetrically arranged reinforcement. Refer to the *Comments* at the end of Example 4–6.

Singly reinforced balanced design:

$$M_{\text{safe}} = Cjd = 0.675(16)(11.00)[23.62] \qquad = 2804 \text{ kip-in.}$$

$$\text{Corresponding } A_s = \frac{2804}{23.62(20)} \qquad = 5.93 \text{ sq. in.}$$

Designing for the remaining M of 519 kip-in.:

$$\text{Additional tensile steel} = \frac{519}{24.04(20)} \qquad = \underline{1.08}$$

$$\text{Total} = 7.01 \text{ sq. in.}$$

Equivalent contribution of the 78.5-kip external force
toward resisting internal tension $= 78.5/20 \qquad = 3.92 \text{ sq. in.}$

$$\text{Required tensile steel area, net} \qquad = 3.09 \text{ sq. in.}$$

Use 2–#11 in tension side.

Required compressive steel area:

[2n *used, as required by ACI new Sec.* 1109(d).]

$$19A'_s[7.75] = (10)1.08[16.29],$$
$$A'_s = 1.20 \text{ sq. in.}$$

Use 2–#7 in compression side.

Comment: As shown by Albert[G] and others, better over-all steel economy can be secured by assuming a neutral axis farther from the compression face than the balanced position conveniently taken above. Such a refinement demands more tensile steel, but greatly reduced compressive steel area.

4–19. Check upon Column Elastic Designing by $Mc/I + N/A$ of Its Cracked Section. When the depth of the tensile cracking is known, or can be closely estimated, the stresses may be found by computing the area, *bending* neutral axis, and moment of inertia of the transformed *cracked section*, and calculating $M_c/I + N/A$. Such a study generally develops additional valuable insight into the internal action of such columns.

Taking the column design of Fig. 4–10 and Example 4–7, a clear understanding of the action may be gained from Fig. 4–11(b) by *first* conceiving only the bending moment, M, to be applied. The member, acting only as a doubly reinforced beam, would then have an open crack extending to the point c and beyond. When next the 78.5-kip compressive force, N, is added, the crack will close between b and c, making that concrete area effective again for resisting direct compression. The compression value at b is offset by a corresponding amount of bending tension, as illustrated, making the combined stress zero at that point.

The greatest value of the method is for making elastic investigations of *round* or irregular-shaped columns subject to heavy bending ($e > \frac{2}{3}t$). For them it is believed to be the best practical method, since the cubic equation algebra of Example 4–6 is then too cumbersome. See Example 4–9 for such an application.

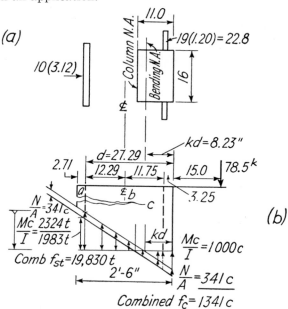

FIG. 4–11. Bending and direct stress analysis.

The results of so checking Example 4–7 are shown in the figure. The inquiring student should verify them as an exercise, since this operation becomes a necessity in dealing with round columns, soon to be considered.

Find, for the three-piece transformed section pictured in Fig. 4–11(a):

Depth of open crack = 30 − 11 = 19 in.
Transformed area = 176 + 31.2 + 22.8 = 230. sq. in.
Neutral axis for bending* only is at 8.23 in. from the compression side.
Corresponding moment of inertia = 14,991 in.⁴
Effective eccentricity of the load = 15. + 8.23 = 23.23 in.
Effective bending moment = 78.5(23.23) = 1826 kip in.

Unit stresses found:

    Extreme concrete fiber = 1341 psi *c* vs. 1350 allowed in designing.
    Compressive steel = 18,940*c* (2*n* plastic consideration) vs. 20,000
       allowed.
    Tensile steel = 19,830 *t* vs. 20,000 allowed.

---

* Remember to include that part of the 11 by 16-in. concrete area which is subject to bending tension.

Comments: Attention is called to the individual stress diagrams, and particularly to the two neutral axes, which *must* be located in succeeding round column problems. The **column neutral axis,** 11 in. inward, is the *axis of zero combined stress,* as established in the preceding Example 4–7. The **bending neutral axis,** 8.23 in. inward, is the *gravity axis* of the section, computed herein as for all beamlike members, and to which the actual eccentricity of the load is measured.

Note particularly that the actual eccentricity of the load with respect to the bending neutral axis of a cracked column is considerably less than if it were uncracked. The resulting smaller actual bending moment makes it possible to use the (larger) uncracked section with the larger bending moment about its bending axis to compute stresses in cracked columns of limited eccentricity with reasonable accuracy.

COMBINED STRESS–MEMBER DESIGN PRACTICE PROBLEMS

Problem 4–12. Redesign the reinforcement for the member of Example 4–7 and Fig. 4–10 if the 78.5-kip load has 12 in. greater eccentricity.

Problem 4–13. Supply the missing background calculations for the results of the $Mc/I + N/A$ check reported in Art. 4–19.

Problem 4–14. Redesign the reinforcement for the member of Example 4–7, taking the steel allowable unit stress at 18,000 psi. Is the total amount of steel required more, or less? Explain clearly how the change comes about.

Problem 4–15. (*Individual*) *Elastic Design of Rigid Frame Column Reinforcement for Heavy Bending.* Given: 3750-lb. concrete, $n = 8$, 50,000 Y.P.

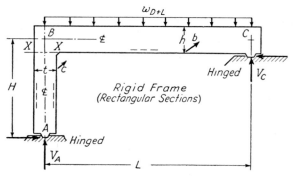

Fig. 4–12.

steel and $1''$ max. aggregate size. It is required to design the column of this rigid frame to have unequal steel contents in the two bending faces.

Method:

(a) First perform a moment distribution to get the bending moment at *B*. Therein use center to center member lengths and plain concrete moments of inertia. Finally draw Ld, V and M diagrams for the column, showing all forces. (Bring these calculations to the instructor for checking before performing item (b).)

(b) Completely design Sec X–X of the column, by the method of Example 4–7. For a start assume $1\frac{1}{2}$ in. fireproofing, #4 stirrups and #10 bars in order to establish a trial d and d'. Consider the allowable stresses as for beam action (actually they are combined stresses) to be $0.45 f'_c$ and $0.4 f_y$. Choose bars and make the final design sketch.

(c) Check the above elastic designing of your column by the $Mc/I + N/A$ cracked section method outlined in Art. 4–19, and finally draw to *large* scale on a separate sheet of $8\frac{1}{2}$ in. $\times$ 11 in. good graph paper *the stress diagrams involved*, as was done in Fig. 4–11.

Case	Center to center lengths		Girder			Column	
	Gdr. L	Col. H	Load w_{D+L}	Width b	Depth h	Width c	Depth t
	Ft.	Ft.	Klf	In.	In.	In.	In.
a	20	$6\frac{1}{2}$	2.20	12	24	12	15
b	22	7	3.20	15	27	13	17
c	24	$7\frac{1}{2}$	3.25	18	30	14	19
d	26	8	3.60	20	32	15	21
e	28	$8\frac{1}{2}$	3.80	22	34	16	22
f	31	10	4.37	23	35	17	26
g	32	$9\frac{1}{2}$	4.20	26	38	19	25
h	34	10	4.40	28	40	20	26
i	27	$8\frac{1}{4}$	3.70	21	33	16	21
j	33	$9\frac{3}{4}$	4.30	27	39	19	26

Part III.   Round (Spiral) Columns with Bending

4–20. Introduction. The investigation of round columns with bending proceeds in the same general manner as for rectangular columns. However, the kern limit for a plain round column is at the edge of the middle quarter of its diameter. Furthermore, the expressions for the moment of inertia of the round concrete section and for the ring of equivalent concrete representing the vertical reinforcement are different from those for rectangular sections.

Only the expression $I = \pi t^4/64$ for a plain round section about its diameter, t, should be memorized. The others follow directly therefrom.

Here again, ACI new Sec. 1109 dictates the use of the interaction formula and permits the assumption of an uncracked section for cases in which e, the resultant eccentricity of the load, does not exceed $\frac{2}{3}t$. For greater eccentricities, the elastic cracked section method must be used, in conjunction with an allowable combined unit stress of $0.45f'_c$.

EXAMPLE 4–8

Investigation of a Spiral Column under Ordinary Bending ($e < \frac{2}{3}t$).
Given the round column of Fig. 4–13, consisting of 3000-lb. concrete and
40,000-psi yield point steel. It is re-
quired to find the maximum safe load
to act at $6\frac{1}{2}$ in. from its center, assuming that an adequate spiral will be
provided. Follow the ACI Code.

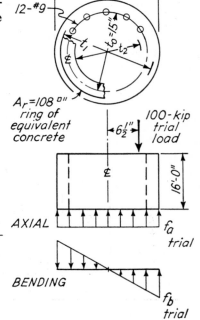

FIG. 4–13. Spiral column with
bending.

Solution:

$$A_g = \pi(10)^2 = 314.2,$$

$$p = \frac{12}{314.2} = 3.82\%$$

Axially:

$$\frac{f_a}{F_a} = \frac{\dfrac{100,000}{\pi(10)^2}}{0.225(3000) + 0.4(40,000)(0.0382)}$$

$$= 0.247$$

Flexurally:
First get I of the uncracked transformed section about the diameter:

Concrete: $I_c = \pi \dfrac{t^4}{64} = A_g \dfrac{t^2}{16}$

$$= 314.2 \frac{(20)^2}{16}$$

$$= 7,850. \text{ in.}^4$$

Equivalent concrete ring of area A_r:

$$I_r = \frac{\pi}{64} (t_1{}^4 - t_2{}^4) = \frac{\pi}{4} (t_1{}^2 - t_2{}^2) \left(\frac{t_1{}^2 + t_2{}^2}{16} \right)$$

$$= A_r \left(\frac{t_0{}^2}{8} \right) \text{ closely } = 9(12) \frac{(15)^2}{8} \qquad = \underline{3,040}$$

$$\text{Total } I = 10,890. \text{ in.}^4$$

$$\frac{f_b}{F_b} = \frac{\dfrac{100,000(6.5)(10)}{10,890}}{1350} = 0.441$$

$$\frac{f_a}{F_a} + \frac{f_b}{F_b} = 0.247 + 0.441 = 0.688$$

Max. safe load N at $6\frac{1}{2}$-in. ecc. $= \dfrac{100}{0.688} = 145.3$ kips   *Ans.*

EXAMPLE 4–9

Investigation of a Spiral Column under Heavy Bending $(e > \frac{2}{3}t)$. Given the 20-in. diameter round column of the preceding Example 4–8, except that the eccentricity, e, with respect to the column center is 20 in., as shown in Fig. 4–14. It is required to find the maximum safe eccentric load. The concrete is 3000-lb., $n = 10$ ACI allowable max. combined $f_c = 1350$, $f_s = 0.4(50,000)$ psi.

Method. The procedure of Example 4–6, wherein the depth of the crack in a rectangular column was found by a cubic equation, cannot be used because it is impossible to so express the areas of the circular segments involved in this case.

In dealing with round columns, Professor J. R. Shank's method will be used:

1) Calculate trial stresses by $N/A \pm Mc/I$, assuming no area lost by cracking, and from the stress diagram determine the approximate depth, kt, of the concrete segment.

2) Compute corrected stresses by $N/A \pm Mc/I$ of the *cracked section*, using Shank's Plate XI of Appendix A for the properties of circular segments.

Solution:

1) *Approximation for depth of the segment:*

$$\frac{N}{A} = \frac{100,000}{314 + 108} = 237.c$$

Get I (uncracked):

Concrete: $\dfrac{\pi t^4}{64} = \dfrac{\pi (20)^4}{64} = 7,850$

Ring: $\dfrac{A_r t_0^2}{8} = \dfrac{108(15)^2}{8} = 3,040$

Uncracked $I = 10,890$

$$\frac{Mc}{I} = \frac{100,000(20)(10)}{10,890} = 1,840$$

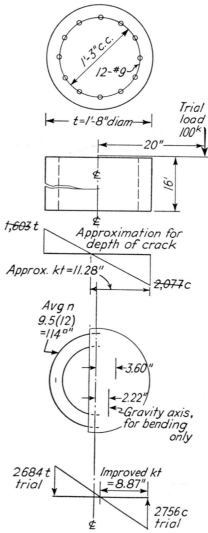

Fig. 4–14. Spiral column under heavy bending.

From the trial combined stresses of $1603t$ and $2077c$ on the left and right sides, respectively, find the approximate $kt = 11.28$ in.

2) *Cracked Section Calculation.* Refer to Plate XI of Appendix A.

$$\frac{kt}{t} = \frac{11.28}{20} = 0.564; \quad \text{area coefficient} = 0.46.$$

Useful concrete area $= 0.46(20)^2 = 184$ sq. in.

$$\text{Corr. } \frac{N}{A} = \frac{100,000}{184 + 114^*} = 336 \text{ psi } c. \text{ (trial)}$$

To get I, we must first find gravity axis of *cracked section.* From Plate XI:

Ctr. of gr. of segment $= 0.36(10)$
$$= 3.60 \text{ in. from center of column.}$$

Moments of areas about the center of the column:

Segment $184 \times 3.60 = 662$ *Cracked section ctr. of*
Ring $114 \times \quad 0 = \quad 0$ *gr. is 2.22 in. from*
         $298 \qquad\qquad 662.$ *the axis of the column.*

Moment of inertia of cracked section, about the gravity axis:

$$\text{Seg't.} \begin{cases} (0.16)(10)^4 = 1600. \\ (184)[1.38]^2 = \;\; 351. \end{cases} \qquad \text{Refer to Plate XI of Appendix A.}$$

$$\text{Ring*} \begin{cases} \dfrac{114(15)^2}{8} = 3207. \\[2mm] 114[2.22]^2 = \;\; \underline{561.} \\[1mm] \qquad\qquad I = 5719. \text{ in.}^4 \end{cases}$$

	Under 100-kip Trial Load	
	Lb./sq. in.	
	Bend-ing	Com-bined

Trial concrete stresses:

Right fiber $\dfrac{Mc}{I} = \dfrac{100,000(20.0 - 2.22)(10.0 - 2.22)}{5719} = $ $2420.c$ $2756.c$

Left fiber at steel $\dfrac{Mc}{I} = \left[\dfrac{7.50 + 2.22}{10.0 - 2.22}\right](2420) = $ $3020.t$ $2684.t$

Trial steel stresses:

Right side: $f_{sc} = 10\left[\dfrac{8.87 - 2.50}{8.87}\right](2756) = 19,750.^* \text{ psi } c$

Left side: $\;\; f_{st} = 10(2684) \qquad\qquad\qquad = 26,840.t$

---

* To simplify this example of the application of Appendix Plate XI to the investigation of such eccentrically loaded round columns, $2n$ was not used to transform the areas of the bars in compression, as now required by ACI Sec. 1109(d). This may be done by including an additional half-ring item in the above *area, neutral axis,* and *moment of inertia* calculations, and using $2n$ in calculating the compressive steel stress.

Max. Safe Load: Since the most critical *trial* unit stress is that of the extreme compressive fiber of concrete:

Max. safe load at 20 in. from the column center $= \dfrac{1350}{2756} (100) = 49.$ kips *Ans.*

The corresponding steel stresses then are

$$f_{sc} = \quad 9,700 \text{ psi } c \quad \text{(See footnote, p. 118)}$$
$$f_{st} = 13,150t$$

Comments: An improved calculation for depth of the segment, made from the combined stress variation shown at the bottom of Fig. 4–14, yields:

$$\frac{kt}{2756} = \frac{17.5}{2756 + 2684} ; \quad \text{improved } kt \text{ value} = 8.87 \text{ in.}$$

Since this improved kt value is 2.41 in. less than the trial one used throughout the calculations, it means that we have appreciably less concrete segment area than was used in the calculations. Therefore the column was completely recalculated, starting with the 8.87-in. kt value. Although the axial concrete stress was greater, the bending stress in the extreme compressive fiber proved to be less than before, principally because its distance from the neutral axis for bending was decreased. Consequently, the recalculated maximum safe load proved to be practically the same as that originally calculated.

An easier way of justifying the original calculation is to compute, *from a stress diagram of the safe load stresses,* the tensile stress in the concrete at the boundary of the *trial* segment (11.28 in. from the right side in the above case). If this stress proves less than the $0.08f'_c + 150$ psi (tensile) minimum modulus of rupture strength (Fig. 13–12) of the concrete used, the column will not crack beyond this point, and the original calculations may well be regarded as satisfactory.

ROUND (SPIRAL) COLUMN BENDING
INVESTIGATION PROBLEMS

Problem 4–16. Reinvestigate the safe load of the column of Example 4–8 with 6½-in. eccentricity by the elastic cracked section method, utilizing the Shank chart of Appendix A for the properties of circular segments, and the former ACI allowable combined unit stress, f_p, of 1210 psi from Plate X of Appendix A.

Ans. 130 *kips by first solution, and* 127 *kips by the (improved) second solution.*

Problem 4–17. Given a round column of 24-in. outside diameter containing ten #10 bars on an 18-in. bar center diameter. The concrete is 3750-lb., $n = 8$, and the bars are hard grade of 50,000-psi yield point. Assuming that the column contains a suitable spiral reinforcement, calculate by the ACI interaction approximation to creep the maximum safe load which can act at its kern limit.

Problem 4–18. Reinvestigate for the maximum safe load for the column of Example 4–9, using the 8.87-in. improved value of kt, the depth of the concrete segment, from the beginning in order to check the statements of the first paragraph of the "Comments."

Problem 4–19. Re-perform the investigation of Example 4–9, using $2n$ for the bars in compression, as suggested in the footnote on p. 118. Prepare a tabular comparison of the safe loads and the corresponding stresses found in the two cases, and discuss.

Design of Round (Spiral) Columns with Bending

4–21. The Designing of Spiral Columns Under Ordinary Bending ($e < \frac{2}{3}t$) by the ACI Interaction Method. As in the case of tied columns, ACI Sec. 1109(a) permits the assumption of an uncracked section. Such designs are evolved in the same way as the tied column one was in Example 4–5, except that:

1) In the equivalent axial load formula (20), the round column B values of 5 to 6 should be used.
2) Steel percentages of from 1 to 8 per cent may be used.
3) The 0.8 tied column handicap coefficient is not to be used in computing F_a, the allowable unit axial stress.

Multistory building columns are usually subject to bending and to percentage-wise reduction of their design (axial) live load. For an example of such round column designing refer to Arts. 7–19 and 7–20, and to Calculation Sheet 7/7 of Example 7–2 in the latter part of Chapter 7.

Problem 4–20. Redesign the 18 by 18-in. square tied column of Example 4–5 as a round spiral one. $N = 120$ kips, $M = 75$ kip-ft. The specification is $f'_c = 3000$, $n = 10$, and steel $f_y = 50,000$ psi. Provide about 2 per cent of reinforcement centered $2\frac{1}{2}$ in. from the outside surface.

Ans. *Make column* 20 *in. in diameter, and use* 10–#8 *bars.*

Problem 4–21. (*Individual*) The concrete is $f'_c = 3750$, $n = 8$. The reinforcement is hard grade at 50,000 psi yield point. Consider the aggregate maximum size to be 1 in. Refer to Example 4–7 for general procedure.

Required:

(a) To design the smallest diameter ACI 2 to $2\frac{1}{2}\%$ spiral column to suit your situation. Work to an even inch of diameter. Provide an even number of standard bars, all one size. For minimum spacing and cover for bars refer to ACI Secs. 507(b) and 1103(b). Allow for splicing of the bars. Also allow for a spiral winding not to exceed $\frac{1}{2}$ in. in diameter (not being designed).

(b) Demonstrate the safety and economy of your design by making an independent final investigation, as in Art. 4–19. See that your *final design sketch* meets the *requirements* thereof, following Art. 2–7 of the textbook, including the clear spacing dimension at splices.

Case	Design Load in kips	Design BM in kip-ft.
(a)	54	31.5
(b)	92	69.0
(c)	114	95
(d)	140	128
(e)	164	164
(f)	194	210
(g)	229	267
(h)	257	321
(i)	300	400
(j)	342	485

4–22. The Designing of Round (Spiral) Columns Subject to Heavy Bending. When $e > \frac{2}{3}t$, all columns must be designed elastically. In rectangular columns so loaded, the computed maximum bending unit stress may be three or more times the axial stress (Example 4–7). In round columns (Example 4–9) it may be six or eight times the axial because of their relatively smaller moment of inertia. Thus, square or rectangular ones are much more suitable in such extreme bending situations. If such a round column *must* be proportioned, refer to the CRSI *Design Handbook* for trial dimensions. A final design may then be evolved algebraically by the elastic cracked section method of Example 4–13 of the (1950) first edition of this textbook, by substituting the current $0.45f'_c$ allowable combined unit stress for the former f_p value used therein.

Alternatively, the trial section may be investigated by the $N/A + Mc/I$ method of Example 4–9, using Plate XI of Appendix A for the properties of circular segments.

4–23. Final Comments on Reinforced Concrete Columns. In the past, all column designing was based upon n, the *elastic* modular ratio, as in beam design. Now, as a result of comprehensive tests, the standard specifications present a *creep* type of formula for the design of axially loaded columns, which is based only upon the strengths of the steel and the concrete, and on safety factors, with n conspicuously absent. Since the f_s/f_c ratio varies considerably with the amount of load, the formula should not be used to compute *unit stresses* except at the safe load level.

Spiral columns, because of their superior continuous hooping, enjoy a 25 per cent safe load advantage over columns with individual lateral ties. Both systems of lateral support are provided empirically without any attempt to compute stress.

The current safe load formulas for columns are intended for use with concrete areas which include a normal amount of shell, or fireproofing concrete, as distinguished from the earlier practice of excluding it.

Columns subject to bending should first be examined to determine what the resulting eccentricity of the load is with respect to the depth of the column, since an entirely different method of calculation is used when the eccentricity exceeds two-thirds of the column depth.

Columns subject to bending of such magnitude that the resultant eccentricity of the load is less than two-thirds of the column depth are now computed by the ACI creep type of formula so far as axial load is concerned; but for the bending moment the elastic method (employing n) is used, and the section is considered to be uncracked throughout both calculations. The interaction method is used to judge the adequacy of such a column, instead of an allowable combined unit stress, as formerly.

The present inconsistency of using both the creep and the elastic methods in analyzing a column subject to bending is great, since the introduction of some bending should not make a fundamental difference in the internal action. This current practice may well be looked upon as a phase in the transition of both beam and column designing from elastic to creep action in the not too distant future.

The best thought is that columns believed to be carrying only axial load really should be designed for a small amount of bending moment, such as that represented by a load eccentricity, e, of $0.10t$ for rectangular ones, and $0.05t$ for round columns.

When the resultant eccentricity of the load exceeds two-thirds of the depth of the column, the accepted elastic cracked section method employing n is still to be used, throughout. The corresponding allowable *combined* unit stress is now $0.45f'_c$.

Although the tensile cracking of a concrete column due to bending decreases the strength of its cross section, the weakening is partially offset by the accompanying decrease in the effective eccentricity of the load as the gravity (bending) axis of the section moves toward it. (Refer to Fig. 4–11 and Art. 4–19.) It is because of this peculiarity of cracked columns that the practice of computing all the factors in the Mc/I expression *about* the central axis of the *assumedly* uncracked column gives bending unit stresses which are substantially correct, especially when we recognize that creep also takes place.

Columns which are part of a rigid frame, and over which the bending moment is not uniform from top to base, are subject to transverse shear and should have correspondingly more lateral steel if a shear study indicates the need for diagonal tension reinforcement.

Corner columns, subjected to bending about both coordinate axes, may also be computed as if uncracked if the component eccentricity/depth ratios do not exceed two thirds.

The purely elastic methods of column analysis and design are now passé, except for the cases of excessive bending.

BIBLIOGRAPHY

A) SHANK, J. R.   The Mechanics of Plastic Flow of Concrete, *Proc. American Concrete Institute*, 1936, Vol. 32, p. 149.

B) RICHART, FRANK E., and BROWN, REX L.   An Investigation of Reinforced Concrete Columns.   *University of Illinois Engineering Experiment Station, Bulletin No.* 267, 1934.

C) BOYD, JAMES E., and FOLK, S. B.   *Strength of Materials.*   5th ed.   New York: McGraw-Hill Book Co., Inc., 1950.   Chap. XII.

D) WESSMAN, HAROLD E.   Reinforced Concrete Columns under Combined Compression and Bending, *Proc. American Concrete Institute*, 1947, Vol. 43, p. 1.

E) HOGNESTAD, EIVIND.   A Study of Combined Bending and Axial Load in Reinforced Concrete Members, *University of Illinois Engineering Experiment Station, Bulletin No.* 339, 1951.

F) ANDERSON, PAUL.   A Graphical Method of Analyzing Eccentrically Loaded Concrete Sections, *Civil Engineering*, Jan., 1940, p. 37.

G) ALBERT, ODD.   Economy Method for Computing Steel for Reinforced Concrete Columns, *Civil Engineering*, Feb., 1943, p. 104.

QUESTIONS

1. Define a pier, column, long column, tied column, spiral column, lateral tie, spiral, shell concrete, and reinforcement.

2. Are all rectangular columns tied columns, and all round columns spiral columns?   Explain.

3. Distinguish clearly between the performances of the two types of columns as load is increased.

4. Explain, in order, the significant stages of the performance of an axially loaded tied column from low load to failure, particularly with respect to the interaction of the steel and the concrete.

5. Explain clearly the contribution of the concrete of a spiral column to load-carrying capacity, from no load to failure load.   Tell exactly what elements of the column are helping to support the load just before column failure, and why.

6. State the two widely different formulas for the safe load of axially loaded columns and discuss the (a) limitations and (b) field of usefulness of each.

7. State all the advantages of each type of column over the other.

8. State how the percentage of steel is computed (a) in columns, and (b) in beams.

9. Tell how to determine how many lateral ties are necessary at a section of any given column.

10. Define creep of concrete.   What has been its influence upon the design of (a) axially loaded columns, (b) eccentrically loaded columns?

11. Is there danger of overstress in either material if creep is disregarded in column design?   Explain.

12. Define the kern limit of a section.   What effect, if any, does the amount of reinforcement have upon it?

13. Can the kern limit of a reinforced concrete section be smaller than that of a plain concrete section? Explain.

14. In an eccentrically loaded column, what is the effect of creep upon (a) the compressive concrete stress, (b) the compressive steel stress, and (c) the tensile steel stress?

15. Outline fully how to design rectangular reinforced concrete columns for bending and direct load.

16. To what extent, if any, might the designing of a rectangular column subject to heavy bending differ from the designing of a beam subject to appreciable direct force?

17. Derive the expression for the moment of inertia of an uncracked, round, reinforced concrete column.

18. Is the spiral reinforcement of a column completely disregarded in investigating its strength? Explain.

19. Tell how to determine the depth of cracking of a round column subject to bending tension.

20. Explain the *interaction formula* as used in reinforced concrete column design. In what other work is it used?

21. Outline fully how to find the maximum safe eccentric load for a square *corner column* subject to somewhat different bending moments in the two coordinate directions.

22. Knowing the required percentage of spiral reinforcement for a column, tell how to determine the diameter and vertical spacing (pitch) thereof.

23. Distinguish clearly between the following axes of a column: longitudinal, major, minor, gravity, and neutral axis.

CONTINUATION PROBLEMS

Unless otherwise directed, take 3750-lb. concrete, $n = 8$, 50,000-psi yield point steel, 1-in. maximum aggregate size, and follow the ACI Code in performing the following solutions.

Problem 4–22. Design an axially loaded round spiral column for 475 kips:
(a) With the 1 per cent minimum steel content,
(b) With the 8 per cent maximum steel content, noting the wide difference in column diameters.
(c) Make a detailed scale layout of the column cross section computed in (b) and determine how the steel shall be arranged. Refer to ACI Code Sec. 1103(b) and (d) and Sec. 507(b).

Problem 4–23. A round spiral column 26 in. in diameter containing eight #11 bars on a 20½-in. bar center diameter is laterally unsupported over its 27-ft. height. Refer to ACI Sec. 1107 on long columns and determine:
(a) Its maximum safe axial load,
(b) Its maximum safe load at 8 in. eccentricity.
Allow for the dead load of the column.

Problem 4-24. A 24-in. diam. round spiral column design, with a 21-in. core diam., ten #7 vertical bars, and a #4 spiral of the same steel at $3\frac{1}{4}$-in. pitch, is said to be inadequate to carry a 600-kip load.

(a) Verify the above statement.

(b) Since architectural considerations require that the column be *squared* with additional concrete, compute the strengthening effect thereof, and if adequate, correspondingly increase the spiral steel content. Refer to ACI Secs. 1103(d) and 1100.

Partial answer. The plan is feasible. No additional vertical reinforcement is needed.

Problem 4-25. (*Individual*) Design the smallest square tied column that will be free of tension. Work to a whole inch of outside dimension. Center the bars $2\frac{1}{2}$ in. from the outside faces.

Design the ties also.

Case	Load	Design M
(a)	275^k	$60^{k\text{-}ft}$
(b)	315	75
(c)	410	103
(d)	445	125
(e)	530	160
(f)	600	170

Problem 4-26. A column 12 in. wide by 22 in. deep carries a load of 24 kips applied 26 in. from its central axis, or 15 in. beyond its face. The allowable combined $f_c = 800$, $f_s = 20,000$, $n = 15$.

Calculate the unequal amounts of balanced section reinforcement required along each of the 12-in. sides, assuming bar centers 2 in. from the outside.

Ans.   1.43 sq. in. of compressive steel.
1.18 sq. in. of tensile steel.

CHAPTER 5

CONTINUITY

5-1. Introduction. Before considering the continuity of the members in reinforced concrete construction, and the methods for evaluating the bending moments therein, one needs to have the mechanics and curve

Hardy Cross, Emeritus Professor of Civil Engineering, Yale University. A well-recognized authority on continuity who presented the moment distribution method of analysis in 1929. His paper, *Why Continuous Frames*, won him the 1935 Wason Medal of the American Concrete Institute.

geometry of simple span beams clearly in mind. **Elasticity,** as revealed in the deflection curve, is the basis for all studies of continuity. The common lack of comprehension of the relationship of the deflection curve to the other four beam curves is understandable, since one or two of the latter curves are usually omitted from textbook illustrations, and the remaining ones are frequently shown in an illogical order.

126

The following paragraphs present an orderly procedure for drawing beam curves which leads easily from the known *load curve* to the **deflection curve.** For all who need to review the subject it is recommended as a coherent summary of simple beam mechanics, which will be quite useful in solving the forthcoming problems in continuity.

EXAMPLE 5–1

Given the simple beam of Fig. 5–1, of 20-ft. span, carrying a uniformly distributed downward load of 3 kips per lin. ft. Required to draw all five beam curves, to write their equations, and to evaluate the maximum ordinates thereof. The solution will be found in the following articles.

5–2. The Relationship of Beam Curves. Figure 5–1 illustrates Professor More's[A] "five-rung ladder" of beam curves, taking a uniformly loaded simple span. The three lower curves, *load, shear,* and *moment,* are the familiar statics curves. They lead upward to the **theta** and **deflection** curves needed to express *elastic* relationships.[1]

When the five curves of any beam are arranged in the natural order shown, each curve is the summation, or integral, of the one immediately below it. The equation of the load curve is written first, and successive integrations thereof yield the equations of all the higher curves. The constant terms are found by inspection.

To write beam curve equations, establish an origin at the left end and consider upward ordinates and rightward abscissae positive. This also makes counterclockwise angles and slopes inclined upward to the right positive, as in mathematics. When concentrated loads are encountered, establish a new origin at that point for the portion of beam to the right.

5–3. Signs Convention for Beam Curves. In drawing beam curves the following situations are always considered *positive,* and pictured *above* the beam (X) axis:

Upward deflections.

Counterclockwise angles, in radians, as in mathematics.

Bending moments compressive upon the top fiber.

Upward shears, to the left of a section.

Upward acting loads[2] and reactions.

---

[1] The modulus of elasticity, E, and moment of inertia, I, are usually constants and are so considered here.

The *ascending* order of the beam curves, as depicted in Fig. 5–1, is in accordance with established *engineering problems* philosophy, which sets higher order curves above lower order ones. If preferred, the descending order may be used, and the accompanying statements and laws correspondingly changed.

[2] Note carefully that the downward loading in Fig. 5–1 is negative, so it must be shown *below* the X-axis.

5–4. The Laws of Related Beam Curves. The following laws[A] follow from the beam curves relationships and make it possible to determine completely the curves for the simpler forms of loading without writing

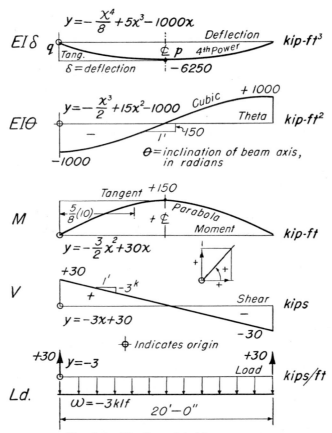

Fig. 5–1.   The five related beam curves.

equations or performing integrations:

I. The **ordinate** at any point on any curve equals the **slope** at the corresponding point on the **next higher** curve.

II. The **area**[3] between any two ordinates of any curve equals the **change in ordinate** between the corresponding two points on the **next higher** curve.

---

[3] Laws II and III were first presented as applicable only to the moment, theta, and deflection curves by Prof. C. E. Greene at the University of Michigan, and called the *moment-area* principles.   For their derivation see any standard text on strength of materials.   As phrased here they constitute the three *generalized moment-area laws.*

III. The **ordinate distance** of any point *q* on any curve, measured **from** a tangent drawn to the curve at any other point *p,* is equal to the **moment of the area of the second lower curve** between the two points, **about** the point *q*.

In Fig. 5–1, by Law I, the load curve *uniform negative ordinate* of three (-3 kips) establishes the shear curve *uniform negative slope* of three (-3). The known 30-kip reaction locates the shear curve vertically. Since the beam is simply supported, the moment curve will pass through the end origin. By Law I, since the *ordinates* of the shear curve decrease uniformly to zero at midspan, the *slope* of the moment curve must also decrease uniformly to zero at midspan. From Law II, the 150 kip-ft. (positive) area of the left half of the shear curve equals the rise of the moment curve from the left end to midspan.

Since the *ordinates* of the moment curve increase from zero at the left end to 150 at midspan, the *slopes* of the $EI\theta$ curve correspond. The *position* of the $EI\theta$ curve vertically may be fixed by anticipating the shape of the $EI\delta$ curve (the sag of the beam) and noting that, by Law I, the $EI\theta$ ordinate must be zero at midspan. The value of $EI\theta$ at the left end may be computed by Law II from the area of the moment curve, which is $\frac{2}{3}(150)(10)$; or, by Law III, from the moment of the area of the corresponding shear curve about the midspan point, which is $(\frac{30}{2})(10)[6.67]$.

The value of $EI\delta$ at midspan is, by Law III, the moment of the area of the moment curve between *p* and *q*, *about q*, equals $(\frac{2}{3})(150)(10)$ [6.25] or $+6250$ kip-ft.[3] The positive sign indicates an upward measurement *from* the tangent *toward* the curve. Also consult Appendix D.

*Learn to draw the curves in their correct relation by inspection. Do not plot laboriously to scale. Always show all loads and reactions acting **away** from the beam axis. Ordinates on one curve equal slopes above. Areas equal ordinate changes above. Calculate deflections by the law of the tangent (Law III).*

For nonuniform loading distributions, write the equations of the curves along the *X*-axis and integrate them to get areas and centroids. Highly irregular loadings require finite integration.

BEAM CURVES PROBLEMS

Problem 5–1. For the Fig. 5–2 case assigned, draw the five related beam curves, write their equations thereon, and mark the values of all maximum and minimum ordinates on each.

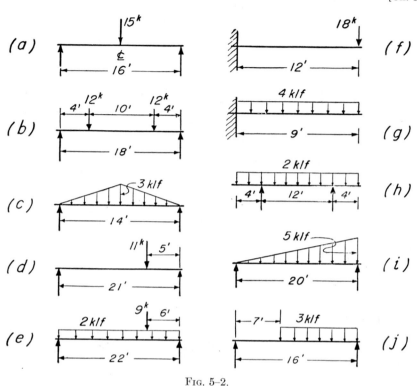

Fig. 5–2.

PRINCIPAL ANSWERS

Case	Max. M in kip-ft.	Max. $EI\delta$ in kip-ft.[3]
a	60.0	1,280
b	48.0	1,816
c	49.0	
d	41.9	
e	149.7	
f	216.0	10,580
g	162.0	3,280
h	20.0	
i	128.3	
j	62.8	

5–5. Fixed End Moments. Figure 5–3 illustrates at (a) and (b) two cases of construction in which the *ends* of beams are so thoroughly anchored in fixed walls that they *cannot rotate* under load. Such beams are called *fixed end beams*, and the end moments developed are called **fully fixed end moments**, or just *fixed end moments*. One must be able to

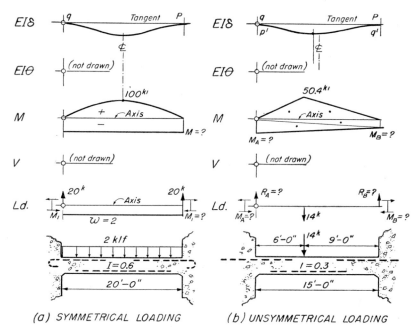

(a) SYMMETRICAL LOADING   (b) UNSYMMETRICAL LOADING

FIG. 5–3. Finding fixed end moments from the beam curves laws.

evaluate these moments in order to design the tensile reinforcement needed at the ends and elsewhere.

EXAMPLE 5–2

Given the two fixed end beams of Fig. 5–3(a) and (b) loaded as shown. Required to find the fixed end moments.

Solution for Symmetrical Loading. To find the fixed end moments for the uniformly loaded beam at (a), consider that the unknown fixed end moments, M_1, are merely additional loads, sometimes called **moment-loads.** We shall then be able to study the effect of the 2-klf uniform loading, and the end moment loading, separately, and finally combine their two effects. When only the uniform load is on the beam, the positive simple beam bending moment curve prevails, as shown. Upon removing the uniform load, and applying only the end moment loads, M_1, the beam is subject to a uniform negative moment from end to end, as pictured below the beam axis. With *both* types of loading on the beam simultaneously, the *fixed end moment* is the particular value of M_1 which is necessary to hold the beam ends level, as shown in the $EI\delta$ curve. Applying Law III, **the moment area law of the tangent,** to find the deflection at q from a tangent drawn at p, and recognizing both the positive and negative moment curve areas:

$$EI\delta_q = \frac{2}{3}(100)(20)[10] - M_1(20)[10] = 0$$

$$M_1 = 66.7 \text{ kip-ft.}$$

The fixed end moments for any fully distributed uniform loading of w per unit of span L are each $wL^2/12$, or two-thirds of the simple beam bending moment.   (Verify this.)

To find the fixed end moments for any symmetrically arranged loading, merely make the positive and negative moment curve areas equal. The depth of the negative moment rectangle will be the fixed end moment.

Problem 5-2. Find the fixed end moments for cases (a), (b), and (c) of Fig. 5-2, Problem 5-1.

Ans. 30.0, 37.33, *and* 30.62 *kip-ft., respectively.*

Solution for Unsymmetrical Loading. In Fig. 5-3(b) the unequal fixed end moments due to the unsymmetrically placed 14-kip load are needed. The positive portion of the moment curve is the simple beam bending moment curve, with a maximum value of $\dfrac{14(9)(6)}{15} = 50.4$ kip-ft. The alternate effect of the two fixed end moments, M_A and M_B, is pictured negatively, using convenient triangles.

Applying Law III to the moment curve areas, first about point q, and then about q':

$$\frac{50.4}{2}(6)[4] + \frac{50.4}{2}(9)[6+3] - M_A\left(\frac{15}{2}\right)[5] - M_B\left(\frac{15}{2}\right)[10] \equiv 0$$

$$\frac{50.4}{2}(6)[2+9] + \frac{50.4}{2}(9)[6] - M_A\left(\frac{15}{2}\right)[10] - M_B\left(\frac{15}{2}\right)[5] \equiv 0$$

Simplifying and solving simultaneously:

$$M_A = 30.24 \text{ kip-ft.}, \qquad M_B = 20.16 \text{ kip-ft.}$$

The area of the negative moment trapezoid will be found equal to that of the positive moment triangle, the same as for symmetrical loadings. Law III has served only to determine the inequality of the fixed end moments.

To find the fixed end moments due to an unsymmetrically located concentrated load, set the area of the negative moment trapezoid equal to the area of the positive moment triangle, and the end values of negative moment in inverse ratio to the subdivided span distances.

Summary. In practical designing, the loadings commonly encountered are combinations of uniform and concentrated loads, for which the fixed end moments may be computed separately, as above, and later combined. When water or earth pressure is involved, the resulting triangular load distribution requires an integration to find the positive moment area, and the application of Law III to find the fixed end moments. See also Bibliography reference F.

Problem 5–3. Find the fixed end moments for cases (d) to (j), inclusive, of Fig. 5–2, Problem 5–1.

Answers: (Moments at left and right supports, respectively, in kip-ft.)

(d) 9.98 *and* 31.92　　　　　　(h) 24 − 16 = 8 *at each support.*
(e) 91.38 *and* 109.25　　　　　(i)
(f) 216.0　　　　　　　　　　　(j)
(g) 162.0

5–6. Continuity in Reinforced Concrete. The monolithic nature of reinforced concrete construction renders it initially continuous from member to member in spite of any simplifying assumptions to the contrary. If a beam or slab extending over several supports is designed as an assemblage of simple spans with steel in the bottom only, it will not so perform until after unsightly tension failure cracks have occurred in the top at the interior supports. Obviously one needs to be able to compute quickly the negative bending moments at the supports and provide steel in the top to resist them.

Consider the two-span continuous beam of Fig. 5–4(a). One cannot compute the reactions at A, B, and C, much less find the bending moments, by applying the three fundamental laws of static equilibrium: $\Sigma H = 0$, $\Sigma V = 0$, and $\Sigma M = 0$. (Try it.) This does not mean that the reactions and moments, when finally found, will not satisfy the demands of these three laws. The point is that they are insufficient for a solution of this problem, and that some additional *elastic* laws involving the geometry of bending must be employed.

5–7. Continuity Methods. Three of the most commonly used methods for analyzing continuous structures are presented herein, namely, **moment distribution, moment areas, and slope deflection.** The moment distribution method is relatively new, requires only simple arithmetic, has tremendous education and practical value, and should be mastered by every structural engineer. The other two methods are algebraic, since they require the setting up and solving of several simultaneous equations. They are too laborious for most structures involving more than five or six members, but are valuable for checking. All three methods are equally sound and accurate, but the moment distribution method has the added practical advantage of yielding an approximate answer almost immediately, yet any desired precision may be achieved by continuing the process.

5–8. Continuity Analysis by the Moment Distribution Method. This method will be illustrated in detail in the following example:

EXAMPLE 5–3

Given the continuous beam and loadings of Fig. 5–4(a). **Required to find the bending moments at the supports by the *moment distribution* method, and to check them by the *moment-area* method.**

Solution by Moment Distribution.[B]

Procedure

1. Make a working sketch of the structure, as at (b), predicting the *bending* of the flexible members and the *rotation* of the rigid "joints," such as *A* and *B*, and others, such as *C*, which cannot, depending upon the construction.

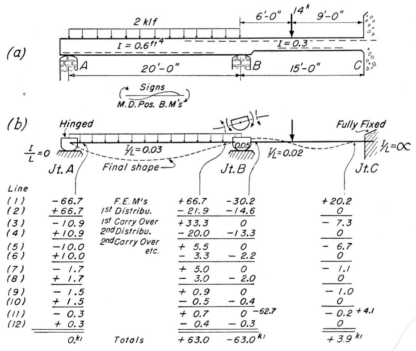

Fɪɢ. 5–4(a, b). Continuous beam analysis by moment distribution.

2. Compute the *stiffness*[4] factors, I/L, for each member, and sum them about each joint.

3. Conceive *all* joints temporarily locked against rotation, as if clamped to a drawing board, and set down at each end of each member the corresponding *fixed end moment* due to the given loading. (Refer to Art. 5–5 and Fig. 5–3.)

4. Signs. In the moment distribution process, **moments acting clockwise upon the ends of members, and externally to them, are considered positive.** For downward loading this makes the fixed end moments upon the left ends of members negative, as shown in line (1) of the tabulation.

5. Release the joints one at a time. Each will then rotate until enough change in end moment develops in the ends of the adjacent members to replace that previously exerted by the external clamps. The algebraic sum of the fixed end moments at a joint will be **distributed** among the connecting members **in the ratio of their stiffnesses,**[5] as in line (2). At joint B, $66.7 - 30.2 = 36.5$ clockwise kip-ft. must be developed upon the joint, or counterclockwise upon the ends of the two members, in the ratio $\frac{3}{5}$ to $\frac{2}{5}$, or -21.9 and -14.6 at the left and right, respectively.

All the items at a joint are next summed to zero for a check, and a line drawn underneath, signifying this balanced condition at the end of the **cycle.** Upon leaving a joint, conceive it to be relocked in its tilted position.

At fully fixed joints, such as C, *all* the joint moment is distributed into the rigid mass, due to its infinite stiffness, but the corresponding column of figures is usually omitted.

6. *Carry over* from each end of each member to the other, one half of the *distribution* item and set it down in line (3), maintaining the sign. For example, it may be proved that when joint B was released and rotated, the -14.6 kip-ft. induced at the left end of BC also induced -7.3 kip-ft. at the right end, C. *Moments are never carried across a joint.*

7. The carry-over moments just written stand as leftover fixed end moments, and are *distributed* in line (4) exactly as was done in line (2).

8. Continue to carry over and distribute until the change in the moment total, per cycle, at all joints becomes insignificant, say 1 per cent of the total, as may be seen at joint B at the end of the sixth cycle. Applying this criterion rigidly at joint C, one sees that the whole process should have been continued.

5–9. Continuity Shear and Moment Diagrams.
After the bending moments at the ends of the members have been found, a designer needs shear diagrams to compute the diagonal tension reinforcement, and moment diagrams for finding the size and required length of both top

---

[4] Use the uncracked plain concrete moment of inertia, $bh^3/12$ for rectangular sections, since only relative values are needed.

[5] For derivation of stiffness and carry-over factors for prismatic members see Appendix B.

A *distribution* item represents the *change* in moment upon each member end due to the rotation of the joint. See the dashed line arrows in the inset view above joint B.

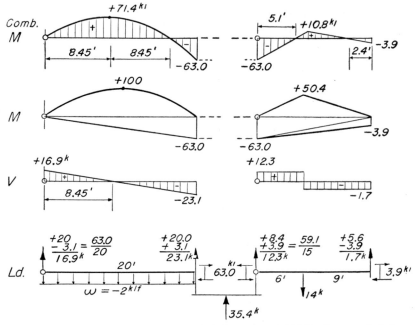

FIG. 5–4(c). Continuous beam analysis by moment distribution concluded.

and bottom flexural (main) reinforcement. These are easily found by statics, as in Fig. 5–4(c), by *beginning* at the bottom *with the load diagram*. To find the true reactions, the moments already found at the supports need to be shown on the loading diagram as "moment load" horizontal couples. This also avoids confusion in drawing the moment diagrams, since *it is necessary at this point to revert to the well-established convention that bending moments producing compression along the top of a member are positive.*

Always draw the **combined bending moment** diagrams. They, and they only, show how much positive bending moment must be designed for and where bars may, theoretically, be discontinued.

MOMENT DISTRIBUTION PROBLEMS

Solve the following continuity problems of Fig. 5–5 by moment distribution, and finally draw true load, shear, moment, and combined moment diagrams for each span, marking maximum, minimum, and end values thereon.

Problem 5–4. Assume uplift cannot occur at C. Dimensions of members are given in Fig. 5-5(a).

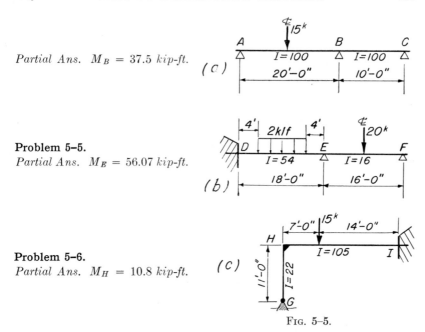

Partial Ans. $M_B = 37.5$ kip-ft.

Problem 5–5.
Partial Ans. $M_E = 56.07$ kip-ft.

Problem 5–6.
Partial Ans. $M_H = 10.8$ kip-ft.

FIG. 5–5.

Problem 5–7. (Individual) Given the continuous beam cases shown in Fig. 5–6. All spans are 18 ft. The moments of inertia are uniform. The loaded spans (pictured) carry 1 kip per lin. ft. Consider that uplift cannot occur at any support. Assume the end supports hinged.

Required, for the case assigned, using the moment distribution method:

(a) Find the negative bending moments at the supports, and also the maximum positive bending moments in the central portion of each span.

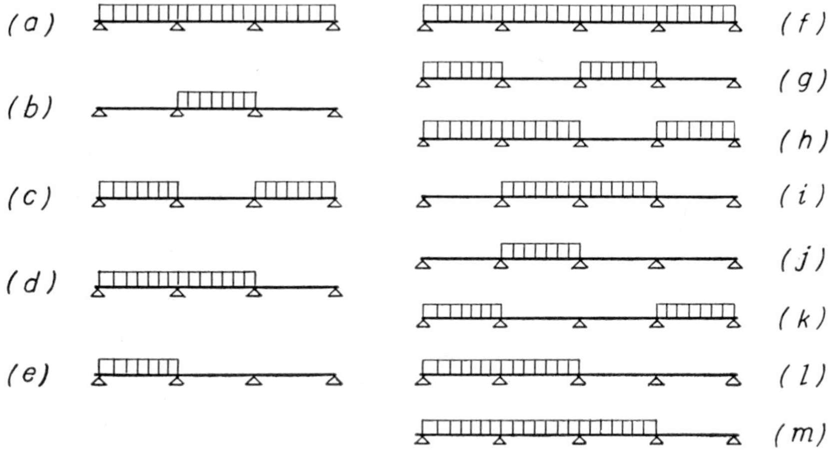

FIG. 5–6.

Pursue until the change in moment total, per cycle, does not exceed 1% in any column of figures.

(b) Draw true load, shear, moment, and combined moment diagrams for each span, marking maximum and minimum values thereon.

(c) Restate the maximum positive and negative moments found in (a) in terms of wL^2, e.g., $0.08wL^2$, *and put all such coefficients on the combined moment diagram* of (b).

Problem 5–8. Summarize the maximum bending moments found in the cases of Problem 5–7 and evolve loading criteria for (a) maximum positive moment and (b) maximum negative moment. Compute combined bending moment coefficients for a LL/DL ratio to be assigned by the instructor.

5–10. (Check) Continuous Beam Analysis by the Moment-Area Method.[6] To check the continuous beam analysis of Example 5–3, Fig. 5–4(a), by the moment-area method, draw separate positive and (unknown) negative moment curves for each member, as in Fig. 5–7.

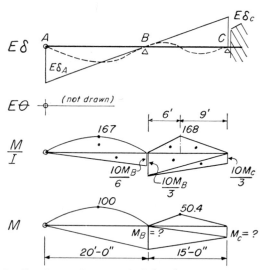

FIG. 5–7. Continuous beam analysis by the moment-area method.

Next construct the corresponding M/I curve to recognize the moment of inertia variation, and sketch the related $E\delta$ curve.

Always apply the beam curves law of the tangent (III) to tangents drawn to the $E\delta$ curve where the moments are unknown.

Using the tangent drawn at B:

$$E\delta_A = \frac{2}{3}(167)(20)[10] - 1.67M_B(10)[13.33]$$

$$E\delta_C = 84(6)[11] + 84(9)[6] - 3.3M_B(7.5)[10] - 3.3M_C(7.5)[5]$$

---

[6] See footnote 3.

Also, from similar triangles:

$$\frac{\delta_A}{\delta_C} = -\frac{20}{15}$$

(The minus sign indicates the difference in the direction of measurement of the deflections.)

Eliminating the deflections and simplifying:

$$1.25M_C + 4.17M_B = 267.4 \tag{5-1}$$

Using a tangent drawn at C:

$$E\delta_B = 84(6)[4] + 84(9)[9] - 3.3M_B(7.5)[5] - 3.3M_C(7.5)[10] = 0$$

or
$$2.5M_C + 1.25M_B = 88.2 \tag{5-2}$$

Solving the two equations simultaneously (compare with Fig. 5–4):

$$M_B = 63.1, \qquad M_C = 3.8 \text{ kip-ft.}$$

Problem 5–9. Check Problems 5–4 and 5–5 by the moment-area method.

5–11. Translational Moment Distribution. The basic procedure for moment distribution outlined in Art. 5–8 is strictly applicable only when the joints of a structure *merely rotate* about a fixed axis. Such a condition exists in a symmetrical rigid* frame carrying a symmetrical vertical loading, such as Problem 5–20, since the shortening of the column members is always disregarded as being relatively insignificant.

If a rigidly constructed frame is unsymmetrically loaded, as in Fig. 5–8(a) and (b), or is unsymmetrical in form as in (c), its upper portion will shift sidewise when loaded, and the axes of rotation of the two

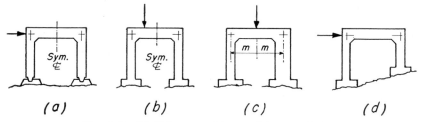

(a)   **(b)**   **(c)**   **(d)**

Fig. 5–8. Rigid frames subject to joint translation.

upper corner joints will be displaced horizontally, or **translated**. The same condition will exist at (d), where both form and loading are unsymmetrical. These movements affect the bending moments in the members. For all such cases, the following *extended* moment distribu-

---

* When the connections, or *joints*, between members are so rigid that no relative angular movement occurs between the axes of the ends of the members when load is applied, the structure is said to be *continuous* if a beam, or *rigid* if a frame.

tional procedure, developed by Prof. Clyde T. Morris[A] for the analysis of wind stresses in building frames, works well.

EXAMPLE 5–4

Given the unsymmetrical rigid frame of Fig. 5–9(a) subject to a 16-kip lateral road. Required to find the bending moments at the ends of the members by translational moment distribution.

Procedure

1. Make a working sketch of the structure as at (b), showing the side sway greatly exaggerated in order to portray clearly the rotation of the joints and the bending of the members. Compute the stiffness factors, I/L.

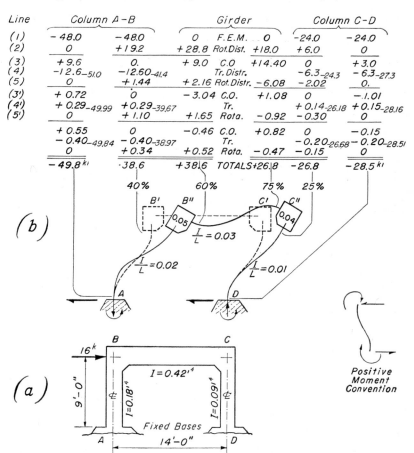

Line	Column A–B		Girder		Column C–D	
(1)	− 48.0	− 48.0	0 F.E.M. 0		−24.0	− 24.0
(2)	0	+19.2	+ 28.8 Rot.Dist. +18.0		+6.0	0
(3)	+9.6	0.	+ 9.0 C.O +14.40		0	+3.0
(4)	−12.6−51.0	−12.60−41.4	Tr. Distr.		−6.3−24.3	− 6.3−27.3
(5)	0	+1.44	+ 2.16 Rot.Distr. −6.08		−2.02	0.
(3′)	+ 0.72	0	− 3.04 C.O. +1.08		0	−.1.01
(4′)	+ 0.29−49.99	+0.29−39.67	Tr.		+ 0.14−26.18	+0.15−28.16
(5′)	0	+1.10	+1.65 Rota. −0.92		−0.30	0
	+ 0.55	0	−0.46 C.O. +0.82		0	−0.15
	− 0.40−49.84	− 0.40−38.97	Tr.		−0.20−26.68	−0.20−28.51
	0	+0.34	+0.52 Rota. −0.47		−0.15	0
	− 49.8 ki	·38.6	+38.6 TOTALS +26.8		−26.8	−28.5 ki

FIG. 5–9. Analysis of a laterally loaded rigid frame by translational moment distribution.

2. To find the translational fixed end moments, conceive the joints to be held vertical by some external means while being displaced laterally to $B'C'$ in the direction of the load. This movement does not deform the girder member, lying in the direction of the displacement, or induce any moment into it. It may be proved that such lateral displacement of the column tops induces end bending moments proportional to I/L^2 (law of the tangent). Equal length columns will assume fixed end bending moments proportional to their moments of inertia, I.

For equilibrium, the sum of the moments at the top and base of all columns of a frame story must equal "the shear in the story times the story height," or 144 kip-ft. in this case. This accounts for the two -48 and -24 kip-ft. items at the top and bottom of the left and right hand columns respectively, line (1) of the tabulation.

3. Allow the joints to rotate, while remaining in the same location. Distribute the fixed end moments as usual, in line (2), and relock each joint in its rotated position.

4. Carry over one-half of the distribution items, line (3), as formerly.

5. The sum of the moments now at the ends of the columns is different from the story moment, so a corrective story column moment must be introduced: and **translationally distributed** thereto. In this case the situation is 106.2 versus 144 kip-ft. This means that additional translation must occur to build up 37.8 kip-ft. more moment at the tops and bases of the columns, line (4), distributed as in step (2) above. See column items -12.6 and -6.3 and the new position of the joints at B'' and C''.

6. Again make a *rotational distribution*, line (5), of all the moments accumulated at each joint since it was last allowed to rotate, and then relock.

7. Repeat the carry over—translational distribution—rotational distribution cycle until the change in moment totals per cycle comes within the percentage of error to be tolerated.

8. Make a partial check by computing the horizontal reactions at the base of the frame from the final column moments and comparing with the applied lateral load. $(\Sigma H \equiv 0.)$

The translational moment distribution method is unexcelled for the analysis of most quadrilateral frames subject to sidesway, such as multistory (building) wind bents, rigid frame bridges, and Vierendeel trusses. Frames with a large number of members, which defy analysis by algebraic methods within a reasonable time, can be investigated rapidly.

TRANSLATIONAL MOMENT DISTRIBUTION PROBLEMS

Find the moments in the members of these frames of Fig. 5–10 by translational moment distribution. Draw the moment diagrams on a sketch of the frame, and compute the contraflexure point locations. Consider all column bases fixed.

Problem 5–10.
Partial Ans. $M_B = 76.5$ *k-ft.*

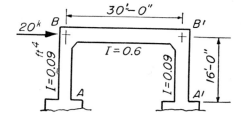

Problem 5–11.
Partial Ans.
$M_D = 75.07$ *k-ft.*

Problem 5–11(a).
Alternately consider column bases hinged. See Appendix B.

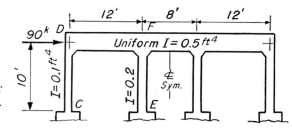

Fig. 5–10(a) and (b).

PLATE 5–1. Precast rigid frame factory building in England. The *gable frames* were cast in three pieces, there being a single-lap, bolted concrete splice in the vicinity of the contraflexure point, underneath the glass roof sections shown. Note the tapered, rigidly connected column portion of the frames.

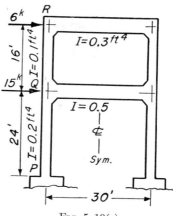

Problem 5–12.

Find the moments in all the members.

FIG. 5–10(c).

5–12. (Check) Rigid Frame Analysis by the Slope Deflection Method.
This method, developed by Prof. G. A. Maney,[c] is presented for analyzing or checking relatively simple rigid frames with or without sidesway. It states that the moments at the ends of a member are a simple function of the joint rotation angles, θ, and the translational (story) deflection angle, d/L. The number of rotating joints plus the number of stories swayed equals the number of unknowns to be solved.

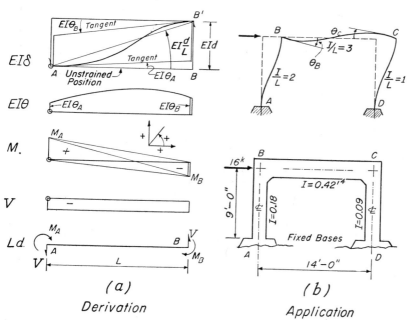

(a)
Derivation

(b)
Application

FIG. 5–11. Rigid frame analysis by slope defection.

Figure 5–11(a) shows the related curves for a column member, one end of which has been displaced an amount d. Applying the law (III) of the tangent:

The ordinate to B' from the tangent at A equals:

$$EId - EI\theta_A L = M_A \left(\frac{L}{2}\right)\left(\frac{2L}{3}\right) - M_B \left(\frac{L}{2}\right)\left(\frac{L}{3}\right) \tag{5-3}$$

Similarly, the ordinate to A from the tangent at B' equals:

$$-(EId - EI\theta_B L) = M_A \left(\frac{L}{2}\right)\left(\frac{L}{3}\right) - M_B \left(\frac{L}{2}\right)\left(\frac{2L}{3}\right) \tag{5-4}$$

Simplifying and solving Eqs. 5–3 and 5–4 simultaneously:

$$-M_A = 2E\frac{I}{L}\left(2\theta_A + \theta_B - 3\frac{d}{L}\right)$$

$$-M_B = 2E\frac{I}{L}\left(2\theta_B + \theta_A - 3\frac{d}{L}\right)$$

In the literature of slope deflection, *clockwise* angles and moments upon the ends of members are considered positive. Then since we applied clockwise moments in Fig. 5–11(a):

$$M_{AB} = \frac{2EI}{L}\left(2\theta_A + \theta_B - 3\frac{d}{L}\right) \tag{5-5}$$

The slope deflection formulas.*

$$M_{BA} = \frac{2EI}{L}\left(2\theta_B + \theta_A - 3\frac{d}{L}\right) \tag{5-6}$$

When there is no angular displacement of the line joining the two ends of a member with respect to its unstrained direction, as in the case of the girder member, BC, of Fig. 5–11(b):

$$M_{BC} = \frac{2EI}{L}(2\theta_B + \theta_C) \tag{5-7}$$

$$M_{CB} = \frac{2EI}{L}(2\theta_C + \theta_B) \tag{5-8}$$

EXAMPLE 5–5

Given the frame and loading of Example 5–4 and Fig. 5–11(b). Required to find the moments at the ends of the members by slope

---

* If a member carries intermediate load, an additional term must be appended to Fors. 5–5 and 5–6, namely the corresponding fully fixed end moment. See Art. 5–13.

deflection, and to compare them with those previously found by moment distribution.   Consider clockwise angles and moments upon the ends of the members as positive.

Solution: Having sketched the deformed frame and computed the stiffnesses, I/L, write the slope deflection equations for each member:

$$M_{AB} = 0.04E\left(2\theta_A + \theta_B - 3\frac{d}{L}\right)$$

$$M_{BA} = 0.04E\left(2\theta_B + \theta_A - 3\frac{d}{L}\right)$$

$$M_{BC} = 0.06E(2\theta_B + \theta_C)$$

$$M_{CB} = 0.06E(2\theta_C + \theta_B)$$

$$M_{CD} = 0.02E\left(2\theta_C + \theta_D - 3\frac{d}{L}\right)$$

$$M_{DC} = 0.02E\left(2\theta_D + \theta_C - 3\frac{d}{L}\right)$$

The angles θ_A and θ_D are zero in this example.

Next write the static equations for moments upon each joint, and the story moment upon the structure:

$$M_{BA} = -M_{BC} \tag{5-9}$$

$$M_{CD} = -M_{CB} \tag{5-10}$$

$$M_{AB} + M_{BA} + M_{CD} + M_{DC} = -16(9) \tag{5-11}$$

Substituting the above six slope deflection equations into Eqs. 5–9, 5–10, and 5–11, and simplifying, we obtain:

$$0.20E\theta_B + 0.06E\theta_C - \frac{4}{300}Ed = 0 \tag{5-9a}$$

$$0.06E\theta_B + 0.16E\theta_C - \frac{2}{300}Ed = 0 \tag{5-10a}$$

$$0.12E\theta_B + 0.06E\theta_C - 0.04Ed = -144 \tag{5-11a}$$

Solving simultaneously:

$$E\theta_B = 278.5, \qquad E\theta_C = 85.6, \qquad Ed = 4564.$$

Resubstituting in the original six equations and comparing:

Method	Bending Moments, in kip-ft.			
	M_A	M_B	M_C	M_D
Slope deflection	49.71	38.57	27.00	28.71
Moment distribution—4 cycles	49.8	38.6	26.8	28.5

SLOPE DEFLECTION PROBLEMS

Problem 5–13. Refer to Fig. 5–10 and solve Problems 5–10, 5–11, 5–11(a), and 5–12 by the slope deflection method. In addition, taking E_c at 3000 kips per sq. in., evaluate the θ's and d's, converting radians to degrees, and draw the deformed shape of the structure with all angles and deflections exaggerated 500 times.

5–13. Continuous Beam Analysis by Slope Deflection. When the load is applied at intermediate points along a member of a rigid frame, instead of at the joints, additional moments are induced at the joints because of the continuity. Such a moment, known as C in slope deflection literature, is actually the *fixed end moment* of the loading for the member end under consideration. Regarding signs, assuming downward loading, that for the left end will be negative, and for the right end positive, as in the moment distribution method.

When there is no translation of joints, as in a continuous beam, the bending moments develop entirely from the C-values.

EXAMPLE 5–6

Given the continuous beam and loading of Fig. 5–4(a). Required to check the bending moments by the slope deflection method.

Solution: From Art. 5–12, the slope deflection equations are:

$$M_{AB} = 0.06E(2\theta_A + \theta_B) - 66.7 = 0 \qquad (5\text{–}12)$$

$$M_{BA} = 0.06E(2\theta_B + \theta_A) + 66.7 \qquad (5\text{–}13)$$

$$M_{BC} = 0.04E(2\theta_B + \theta_C) - 30.2 \qquad (5\text{–}14)$$

$$M_{CB} = 0.04E(2\theta_C + \theta_B) + 20.2 \qquad (5\text{–}15)$$

Combining Eqs. 5–13 and 5–14, recognizing that $M_{BA} = - M_{BC}$, we get:

$$E\theta_A + 3.33E\theta_B = -609. \qquad (5\text{–}16)$$

Solving Eqs. 5–12 and 5–16 simultaneously yields:

$$E\theta_A = +760, \qquad E\theta_B = -411 \quad \text{(kip and foot units)}.$$

By substituting in the original equations:

	By Moment Distribution	By Moment Areas
$M_{BC} = - 63.1$ kip-ft.	−63.1	−63.1
$M_{CB} = + 3.8$	+3.9	+3.8

5–14. Moment Distribution Analysis of Continuous Beams and Frames Having Nonprismatic (Haunched) Members.[A] **(Author's Method)** If the cross section of a member varies along its length, as in Fig. 5–12, the fixed end moments, stiffness, and carry-over factors will be different from those of the common *prismatic* member, which has a uniform moment of inertia throughout. In comparatively few cases is it possible and feasible to write the equation of moment of inertia variation and perform the necessary integrations to find the required constants mentioned above. The helpful tables and diagrams prepared by some investigators[D] cannot well cover all the possibilities.

The method presented here was developed in 1931.[A] It permits any conceivable variation of the moment of inertia. In computing the stiffness of reinforced concrete members, the moment of inertia of the plain concrete section is usually taken, since its use in deflection formulas produces a fair check upon deflection test data secured at working loads.

When a member is unsymmetrical about its center line of span there will be different stiffness and carry-over factors for the two ends, and symmetrically placed loads will cause fixed end moments of different values. In such cases most of the work centers around the finding of these six constants, after which a simple moment distribution is performed. The method involves the application of the laws of related beam curves, Art. 5–4, to M/I and deflection curves, usually referred to as the *moment-area* principles,[3,5] as will be seen.

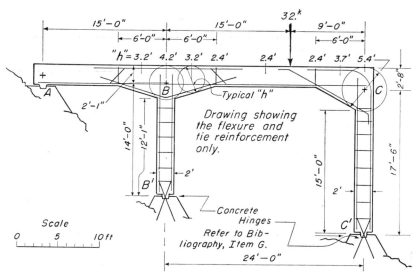

FIG. 5–12. Rigid frame with haunched members. (EXAMPLE 5–7.)

EXAMPLE 5-7

Given the haunched membered rigid frame of Fig. 5–12. It is required to find the bending moments therein due only to the single concentrated load shown, by haunched beam moment distribution. (The solution is discussed in the following articles.)

5-15. Determination of the M/I Curves from the Effective Cross Sections. Referring to Fig. 5–12, the flexural *effective depth*, h, at a section of a haunch of the girder member BC was considered to be the diameter of the inscribed circle having its center on the section. This or similar construction should always be used to find effective cross sections, shown in Fig. 5–13(a). At (c) are shown the moments of inertia calculated therefrom, taking a one-foot width. Any convenient number of *equidistant* sections may be taken, provided the depth variation gets expressed.

In Fig. 5–13(b) separate bending moment diagrams were drawn for the known loading (positive) and the unknown fixed end moments (negative) M_1 and M_0. If preferred, convenient trial numerical values may be assumed for these restraining moments.

TABLE 5–1

CALCULATION OF $\dfrac{M}{I}$ AREAS, MOMENTS OF AREAS AND CENTROIDS OF AREAS

($S = 3$ FT.)

Arm from Small End "B" to Centroid of Area	Positive M/I		M_1/I		M_0/I	
	Area	Mom. of Area	Area	Mom. of Area	Area	Mom. of Area
0.33 S	—	—	$0.08\ SM_1$	$0.03\ S^2M_1$	—	—
1.00	13.2 S	13.2 S^2	0.32	0.32	$0.05\ SM_0$	$0.05\ S^2M_0$
2.00	62.5	125.0	0.65	1.30	0.22	0.44
3.00	94.0	282.0	0.54	1.62	0.33	0.99
4.00	125.0	500.0	0.44	1.76	0.44	1.76
5.00	156.0	780.0	0.33	1.65	0.54	2.70
6.00	104.0	624.0	0.22	1.32	0.65	3.90
7.00	14.2	99.5	0.03	0.21	0.21	1.47
7.67 S	—	—	—	—	0.04	0.31
Totals	568.9 S	2423.7 S^2	2.61 SM_1	8.21 S^2M_1	2.48 SM_0	11.62 S^2M_0
$\bar{x} =$	4.26 S =	12.78 ft.	3.14 S =	9.42 ft.	4.68 S =	14.04 ft.

Portions (d) and (e) are the desired M/I curves computed by simple division at each section of the member. For example, at the section 6 ft. from the left end, the positive $M/I = 72/1.15 = 62.5$, the $M_1/I = 0.75/1.15 = 0.65$, and the $M_0/I = 0.25/1.15 = 0.22$.

The area "under" each curve was found in Table 5–1 by multiplying the summation of its ordinates by S, the constant 3-ft. distance between ordinates. Moments of M/I areas were also computed in order

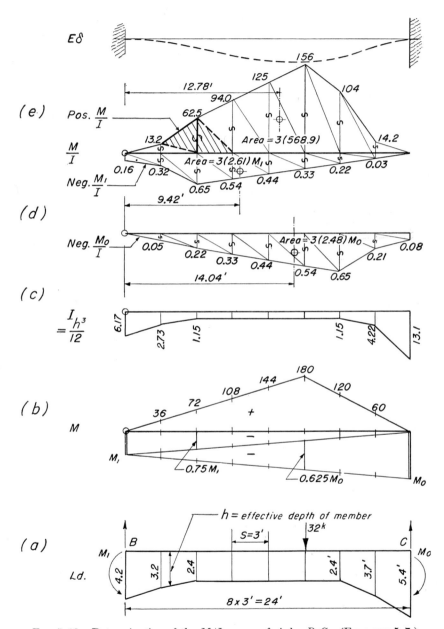

FIG. 5–13. Determination of the M/I curves of girder B–C. (EXAMPLE 5–7.)

to find the needed centroids for use with the moment-area laws. For this purpose the division of the areas into pairs of equal-area triangles, as shown, means that the arm for each pair is the distance to the common ordinate, as shown in the left-hand column of the table. The odd triangular area at one end of each negative M/I diagram received special treatment.

5–16. Determination of Nonprismatic Fixed End Moments. The F.E.M.'s will be found under the condition of zero rotation of the end tangents of the $E\delta$ curve. By moment areas (curves, Law III), the algebraic sum of the moments of the M/I areas about one end must equal zero:

$$2423.7 - 8.21M_1 - 11.62M_0 \equiv 0 \tag{A}$$

Also by moment areas (curves, Law II), the algebraic sum of the M/I areas must equal zero:

$$568.9 - 2.61M_1 - 2.48M_0 \equiv 0 \tag{B}$$

Solving Eqs. (A) and (B) simultaneously, the fixed end moments are:

$$M_1 = 60.2 \text{ kip-ft.}, \qquad M_0 = 166.1 \text{ kip-ft.}$$

5–17. Determination of Nonprismatic Carry-over Factors. Taking a member fixed at one end and hinged at the other, as in Fig. 5–14(a), Professor Cross[B] defined *carry-over factor* as the ratio of the moment at the fixed end to the moment producing rotation at the rotated end. For prismatic members it is $1/2$, as derived in Appendix B, but for non-prismatic members the values must be calculated. In every case the rotated end corresponds to a joint just released for a cycle of moment distribution, while the fixed end represents the remote end of the member. Unsymmetrical members have two carry-over factors, one emanating from each rotated end.

Referring again to Fig. 5–14(a), the problem is to find the fixity moment M_{CB} developed at C by the application of moment M_{BC} at B. The corresponding M/I curve at (b) was taken from Fig. 5–13(d) and (e). Again, applying the moment area law of the tangent, the summation of moments of M/I areas about B must equal zero:

$$2.61M_{BC}(9.42) - 2.48M_{CB}(14.04) \equiv 0$$
$$M_{CB} = 0.706M_{BC}$$

Therefore, the carry-over factor from B to $C = 0.706$.

Similarly, by rotating the end C, while holding end B fixed, as shown in Fig. 5–14(c), the algebraic sum of the moments of the areas about C must equal zero:

$$2.61M_{BC}(14.58) - 2.48M_{CB}(9.96) \equiv 0$$
$$M_{BC} = 0.649M_{CB}$$

Therefore, the carry-over factor from C to $B = 0.649$.

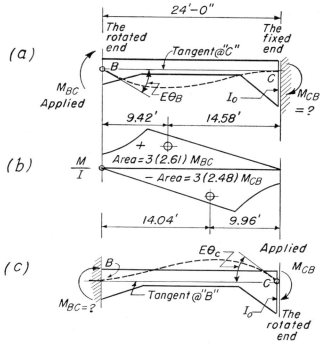

Fig. 5–14. Finding member B–C carry-over factors.

5–18. Determination of Nonprismatic Stiffness Factors. Strictly speaking, the *stiffness* is the amount of moment necessary to rotate the hinged end of a member through a unit angle when the other end is held fixed, as was depicted in Fig. 5–14. The rotated end corresponds to a joint just released for a cycle of moment distribution. The ends of all members connecting directly thereto are rotated through the same angle. Of the whole moment to be distributed, the portion which each such member assumes is proportional to its stiffness, as defined above.

It is proved in Appendix B and its Fig. 3(b) that for a *prismatic* member BC that is fixed at C the moment distributable to end B will be:

$$M_{BC} = E\theta_B \left(\frac{4I}{L}\right). \tag{5–17}$$

Since θ, and E ordinarily, is constant for all members connecting to joint B, the moment distributed to each will be *proportional to I/L.* Accordingly, for prismatic members, I/L is usually said to *be the stiffness factor.*

In the case of nonprismatic members, the coefficient of I/L is not 4. Furthermore, if such a member is unsymmetrical, it will have a different stiffness factor for each end.

When a structure consists of both prismatic and nonprismatic members, as in the present example, it is better to use $4EI/L$ in calculating the stiffness of the prismatic members.* An additional constant, h', the haunching coefficient, may then be computed for the nonprismatic members so that:

$$\text{Stiffness factor for nonprismatic members} = \frac{4h'EI_0}{L}$$

Stiffness Factor Calculation. Assume that the numerical value of h' is not of interest, and that both E and θ_B are taken as unity in Fig. 5–14(a) and (b). Then by curves, Law II, the unity value of $E\theta_B$ must equal the net actual M/I area for the bending situation pictured at (a):

By cross multiplication

$$M_{BC} = \frac{1}{3[2.61 - 0.706(2.48)]}$$

or

Stiffness factor for B end $= 0.391$

Similarly, referring to Fig. 5–14(b) and (c), and rotating end C a unit amount:

$$M_{CB} = \frac{1}{3[2.48 - 0.649(2.61)]}$$

or

Stiffness factor for C end $= 0.426$

Theoretically, the stiffnesses at the two ends of a nonprismatic member must be inversely proportional to the carry-over factors emanating therefrom. Values computed by the numerical method here presented should not deviate materially from this relationship.

The Haunching Coefficient. If the larger end of a member is chosen as the section of reference, calling its moment of inertia I_0, the h''s of both ends will be less than unity, and will indicate the stiffness of the haunched member *relative* to a prismatic one of inertia I_0.

Referring again to Fig. 5–14(a) and (b) and the carry-over factors previously computed, we may state from Formula 5–17:

$$E\theta_B = \frac{M_{BC}}{4h'_B}\left(\frac{L}{I_0}\right)$$

So, from above:

$$3M_{BC}[2.61 - 0.706(2.48)] = \frac{24M_{BC}}{4h_B(13.1)}$$

$$h'_B = 0.179$$

---

* In Fig. 5–15, E was omitted since the same class of concrete was contemplated throughout the structure.

STANDARD HOOKS

180° HOOK
ailing Dimension

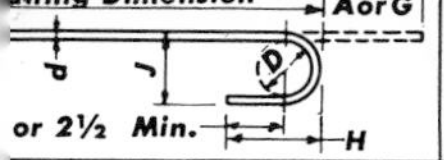

d	HOOK A or G	J	Approx. H
	4	2	3½
	5	3	4
	6	4	4½
	7	5	5
	8	6	6
	10	7	7
	1-1	10	9
	1-3	11¼	10¼
	1-5	1-0½	11¼
	1-7	1-2	1-0¾

D = 6 d for #2 to #7
D = 8 d for #8 to #11

90° HOOK
Detailing Dimension

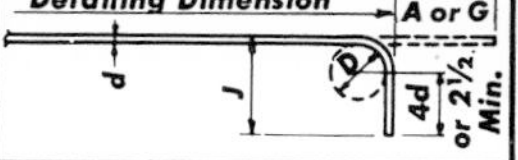

BAR SIZE d	HOOK A or G	J
#2	3	3½
#3	3½	4
#4	3½	5
#5	4	5½
#6	4½	6½
#7	5½	7½
#8	6½	9
#9	7½	10
#10	8½	11½
#11	9	1-0½

D = 7 d for #2 to #7
D = 8 d for #8 to #11

SLANTS

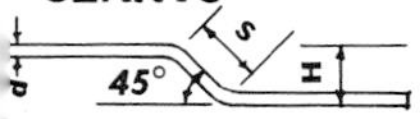

S	H	S
4	1-1	1-6½
5½	1-2	1-8
7	1-3	1-9
8½	1-4	1-10½
10	1-5	2-0
11½	1-6	2-1½
1-0½	1-7	2-3
1-2	1-8	2-4
1-3½	1-9	2-5½
1-5	1-10	2-7

BAR LAPS

Number of Bar Diameters Indicated below, or 12′ whichever is greater.

BAR	20 d	24 d	30 d	40 d
#2	*	*	*	*
#3	*	*	1-0	1-3
#4	*	1-0	1-3	1-8
#5	1-1	1-3	1-7	2-1
#6	1-3	1-6	1-11	2-6
#7	1-6	1-9	2-3	2-11
#8	1-8	2-0	2-6	3-4
#9	1-11	2-4	2-10	3-10
#10	2-2	2-7	3-3	4-3
#11	2-5	2-10	3-7	4-9

* Minimum 12″

CONCRETE REINFORCING STEEL INSTITUTE

38 South Dearborn St., Chicago 3, Ill.

STANDARD A305 REINFORCING BARS

| BAR SIZES | | WEIGHT | NOMINAL DIM.—ROUND S | | |
OLD (Inches)	NEW (Numerals)	POUNDS PER FOOT	DIAMETER INCHES	CROSS SEC. AREA, SQ. IN.	PERIM. INCH
¼	#2	.167	.250	.05	.7
⅜	#3	.376	.375	.11	1.1
½	#4	.668	.500	.20	1.5
⅝	#5	1.043	.625	.31	1.9
¾	#6	1.502	.750	.44	2.3
⅞	#7	2.044	.875	.60	2.7
1	#8	2.670	1.000	.79	3.1
1	#9	3.400	1.128	1.00	3.5
1⅛	#10	4.303	1.270	1.27	3.9
1¼	#11	5.313	1.410	1.56	4.4

The new bar numbers are based on the number of inches included in the nominal diameter of the bar.

Bar #2 in plain rounds only. Bars #9, #10 and #11 c round bars and equivalent in weight and nominal cre sectional area to old type 1″, 1⅛″ and 1¼″ square ba

These weights were adopted as standards by the Institu in 1934 and approved through U.S. Department of Co merce Simplified Practice Recommendation 26.

SPECIAL DEFORMED ROUND STEEL BARS
ASTM Designation (A 408-57T)

| BAR SIZES | | WEIGHT | NOMINAL DIM.—ROUND S | | |
OLD (Inches)	NEW (Numerals)	POUNDS PER FOOT	DIAMETER INCHES	CROSS SEC. AREA, SQ. IN.	PERIM. INCH
1½	14S	7.65	1.693	2.25	5.3
2	18S	13.60	2.257	4.00	7.0

These large bars are outside the scope of ASTM A15 f Billet Steel Bars and ASTM A305 for Deformations.

Similarly, from Fig. 5–14(b) and (c), involving the rotation of end C:

$$h'_C = 0.195$$

Note in this case that haunched member BC is hardly one-fifth as stiff as the corresponding enveloping uniform section member.

5–19. Haunched Member Moment Distribution. Figure 5–15 shows the fixed end moments, carry-over and stiffness factors just computed for member BC, together with similar factors computed elsewhere for member AB. The calculation of the corresponding stiffnesses of the prismatic column members is included.

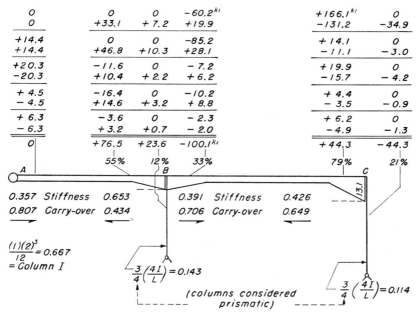

Fig. 5–15. Haunched member moment distribution. (Example 5–7.)

The moment distribution process itself is complicated only by the extra attention necessary to see that the proper carry-over factor is used at each end of the members.

Obviously the plain concrete moments of inertia should not be used to investigate the bending stresses at a section. Their usefulness is limited exclusively to elastic considerations.

HAUNCHED MEMBER PRACTICE PROBLEMS

Problem 5–14. Find the carry-over and stiffness factors for member AB of Example 5–7 by the M/I method demonstrated. Compare your results with the values on Fig. 5–15.

Problem 5-15. In the subsequent Example 5–8, the fixed end moments, carry-over factors, and stiffness factors were found from the charts of Appendix C. Check the six values thereof by working by the M/I method demonstrated. Carefully compute the values of moment of inertia at intermediate points along each member, using the algebraic expression shown on the chart.

5-20. Analysis of a Nonprismatic Membered Rigid Frame, Using the Charts of Appendix C.

To expedite the solution of some of the simpler cases of nonprismatic members, the author has prepared charts of fixed end moment, carry-over, and stiffness factor variation for all ratios of I_{min} to I_{max}, a ratio shown on the charts as I_1/I_0. Only a few of the most common cases of loading and sectional variation are embraced, as will be seen by referring to Plates XII to XIV, inclusive, of Appendix C. The curves were obtained by integration, taking advantage of the regularity of form[7] and loading. Points on these curves may be checked by the foregoing M/I method.[8]

The values shown for stiffness and fixed end moment are coefficients of the corresponding expression for the case of a hypothetical prismatic member of moment of inertia I_0 and loaded in the same way. Therefore all these curves pass through unity when $I_1/I_0 = 1$—a prismatic member.

The carry-over factor was plotted directly, the curve passing through 0.5 when $I_1/I_0 = 1$.

EXAMPLE 5–8

Given the nonprismatic membered rigid frame of Fig. 5–16, loaded as shown. Required to make a moment distribution analysis, using the charts of Appendix C.

---

[7] The equation $I_x = \dfrac{I_0}{1 + ax}$ shows what beam contour was contemplated in working out the values on Plates XIIa and XIV. The graphs can be used without appreciable error for beams not vastly different in shape.

The symbol a is a constant which may be determined for each beam. Suppose that in Plate XIIa the whole span is 20 ft., $I_0 = 1000$, and $I_1 = 500$. Then, with origin at the left end, $I = 500$, where $x = 10$, so $I_x = \dfrac{1000}{1 + 10a} = 500$, from which $a = 0.1$ for this case.

To find I_x at some intermediate point, say, 5 ft. from the left end, use the value of a previously determined, finding $I_x = I_5 = 667$.

Other such points may be found, and the depths sketched to scale according to the cube root of the I's. Comparison can then be made with the contour of the beam.

[8] For a comprehensive set of tables of values covering many more cases of loading and haunching, see the *Handbook of Frame Constants* published by the Portland Cement Association.

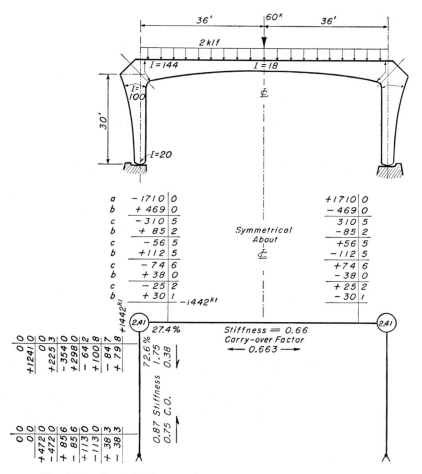

FIG. 5–16. Analysis of a rigid frame having nonprismatic members.

Solution:
Find girder fixed end moments:

Distributed load: $\dfrac{I_1}{I_0} = \dfrac{18}{144} = 0.125$

From Plate XII(a): $c\,\dfrac{wL^2}{12} = 1.19\left(\dfrac{2 \times \overline{72}^2}{12}\right) = 1030$ kip-ft.

Concentrated load:

From Plate XII(a): $c\,\dfrac{WL}{8} = 1.26\left(\dfrac{60 \times 72}{8}\right) = \underline{\;680\;}$ kip-ft.

Total F. E. M.   1710 kip-ft.

Find stiffnesses:

Girder—symmetrical: $I_0 = 144,$ $\dfrac{I_1}{I_0} = 0.125$

From Plate XII(a): $c\,\dfrac{I_0}{L} = 0.33\left(\dfrac{144}{72}\right) = 0.66$ at each end

Column—unsymmetrical: $I_0 = 100,$ $\dfrac{I_1}{I_0} = 0.2$

From Plate XIV: $c\,\dfrac{I_0}{L} = 0.525\left(\dfrac{100}{30}\right) = 1.75$ large end

$0.26\left(\dfrac{100}{30}\right) = 0.87$ small end, not used.

Find carry-over factors:

Girder—symmetrical: $\dfrac{I_1}{I_0} = 0.125$

From Plate XII(a): C.O.F. $= 0.66$ in both directions

Column—unsymmetrical: $\dfrac{I_1}{I_0} = 0.2$

From Plate XIV: C.O.F. $= 0.75$ small end to large
$= 0.38$ large end to small.

With the above information conveniently arranged on the layout sheet, the moment distribution was performed in the usual manner and the bending moment at the upper corner was found to be 1442 kip-ft. At each end of the members, care must be taken that the correct factor is used.

CHART PRACTICE PROBLEM

Problem 5–16. Assuming ⅕-span haunching of both members of Fig. 5–16 instead of the curved variation shown, recalculate Example 5–8, using the corresponding haunched member charts of Appendix C. Make a tabular comparison of the results in the two cases.

5–21. Summary of Continuity. The generalized statement of the moment-area laws enables one to sketch quickly and define the curve geometry of beam action for the usual cases without writing equations and performing integrations.

When members are continuous over more than one span, or are otherwise restrained at their ends, the laws of static equilibrium are insufficient for determining the bending moments therein, and continuity methods based upon the deformed shape of the structure become necessary.

In the *moment distribution* and *slope deflection* methods of continuity analysis, the fully fixed end moments are needed for each span carrying intermediate loads. For prismatic members these may be found geometrically by sketching the rectangular or trapezoidal *negative* bending moment diagram and equalizing the positive and negative moment diagram areas and moments of areas. For nonprismatic members the corresponding irregular M/I areas must be so used.

PLATE 5–2. Continuous reinforced concrete girder highway bridge. Note the curved haunching of the girders.

To ensure a hinged condition at the pier tops the main vertical reinforcement of the pier is often crossed there in scissors fashion, as in Fig. 5–12, and sheet lead laid between the pier top and the underside of the girder. The lead also prevents the development of high stresses in the concrete at the edges of the pier due to girder joint rotation. Obviously such structures do not function as rigid frames.

Carry-over and stiffness factors are needed in moment distribution analyses. For prismatic members the carry-over factor is one half and the stiffness factor is $4I/L$; but for nonprismatic members they must be calculated from M/I diagram areas and moments of areas or by some other means.

In attacking a continuity problem, always sketch a predicted deflected shape of the structure and the contraflexure point locations, since a comparison thereof with the final result develops structural judgment.

The moment distribution method is generally preferred by designers working on structures involving more than a few members. It can easily be adapted to cases in which the joints translate, such as horizontally under wind forces,[A] or vertically due to settlement of supports.[E]

The algebraic methods are most useful, when only a few members are involved, for preparing design charts or tables, and for checking. Everyone should know at least two continuity methods well, so that checks can be made when needed.

BIBLIOGRAPHY

A) LARGE, GEORGE E., and MORRIS, CLYDE T.   The Moment Distribution Method of Structural Analysis Extended to Lateral Loads and Members of Variable Section, *Ohio State University Engineering Experiment Station Bulletin No.* 66, 1931.

See Appendix B thereof in particular for Professor C. C. More's method of presenting the Beam Curves relationships.

B) CROSS, HARDY.   Analysis of Continuous Frames by Distributing Fixed End Moments, *Transactions A.S.C.E.*, 1932, Vol. 96, p. 1.   Note that Cross used a system of signs different from that used throughout this text.

C) WILSON, RICHART, and WEISS.   Analysis of Statically Indeterminate Structures by the Slope Deflection Method, *University of Illinois Engineering Experiment Station Bulletin No.* 108.

D) See discussion by Walter Ruppel of Paper No. 1598, *Transactions A.S.C.E.*, 1927, Vol. 90, p. 152.   "Moments in Restrained and Continuous Beams by the Method of Conjugate Points," by Nishkian, L. B., and Steinman, D. B.

Also the Modified Slope Deflection Equations.   Evans, L. T., *Jour. Amer. Concrete Inst.*, Oct. 1931, p. 109.

Also *Handbook of Frame Constants*.   Portland Cement Association.   Chicago, 1947.

E) LARGE, GEORGE E.   Settlement Stresses in Continuous Frames, *Ohio State University Engineering Experiment Station Bulletin No.* 102, 1939.

F) ZALKIN, JOSEPH.   Determination of Fixed End Moments in Beams with Irregular Loading Without Use of Formulas from Handbooks, *Proc. American Concrete Institute*, 1952, Vol. 48, pp. 186 and 425.

G) MOREELL, BEN.   Articulation for Concrete Structures—The Mesnager Hinge, *Proc. American Concrete Institute*, 1935, Vol. 31, p. 368.

REVIEW QUESTIONS

1. Why should downward loading be shown as hanging from a beam instead of pressing upon it?

2. What do the $EI\theta$ and $EI\delta$ curves represent?   Is the $EI\theta$ curve superfluous?   Explain.

3. State the three Laws of Related Beam Curves.   To which beam curves are they applicable?   Are the moment-area laws as generally applicable? (See Appendix B.)

4. Define fixed end moment, carry-over moment, carry-over factor, stiffness, and stiffness factor.

5. Derive the expressions for carry-over factor and stiffness factor.

6. Are the reactions for a fully fixed beam always different from the simple beam reactions? Explain.

7. In the moment distribution process, why should a joint be considered relocked following a distribution and before proceeding to the next joint?

8. Justify by derivation the use of $(3/4)(I/L)$ for the stiffness of members hinged at their outer ends. Would you use $(3/4)(I/L)$ for a two-span beam hinged at both ends, to avoid dealing with four columns of figures?

9. Since one system of signs for bending moments is used in the moment distribution process, and another for drawing load, shear, and moment curves, how can confusion be avoided in changing from one to the other?

10. In analyzing a six-span continuous beam by moment areas, how many equations must be solved simultaneously? By slope deflection?

11. Taking the symmetrical frame with girder overhangs, as shown in Problem 5–21, Fig. 5–17, show exactly how the moment distribution should be performed at the upper joints.

12. Prove that the translation of the upper joints of an unequal legged rigid frame induces bending moments in the columns proportional to I/L^2.

13. Distinguish clearly between prismatic and nonprismatic members.

14. Are the fixed end moments of a beam dependent only upon the loading and the span? Explain.

15. Is there any error in the method of computing areas and moments of areas used in Table 5–1? Explain.

16. Assume that the beam BC of Example 5–7 is prismatic. Rapidly calculate the fixed end moments. Compare their values with those used.

17. Explain why $(3/4)(4I/L)$ was used for the stiffness of the columns in Fig. 5–15.

18. What stiffness factors would have been found in Example 5–7 if the moment of inertia of the smaller end of member BC had been used as a reference?

19. Deduce qualitatively the effect of haunching upon (a) stiffness factor and (b) carry-over factor, as compared to those for a prismatic beam of the same maximum depth.

PROBLEMS

Problems 5–17 to 5–25. Find the moments in the members of the continuous structures of Fig. 5–17, and finally draw load, shear, and moment diagrams for each member. If a member is also subject to direct load (tensile or compressive), show it also on the load diagram.

Problem 5–26. (*Individual*) Taking a symmetrical beam with straight haunches, compute the uniform load fixed end moments, the carry-over factor, and the stiffness factor for various combinations of end depth/midspan depth and haunch length/span length ratios. Take haunch ratios from 0.1 span to 0.5 span, and depth ratios from 1.1 to 3.0. Get effective depths by the inscribed circle method. Plot charts of your findings as directed by the instructor.

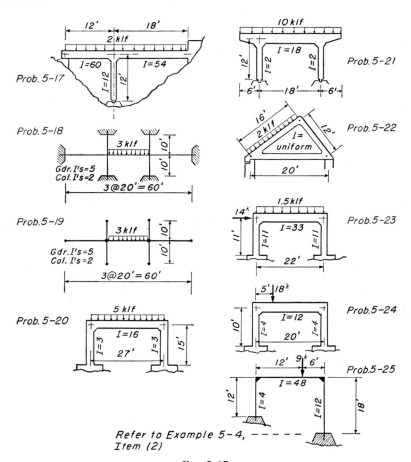

Fig. 5–17.

Problem 5–27. Re-perform the moment distribution of Fig. 5–15, Example 5–7, using the 12 ft. and 15 ft. clear heights of the columns for stiffness calculations. Refer to Fig. 5–12. What difference in bending moments do you find? About what points do the joints rotate? Should we have figured haunches at the tops of the columns too? Discuss.

Problem 5–28. Design rectangular columns for the rigid frame situations shown in Fig. 5–18. Refer to Figs. 5–12 and 5–16 for orientation.

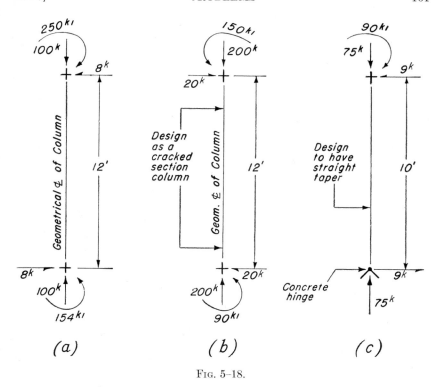

Fig. 5–18.

Take 40,000-psi yield point steel and ACI 3000-lb. concrete and specification.

Design by the demonstrated methods of Chapter 4.   Employ available check methods.

Observe the ACI maximum and minimum percentages of steel.   Refer to ACI new Sec. 1104(b).   Bars may be discontinued where no longer needed.

Provide a minimum of 1½ in. cover over all steel, allowing ½ in. for ties.

Make a final design sketch to scale showing bar sizes, positions, and lengths: also ties, and stirrups if needed.

Suggestion. First draw the resultant force line.

CHAPTER 6

BUILDINGS—
DESIGN OF BEAM AND GIRDER FLOORS, COLUMNS

6–1. Introduction. Reinforced concrete is widely used in building construction because of its firesafety, durability, waterproofness, and relatively lower cost. Its integral form results in continuity between members, which makes for a very rigid structure, usually without the necessity for additional bracing members. Since beams with freely

Arthur J. Boase, 1893–1949, for sixteen years manager of the Structural Bureau, Portland Cement Association. Mr. Boase traveled widely in Europe and South America studying foreign reinforced concrete design practice, and was the author of numerous papers in the field. He was chairman of the ACI committee which formulated the 1947 Building Code and author-chairman of the ACI *Reinforced Concrete Design Handbook* and the *Manual of Standard Practice for Detailing Reinforced Concrete Structures.*

hinged ends are almost unknown in this field, the designer must make practical application of all his knowledge of structural continuity. Furthermore, the columns and walls are generally so rigidly connected to portions of the floor system that the structure is actually a three-dimensional rigid frame.

In **skeleton construction,** illustrated in Fig. 6–1, the relatively thin walls and partitions above ground are supported story by story, through girders, by a forest of columns. It should be clearly distinguished from the older **wall bearing construction** still used for low buildings, in which all or most of the weight of the structure is supported *by* thick bearing walls.

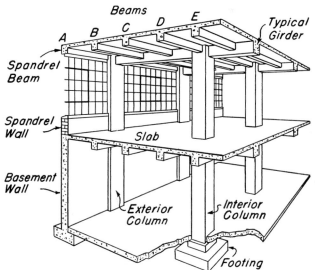

FIG. 6–1. Slab, beam, and girder skeleton construction.

The term **girder** is here applied to horizontal beam-like members extending from column to column, as distinguished from **beams** which typically extend from girder to girder.

The four principal types of reinforced concrete floors are (a) **concrete joist** construction (the pan T-beams of Chapter 2), (b) the **slab, beam, and girder** scheme illustrated in Fig. 6–1, (c) **two-way slab** and girder and (d) **flat slab** (girderless) construction, the latter two taken up in Chapter 7.

6–2. Building Loads. Building design begins with the design of the roof[1] members and progresses downward through the columns, picking

---

[1] Ordinarily, snow load, wind load, dead load, and live load, abbreviated *S.L.*, *W.L* , *D.L.*, and *L.L.*, must all be considered, and sometimes other special loads. Since, for the building to be designed in this chapter, space will permit only the design of *typical* floor and column members, the detailed design of the roof slab and framing, together with discussion of the snow and wind loads to which it is subject, will be omitted. Neither will the overturning effect of the wind on the side of the building be taken up, since the low ratio of height to base width of the structure means that little if any change in the *D.L.* + *L.L.* design will be necessary to provide for it within the $33\frac{1}{3}$ per cent additional allowable unit stress limitation universally permitted.

up the floor loads on the way, to the calculation of footings.   Each member must first of all carry its own weight, or **dead load,** plus that of all other parts of the structure supported by it, including all permanent built-in fixtures.   Extensive tables of weights of building materials will be found in Appendix **K**, and in the American Institute of Steel Construction, *Steel Construction Manual.*   Lightweight, movable office partitions are not considered as dead load, but should be included in the total load.

The **live load** embraces all movable contents of the building, including people, and is stated in pounds per square foot of floor.   Tables thereof for various occupancies as set by building codes will be found in Appendix **K**, and in structural handbooks.   The published values have been set high enough to include the effect of the ordinary concentrated loads involved in each case.   The effect of extraordinary concentrations, such as heavy safes, must be computed separately and included.

Each floor of a building must be designed for the full dead plus live loading.   However, due to the improbability of having full live load on all floors at any instant, members which support several floors, such as columns and footings, are customarily designed for a decreased live loading depending upon the number of floors carried, as shown in the accompanying table:

U. S. DEPARTMENT OF COMMERCE
REPORT OF BUILDING CODE COMMITTEE

Number of Floors Carried by the Member	Permissible Reduction in Total Live Load Carried
1	0%
2	10
3	20
4	30
5	40
6	45
7 or more	50%

6–3. Floor Framing Layouts. Before any detailed designing can proceed, a decision must be made as to the general layout, especially regarding the location of the columns.   Generally, the simplest arrangement is best.   The owner usually wants as few columns as possible, but the decision should be made by the architect after the structural engineer has shown him by rapid preliminary calculations what structural sacrifices are involved in a given proposal, and what alternate layout would be the most economical.   To do this the experienced engineer may study several typical slab, beam, and girder arrangements similar to Fig. 6–1, recognizing that extensive thick solid slabs are uneconomical and should not greatly exceed a 4-in. minimum thickness; that for light loads such slab spans may be 12 ft. or more, for heavy ones perhaps 6 ft.; that beams and girders of more than 20- to 25-ft. span tend to have depths which encroach upon headroom; that when the column spacings are unequal in the two directions it will usually be better to run the girders in the short direction; and that heavy concentrated loads near the center of long spans should be avoided.

EXAMPLE 6–1

The Design of an Industrial Building. Following preliminary studies, it is required to design a four-story manufacturing and storage building according to the floor plan and elevations shown in Fig. 6–4. The given data and the allowable stresses of the ACI Code have been put properly on Calculation Sheet 1 for ready reference.

The manner of determining the bending moments in the slabs and beams differs from that used for the girders and columns, as will be seen.

(A) The Design of Floor Slabs[2] and Beams as Units of a Continuous Horizontal System

6–4. Slab Flexure. A typical floor slab, *EF*, in Fig. 6–4(a), is supported along all four edges, and the length of the long side is more than three times the short side. Accepted[A] theory for such slabs has shown that when the length exceeds 1.5 times the breadth, all the bending may be considered to take place over the shorter distance. We will therefore run all slab flexure steel in the east-west direction.

6–5. Effective Spans for Computing Bending Moments. Whether to use the *center to center lengths* or the *clear lengths* of members of continuous structures in calculating bending moments is a troublesome problem. Obviously, if a member is built integrally between massive supports which do not rotate at all (full fixity), the clear span is the correct one to use. In practical reinforced concrete building construction, most of the floor members are supported by other floor members which themselves rotate or tilt appreciably as the supported member deforms, which suggests the use of a longer effective span.

The 1940 Joint Committee Specification (see Chapter 1), which is conservative and clear, states that "in continuous beams and slabs or elastic

---

[2] Since the *slabs* are not attached directly to the columns flexurally, they form a continuous east-west horizontal member restrained at the supports only by the torsional rigidity of the supporting beams, which is neglected. The same situation exists with respect to the typical *beams*. Neither is considered a part of a vertical rigid frame.

frames the effective span should be taken as the center to center distance between supports." It further states that the (decreased) negative moment at the face of the support *may* be used in proportioning the members.[B]

The ACI Code, to which this text is referred, is similar in Sec. 702(b) 2 and 3, but is somewhat unclear with respect to the designing of slabs.

In the example to follow, center to center span distances will be used throughout to compute stiffnesses and continuity bending moments at the centerline of supports. The smaller (negative) bending moment value computable therefrom at the *face* of the support will be used in designing the end sections of all slabs, beams, and girders.

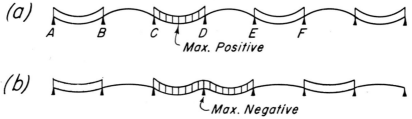

FIG. 6–2.   Loading conditions for maximum live load bending moment.

6–6. Criteria for Maximum Live Load Bending Moments in a Continuous Slab or Beam. Referring to Fig. 6–2(a), and assuming approximately equal spans, it will be evident that the greatest bending will occur in a chosen member, say CD, when some spans are unloaded.

PLATE 6–1.   Reinforced concrete frame apartments built by the New York City Housing Authority.

To produce a maximum positive bending moment in a chosen span of a continuous beam or slab, load that span, and alternate spans.

Correspondingly, for the greatest bending over any chosen support, D, as in (b):

To produce a maximum negative bending moment at a chosen support of a continuous beam or slab, load the two adjacent spans, and alternate spans.

Furthermore it will be found that the influence of loads on any but the *adjacent* "alternate spans" is practically negligible.

6–7. Bending Moment Coefficients for Continuous Slab and Beam Design. The accompanying Fig. 6–3 shows the results of moment distribution studies made upon continuous systems of several equal spans, uniformly loaded according to the live-load criteria of the preceding article. Since, in the columns of the upper table, there is little variation

(Courtesy of the F. & R. Lazarus Company)

PLATE 6–2. Unenclosed parking garage of reinforced concrete.

The round columns support wide shallow continuous girders which in turn carry pan-construction T-beam floors. The end spans are short cantilevers which function to prevent the bending moments in the outermost columns from being greater than those in the interior ones.

Note how reinforced concrete construction may be adapted to a highly irregular parcel of land with pleasing effect.

in the coefficient of wL^2, the maximum values have been underscored (two-span ignored) and used to compute weighted combined coefficients for use with total dead load plus live load, for three ratios of live to dead load. The results appear in the lower table and will be used in the designing.

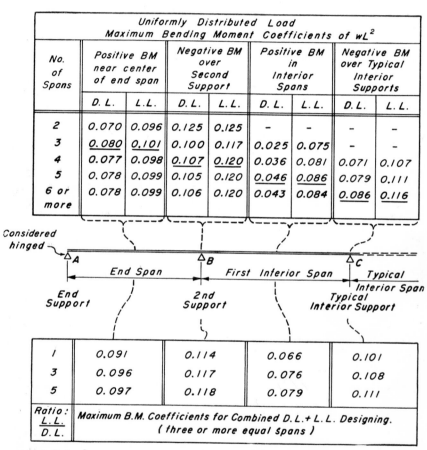

	Uniformly Distributed Load							
	Maximum Bending Moment Coefficients of wL^2							
No. of Spans	Positive BM near center of end span		Negative BM over Second Support		Positive BM in Interior Spans		Negative BM over Typical Interior Supports	
	D. L.	L. L.	D. L.	L. L.	D. L.	L. L.	D. L.	L. L.
2	0.070	0.096	0.125	0.125	–	–	–	–
3	0.080	0.101	0.100	0.117	0.025	0.075	–	–
4	0.077	0.098	0.107	0.120	0.036	0.081	0.071	0.107
5	0.078	0.099	0.105	0.120	0.046	0.086	0.079	0.111
6 or more	0.078	0.099	0.106	0.120	0.043	0.084	0.086	0.116

Considered hinged

A   End Span   B   First Interior Span   C   Typical Interior Span

End Support   2nd Support   Typical Interior Support

1	0.091	0.114	0.066	0.101
3	0.096	0.117	0.076	0.108
5	0.097	0.118	0.079	0.111
Ratio: L.L. / D.L.	Maximum B.M. Coefficients for Combined D.L.+ L.L. Designing. (three or more equal spans)			

FIG. 6–3. Moment coefficients found by *moment distribution* analysis.

6–8. Flexure Design of a One-Way Floor Slab System. Whenever possible, a uniform thickness of slab should be planned for throughout all spans, as it facilitates the simplicity and re-use of the formwork. When spans are equal, the greatest bending moments occur in the end span or at the second support, so the end slab thickness may be maintained throughout the system and the interior slabs under-reinforced.

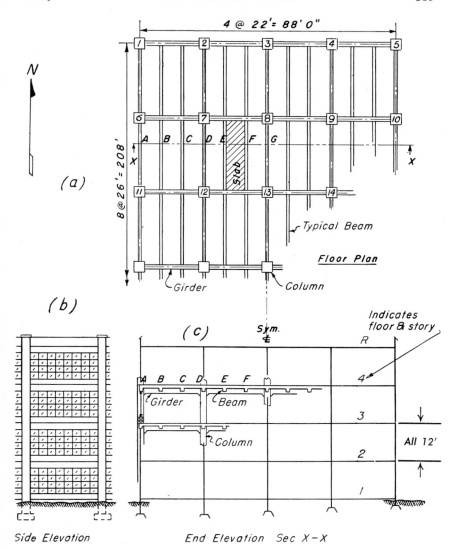

FIG. 6–4.   Floor plan and elevations of building.   (For additional orientation see also Dwg. 19 in the ACI's 1951 *Manual of Standard Practice for Detailing Reinforced Concrete Structures*.)

In very large, lightly loaded floor areas, with relatively few end spans, over-all economy may be facilitated by using a thinner slab largely dictated by the interior spans and over-reinforcing the end spans. Making the end spans shorter than the rest is a good solution.

It is best to underestimate the width of supporting members, as this will result in conservatively high values of slab shear and bending moment at the face thereof which will not need to be revised later on. See the accompanying Calculation Sheet 1, *Data and Spec.*

Design of End Slab A–B (Calculation Sheet 1). The design for positive steel proceeds easily from Art. 6–4 and the bending moments of Fig. 6–3, using the beam charts. Always be sure to take advantage of any increase in d after a slab thickness, t, is chosen. *Repeatedly revise the bending moment to reflect the improved value of dead load until the slab thickness called for by the final design sketch is consistent with the bending moment used.* To save space only the final calculation is shown. The computation of steel area required per inch of slab width is a convenience in trying bar sizes.

Choice of Bar Size. The *minimum* usable size of bar is dictated by ACI Sec. 505, which requires a clear spacing of at least 1.33 in. to allow our 1-in. coarse aggregate to pass between the bars.

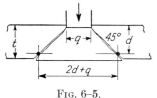

FIG. 6–5.

The *maximum* bar size is set by Sec. 702(e)(3) which limits bar spacings to three times the slab thickness, t, but not more than 18 in. Some such requirement is necessary because large bars may work out to be so far apart that a concentrated load may punch[3] out a frustum of concrete, mostly through diagonal tension failure, as pictured in Fig. 6–5. Even when the "concentrated" load is distributed over a width $q = d$, this consideration shows that bar spacing preferably should not exceed $2\frac{1}{2}d$.

The necessity for safety in bond also can be a guide to suitable bar size. One can compute the required bar perimeter and area at the face of a prominent support, and then select the corresponding bar from Table 1–3 of Chapter 1.

It should also be borne in mind that the smaller sized bars cost more, both in price per pound and in the labor of setting them.

The Design of Negative Steel at Support B. Refer to Calculation Sheet 2. The design bending moment is computed at the *face* of the supporting beam, and will be less than the $0.12wL^2$ value determined from the center-to-center span study to the extent of the beam shear area between the two sections. Actually, the 12-in. beam dimension is only an estimate, so a precise value of the shear area is not possible. Referring also to the sketch at the bottom of Sheet 1, we are reminded also that the actual end shears must be unequal. Only the small shaded

---

[3] The old idea of "punching shear" fracture surfaces *normal to the slab*, as in punching holes in structural steel plates, has long since been demonstrated to be an inaccurate conception for reinforced concrete.

Ex. 6-1	Design of Beam & Girder Floor.	A. E. L.	7-18-'55	$\frac{1}{11}$

○ **DATA & SPEC.**　　Refer to Fig. 6-4 and ACI Code.

Occupancy: Heavy manufacturing and storage @ 300 psf.

Concrete: $f_c' = 3000$-lb., 6 gal. of water per sack of cement, 6_{MIN} sacks per cu. yd., aggregate max. size 1 in.

R/C *Allowable Stresses* : (in psi)　$n = 10$　$f_c = 1350$.
　$v = 90$ psi for concrete alone,
　　$= 180$ to 240 with stirrups.
　$u = 210$ to 300 psi.

Steel: Intermediate grade high bond deformed bars @ 40,000 psi yield point strength. $f_s = f_y = 20,000$ psi.
Estimated Width of Supports ↪ for approximating the clear spans of members:
Beams 12 in., Girders 15 in., Columns 18 in.

○ Ref. ----
ACI
Sec. 703(a)
Floor Slabs are to have an additional $\frac{1}{2}$ in. of wearing surface concrete not counted for strength,
　↪ equals 6 psf additional dead load.

Ref. --- **DESIGN OF END SLAB A-B.**

Text. Art. 6-4,
Fig. 6-3 &
Fig. 6-4.

"Design slab
thicknesses
and bar sp'c'gs
by half-inches."

0.097 in.
Fig. 6-3,
$\frac{L.L.}{D.L.} = 5$

Loads: ↪ working with a one-foot strip:

Wearing surface (D.L.)	6#
Est. Slab D. L.	50
Live Load	300

$\frac{L.L.}{D.L.} = 5 +$

$\omega = 356$ plf of span.

(a) Design of Positive Steel

B.M. $= 0.10 \, \omega L^2 = 0.10 (356)(7.33)^2 = 1915'$#

For Spec. 20 000 - 1350 - 10, balanced

$R = 236$,　bal. $p = 1.36\%$ (Chart)

$d_{req'd} = \sqrt{\dfrac{M}{Rb}} = \sqrt{\dfrac{1915(12)}{236(12)}} = 2.85$ in.

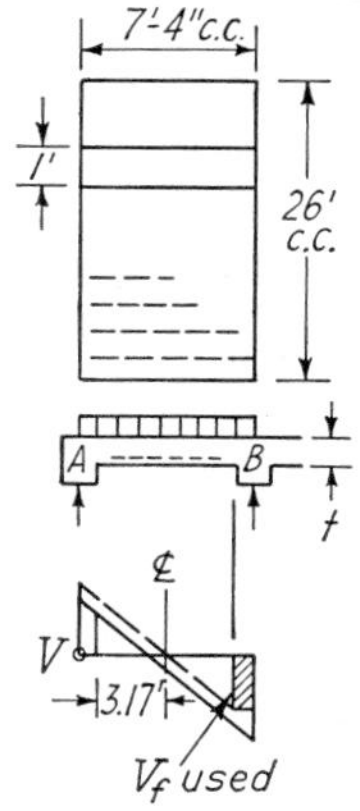

7'-4" c.c.

26'
c.c.

$\frac{1}{2}$'

A ---- B

℄

V_f used

3.17'

---

area was deducted. The design bending moment used is therefore larger than the true value, so the slab design will be safe.

The rest of the flexural designing was performed in the tabular form shown.

Spandrel Effect. The beams within outside walls are called **spandrel beams.** They have considerable torsional rigidity, due partly to being buried in masonry, and cannot rotate enough to satisfy the simple beam end condition usually assumed in the continuity analysis of slabs. The necessity for steel in the top of a slab at such points should never be overlooked if unsightly cracking is to be prevented. The $\frac{1}{24}wL^2$ assumption being used is none too large.

Shrinkage and Temperature Reinforcement. Like other building materials, concrete expands when heated and contracts when cooled. It also contracts in curing with decrease in moisture content, which is known as **shrinkage.** Most of the shrinkage takes place during the first few months, and will recur after a rewetting. The shrinkage of extensive slabs and walls is often opposed by the adjacent stiff members of a structure, so that the whole slab becomes stressed in axial tension and tends to crack. The ACI Code section referred to in Calculation Sheet 2 specifies the amount of such reinforcement. Since it is always installed perpendicular to the flexure steel, it also serves admirably to space it and hold it in place.

SLAB PRACTICE PROBLEMS

Problem 6–1. Perform the flexure design of the floor slabs of Example 6–1, using a stronger concrete assigned by the instructor. Make a tabular comparison of the two designs, and comment thereupon.

Problem 6–2. Redesign the floor slab system of Example 6–1 for flexure, letting the typical interior span set the slab thickness used throughout. Design slab thickness by half-inches. What percentage change do you find in the steel and concrete areas? Would your answer be the same for a building only half as wide?

6–9. Bond Stress and Anchorage in Continuous Structures. In retrospect, we conclude from the flexural design just performed that the deformation of the continuous slab is as pictured in the lower portions of the sketches on Calculation Sheets 3 and 4. Over the beams the slab consists of double cantilevers reinforced in the top with *negative* steel. In addition to their uniformly distributed load, these cantilevers also support a short simple span of slab suspended between contra-flexure points, and reinforced in the bottom with *positive* steel. Once the contraflexure points have been located the problem becomes one of statics alone. However, the solution is complicated by the fact that the maximum bending condition in positive steel occurs under a different arrangement of live load than for negative steel (Art. 6–6). Consequently there are two sets of contraflexure points for slabs, beams, and girders; one for the positive steel and another for the negative steel, as will be seen from the slab sketches on Calculation Sheets 3 and 4. Fortunately, in continuous spans the same arrangement of live load produces both maximum beam shear and bending moment. The proper loading

Ex. 6-1	Design of End Slab Flexure Steel ~ concl.	*H. E. L.*	7-18-'55	2/11

(Positive Steel ~ concl.)

$t_{req'd} = 2.85'' + 0.75''$ fpg. $+ 0.25''$ bar half-dimen. $= 3.85$ in.

Unbal.   **Make $t = 4$ in.** ◄

$$R = \frac{M}{bd^2} = \frac{1915(12)}{(12)(3)^2} = 213.$$ (Corresponding $d = 3.00$ in.)

Find on chart $f_c = 1260$, $f_s = 20,000$, $p = 1.23\%$

A_s per inch of slab width $= pd = 0.0369$ sq. in.

Try $\frac{1}{2}''\phi$: $\dfrac{0.20}{0.0369} = 5.42$ in.   **Use #4 @ 5 in. c.c.** ◄

(b) Design of Negative Steel at "B" $t = 4''$ $d = 3.00$

SHEAR @ INSIDE FACE OF WALL

See Sheet #L sketch.

0.118 in Fig. 6-3

Assuming that *beams* will be 12 in. wide, $V_f = 1130$ #

B.M $= 0.12 \omega L^2 - V\frac{b}{2} = 0.12(356)(7.33)^2 - 1130(0.5) = 1735$ '#

$R = \dfrac{M}{bd^2} = \dfrac{1735}{(3)^2} = 193.$ Find $\begin{cases} f_c = 1180, \ f_s = 20\,000, \ p = 1.10\% \\ A_{s/in.} = 0.033^{\,\square''} \ , 011 \times 3 \end{cases}$

Try $\frac{1}{2}\phi$: $\dfrac{0.20}{0.033} = 6.05''$,   **Use #4 @ 6 in. c.c.** ◄

DESIGN AT INTERIOR SPANS & OTHER SUPPORTS (Summary)

$\omega = 356$ # $L = 7.33'$ $t = 4''$ $d = 3.00''$

Span or Support	Description	Design Bending Moment	$\dfrac{R}{M}{bd^2}$	$\dfrac{P}{\text{in}}\%$	A_s in sq. in. per inch	Theor. Sp'c'g	Steel to Use
B-C etc.	Interior Spans	$0.08\omega L^2 = +1530$ '# (0.079 in Fig. 6-3)	170	0.96	0.0288	6.95''	#4 @ 6½'' bottom
C etc.	Typical Interior Supports	B.M $= 0.11\omega L^2 - V_f \frac{b}{2}$ $= 2110 - 1130(0.5) = -1545$ '#	172	0.98	0.0294	6.80	#4 @ 6½'' -top
A	"Spandrel Effect"	ACI Sec. 701 (c) $\dfrac{\omega \ell'^2}{24} = \dfrac{356(6.33)^2}{24} = 595$ '#	66	0.33	0.010	11.0	#3 @ 11'' -top
All spans	ACI Sec. 707 (a) requires Shrinkage & Temperature reinforcement in all spans ~ at right angles to the flexure reinforcement.		0.20 %of Lt*	0.008			#3 @ 14''

*For these slabs

arrangement not only yields the *length* of bar required for flexure, but also the maximum bond stress.

Negative Steel. If the maximum bond stress in the negative reinforcement exceeds the allowable, smaller bars should be selected. Directly over the beams there will be more than 12 in. of plastic concrete below the bars, so that the $0.07f'_c$ allowable should be taken (ACI Sec. 305). Such bars must always extend beyond the contraflexure point for the 12-diam. *partial anchorage* distance previously discussed in Example 3–4.

At the extreme ends of floor slab systems the top steel was formerly always provided with a standard hook. The 1956 Code is interpreted to call simply for *full anchorage* of deformed bars beyond the inside face of the support. Thus some bending may or may not be necessary, depending upon the width of the supporting member. Refer to the design sketch of Calculation Sheet 4.

Positive Steel. In Calculation Sheet 4 the floor system was reloaded according to the criterion for maximum positive bending moment and the contraflexure points relocated. *The maximum bond stress in the positive reinforcement was computed from the greatest value of V over the positively bent portion.* It proved to be less than half the $0.10f'_c$ allowable. *For end span anchorage at A,* ACI Sec. 902(c) requires that at least one-third of the positive steel be left at the bottom and extended 6 in. into the supporting member.

PRACTICE PROBLEMS

Problem 6–3. Same as Example 6–1 except that the beams are spaced 11 ft. center to center instead of 7 ft., 4 in.

(a) Completely design the slab system for flexure.

(b) Study a typical interior slab for bond, and determine the length and endings of all bars.

(c) Perform (b) for the end span and its supports.

Problem 6–4. (a) Establish the maximum moment and shear diagrams for end slab $A-B$ of Example 6–1, assuming $\frac{1}{24}wL^2$ negative bending moment at A.

(b) Improve the arrangement of the reinforcement, locating the points of bar bending with care. Calculate the maximum bond stresses and redesign the top reinforcing at A, including its anchorages.

Problem 6–5. (*Individual*) *Design of a Slab, Beam, and Girder Industrial Building.* Follow the detailed advice of the instructor regarding the spacing of the beams, class of concrete, maximum size of aggregate, grade of reinforcement, the meaning of code provisions, etc. Make final design sketches to scale, and complete.

Name	Case	Panels, ft.	Live Load, psf	Name	Case	Panels, ft.	Live Load, psf
	a	18.6 × 22.5	195		h	16.0 × 19.0	305
	b	22.5 × 27.0	105		i	21.4 × 25.7	115
	c	19.2 × 23.0	175		j	23.0 × 27.6	100
	d	18.0 × 21.6	210		k	17.6 × 21.0	215
	e	20.0 × 24.0	150		l	19.6 × 23.4	160
	f	17.0 × 20.4	250		m	16.6 × 20.0	260
	g	20.8 × 25.0	130		n	15.6 × 18.8	335

Ex. 6-1	Bond Stress & Anchorage in Typical Interior Slabs	A. E. L.	7-18-'55	3/11

(a) For Negative Steel

With two spans of the slab loaded to produce a maximum negative bending moment and shear at "C", the bending moment at "D" is, from a moment distribution solution (not shown), about $0.05 wL^2$. At "C" it is, from Fig. 6-3, about $0.11 wL^2$

The inequality of these end moments means that the vertical reactions will each differ from $\frac{wL}{2}$ to the extent of:

$$\frac{(0.11-0.05)wL^2}{L} = 0.06 wL$$

The negative bending moment of $0.076 wL^2$ was then found by proportion, utilizing the negative moment trapezoid.

Next, considering the simple beam span L' suspended between contraflexure points:

$$\frac{wL'^2}{8} = 0.049 \, wL^2, \qquad L' = 0.62 L, \text{ and the left-hand contra-flexure point is at } 0.25L.$$

Diagonal Tension:

$$\text{Max. } v = \frac{V_f}{bjd} = \frac{1280}{12(\frac{7}{8})(3)} = 41 psi., < 90, \therefore \text{ no stirrups are needed}$$

Bond Stress:

$$\text{Max. } u = \frac{V_f}{\Sigma_0 jd} = \frac{1280}{\frac{1}{2}\pi(\frac{12}{6.5})(\frac{7}{8})(3)} = 168 psi., < 210 \therefore O.K.$$

Anchorage:

Extend bent-up bars 12 diam. beyond contraflexure point: $= 22 + 6 = 2'\text{-}4''$ from ℄ of beam.
This is quite adequate for the req'd. $8\frac{1}{2}$ in. _full_ anchorage required outside the face of the 12 in. beam.
ALTERNATE DESIGN   Could use separate straight top bars $2(22+6) = 4'\text{-}8''$ long.

(left margin annotations:)
0.56 L
0.31
0.25 L

ACI
Sec. 902(a)

(Problem 6–5 *continued*)

Note: For these cases conservatively underestimate the widths of supporting members as follows: beam stems at 10 in., girder widths at 12 in. and columns at 15 in. square.

(a) *Slab Design.* Perform the complete flexural design for all panels, the bond and anchorage studies of typical interior panels, and the arrangement of the reinforcement, including that at the ends of the system. Bend up the reinforcement in all spans.

(**Problem 6–5** *concluded*)

(b) *Beam Design*. Design a typical interior one, following the methods of Example 6–1. (If the designing of the slab has not been performed, consult the instructor for a thickness to assume.) Make independent final investigations of your beam.

(c) *Girder Design*. Design an interior one, as a rigid frame element. Utilize the beam loads already worked out.

(d) *Column Design*.

(1) Design an interior one selected by the instructor.

(2) Design an exterior one. Refer to Art. 7–21.

6–10. Arrangement of Slab Steel.

Upon starting the final design sketch on Calculation Sheet 4 it became evident that, in the B–C–D vicinity, bending up half the bottom bars exactly met the top steel requirement. Although some designers would not bother to bend bars only 2 in., it does largely eliminate the problem of holding separate short top bars in place. Furthermore, the overlap of the two differently spaced groups over the support B provides a little more than the required amount of steel. The vertical "tick" marks at the quarter points of the spans serve as a guide for locating bendup points.

At A, the end of the system, #3 bars at 11-in. spacing would satisfy the requirement for top steel computed at the bottom of Sheet 2, without the aid of bent-up bars. Half of the bottom steel might have been cut off in the neighborhood of the outer quarter point, but the practice is frowned upon by many as productive of unsightly cracks *in the bottom* at that point. They also consider that the *trussing* so accomplished by bending bars upward is well worth the cost of making the bend.

The reader is cautioned not to rely upon bent bars alone in the top at A. Such a practice leaves that tensile locality unreinforced for several inches just outside the lower bendup point, namely, the outer contraflexure point. At *interior* supports this situation does not arise if the overlapping bars from the adjacent spans are extended at least 12 diameters beyond the contraflexure points, as shown in the drawing.

In large work the end span situation should be carefully studied by evaluating the effect of wall loads and restraints, and performing a *moment distribution*. The contraflexure point locations so found are likely to be appreciably different from the quarter-point ones usually assumed elsewhere.

The number of slab spans over which a single bottom bar can be extended depends upon the bar length, which may be from 35 to 60 ft. or more, depending upon the length of the railroad car, or other shipping and handling situations. Of course, if the bar spacing in one span is not a multiple of that in the adjacent one, the bars must end at the support, as shown at B.

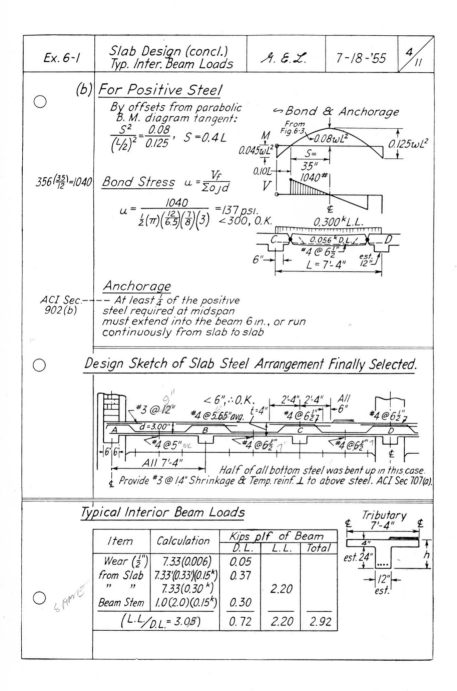

	Slab Design (concl.) Typ. Inter. Beam Loads	∜. E. L.	7-18-'55	4/11
Ex. 6-1				

(b) For Positive Steel

By offsets from parabolic B. M. diagram tangent:

$$\frac{S^2}{(L/2)^2} = \frac{0.08}{0.125}, \quad S = 0.4L$$

$356\left(\frac{35}{12}\right) = 1040$

Bond Stress $u = \dfrac{V_f}{\Sigma_0 jd}$

$$u = \frac{1040}{\frac{1}{2}(\pi)\left(\frac{12}{6.5}\right)\left(\frac{7}{8}\right)(3)} = 137\ psi. \quad < 300,\ O.K.$$

↪ *Bond & Anchorage*

From Fig 6-3

$0.045wL^2$ $0.08wL^2$ $0.125wL^2$

$S = 35"$

$0.10L$ $1040^{\#}$

$0.300^k L.L.$

$0.056^k D.L.$

#4 @ $6\frac{1}{2}"$ est. 12"

$6"$ $L = 7'-4"$

Anchorage

ACI Sec. 902(b) — At least $\frac{1}{4}$ of the positive steel required at midspan must extend into the beam 6 in., or run continuously from slab to slab

---

Design Sketch of Slab Steel Arrangement Finally Selected.

#3 @ 12"   < 6", ∴ O.K.   2'-4" 2'-4" All -6"

#4 @ 5.65" avg. $t = 4"$ #4 @ $6\frac{1}{2}"$ #4 @ $6\frac{1}{2}"$

$d = 3.00"$ A   B   C   D

#4 @ 5" o.c.   #4 @ $6\frac{1}{2}"$ #4 @ $6\frac{1}{2}"$

$6'6"$ All 7'-4"

Half of all bottom steel was bent up in this case.
Provide #3 @ 14" Shrinkage & Temp. reinf. ⊥ to above steel. ACI Sec 707(a).

Typical Interior Beam Loads

Tributary 7'-4"

est. 24"   12" est.

Item	Calculation	Kips plf of Beam		
		D.L.	L.L.	Total
Wear ($\frac{1}{2}"$)	7.33(0.006)	0.05		
from Slab	7.33'(0.33')(0.15^k)	0.37		
" "	7.33(0.30^k)		2.20	
Beam Stem	1.0(2.0)(0.15^k)	0.30		
(L.L./D.L. = 3.05)		0.72	2.20	2.92

6–11. Design of a Typical Interior Beam. (Calculation Sheet 5) The typical *beam* at *E* in Fig. 6–4(a) is of T-shape, and continuous. It rests upon east-west *girders* at the third points of their spans, but is not directly connected to the columns, so no rigid frame action is considered. As with slabs, the live load may be either on or off a given span. Referring to Fig. 6–3, and taking the L.L./D.L. ratio of 3, the bending moments at the centerline of span and of support will be found to be as shown on the sketch in Calculation Sheet 5. The design negative bending moment, M_f, was found by assuming a girder width of 15 in. and computing offsets from the horizontal tangent to the parabolic moment diagram.

The beam dead load was computed in the preceding table after estimating that the stem thereof would be about 12 by 24 in. The 12-in. dimension was suggested by the necessity for covering four large bars whose exact size was still unknown.

The slab was considered to act flexurally with the stem of the beam in this case, namely, T-beam action, since the slab was not already stressed in *this* direction by the one-way flexure (Art. 6–8) at right angles thereto.

At this point it was noted that the beam had to meet three strength requirements, namely, diagonal tension, bending at the centerline of span, and bearing at the face of the support. Accordingly Eqs. (1), (2), and (3) were approximated and set up as guideposts for judging proposed cross sections.

By comparing Eqs. (2) and (3) it was found that $1\frac{1}{3}$ times as much top steel was needed at the support as in the bottom at midspan. The *number* of bars at midspan should be *four*, since ACI Sec. 902(b) will permit as much as 75 per cent thereof to be bent up from interior spans to serve as negative reinforcement. The choice of *size* of such bars is governed by the depth of beam which can be tolerated in each case.

When #9 bars were chosen, the other dimensions followed, as shown. The *concrete compressive stress at the bottom fiber* at the face of the support usually tends to be critical. A good guide to the necessary width of stem, b', is to take the width required if the beam were to be singly reinforced, and to deduct from it the equivalent width represented by the transformed area of the proposed compression (bottom) steel, divided by kd. In this case:

$$16.2 - \frac{[2(10) - 1](2)(1 \text{ sq. in.})}{0.403(24.43)} = 12.3 \text{ in.}$$

13 in. was tried.

Generally, if one takes enough stem width to properly *space* and *fireproof* the reinforcement of a single-layer *midspan* section, the con-

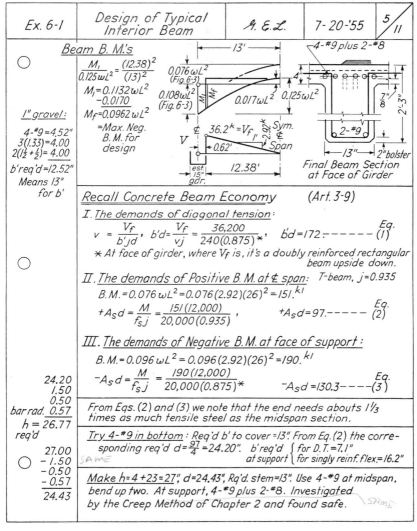

Ex. 6-1	Design of Typical Interior Beam	A. E. L.	7-20-'55	5/11

Beam B. M.'s

$\dfrac{M_1}{0.125\omega L^2} = \dfrac{(12.38)^2}{(13)^2}$

$M_1 = 0.1132\,\omega L^2$
$\quad -0.0170$
$M_f = 0.0962\,\omega L^2$
= Max. Neg.
B.M. for
design

$0.076\,\omega L^2$ (Fig. 6-3)

$0.108\,\omega L^2$ (Fig. 6-3)

$0.017\,\omega L^2$ $0.125\,\omega L^2$

⊄ $36.2^k = V_{f_1}$ Sym.
V   ⊄ Span
← 0.62'

est. 15" gdr.   12.38'

1" gravel:

4-#9 = 4.52"
3(1.33) = 4.00
2(1½ + ½) = 4.00
b'req'd = 12.52"
Means 13"
for b'

4-#9 plus 2-#8

2-#9

← 13" → 2" bolster

Final Beam Section
at Face of Girder

Recall Concrete Beam Economy   (Art. 3-9)

I. The demands of diagonal tension:

$v = \dfrac{V_f}{b'jd}, \quad b'd = \dfrac{V_f}{vj} = \dfrac{36,200}{240(0.875)*}, \quad b'd = 172. - - - - - (1)$

* At face of girder, where V_f is, it's a doubly reinforced rectangular beam upside down.

II. The demands of Positive B.M. at ⊄ span: T-beam, j = 0.935

$B.M. = 0.076\,\omega L^2 = 0.076(2.92)(26)^2 = 151.^{kl}$

$+A_s d = \dfrac{M}{f_s j} = \dfrac{151(12,000)}{20,000(0.935)}, \quad +A_s d = 97. - - - - - (2)$

III. The demands of Negative B.M. at face of support:

$B.M. = 0.096\,\omega L^2 = 0.096(2.92)(26)^2 = 190.^{kl}$

$-A_s d = \dfrac{M}{f_s j} = \dfrac{190(12,000)}{20,000(0.875)*} \quad -A_s d = 130.3 - - - - (3)$

24.20
1.50
0.50
bar rad. 0.57
h = 26.77
req'd

From Eqs. (2) and (3) we note that the end needs abouts 1⅓ times as much tensile steel as the midspan section.

27.00
− 1.50
−0.50
−0.57
24.43

Try 4-#9 in bottom: Req'd b' to cover = 13". From Eq. (2) the corresponding req'd $d = \dfrac{97}{4} = 24.20$". b'req'd { for D.T. = 7.1"   SAME   at support { for singly reinf. flex. = 16.2"

Make h = 4 + 23 = 27", d = 24.43", Rq'd. stem = 13". Use 4-#9 at midspan, bend up two. At support, 4-#9 plus 2-#8. Investigated by the Creep Method of Chapter 2 and found safe.   SAME

---

crete stresses at the support will turn out well. Refer to the calculation in the upper margin of Calculation Sheet 5.

The negative steel requirement was met by bending up half the bottom steel from each side and adding two #8 straight bars over the support at the edge of the slab, as shown in the sketch.

A final *investigation* should always be conducted as a check, particularly at the face of the support, where f_c tends to be high (Problem 6-6).

Stirrups. Near the ends of *continuous* spans the diagonal tension region lies in the *upper* portion of the member instead of the lower.

Consequently, stirrups really should be located therein with their open ends downward, since their anchorage must be achieved *below* the neutral axis. However, such an arrangement is impractical for getting the flexure bars into the forms. The arrangement shown in Sheet 5 may be used (a) if each upper leg of the stirrup represents a *full anchorage* distance and (b) some parallel horizontal bars exist in the top which can tie the upper halves of the stirrups together, such as our slab bars. See also Sheet 6.

6–12. Beam Design Sketch. Calculation Sheet 6 illustrates how a single moment curve may be utilized to determine the flexural bend-up limits for both positive and negative steel by shifting the X-axis thereof.

In continuous beams and girders, the areas of positive and negative steel needed at all points to satisfy flexural requirements dictate rather closely where bars may be bent up. Consequently they often cannot be spaced properly for resisting diagonal tension. On this account many designers omit to rely upon them as web reinforcement, as has been done in this case.

The separate shear* diagrams for positive and negative steel were utilized to show the computed unit bond stresses on both sides of the points of bar bending. The top steel bond stress is limited to $0.07f'_c$, but the bottom steel is permitted $0.10f'_c$. All the bond stresses proved safely low. For a more refined treatment refer to Bibliography reference C.

Anchorage of Flexural Compressive Steel. The computed compressive stress in the bottom steel at the face of the supporting girder is 17,600 psi, for which the fundamental calculation requires 16.6 in. of anchorage. ACI Sec. 1103(c), which governs the splicing of column bars, may be applied. It requires 20 diam., or 22.6 in., which was used to set the 15 plus 8-in. dimension shown. The end bearing value of such bars is always disregarded.

BEAM PRACTICE PROBLEMS

Problem 6–6. Taking the typical interior beam designed in Calculation Sheet 5, investigate the bending stresses at the face of the girder support (a) by the creep method of Chapter 2 and (b) by the elastic method. Note that there will be only two effective bars in the bottom at this section.

$Ans.$ (a) $kd = 9.49$ in., $f_c = 1210$, $f_s = 19,050$, f_s $(comp.) = 17,620$ psi
(b) $kd = 10.09$ in., $f_c = 1360$, $f_s = 19,300$, f_s $(comp.) = 10,120$

Investigate the beam for bending at the centerline of span. Observe ACI Code, Sec. 705(a). $Ans.$ $b = 77$ $in.$, $f_c = 455$, $f_s = 19,800$ psi.

---

* To guard against possible lack of uniformity of the loading some codes require flexural members to be designed to a larger shear diagram defined by assuming a value of $\frac{1}{4}V_f$ at midspan.

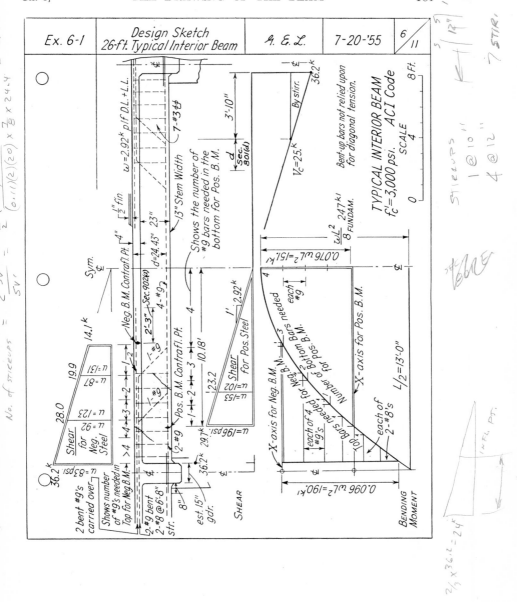

Problem 6–7. Following up Problem 6–3(a), completely design the corresponding typical interior beam for the 11-foot spacing.

Problem 6–8. Following up Problem 6–1, redesign the typical interior beam of Example 6–1, using the stronger concrete assigned by the instructor. Make a tabular comparison of the two designs and comment upon it.

(B) The Design of Girders and Columns as Rigid Frame Members

6–13. Bending Moments in an Interior Girder. Calculation Sheet 7 shows the loads, shears, and (fully) fixed end moments for Interior Girder 8–9. The design bending moments will be calculated therefrom, recognizing the stiffening effect of the columns upon the performance of the girder, namely **rigid frame action.** Note that the *typical* beams of Fig. 6–4(a) are not restrained by columns.

The ACI Code, Sec. 702, permits analyses which embrace only those portions of the structure which are adjacent to the stressed point being studied. The time-saving advantage of such short cuts is illustrated in the following moment distribution analyses to determine the maximum positive and the maximum negative live load bending moments in Girder 8–9.

Dead Load Bending Moment. The first step in making a short-cut analysis of a continuous structure consisting of many members is to **predict and sketch the rotation of the joints and the bending of the members** in the vicinity of the point being studied, as has been done for the dead loading at the bottom of Calculation Sheet 7. It will then be apparent that the analysis can be narrowed down to a study of the accompanying two-span auxiliary cut-out, involving hinged ended columns 6 ft. long, without appreciable error.

The actual performance of this dead load moment distribution will be left to the student as an exercise (Problem 6–9). The author has found by experience that for such a member the dead load fixed end moment itself is close enough to the negative bending moment obtainable by a moment distribution, except when the columns are relatively flexible. Call 112 kip-ft. the girder dead load bending moment at the centerline of columns.

Although the general moment distribution method of analyzing continuous structures as presented in Chapter 5 is quicker than most others, it too becomes laborious when applied to rigid frames consisting of more than a dozen members. Since the present relatively simple building frame consists of 45 members, the need for some simplification of the calculations is apparent, particularly in connection with studies of the effect of live loading. A short-cut method involving only the members in the close vicinity of the one being studied, and which gives results well within the desired 1 per cent accuracy so often referred to, will be presented herein. It is based upon the observation that members and loads more than two member lengths distant from the ends of the member being studied exert only a negligible influence upon it, and may be disregarded.

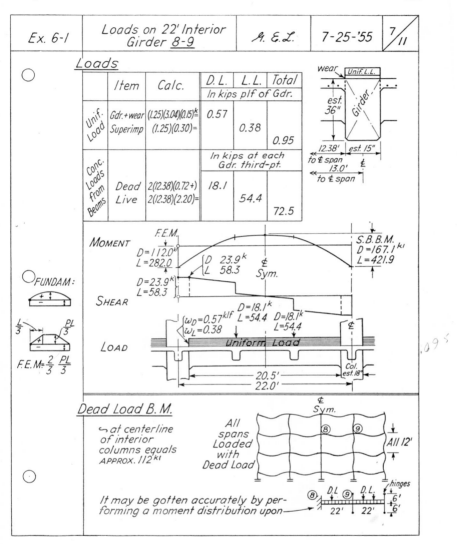

| Ex. 6-1 | Loads on 22' Interior Girder 8-9 | | 𝒜. 𝓔.𝓛. | 7-25-'55 | 7/11 |

Loads

	Item	Calc.	D.L.	L.L.	Total
			In kips plf of Gdr.		
Unif. Load	Gdr.+wear	(1.25)(3.04)(0.15)ᵏ=	0.57		
	Superimp	(1.25)(0.30)=		0.38	
					0.95
Conc. Loads from Beams			In kips at each Gdr. third-pt.		
	Dead	2(12.38)(0.72+)	18.1		
	Live	2(12.38)(2.20)=		54.4	
					72.5

FUNDAM:

$$F.E.M. = \frac{2}{3}\frac{PL}{3}$$

Dead Load B.M.

⤶ at centerline of interior columns equals APPROX. 112ᵏˡ

All spans Loaded with Dead Load

It may be gotten accurately by performing a moment distribution upon—➤

6-14. Girder Live Load Maximum Positive Bending Moment by "Three-Zone Cut-out" Moment Distribution. This method was proposed by the author in 1949 and its accuracy was verified thoroughly by Mr. George E. Sutila and his thesis work.[D] Calculation Sheet 8 illustrates the complete calculation required to so find the maximum live load positive bending moment in Girder 8–9 of the frame under consideration.

Procedure

1. Make a sketch of the frame, and load it for maximum bending moment at the point in question, as in Calculation Sheet 8, by referring to Mr. Sutila's live loading patterns of Appendix E.

2. Identify the following zones on the sketch:

Zone I is that area occupied by the particular loaded member (or members) being studied to find a maximum live load bending moment.

Zone II includes all the (unloaded) members which abut Zone I.

Zone III includes all the members which abut the outer boundary of Zone II. Some of them will be loaded members.

3. Compute the stiffnesses, I/L, of all the members in the three zones, and the fixed end moments for the loaded spans thereof.

· 4. Upon each loaded member of Zone III perform one cycle of moment distribution, setting down a distribution item only for the outer end of the adjoining Zone II member. Carry over half this item to the inner end of each Zone II member, for later adding to the fixed end moment of the live loading at that floor joint.

5. Next discard the Zone III members, hinge the outer ends of all Zone II members, and recalculate all stiffnesses, using $\frac{3}{4} \, I/L$ for the hinged ended members so that there will be no *distributing* to do at the remote (hinged) ends.[4]

6. At each end of the Zone I member, sum the fixed end moment and the carried-in moment, or moments, from item 4; and perform a simple moment distribution to convergence.

Comments. Calculation Sheet 9 shows a similar study made to find the maximum live load *negative* bending moment in the same member (8–9). Note in this latter case that Zone I consists of two loaded members. The rest of the process is the same as before.

A study of the cut-out moment distribution process will show that if the moment distribution is performed upon the hinged ended two-zone cut-out without including the *carried-in moments* from Zone III, the resulting design bending moments will both be appreciably smaller than the true values, i.e., in error on the danger side.

It should be remembered that the Sutila loading patterns and the Three-Zone Cut-out method give precise results only for structures having *uniform* spans, story heights, live loadings, and stiffness factors, but that they may also be used judiciously for cases in which there are reasonable deviations therefrom without much sacrifice of precision.

An investigation disclosed that the sidesway due to the dissymmetry of the loads had a negligible effect upon the girder bending moments. Refer to Art. 5–11.

---

[4] See Appendix B. When $\frac{3}{4}I/L$ is used to calculate the stiffness of a hinged ended member, no moment is ever to be carried over to the hinged end thereof.

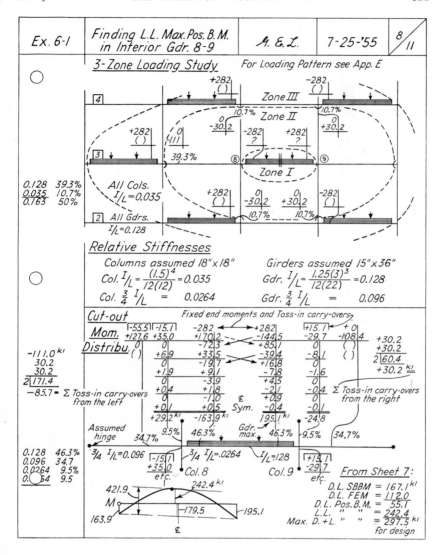

CUT–OUT MOMENT DISTRIBUTION PRACTICE PROBLEMS

Problem 6–9. Find the dead load bending moments at the ends of Girder 8–9 by performing a moment distribution upon the cut-out portion of the structure shown at the extreme bottom of Calculation Sheet 7. Compare with the fixed end moment value. By what percentage would your determination increase or decrease the dead plus live bending moments used in designing the girder?

PLATE 6–3. Royal Canadian Air Force airplane hangar with superstructure built entirely of precast reinforced concrete elements. It can be dismantled and re-erected elsewhere. Two three-hinged (side) frames support the main three-hinged arch.

Three bents were tested to secure deflection and recovery data under 1½ times the design loading. The photograph shows the continuous loading platform upon which sacks of cement were placed to make up the test load. The central tower was used for erection and later for observing deflections. Reported to the ACI by Otto Safir, consulting engineer of Vancouver, British Columbia.

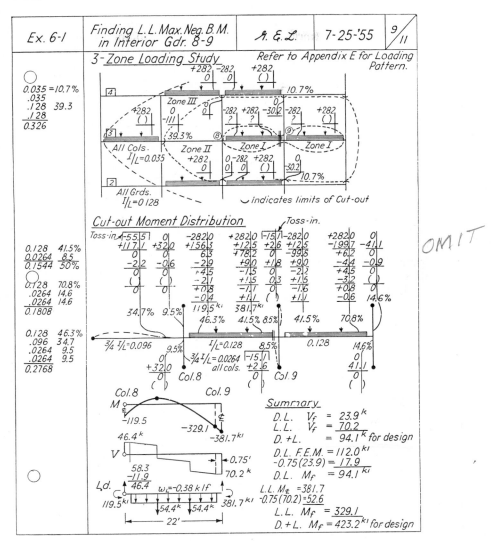

Problem 6–10. Find the design maximum live load bending moments, positive and negative, in Girder 8–9 by a two-zone cut-out as in the lower portion of Calculation Sheets 8 and 9, but ignoring the effect of loads in Zone III.

By what percentage do they differ from the original values, and in which direction?

Problem 6–11. Compute by three-zone cut-outs the live load maximum positive and negative bending moments in exterior Girder 9–10. Refer to Appendix E.

6–15. Design of Interior Girder 8–9. Calculation Sheet 10 includes the three guiding expressions, Eqs. (4), (5), and (6), for proportioning the girder. The necessity for the girder steel to clear both the beam and column steel is an added influence on design. If the girder width can be held to 3 in. less than the anticipated column width, the two groups of bars can usually be reconciled, as shown in the design sketch at the bottom of Calculation Sheet 11.

The negative depth, $-d$, at the end of the girder had to be appreciably less than the positive one at midspan due to the necessity for having two layers of negative steel, and to keep it below the intersecting #9 *beam* bars. This disadvantage was partially offset by locating two-thirds of the negative steel in the upper layer, which put the centroid of the group in a high position.

Most of the girder designing was closely similar to that of the *beam*.

Since nearly one and one-half times as much steel was needed in the top over the support as in the bottom at midspan, another solution would have been to bend up three bars from adjacent girders, leaving only one in the bottom at the supports. However, it was found by investigation that three effective bars were needed to resist the compression in the bottom at supports; while a *lengthy overlapping* of the single bottom bars could provide only two effective bar areas. Since supplementary straight bar reinforcement was needed, it was decided to return to the more conventional plan shown, namely, only four bent, plus two straight, bars in the *top*, and one long overlap in the bottom at the support to produce a total of three effective compression bars.

GIRDER PRACTICE PROBLEMS

FOR MON

Problem 6–12. Taking the interior girder as designed and sketched in Calculation Sheet 10, investigate the bending stresses at the face of the column support by the creep method of Art. 2–12, Chapter 2.

Ans. $kd = 11.74$ $in.$, $f_c = 1160$, $f_s = 19,400$, f_s (*comp.*) $= 17,900$ $psi.$

Investigate also at the centerline of span, using the chart.

Ans. $R = 214$, $p = 1.25\%$, $f_c = 1260$, $f_s = 19,800$ $psi.$

Problem 6–13. (*Individual*) Design the typical interior girder for your *individual* structure, as stated in (c) of Problem 6–5.

Problem 6–14. Make a design drawing similar to Calculation Sheet 6 for the Interior Girder 8–9 designed in this chapter.

Problem 6–15. Completely design the Exterior Girder 9–10 of the structure of Example 6–1. Be sure to find the dead load bending moments by moment distribution. For computing the exterior column stiffness, assume, for a start, that due to greater bending it will be as large as the interior column.

Problem 6–16. Following up Problem 6–3(a) for the slab, and Problem 6–7 for the beam, completely design the corresponding interior girder for the 11-ft. beam spacing.

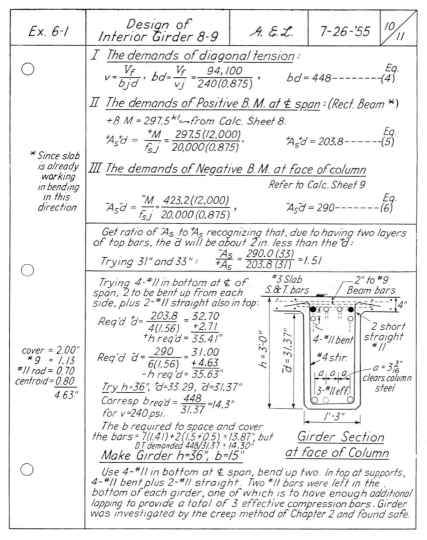

| Ex. 6-1 | Design of Interior Girder 8-9 | 𝓐. 𝓔. 𝓛. | 7-26-'55 | 10/11 |

I *The demands of diagonal tension:*

$$v = \frac{V_f}{bjd}, \quad bd = \frac{V_f}{vj} = \frac{94,100}{240(0.875)}, \qquad bd = 448 ------(4)$$

II *The demands of Positive B. M. at ℄ span : (Rect. Beam ✱)*

+B. M. = 297.5 ᵏˡ↪from Calc. Sheet 8.

$$^+\!A_s \, ^+\!d = \frac{^+M}{f_s j} = \frac{297.5(12,000)}{20,000(0.875)}, \qquad ^+\!A_s \, ^+\!d = 203.8 ------(5)$$

✱ *Since slab is already working in bending in this direction*

III *The demands of Negative B. M. at face of column*

Refer to Calc. Sheet 9

$$^-\!A_s \, \bar{d} = \frac{^-M}{f_s j} = \frac{423.2(12,000)}{20,000(0.875)}, \qquad ^-\!A_s \bar{d} = 290 ------(6)$$

Get ratio of $^-\!A_s$ to $^+\!A_s$ recognizing that, due to having two layers of top bars, the $\bar{d}$ will be about 2 in. less than the $^+\!d$:

Trying 31" and 33" : $\dfrac{^-\!A_s}{^+\!A_s} = \dfrac{290.0(33)}{203.8(31)} = 1.51$

cover = 2.00"
#9 = 1.13
#11 rad = 0.70
centroid = 0.80
4.63"

Trying 4-#11 in bottom at ℄ of span, 2 to be bent up from each side, plus 2-#11 straight also in top:

Req'd $^+\!d = \dfrac{203.8}{4(1.56)} = \dfrac{32.70}{+2.71}$
$^+\!h$ req'd = 35.41"

Req'd $\bar{d} = \dfrac{290}{6(1.56)} = \dfrac{31.00}{+4.63}$
$^-\!h$ req'd = 35.63"

Try h=36", $^+\!d$=33.29, $\bar{d}$=31.37"

Corresp b req'd $= \dfrac{448}{31.37} = 14.3$"
for v=240 psi.

The b required to space and cover the bars $= 7(1.41)+2(1.5+0.5) = 13.87$", *but*
D.T. demanded 448/31.37 = 14.30"

Make Girder h=36", b=15"

#3 Slab S.& T. bars   *2" to #9 Beam bars*

h=3'-0" $\bar{d}$=31.37"

4"
4-#11 bent
#4 stir.
3-#11 eff.

2 short straight #11

$a = 3\frac{3}{16}$ clears column steel

1'-3"

Girder Section at face of Column

Use 4-#11 in bottom at ℄ span, bend up two. In top at supports, 4-#11 bent plus 2-#11 straight. Two #11 bars were left in the bottom of each girder, one of which is to have enough additional lapping to provide a total of 3 effective compression bars. Girder was investigated by the creep method of Chapter 2 and found safe.

6–16. Summary of Floor Designing. Floors to carry moderate to heavy loadings, with approximately square bays between columns, may be designed using beams and girders. The girders should preferably extend in the shorter direction. The slabs will be pronouncedly rectangular and should have one-way steel in the shorter direction. If the beams are omitted, the resulting squarish slabs must be designed with two-way reinforcement, as in Chapter 7.

The probability of loaded and unloaded continuous spans of live load throughout has led to the use of convenient arbitrary bending moment coefficients. The novice will do well to study the underlying mechanics thereof before blindly accepting published coefficients. When span lengths differ widely, moment distribution studies for maximum bending moments should be made, employing the aforementioned equal-span loading criteria as guides.

In designing for floor continuity, it is probably best to use center to center spans and story heights in the determination of the bending moments, but to use the decreased value at the face of the support for the design negative bending moment, as has been done throughout the present designing.

Whether to use the thicker exterior slab thickness throughout a floor to save formwork depends partly upon the width of the structure. Refer to Fig. 6–4(a). A structure with a preponderance of interior spans should ordinarily not be so designed. Alternate schemes should be worked out and costs compared.

The designer's choice of flexural steel bar size should be made in conjunction with the selection of the span-to-span bent-up bar arrangement. In slabs it is often convenient to bend up half the positive steel. Furthermore, in beam and girder design, four bars of some size at the center of the span should be considered early, since, if necessary, three of them may be bent up [ACI, Sec. 902(b)]. An early calculation of the required ratio of the positive and negative steel contents needed speeds a decision upon bar arrangement.

Since all the girders extend from column to column, their design involves *rigid frame* action. In calculating relative stiffnesses, I/L, it is customary, convenient, and in accordance with test results to use the plain concrete section in calculating moment of inertia. If, as in the present case, the slab has already been relied upon for flexure in the direction of the girder, the girder should be designed as a rectangular beam.

The pattern of loaded and unloaded girder spans of live load leads easily to an accurate short-cut form of moment distribution, involving only a three-zone study of members in the immediate vicinity of the one being studied, so that it is not necessary to consider the whole frame. For preliminary designs the effect of the more remote "Zone 3" may be ignored, and a hinged ended two-zone solution quickly performed, which, when combined with the dead load moment, will give a total bending moment that will seldom be more than 5 per cent in error, but on the side of danger.

All reinforced concrete flexural members must be examined for four strength factors, namely, *bending* over a span, *diagonal tension* in the concrete, *bond* of the concrete to the steel and *anchorage* of the ends of the bars against slippage.

6–17. Bending Moments in Building Columns. Space limitations have not permitted the inclusion of the design of the roof members, followed by the design of the exterior and interior columns in all stories.[5] Nevertheless, preliminary studies have yielded sufficient data on member sizes to justify the preparation of the accompanying tentative table of interior column loads from Fig. 6–6. It is proposed to make a trial design of Interior Column 8 in the third story, and to demonstrate that its reinforcement clears the beam and girder steel at the floor levels.

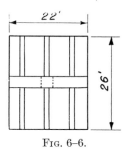

Fig. 6–6.

The ACI Method. Given equal loads, spans and story heights, the interior columns of buildings were formerly considered free of bending,

TABLE OF INTERIOR COLUMN LOADS—KIPS

Story	Source of Load	Interior Column Load, in kips			Roof L.L. @ 20 lb., Snow @ 40 lb. psf
		D.L.	L.L.	Total	
4th	Roof Slab and Beams	11.2	*10.8	22.0	Roof
	Roof Girder	30.9	*23.6	54.5	
	Estimated Column Wt.	4.0		4.0	
				80.5	
3rd	4th Fl. Slab and Beams	17.7	53.9	71.6	4th
	4th Fl. Girder	47.8	116.6	164.4	
	Estimated Column Wt.	4.5		4.5	
				321.0	
					3rd

* Including snow load.

and designed only for axial loads. Due to the live load unbalance created by adjacent loaded and unloaded spans, the practice is no longer per-

---

[5] For an example of multistory column designing, including the use of the live load reduction percentages tabulated in Art. 6–2, refer to Arts. 7–18, 7–19, and 7–20, and especially to Calculation Sheet 7/7 of Example 7–2 in the latter portion of Chapter 7.

mitted in rigid frame structures. Section 1108 of the ACI Code states in part:

Columns shall be designed to resist the axial forces from loads on all floors, plus the maximum bending due to loads on a single adjacent span of the floor under consideration.

In the case of the third story of Column 8, and referring to the upper checkerboard-loaded sketch of Calculation Sheet 8, the quoted clause of the Code is interpreted to mean that the column is to be designed for the whole tributary dead and live *axial* load of the roof and fourth floor, plus the additional *bending* effect of third floor live load only on span 7–8 (or 8–9).

The moment distribution previously performed in the lower portion of Calculation Sheet 8 does not represent the case at hand because of the initial inclusion of the toss-in moments of -55.5, -15.1 and $+15.1$ kip-ft., due to loads on *other* spans. When it was re-performed to exclude them, the moment sum at the base of Column 8 changed from the 29.2 value to 34.8 kip-ft., which was used in the designing, in combination with the 321-kip total tributary axial load.

The Cut-out Method. An alternate design bending moment may be calculated by referring to Sutila's *column* loading criteria, case (m) of Appendix E, making the preliminary three-zone loading study and performing the cut-out moment distribution. It will be found that the column moment is then about *twice* the 34.8 kip-ft. value gotten above by the ACI method. However, the *axial* load under this Sutila loading will be only about half the former 321-kip value, so *the two methods call for closely the same column section.*

6–18. Designing an Interior Column. In the upper portion of Calculation Sheet 11 the column bending moment was recalculated to the clear height value of 30.4 kip-ft. and incorporated into the *equivalent axial load* formula (20) of ACI Sec. 1109. From it the 20 by 18-in. trial section with 10–#11 bars was evolved as in Example 4–5 of Chapter 4. The interaction investigation demonstrated its safety.

As shown, a *scale* design sketch is necessary to demonstrate that beam, girder, and column bars do not interfere. Usually, if the beam and girder widths have been kept to fully 3 in. less than the least column dimension, no rearranging is necessary. The bar spacings that were computed indicate that there will be room for splicing the column bars in the usual location just above each floor, where there are no beam or girder bars.

COLUMN PRACTICE PROBLEMS

Problem 6–17. Recompute in Example 6–1 the design axial load and the bending moment for Column 8 in the third story using the Cut-out Method

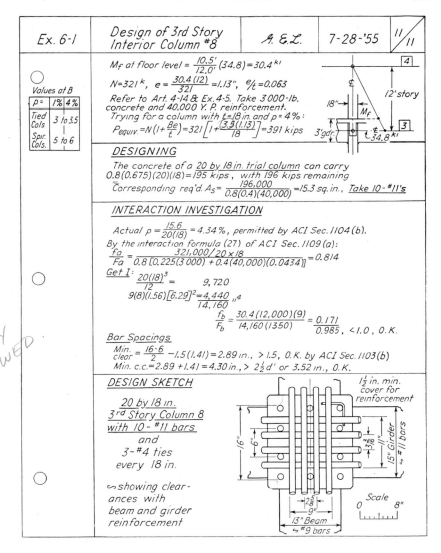

| Ex. 6-1 | Design of 3rd Story Interior Column #8 | *A. E. L.* | 7-28-'55 | 11/11 |

Values at B

	p =	1%	4%
Tied Cols		3 to 3.5	
Spir. Cols.		5 to 6	

M_f at floor level $= \dfrac{10.5'}{12.0'}(34.8)=30.4^{k'}$

$N=321^k$, $e=\dfrac{30.4(12)}{321}=1.13''$, $e/t=0.063$

Refer to Art. 4-14 & Ex. 4-5. Take 3000-lb. concrete and 40,000 Y. P. reinforcement.
Trying for a column with $t=18$ in. and $p=4\%$:

$P_{equiv.}=N\left(1+\dfrac{Be}{t}\right)=321\left[1+\dfrac{3.5(1.13)}{18}\right]=391$ kips

[4]
12' story
18"
M_f
3'gdr.
[3]
$34.8^{k'}$

DESIGNING

The concrete of a 20 by 18 in. trial column can carry
$0.8(0.675)(20)(18)=195$ kips, with 196 kips remaining

Corresponding req'd $A_s = \dfrac{196,000}{0.8(0.4)(40,000)}=15.3$ sq. in., Take 10-#11's

INTERACTION INVESTIGATION

Actual $p=\dfrac{15.6}{20(18)}=4.34\%$, permitted by ACI Sec. 1104(b).

By the interaction formula (27) of ACI Sec. 1109(a):

$\dfrac{fa}{Fa}=\dfrac{321,000/20\times18}{0.8[0.225(3000)+0.4(40,000)(0.0434)]}=0.814$

Get I:

$\dfrac{20(18)^3}{12}=\quad 9,720$

$9(8)(1.56)[6.29]^2=\underline{4,440}$ $_{in}^4$
$\qquad\qquad\qquad 14,160$

$\dfrac{fb}{F_b}=\dfrac{30.4(12,000)(9)}{14,160(1350)}=\dfrac{0.171}{0.985}$, <1.0, O.K.

Bar Spacings

$\dfrac{Min.}{clear}=\dfrac{16-6}{2}-1.5(1.41)=2.89$ in., >1.5, O.K. by ACI Sec. 1103(b)

Min. c.c.$=2.89+1.41=4.30$ in., $>2\frac{1}{2}d'$ or 3.52 in., O.K.

DESIGN SKETCH

20 by 18 in.
3rd Story Column 8
with 10 - #11 bars
and
3 - #4 ties
every 18 in.

↪showing clearances with beam and girder reinforcement

1½ in. min. cover for reinforcement
16"
6"
15" Girder
#11 bars
$2\frac{5}{8}''$
9"
13" Beam
↪#9 bars
Scale
0   8"

DY WED

outlined in Art. 6–17, and use them to perform an interaction investigation upon the 20 by 18-in. column developed in Calculation Sheet 11. Did it prove safe?

Problem 6–18. Design the second story of Column 8 by the ACI method, using 5000-lb. concrete, $n = 6$, and 50,000-psi yield point steel. Endeavor to maintain the 20 by 18-in. size. Employ the live load reduction percentage referred to in the footnote to the table of Art. 6–17.

Will the ACI method bending moment be the same as in the third story?

PLATE 6–4. Self-supporting reinforced concrete spiral stairs, Port Museum, The Hague, Netherlands. Photograph by G. T. Hamer.

Problem 6–19. (*Individual*) Design the typical interior column in the third story of your individual structure, as stated in Problem 6–5(d).

BIBLIOGRAPHY

A) WESTERGAARD and SLATER. Moments and Stresses in Slabs, *Proc. American Concrete Institute*, 1921, Vol. 17, Art. 7, p. 430.
B) FLORIS, A. More Exact Analysis Proposed for Continuous Beams Over Flat Supports, *Civil Engineering*, May, 1948, p. 45.
C) MYLREA, T. D. Bond and Anchorage, *Proc. American Concrete Institute*, 1948, Vol. 44, p. 52.
D) *Accuracy of Live Load Bending Moments Obtained from Cut-Out Portions of Extensive Rigid Frames as Revealed by the Superposition of Moment Patterns.* A thesis presented by G. E. Sutila in partial fulfillment of the requirements for the master of science degree at Ohio State University in 1949.
E) RICHART, FRANK E. A Study of Bending Moments in Columns, *Proc. American Concrete Institute*, 1924, Vol. 20, p. 495.
F) PORTLAND CEMENT ASSN. 16mm sound color film obtainable on loan: "Tilt-up Sandwich Wall Construction," 10 min.

QUESTIONS

1. Distinguish clearly between skeleton and wall bearing building construction.

2. State the loading criteria for (a) maximum positive and (b) maximum negative bending moment in a continuous beam or slab.

3. What is meant by the term *spandrel effect?*

4. Draw the bending moment diagram for the end slab of the building (a) as for positive steel designing and (b) as for negative steel designing, marking the maximum, minimum, and end values thereon.

5. Why is it necessary to draw two bending moment diagrams for all floor elements?

6. Tell exactly how to terminate both the top and bottom slab reinforcement at the end of a floor system employing high bond deformed bars.

7. Tell in how many ways the locations of the contraflexure points in a continuous slab or beam are useful.

8. Why was the floor girder designed as an element of a continuous frame, while the slabs and beams were not?

9. Given all the forces, describe fully how to *design* a span of a continuous reinforced concrete beam or girder with facility.

10. What use was made of the two shear diagrams on Calculation Sheet 6?

11. Account for the type of stirrup shown in the design sketch on Calculation Sheet 5. Need all the "Beam" stirrups be of this type? Explain.

12. For what type of structure and loading is the 3-zone cut-out moment distribution advantageous? How would you find the dead load bending moments in a building frame consisting of widely different spans?

13. Can the interior columns of continuous equal-span reinforced concrete rigid frames be designed for axial load only? Tell why.

14. Are columns ever designed for only half the full tributary live load? Explain.

15. Explain the two general methods for determining the bending moments in the columns of a continuous reinforced concrete frame.

REVIEW PROBLEMS

Problem 6–20. A five-span continuous beam consists of center-to-center spans, L, as follows: 24 ft., 20 ft., 24 ft., 20 ft., and 24 ft. Consider the ends hinged. The live load is 3 kips per ft., dead load 1 kip per ft. Calculate the maximum dead load plus live load bending moments, both positive and negative:

(a) Using center-to-center span distances throughout.

(b) Assuming supports 12 in. wide, working with clear spans, l' throughout.

Tabulate a comparison of the (a) and (b) results with ACI, Clause 701(c) and Fig. 6–3 of this text, and discuss.

Problem 6–21. Design the roof, including the slab, typical interior beam, interior girder, and a typical interior fourth-story column for the structure of Example 6–1. Assume roof covering at 5 psf. Is the design an economical one? Comment.

Problem 6–22. Redesign the structure of Example 6–1 for 150 psf live load instead of 300.

Problem 6–23. Redesign the structure of Example 6–1 on the same 22 by 26-ft. column centers, but with the girders spanning the 26-ft. direction. Tabulate a comparison of the two designs.

Problem 6–24. Redesign the complete floor system of Example 6–1, spacing the beams at 11 ft. 0 in. center-to-center instead of 7 ft. 4 in. Take the class of concrete and live loading assigned by the instructor. Refer to Calculation Sheet 1 for decisions on the rest of the starting data.

CHAPTER 7

TWO–WAY AND FLAT SLAB FLOORS

7–0. Introduction. Thus far, rectangular floor slabs with flexure steel in only one direction, called *one-way slabs*, have been considered. If the slabs are square, or approximately so, it is more economical to run the steel in both horizontal directions. Such slabs are of two

Dr. H. M. Westergaard, 1889–1950, Gordon McKay Professor of Civil Engineering, Harvard University; formerly Professor of Theoretical and Applied Mechanics, University of Illinois. While at Illinois he made the original general mathematical studies of slab performance which became the basis for the procedures now used to design two-way and flat slab floors.

types, depending upon how they are supported. When the slabs are *directly supported along all four edges*, as by girders extending between columns, they are called **two-way slabs.** Figure 7–1 is an illustration thereof.

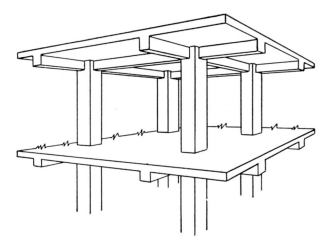

Fig. 7–1. Two-way slab floor construction.

The other type of construction, known as **flat slab,** is shown in Fig. 7–3. It consists of slabs reinforced in two or more directions, which are *supported only at their corners* by the columns, there being no beams or girders whatever. When there are a number of such spans in both directions, this construction is quite economical, as will be seen.

Part I. Two-Way Slab Floors

7–1. Two-Way Slabs. As presented by Dr. H. M. Westergaard,[A, B] the precise mathematics of two-way slab performance is too cumbersome for everyday use. However, his findings serve admirably as a standard by which to judge the convenient approximate methods which have been devised. Because of their relative simplicity, these methods also serve to give the engineer a fairly good conception of two-way slab action. Two such methods will be discussed briefly.

The "crossed sticks" method, illustrated in Fig. 7–2(a), states that since the two central strips must deflect the same amount, the whole load w, per square foot of floor, may be divided between the shorter and longer spans inversely as the fourth power of the span distances, S and L of Figs. 7–1 and 7–2, as set by uniformly loaded beam deflection formulas. Thus, if the longer side of a slab is $1\frac{1}{2}$ times the shorter, only $\dfrac{1}{1 + (1.5)^4}$, or $0.165w$ would be applied to the longer span central strips, while $0.835w$ would be assigned to the shorter ones. For a square slab, this method gives a simple span bending moment of $0.0625wS^2$ per ft. of strip width in each direction. The method is conservative, since supporting vertical shear is contributed along the edges of the strips by the four remaining quadrants of slab, e, f, g, and h, which is ignored.

The "*diagonals*" *method*, recorded by Seely,[c] asserts that the diagonals of the slab approximately define the dangerous sections and suggests that the two-way steel really should be run perpendicular thereto.

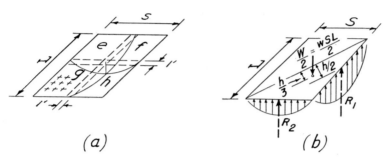

(a)   (b)

Fig. 7–2. Concepts of two approximate methods of two-way slab analysis.

Taking half a slab for study in Fig. 7–2(b), the maximum simple span bending moment total over the whole length of the diagonal will be $W(h)/2(6)$ or $wSLh/12$, regardless of what the distribution of the reactions along the girders may be. By similar triangles:

$$h = \frac{SL}{\sqrt{S^2 + L^2}} = \frac{\text{whole slab area}}{\text{length of the diagonal}}$$

Although the bending moment is not uniformly distributed, the *average* bending moment across the diagonal, per unit of length of diagonal, would be, from the above:

$$M_{\text{avg}} = \frac{wS^2}{12} \left(\frac{L^2}{S^2 + L^2} \right)$$

which for a square slab reduces[1] to $0.042wS^2$. It will be noted that this calls for a thinner slab and a smaller steel percentage than the "crossed sticks" method. Unfortunately, such a diagonal arrangement of the steel is somewhat inconvenient.

Comments. Neither of the above methods is accurate, as they naïvely overlook important aspects of two-way action. Westergaard recognized that a two-way slab would be stronger than the above calculations indicate, due to the help that each resisting strip receives from the one normal to it, namely the effect of Poisson's ratio and interband readjustments. Extension in one direction is accompanied by offsetting

---

[1] Equals the *average* bending moment used in the coordinate directions in "Method 2" of ACI Code, Sec. 709.

contraction in the other, and vice versa. On this account there is relatively less total tensile deformation and cracking in two-way reinforced slabs. Furthermore, if the north-south steel at a certain point tends to yield, the east-west bars come to the rescue by assuming a larger share of the load.

Problem 7–1(a) Taking a panel S feet square, and a uniform loading of w pounds per square foot of slab, find the total simple span bending moment across a right section through the center of the slab. Consider a parabolic distribution of the reactions to the girders, and coordinate reinforcement.

$$Ans. \; \tfrac{3}{64}wS^3.$$

(b) Assuming a parabolic distribution of the bending moment across the width of the slab, calculate the maximum bending moment per foot of width at the center section and compare it with that calculated by the "crossed sticks" method. Which is greater?

(c) Why cannot one use this method when the slab is rectangular?

7–2. Bending Moments in Two-Way Slabs. The ACI Code, Sec. 709, presents two methods for designing two-way slabs, of which "Method 2" is the simpler. It will be illustrated herein. It was originally a Joint Committee Specification method. Bending moment coefficients based upon Westergaard's findings have been tabulated for ready use. Special attention has been given to the effect of continuity between slabs, and a simple approach devised. Referring to Sec. 709 and the accompanying abstracted *portion* of the table, one sees that for a simply supported square slab the design positive bending moment is, from "Case 5," $0.05wS^2$ per foot of width for the central half of the slab, and two-thirds of this figure for the rest, an average of $0.042wS^2$. On the other hand, if the slab is fully restrained (fixed) along all four edges, the center strip is designed for only $0.025wS^2$ positive bending moment, as may be seen from "Case 1" for interior panels. For the three intermediate cases of *partial* restraint, a straight-line interpolation between the above mentioned positive bending moment coefficients was evidently taken. The loading criteria for maximum live load bending moment in continuous spans were recognized by Westergaard and the coefficients set large enough to embrace all ordinary cases.

EXAMPLE 7–1

Given the building of Example 6–1 and Fig. 6–4 to redesign for two-way slab floors. The column centers are 22 by 26 ft., the live load is 300 psf, the concrete is 3000-lb., all as shown in the upper portion of Calculation Sheet 1 of Chapter 6. The ACI Code is to be followed. See the solution in the following articles.

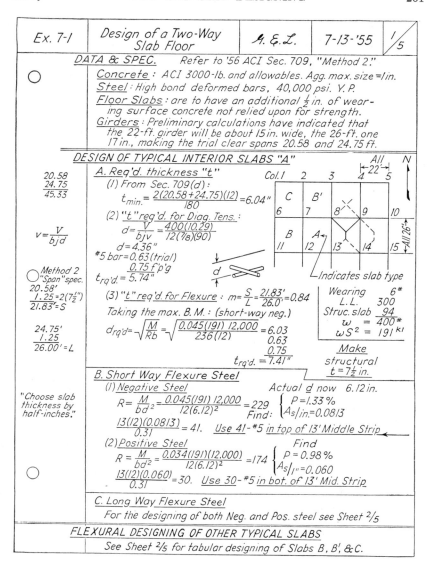

Ex. 7-1	Design of a Two-Way Slab Floor	*A. E. L.*	7-13-'55	1/5

DATA & SPEC.   Refer to '56 ACI Sec. 709, "Method 2."

Concrete : ACI 3000-lb. and allowables. Agg. max. size =1in.
Steel : High bond deformed bars, 40,000 psi. Y. P.
Floor Slabs : are to have an additional $\frac{1}{2}$ in. of wearing surface concrete not relied upon for strength.
Girders : Preliminary calculations have indicated that the 22-ft. girder will be about 15 in. wide, the 26-ft. one 17 in., making the trial clear spans 20.58 and 24.75 ft.

DESIGN OF TYPICAL INTERIOR SLABS "A"

A. Req'd. thickness "t"   Col.1   2   3   4   5

20.58
24.75
45.33

(1) From Sec. 709(d) :
$$t_{min.} = \frac{2(20.58+24.75)(12)}{180} = 6.04''$$

(2) "t" req'd. for Diag. Tens. :

$v = \frac{V}{bjd}$

$$d = \frac{V}{bjv} = \frac{400(10.29)}{12(7/8)(90)}$$
$$d = 4.36''$$
#5 bar = 0.63 (trial)

Method 2
"Span" spec.
20.58'
$\frac{1.25}{21.83'} = 2(7\frac{1}{2}'')$
= S

24.75'
$\frac{1.25}{26.00'} = L$

$\frac{0.75 f'p'g}{t_{rq'd.} = 5.74''}$

(3) "t" req'd. for Flexure : $m = \frac{S}{L} = \frac{21.83'}{26.0'} = 0.84$

Taking the max. B. M. : (short-way neg.)
$$d_{rq'd} = \sqrt{\frac{M}{Rb}} = \sqrt{\frac{0.045(191)\,12,000}{236(12)}} = 6.03$$
0.63
0.75
$t_{rq'd.} = 7.41''$

"Choose slab thickness by half-inches."

B. Short Way Flexure Steel   Actual d now 6.12 in.

(1) Negative Steel
$$R = \frac{M}{bd^2} = \frac{0.045(191)\,12,000}{12(6.12)^2} = 229$$ $\begin{cases} P = 1.33\% \\ A_s/in. = 0.0813 \end{cases}$
Find:
$\frac{13(12)(0.0813)}{0.31} = 41.$ Use 41-#5 in top of 13' Middle Strip

(2) Positive Steel   Find
$$R = \frac{M}{bd^2} = \frac{0.034(191)(12,000)}{12(6.12)^2} = 174$$ $\begin{cases} P = 0.98\% \\ A_s/_{1''} = 0.060 \end{cases}$
$\frac{13(12)(0.060)}{0.31} = 30.$ Use 30-#5 in bot. of 13' Mid. Strip

C. Long Way Flexure Steel
For the designing of both Neg. and Pos. steel see Sheet 2/5.

FLEXURAL DESIGNING OF OTHER TYPICAL SLABS
See Sheet 2/5 for tabular designing of Slabs B, B', & C.

All 22
N
↑
All 26

C   B'
6   7   8   9   10
B   A
11 12 13 14 15

Indicates slab type

Wearing   6#
L.L.   300
Struc. slab   94
ω = 400#
ωS^2 = 191 k/
Make structural
$t = 7\frac{1}{2}$ in.

7-3. Design of a Two-Way Slab Floor. A start was made upon Example 7–1 by estimating the slab thickness in order to calculate a trial dead load. Next the total load was distributed to the girders, according to the 45° division pictured on Calculation Sheet 1/5. This enabled the designer to compute the 15- and 17-in. tentative widths of the girders, and so determine the clear spans needed for computing maximum slab shear. Follow Calculation Sheet 1/5, item A, closely.

Designing for Diagonal Tension. Having the slab shear at the inside faces of the girders, the total slab thickness required for safety in diagonal tension was independently calculated to be 5.74 in. Most designers measure *d* upward from the centroid of the areas of the two crossed bars, as in this case. This practice makes it unnecessary for them to know which bar group finally will be uppermost.

Designing for Flexure. A trial bending calculation having indicated that the structural thickness of the slab would have to be made about $7\frac{1}{2}$ in., *S*, *L*, and *m* were then closely calculated, in the left margin, and the design bending moment coefficients were interpolated from the Code and set down in the accompanying Table 7–1 for convenient reference.

As in one-way slabs, the controlling slab thickness required for flexure is set by the unit bending moment in the shorter direction. It proved to be 7.41 in. in the case of slabs A, and overruled the 5.74 in. demand of diagonal tension.[2] Consequently these slabs were made $7\frac{1}{2}$ in. thick. The design shears and bending moments were next revised so as to be consistent with the slab thickness just chosen, and the intervening calculations were then quickly corrected, using colored pencil. Only the resulting final values are shown.

As depicted in Calculation Sheet 1/5, items B and C, slab A was next reinforced for flexure. The required amount of steel per *inch* of slab width was computed, and divided into the width of the *middle strip* of slab to find the required number of bars of any proposed size. The #5 bar proved generally suitable. (Refer to Chapter 6, Art. 6–8, fifth paragraph.) The steel was next located on the design sketch of Calculation Sheet 3/5.

Tabulated Flexural Designing. Once the pattern of calculations has been set, much time and space may be saved by performing the rest of the work in tabular form. Calculation Sheet 2/5 includes the flexural designing of all the slabs. There was little variation in required slab thickness from panel to panel in this floor, so all except the corner slabs were made $7\frac{1}{2}$ in., exclusive of the $\frac{1}{2}$-in. wearing surface.

Note that both the short and long span middle strip bending moments are calculated by applying the tabulated coefficients to the short span moment wS^2.

In the designing tabulation, the sketches under "Remarks" serve to orient the reader as he deals with exterior slabs. The lack of full restraint at one or more edges means that larger bending moments must be designed for elsewhere. Obviously the method is somewhat empirical.

---

[2] As well as the Sec. 709(d) minimum thickness required to prevent excessive deflection.

Ex. 7-1 — Tabular Summary of Two-Way Slab Designing | A. E. L. | 7-13-'55 | 2/5

One-foot strips studied: $S = 21.83'$, $L = 26.0'$, $m = 0.84$. $w_{D+L} = 400$ psf, $wS^2 = 191$ k.i. *** Depth $d = 6.12$ and 7.12 in. **

Slab Type	Steel considered	Short Span Flexural Design – for 13' Middle Strip *										Long Span Flexural Design – for 11' Middle Strip *					Remarks
		C from table	M = CwS²/… -ki	Req'd bal. d -in.	t req'd √(M/Vb) -in.	t used -in.	d used in.	R = CwS²/bd²	Corresp. p-%	A_s per inch	Req'd Steel Content *	C from table	R = CwS²/bd²	Corresp. p-%	A_s per inch	Req'd Steel Content *	
A — Typ. inter. slabs	Top	0.045	−8.60	6.03	7.41	7.50	6.12	229	1.33	0.083	41-#5	0.033	168	0.95	0.058	25-#5 Top	The one typical interior slab sketched in Calc. Sheet 4
	Bot.	0.034	+6.50	—			6.12	174	0.98	0.060	30-#5	0.025	127	0.72	0.044	19-#5 Bot.	
B — West exter. slabs	Top	0.052	−9.93	6.49	7.87	7.50	6.12	265	2.00	0.122	△ 62-#5 inter. sup.	0.041	210	1.20	0.0735	31-#5 Top	*(For elaboration see Calc. Sheet 1)* — West Wall, 22' × 26', N↑
	Bot.	0.039	+7.45	—			6.12	199	1.14	0.070	35-#5	0.031	158	0.89	0.0545	23-#5 Bot.	
B' — North exter. slabs	Top	0.052	−9.93	6.49	7.87	7.50		Same as for Slabs "B"			62-#5	0.041	Same as for Slabs B			△ 31-#5 inter. sup.	North Wall, 26' × 22', N↑
	Bot.	0.039	+7.45	—							35-#5	0.031				23-#5 Bot.	
C ** — Corner slabs	Top	0.061 **	−12.05 **	7.14	8.52	8.50 ××	7.12	238	1.41	0.100	△ 50-#5 inter. sup.	0.049	190	1.09	0.078	△ 33-#5 Top inter. sup.	N. Wall / W. Wall, 22' × 26', N↑
	Bot.	0.046 **	+9.05 **	—			7.12	178	1.01	0.072	36-#5	0.037	143	0.80	0.057	24-#5 Bot.	

* --- 1/3 as much steel to be used in each of the two corresponding Column Strip bands. See Spec. "Method 2", and Sheet 3/5

△ Half as much steel to be used in the top at the outer support.

** The corner slabs had to be made 1 in. thicker than the rest. For them $wS^2 = 197$ k.i.

At the corner slab C, large flexural steel contents were avoided by increasing the slab thickness. Since there are only four of them in each floor the quantity of concrete was not greatly increased.

TABLE 7–1

TWO-WAY SLAB BENDING MOMENT COEFFICIENT, C,
("Method 2," American Concrete Institute Building Code, Section 709)

| | For Short Span S | | | For Long Span L all values of m |
| | Values of $m = \dfrac{S}{L}$ | | | |
	Square 1.00 Slab	0.84*	0.50 and less	
Case 1: Interior panels Negative moment at:				
Continuous edge	0.033	0.045	0.083	0.033
Discontinuous edge	—	—	—	—
Positive moment at midspan	0.025	0.034	0.062	0.025
Case 2: One edge discontinuous Negative moment at:				
Continuous edge	0.041	0.052	0.085	0.041
Discontinuous edge	0.021	0.026	0.042	0.021
Positive moment at midspan	0.031	0.039	0.064	0.031
Case 3: Two edges discontinuous Negative moment at:				
Continuous edge	0.049	0.061	0.090	0.049
Discontinuous edge	0.025	0.030	0.045	0.025
Positive moment at midspan	0.037	0.046	0.068	0.037
Case 4: Three edges discontinuous Negative moment at:				
Continuous edge	0.058	0.071	0.098	0.058
Discontinuous edge	0.029	0.035	0.049	0.029
Positive moment at midspan	0.044	0.054	0.074	0.044
Case 5: Four edges discontinuous Negative moment at:				
Continuous edge	— —	—	—	—
Discontinuous edge	0.033	0.041	0.055	0.033
Positive moment at midspan	0.050	0.061	0.083	0.050

* Interpolated from ACI Code, Sec. 709, Table 3.

7–4. Two-Way Slab Steel Arrangement. The layout on Calculation Sheet 3/5 was begun by first lightly sketching in assumed contraflexure points at the quarter-points of each span and locating the middle strip positive steel for typical interior slabs, such as slab A. Enough of this steel was next bent up just outside the quarter-points to take care of the negative steel requirement at typical interior supports, located two spans or more from the outside walls. This usually meant that about two-thirds of the positive steel was bent up, and continued past the next quarter-point. Since ACI Code, Sec. 709, "Method 2" makes no men-

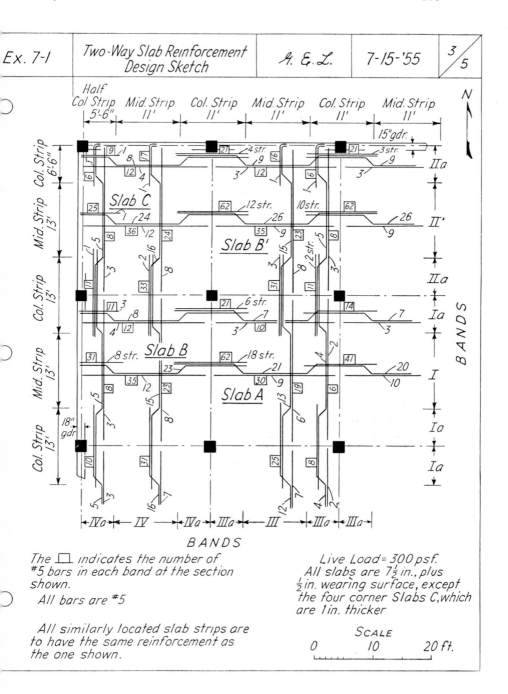

| Ex. 7-1 | Two-Way Slab Reinforcement Design Sketch | 𝒜. 𝓔. 𝓛. | 7-15-'55 | 3/5 |

The ⬚ indicates the number of #5 bars in each band at the section shown.

All bars are #5

All similarly located slab strips are to have the same reinforcement as the one shown.

Live Load= 300 psf.
All slabs are 7½ in., plus ½ in. wearing surface, except the four corner Slabs C, which are 1 in. thicker

SCALE
0   10   20 ft.

tion of anchorage, Sec. 902 may be presumed to apply. It requires that in interior spans at least one-fourth of the positive steel area must be left in the bottom, and continued into the supporting member. When the bars left over for bending-up were insufficient to take care of the negative bending moment over a support, short straight bars were added.

End Span Steel. ACI Sec. 902(c) demands that in end spans one-third of the positive reinforcement shall extend along the bottom of the member and into the outer (end) support. The bending up of two-thirds of the bottom steel from the exterior slab, plus three-fourths of that from the interior one, often is insufficient to reinforce the top of the slab at the first interior (or second) support, so short straight bars are added, as in this case.

Still concentrating upon the steel needed for middle strips, a few straight bars were necessary in the top over the end supports to help resist the half-value of negative bending moment assigned to such points. A few such bars are always necessary to reinforce the portion of the slab between the upper bar bend point and the contraflexure point.

Choice of Bar Size. The *minimum* usable size of slab bar will be the one which barely meets the minimum spacing requirements of ACI Sec. 505(a). In this case they would demand a clear spacing of 1.33 in. to allow our one-inch aggregate stones to pass through.

The *maximum* bar size will be set by the 18-in. spacing permitted by ACI Sec. 702(e)(3), or by the perimeter required for safe bond values.

Examination of the bond stress formula, $u = V/\Sigma_0 jd$, suggests that the portion of the structure where V is large but bars are scarce will be the governing locality. In two-way slab floors it tends to be in the top steel at the extreme ends of long-span middle strips. Thus the steel for a portion such as our slab B′ should be designed for flexure as early as possible in the designing process, so that the bond stress check upon the bar size tentatively selected can then be made.

Check for Bond. In this case, working at the face of the 22-ft. girder at the north wall, taking the loading distribution pictured in Calculation Sheet 1/5 and the 16–#5 bars originally selected:

$$u = \frac{V}{\Sigma_0 jd} = \frac{400(11)[\tfrac{3}{4} \times 11 - 0.63]}{16(\tfrac{5}{8})(\pi)(\tfrac{7}{8})(6.12)} = 199. \text{ psi}$$

$$< 210, \therefore \text{ O.K.}$$

Slabs B and C were also similarly examined. Their maximum bond stresses turned out 138 and 166 psi, respectively.

Anchorage of Reinforcement. A cue for the anchorage of two-way slab steel is provided at the left side of Fig. 7–6, prepared for flat slab construction.

At the extreme ends of all two-way slab design strips the *top bars* shall have full anchorage beyond the inside face of the girder, by bending them if necessary. In the case at hand the required anchorage distance would be

$$\frac{f_s}{4u}\,(d') = \frac{20,000}{4(210)}\,(\tfrac{5}{8}) = 15 \text{ in.}$$

Therefore, in Calculation Sheet 3/5, the N-S bars extending into the 15-in. girder are shown bent; but the E-W bars extending into the 18-in. girder did not require it.

At intermediate points the ends of top bars should be extended 12 diam. beyond the assumed quarter-span contraflexure point.

The ends of all *bottom bars* should be embedded into the girders 6 in., or made continuous.

TWO–WAY SLAB PRACTICE PROBLEMS

Problem 7–2. Design the typical interior two-way roof slab for the building of Example 7–1. Take 40-lb. snow and 20-lb. live load per sq. ft. Include 5 psf for roof covering. Take ACI 3000-lb. concrete and specification. Make rough estimates of girder depths and widths before proceeding. Prepare a final design sketch similar to Calculation Sheet 3/5, including the steel over the columns. Comment upon the economy of your design.

Problem 7–3. Same as Example 7–1, except that the floor live load is only 100 psf. Design a typical interior panel of floor slab and tabulate a comparison of quantities with those of Example 7–1.

7–5. The Design of Interior Girders for the Two-Way Slab Floor. The *tributary areas* method, recommended by the ACI for allocating load to such girders, results in a triangular distribution along the short spans. This work was begun on Calculation Sheet 5/5, taking Girder 8–9 as typical. The left-hand column on Calculation Sheet 4/5 shows the necessary fundamental expressions.

7–6. Maximum Bending Moments in the 22-ft. Girder. In the second column on Calculation Sheet 4/5, the fully fixed end condition has been called the maximum bending moment condition for *dead load*, as formerly, since it is impossible to remove it from any span.

The maximum *live load* bending moments and shears were determined by applying the criteria applicable to systems consisting of loaded and unloaded spans. In Chapter 6 these same 22-ft. span frames were studied for maximum moments using the "cut-out" moment distribution[3] approximation, although the loading differed.

---

[3] Students who are unfamiliar with the girder designing of Chapter 6 will first need to study it.

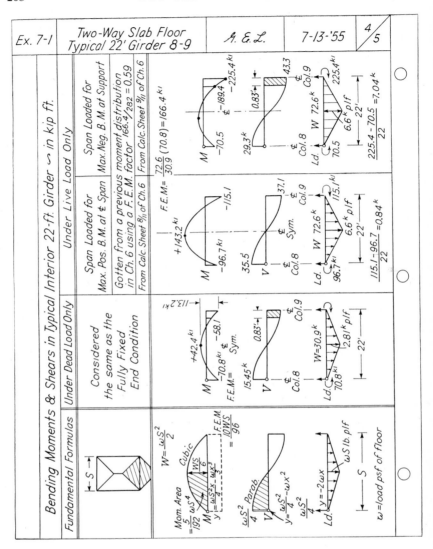

Maximum L. L. Positive B. M. By referring to Calculation Sheet 8 of Chapter 6, one sees a moment distribution study for maximum positive bending moment.

Its results have been adapted to the present need by applying a factor, 0.59, which represents the ratio of the fixed end moments in the two cases, as shown in the third and fourth columns of Calculation Sheet 4/5 of the present Chapter 7.

The Maximum L. L. Negative B. M. was found correspondingly, using the former results on Calculation Sheet 9 of Chapter 6. The drawing of

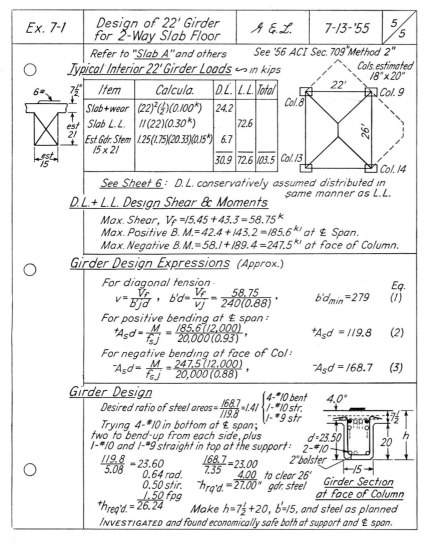

| Ex. 7-1 | Design of 22' Girder for 2-Way Slab Floor | A.E.L. | 7-13-'55 | 5/5 |

Refer to "*Slab A*" and others   See '56 ACI Sec. 709 "Method 2"

Typical Interior 22' Girder Loads ↝ in kips   Cols. estimated 18"×20"

Item	Calcula.	D.L.	L.L.	Total
Slab+wear	$(22)^2(\tfrac{1}{2})(0.100^k)$	24.2		
Slab L.L.	$11(22)(0.30^k)$		72.6	
Est. Gdr. Stem 15 x 21	$1.25(1.75)(20.33)(0.15^k)$	6.7		
		30.9	72.6	103.5

See Sheet 6 : D.L. conservatively assumed distributed in same manner as L.L.

D.L.+ L.L. Design Shear & Moments

Max. Shear, $V_f = 15.45 + 43.3 = 58.75^k$
Max. Positive B.M. = 42.4 + 143.2 = 185.6 ^{kl} at ₵ Span.
Max. Negative B.M. = 58.1 + 189.4 = 247.5 ^{kl} at face of Column.

Girder Design Expressions (Approx.)

For diagonal tension ·   Eq.
$$v = \frac{V_f}{b'jd}, \quad b'd = \frac{V_f}{vj} = \frac{58.75}{240(0.88)}, \quad b'd_{min} = 279 \quad (1)$$

For positive bending at ₵ span:
$$+A_sd = \frac{M}{f_sj} = \frac{185.6(12,000)}{20,000(0.93)}, \quad +A_sd = 119.8 \quad (2)$$

For negative bending at face of Col:
$$-A_sd = \frac{M}{f_sj} = \frac{247.5(12,000)}{20,000(0.88)}, \quad -A_sd = 168.7 \quad (3)$$

Girder Design

Desired ratio of steel areas = $\frac{168.7}{119.8} = 1.41$ { 4-#10 bent, 1-#10 str., 1-#9 str.

Trying 4-#10 in bottom at ₵ span; two to bend-up from each side, plus 1-#10 and 1-#9 straight in top at the support:

$\frac{119.8}{5.08} = 23.60$	$\frac{168.7}{7.35} = 23.00$
0.64 rad.	4.00 to clear 26'
0.50 stir.	$-h_{rq'd.} = 27.00"$ gdr. steel
1.50 fpg	
$+h_{req'd.} = 26.24$	

4.0"   d = 23.50   2-#10 2"bolster   h   20   15   7½

Girder Section at face of Column

Make h=7½+20, b'=15, and steel as planned
Investigated and found economically safe both at support and ₵ span.

---

the beam curves, in the last column on Calculation Sheet 4/5 of the present chapter, was complicated by the inequality of the end reactions, the dissymmetry of the bending moment diagram, and the necessity for recalculating the bending moment to the face of the column using shear areas. Small approximations were made.

The **22-ft. girder** designing proper appears on Calculation Sheet 5/5 and follows a pattern already familiar. The single tier of top steel was centered 4 in. from the top so that it could be straddled by a double tier in the top of the 26-ft. girder yet to be designed.

7–7. The Design of the 26-ft. Girders and the Columns. In the case of this longer girder no earlier study of loads and bending moments existed, so they had to be calculated anew, and the designing performed. Because of its similarity to other girder designing performed in this and Chapter 6, the work will only be outlined and the results reported.

Both the live load and the (conservatively predicted) dead load were considered to be trapezoidally distributed. They proved to be 99 kips and 50.8 kips, respectively.

For the rigid frame action, the stiffnesses of the girder and columns were taken to be the same as those used in Chapter 6. The ensuing three-zone live loading cut-out moment distribution studies yielded a design maximum positive bending moment of 265.6 kip-ft., and a maximum negative bending moment at the face of the column of 326.0 kip-ft.

The combined maximum shears and moments used in designing were $V = 84.5$ kips, Pos. B.M. = 346.3 kip-ft. and Neg. B.M. = 444. kip-ft. These yielded the following familiar approximate design expressions:

$$b'd = 396, \qquad Pos.\ A_sd = 224, \qquad Neg.\ A_sd = 300$$

The resulting effective section at midspan consisted of a T-shaped section with a flange 6 ft. by 6 in. by $7\frac{1}{2}$ in., and a stem 18 in. by 2 ft. 7 in., making the total structural depth, $h = 3$ ft. $2\frac{1}{2}$ in. Four #11 bars were used.

The corresponding negative moment section at the face of the column had two #11 bars in the bottom, on 2-in. bolsters. The top steel consisted of four #11 bent-up bars plus two #10 straight bars, all straddling the transverse top bars from the 22-ft. girders, which were centered 4 in. from the top.

This design was thoroughly investigated and proved economically safe. Its dimensions were consistent with those used to compute the dead load.

The *interior columns* may be expected to be closely the same size as the one designed for the slab, beam, and girder floor of Chapter 6, so there should be no tendency for interference of the bars.

The *exterior columns* will be subject to somewhat less axial load, a portion of which will be eccentric wall load, and to greatly increased floor bending moment due to both live and dead load. The designing of such columns is taken up at length in Art. 7–21.

GIRDER PRACTICE PROBLEMS

Problem 7–4. Supply the detailed design calculations for the 26-ft. typical interior girder of Example 7–1. Refer to Art. 7–7 and Chapter 6, accounting for all values used.

Problem 7–5. Design the two typical interior roof girders for the structure of Example 7–1. Refer to Problem 7–2, wherein the two-way roof slab was designed.

Problem 7–6. Design the two typical interior floor girders for the structure of Example 7–1, except that the live load is only 100 psi, as in Problem 7–3, wherein an interior panel of floor slab was redesigned.

7–8. Summary of Two-Way Slab Floor Designing. Two-way flexural members are quite efficient, since by Poisson's ratio the major extension of the material in one direction is accompanied by an appreciable minor contraction at right angles thereto which has a supporting effect in the latter direction and thus decreases the amount of bending moment which must be designed for.

If floor slabs are square, or less than 1.5 times as long as wide, there is bending in both coordinate directions which must be taken care of by a two-way system of reinforcing steel.

In two-way slabs the intensity of the bending moment is much greater in the direction of the shorter dimension.

In arranging reinforcement, part of the bars are bent up at assumed quarter-span contraflexure points, and extended over the girders to and beyond the next quarter-span point.

A squarish slab which is supported along all four sides tends to curl up at the corners when loaded. Consequently it is customary in designing to assume a triangular, trapezoidal, or parabolic distribution of the pressure between slab and supporting member, with zero values at the slab corners, as in the girder designing illustrated. This phenomenon is also recognized somewhat in ACI slab design by providing a greater steel content throughout the central half of the slab.

The bending moment coefficients tabulated under ACI Method 2 presuppose that the slab will be placed monolithicly with the supporting girders or walls; otherwise additional reinforcement must be provided in the corners of the slab according to ACI Code, Sec. 709(b).

Unit shearing stress as a measure of diagonal tension in two-way slabs may be calculated at the face of the girder, assuming a 45° division of tributary slab areas carrying uniformly distributed load.

Bond stress in continuous two-way slab reinforcement tends to be high in the top steel at the face of the end supports. Smaller bars must sometimes be provided at such points.

BIBLIOGRAPHY

(*See page* 240)

TWO–WAY SLAB QUESTIONS

1. Distinguish clearly between one-way, two-way, and flat slab floors.
2. Exactly what is meant by "the effect of Poisson's ratio" upon slab performance? Is the effect the same in two-way footings? Explain.
3. Why do two-way slabs tend to curl up at the corners? In what two ways is this tendency dealt with in construction?
4. Why do bond stresses tend to be high in the top of continuous slabs, at the extreme ends thereof? (See ACI *Manual of Standard Practice* for treatment of bar ends at such points.)

5. What practical limitations, if any, affect the choice of a two-way slab when the lengths of the two sides are quite unequal?

6. Tell how to determine systematically the proper size of bar for a given floor.

7. What three factors influence the choice of slab thickness?

8. Referring to the sketches of Calculation Sheet 2/5, truly should Slabs B and B' have the same reinforcement at midspan and at corresponding interior supports? Explain.

TWO–WAY SLAB PROBLEMS

Problem 7–7. Redesign the typical interior roof panel of Example 7–1 and Problem 7–2 as a pan T-beam system spanning the 22-ft. direction. Refer to Fig. 2–15. Take ACI 3000-lb. concrete and specification. Be sure to consider diagonal tension, and if tapered pans are needed, the instructor will indicate the increased beam stem width attainable therewith.

Make a tabular comparison of the required quantities of material with the results of Problem 7–2, the two-way slab design, and comment. Also secure data upon form costs in the two cases.

Problem 7–8. (*Individual*) *Design of a Two-Way Slab Floor.* Design the two-way slabs and typical long and short girders for your assigned case. Consult the instructor for the aggregate maximum size, the class of concrete, and any other starting information needed. Take high bond deformed bars and the ACI Code.

Name	Case	Panels, ft.	Live Load, psf	Name	Case	Panels, ft.	Live Load, psf
	a	18.6 × 22.5	195		h	16.0 × 19.0	305
	b	22.5 × 27.0	105		i	21.4 × 25.7	115
	c	19.2 × 23.0	175		j	23.0 × 27.6	100
	d	18.0 × 21.6	210		k	17.6 × 21.0	215
	e	20.0 × 24.0	150		l	19.6 × 23.4	160
	f	17.0 × 20.4	250		m	16.6 × 20.0	260
	g	20.8 × 25.0	130		n	15.6 × 18.8	335

Summarize your slab calculations and designing as in Calculation Sheets 2/5 and 3/5.

Part II.   Flat Slab Floors and Columns

7–9. Flat Slabs. When reinforced concrete floor slabs are supported only by columns, the construction is known as **flat slab.** As shown in Fig. 7–3, the columns are usually round and are conically enlarged at their tops to form a **capital.** The effective spans are shortened thereby, preventing high diagonal tension and bending stresses. Flat slabs are also distinguished by being supported only at the corners, along the quarter-circle boundary of the capital, as illustrated in Fig. 7–4. The "Mushroom system," an early form of flat-slab construction, was originated by Dr. C. A. P. Turner, a member of ASCE. Four-way reinforcement was used.

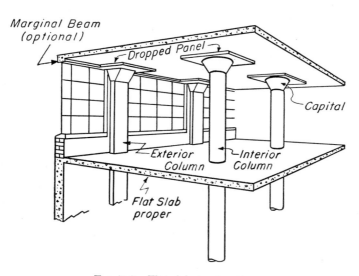

FIG. 7–3. Flat-slab construction.

Continuity is a prerequisite to economical use of flat-slab construction, a minimum of four spans being preferable. Furthermore, the column spacing should be approximately uniform in each direction. The presence of several large openings in a floor destroys the continuity. Flat slab construction is most advantageous for live loadings exceeding 125 psf.

Flat-slab formwork is relatively simpler and cheaper than if beams and girders are used. The absence of girders also means that for the same clear story heights the structure will be only 90 per cent as high, which decreases wall, column, and footing costs. The unbroken ceiling expanse not only presents a better appearance, but also facilitates better lighting, simplifies the installation of piped services, and improves ventilation. The decreased number of edges increases the fire resistance.

7–10. Reinforcement of Flat Slabs. When the reinforcement runs in only two directions, as in Fig. 7–4, it is said to be a **two-way** system. The four-way system was a variation in which the middle-strip bands of steel between the columns were replaced by bands at 45° thereto which also passed over the columns and created such a congestion of bars at that point that the effective depth of the slabs was considerably diminished.

There is also a three-way system in which the lines of columns are at the apices of equilateral triangles, and the reinforcement runs in three directions. Such an arrangement is convenient for garages because turns of only 60° are needed to pass from one bay to another.

Ordinarily flat slabs are proportioned so that diagonal tension reinforcement is not needed.[D] **Dropped panels,** pictured in Fig. 7–3, serve to improve shear and bending resistance near the (column) supports by increasing the effective thickness of the slab. The critical sections for diagonal tension are a short distance outside (a) the capital and (b) the *drop*, as it is usually called. With the longer spans and lighter loadings, drops become unnecessary.

7–11. Design of Flat Slabs. There are two well-recognized methods for designing flat-slab floors. The more general and accurate one, called the **elastic method,** requires that the structure be designed as a rigid frame continuous from story to story, as well as horizontally. It *must* be used when the span lengths are irregular and/or the panels of floor are far from square. This method is broadly outlined in the Code, but considerable skill is required to use it intelligently.

The **empirical method,** embracing tables of *moment coefficients*, may be used if the structure comes within the following limitations:

(a) The construction shall consist of at least three continuous panels in each direction.

(b) The ratio of length to width of panels shall not exceed 1.33.

(c) The grid pattern shall consist of approximately rectangular panels, the successive span lengths of which, in each direction, shall not differ from the longer span by more than 20 per cent. Within these limitations, columns may be offset a maximum of 10 per cent of the span, in the direction of the offset, from either axis between center lines of successive columns.

(d) The structure shall not be over 125 ft. in height, nor have a story greater than 12 ft. 6 in.

(e) Proper account must be taken of wind and earthquake forces, as required by other sections of the Code. Refer to the 1956 ACI Code, Sec. 1004(a).

The basic floor panel bending moment, M_o, to which the moment coefficients of the *empirical method* are applied, will now be established.

7–12. Simplified Flat-Slab Panel Bending Moment. A static analysis was begun for a square panel of flat slab at (a) in Fig. 7–4. The ACI standard notation was used, in which c is the diameter of the column capital. The portion of the dead and live load which lies directly over the column capital is carried directly by the columns and was purposely excluded from the load, W, which is considered to be uniformly distributed only over the area pictured, and so productive of bending in the slab. The centroids of the reaction forces acting upward around the quarter-circles at the boundaries of the capitals are at some distance, a, from the column centers.

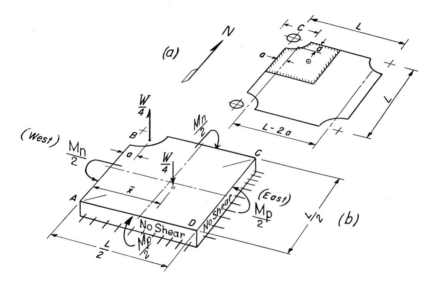

FIG. 7–4. Free body sketch of a square flat-slab quadrant.

One quadrant[4] of the slab has been taken out at (b) for the study of bending moments in the east-west direction only. The load $W/4$ acts at a point $\bar{x}$ distance from the line of column centers, as defined by the center of gravity of the quadrant. Since the slab is continuous, positive and negative bending moments, M_p and M_n, must exist in the panel in both coordinate directions. The half-values shown are for the quadrant only. $M_n/2$ is understood to include the component, in the coordinate direction, of whatever negative bending moment there is upon the adjacent curved boundary. *From symmetry, there can be no vertical shear on any of the four* plane *vertical surfaces shown.* Taking moments about the diagonal AC:

$$\frac{W}{4} \left(\bar{x} - a \right) \sec 45° = \left(\frac{2M_p}{2} + \frac{2M_n}{2} \right) \cos 45°.$$

[4] This quadrant free body approach is that of Professor P. W. Ott, Department of Mechanics, Ohio State University.

Letting the sum of the positive and negative bending moments per panel, in each direction, be M_s, and taking a half-panel for study:

$$M_s = M_p + M_n = \frac{W}{2} (\bar{x} - a).$$

From mechanics:

$$W = w \left(L^2 - \frac{\pi}{4} c^2 \right)$$

where w is the load per square unit.

By taking moments of areas about AB:

$$\bar{x} = \frac{\dfrac{L^2}{2} \left(\dfrac{L}{4} \right) - \dfrac{\pi c^2}{8} \left(\dfrac{2c}{3\pi} \right)}{\dfrac{L^2}{2} - \dfrac{\pi c^2}{8}} = \frac{3L^3 - 2c^2}{3(4L^2 - \pi c^2)}$$

since $a = c/\pi$ from mathematics. Therefore:

$$M_s = \frac{wL^3}{8} \left[1 - \frac{4c}{\pi L} + \frac{1}{3} \left(\frac{c}{L} \right)^3 \right].$$

From which by approximations,

$$M_s = 0.125WL \left(1 - \frac{2c}{3L} \right)^2.$$

As in the case of two-way slabs, the above static analysis gives bending moment values greater than Westergaard's[B] precise three-dimensional mathematical analysis, which recognized the effect of Poisson's ratio upon the deformations, stress readjustments resulting from creep action, and the results of tests. Accordingly, Westergaard and Slater[A] recommended:

$$M_o = 0.09WL \left(1 - \frac{2c}{3L} \right)^2 --- \text{obsolete} -------- (7)$$

wherein M_o was the arithmetical sum of the design positive and negative bending moments in each coordinate direction of a *square panel* having sides L, and capitals of diameter c.

More recently DiStasio[E] showed the need for an additional coefficient:

$$F = 1.15 - \frac{c}{L}, \qquad \text{minimum value unity,}$$

as capitals sometimes came to be omitted and the dimension of the column was then used as c, so:

$$M_o = 0.09WLF \left(1 - \frac{2c}{3L} \right)^2 --- (1956 \text{ ACI}) ------ (8)$$

PLATE 7-1. Reinforced concrete pergolas, Bellevue Park, Cincinnati. A decorative application of the flat-slab principle.

If the panels are rectangular, of length L and breadth B, the design bending moments in each direction will be respectively:

$$M_{oL} = 0.09WLF\left(1 - \frac{2c}{3L}\right)^2 \tag{9}$$

$$M_{oB} = 0.09WBF\left(1 - \frac{2c}{3B}\right)^2 \tag{10}$$

in both of which $W = w\left(BL - \frac{\pi}{4}c^2\right)$, and $F = 1.15 - \frac{c}{B}$, min. value 1.00, in the case of Formula (10).

Note that in flat slabs the greater bending moment occurs over the longer span, which is not the case in two-way slabs. It makes a great difference whether a slab is supported at the four corners or along all four sides.

EXAMPLE 7–2

Given the 22 by 26 ft. column-centered storage and manufacturing building previously designed with beam and girder floors in Example 6–1 of Chapter 6, and for two-way slabs in Example 7–1 of this chapter. Required: to redesign for flat-slab floors, using the tables of moment coefficients. The live load is 300 psf. Use ACI 3000-lb. concrete and specification.

7–13. Design of a Flat-Slab Floor. (Example 7–2.) Calculation Sheet 1/7 illustrates the general arrangement, assuming that dropped panels, or "drops," will be necessary. It is customary to make the exterior columns rectangular, with pyramidal capitals or "caps" to better suit the architectural situation at the exterior walls.

The edges of the floor will be stiffened by *marginal beams* which are shown upturned in the illustration, instead of in the usual downturned position, to improve the natural lighting.

Attention is directed to the allowable stresses, minimum slab thicknesses, and the old rules-of-thumb for trial dimensions of capitals and dropped panels.

The actual designing consists of two principal steps: (a) the determination of the concrete dimensions, namely slab thickness, length, width and thickness of the drops, and the diameter of the caps. The second step, (b), consists in calculating and arranging the required amount of steel.

7–14. Panel Load and Moment from Trial Slab Thickness. As shown in Calculation Sheet 1/7, and later in Sheet 4/7, the 1956 ACI Code enables one to quickly determine a slab thickness, t_2, which will be closely

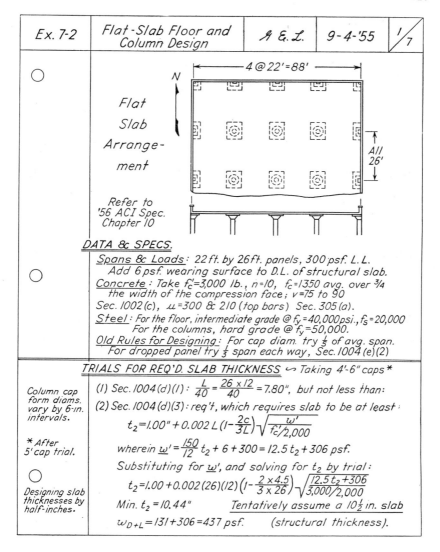

| Ex. 7-2 | Flat-Slab Floor and Column Design | A. E. L. | 9-4-'55 | 1/7 |

Flat Slab Arrange- ment

N

— 4 @ 22' = 88' —

All 26'

Refer to '56 ACI Spec. Chapter 10

DATA & SPECS.

Spans & Loads: 22 ft. by 26 ft. panels, 300 psf. L. L.
   Add 6 psf. wearing surface to D.L. of structural slab.
Concrete: Take $f_c'=3{,}000$ lb., $n=10$, $f_c=1350$ avg. over ¾ the width of the compression face; $v=75$ to 90
Sec. 1002(c), $u=300$ & 210 (top bars) Sec. 305(a).
Steel: For the floor, intermediate grade @ $f_y=40{,}000$psi., $f_s=20{,}000$
   For the columns, hard grade @ $f_y=50{,}000$.
Old Rules for Designing: For cap diam. try ⅕ of avg. span.
   For dropped panel try ⅓ span each way, Sec. 1004(e)(2)

TRIALS FOR REQ'D. SLAB THICKNESS ↪ Taking 4'-6" caps *

Column cap form diams. vary by 6-in. intervals.

(1) Sec. 1004(d)(1): $\dfrac{L}{40}=\dfrac{26\times 12}{40}=7.80''$, but not less than:

(2) Sec. 1004(d)(3): req't, which requires slab to be at least:

$$t_2=1.00''+0.002\,L\left(1-\tfrac{2c}{3L}\right)\sqrt{\dfrac{w'}{f_c'/2{,}000}}$$

* After 5' cap trial.

wherein $\underline{w}'=\dfrac{150}{12}\,t_2+6+300=12.5\,t_2+306$ psf.

Substituting for $\underline{w}'$, and solving for t_2 by trial:

Designing slab thicknesses by half-inches.

$$t_2=1.00+0.002(26)(12)\left(1-\tfrac{2\times 4.5}{3\times 26}\right)\sqrt{\dfrac{12.5\,t_2+306}{3{,}000/2{,}000}}$$

Min. $t_2=10.44''$ *Tentatively assume a 10½ in. slab*

$w_{D+L}=131+306=437$ psf.   (structural thickness).

---

correct for the most critical section thereof. It largely makes unnecessary the estimating of slab thickness and the computing of trial dead-load panel load and bending moment, the error in which is not soon revealed.

The t_2 Trial for Slab Thickness. Having computed the $L/40$ minimum thickness of 7.80 in., consider the t_2 formula. By expressing w', the total load per square foot of floor, in terms of t_2 and the known live loading, and assuming only the diameter of the capital, the formula yields t_2; from which the panel load W, and the panel bending moment M_o follow. In this example these values were only slightly affected when it later became necessary to change the diameter of the capitals to the next smaller (4 ft. 6 in.) size. The background of the development of the t_2 formula will be discussed in a later section.

Panel Load and Bending Moment. In computing the panel load W at the top of Sheet 2/7, the small sketch reminds the reader that only the load outside the limits of the column capital causes bending in the slab, since the rest of it gets into the column *directly.* Refer to Fig. 7–4.

In computing M_o, the new coefficient $F = 1.15 - \dfrac{c}{L}$ becomes 1.07

if capitals are omitted from a structure consisting of 16-in. columns on 16-ft. centers. It expresses the effect of an increased effective span upon the magnitude of the bending moment.

7-15. Designing the Flat-Slab Concrete. Note in Sheet 2/7 that for calculation purposes the panels are divided into *column strips* and *middle strips,* each a half-span in width, as in two-way slab designing, to each of which design moments are assigned.

The third and last trial for required slab thickness at midspan called for about $8\frac{1}{2}$ in., as demanded by flexure. Here, for the first time, an allowance is being made for the proven variation[A] in f_c across the width of slab strips and drops by using only three-fourths of the strip width in the flexure formula. It leads to a more realistic value of the safe total compressive force, C. *This three-fourths width is used only in determining the* **concrete dimensions.**

Since the $10\frac{1}{2}$-in. thickness earlier determined must be adopted, it is evident that at midspan we have appreciably more slab thickness than needed for a *balanced* section. However, at an intermediate section through the edge of the drop, where the thickness will be the same, the (negative) bending moment value is always greater. The t_2 formula was carefully devised to allow for this, as will be seen later.

Depth "d" versus Bar Size. The slab depth to the centroid of the reinforcement is partly determined by the *diameter* of the bars. In slabs, the maximum suitable bar size is set either (a) by bond requirements or (b) by the limitation on bar spacing. At this early stage only the latter can be utilized. A choice was therefore made by selecting a bar which could work economically at the $2t$ maximum spacing in a locality subject to very small bending moment. Later on, after a pattern of bar groups has been established, a corresponding investigation utilizing the allowable bond stress will be made.

Note that the average depth to the crossed-bar centers is conveniently being used in these calculations.

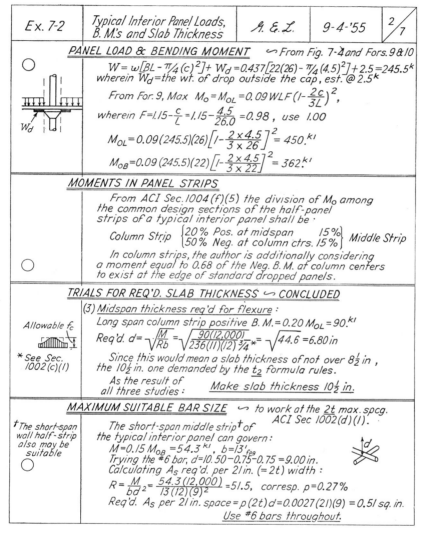

Ex. 7-2	Typical Interior Panel Loads, B. M.'s and Slab Thickness	*A. E. L.*	9-4-'55	2/7

PANEL LOAD & BENDING MOMENT　　⌐ From Fig. 7-4 and Fors. 9 & 10

$$W = w[BL - \pi/4 (c)^2] + W_d = 0.437[22(26) - \pi/4 (4.5)^2] + 2.5 = 245.5^k$$
wherein W_d =the wt. of drop outside the cap, est. @ 2.5^k

From For. 9, Max $M_O = M_{OL} = 0.09\,WLF\left(1 - \frac{2c}{3L}\right)^2$,

wherein $F = 1.15 - \frac{c}{L} = 1.15 - \frac{4.5}{26.0} = 0.98$, use 1.00

$$M_{OL} = 0.09(245.5)(26)\left[1 - \frac{2 \times 4.5}{3 \times 26}\right]^2 = 450.^{kI}$$

$$M_{OB} = 0.09(245.5)(22)\left[1 - \frac{2 \times 4.5}{3 \times 22}\right]^2 = 362.^{kI}$$

MOMENTS IN PANEL STRIPS

From ACI Sec. 1004 (f)(5) the division of M_O among the common design sections of the half-panel strips of a typical interior panel shall be ·

Column Strip $\begin{Bmatrix} 20\% \text{ Pos. at midspan} & 15\% \\ 50\% \text{ Neg. at column ctrs.} & 15\% \end{Bmatrix}$ Middle Strip

In column strips, the author is additionally considering a moment equal to 0.68 of the Neg. B. M. at column centers to exist at the edge of standard dropped panels.

TRIALS FOR REQ'D. SLAB THICKNESS　⌐ CONCLUDED

(3) *Midspan thickness req'd for flexure* :

Allowable f_c

Long span column strip positive B. M. = 0.20 M_{OL} = 90.^{kI}

Req'd. $d = \sqrt{\dfrac{M}{Rb}} = \sqrt{\dfrac{90(12,000)}{236(11)(12)\,3/4}}* = \sqrt{44.6} = 6.80\,in$

* See Sec. 1002 (c)(1)

Since this would mean a slab thickness of not over $8\frac{1}{2}$ in , the $10\frac{1}{2}$ in. one demanded by the t_2 formula rules.

As the result of all three studies :　　__Make slab thickness $10\frac{1}{2}$ in.__

MAXIMUM SUITABLE BAR SIZE　⌐ to work at the 2t max. spcg.
　　　　　　　　　　　　　　　　　　　　ACI Sec 1002(d)(1).

†The short-span wall half-strip also may be suitable

The short-span middle strip†of the typical interior panel can govern :

$M = 0.15\,M_{OB} = 54.3^{kI}$, $b = 13'_{fpg}$
Trying the #6 bar, $d = 10.50 - 0.75 - 0.75 = 9.00\,in.$
Calculating A_s req'd. per 21 in. (= 2t) width :

$R = \dfrac{M}{bd^2} = \dfrac{54.3(12,000)}{13(12)(9)^2} = 51.5$, corresp. $p = 0.27\%$

Req'd. A_s per 21 in. space = $p(2t)d = 0.0027(21)(9) = 0.51\,sq. in.$

　　　　　　　　__Use #6 bars throughout.__

The Long-Span Column Strip. At the top of Calculation Sheet 3/7 the required total thickness, t_1, over the columns was computed in the familiar manner, and found to be considerably more than the $10\frac{1}{2}$ in. taken for the midspan section of the column strip. A total thickness of $10\frac{1}{2}$ in. plus a 4-in. drop, or $14\frac{1}{2}$ in., was tentatively decided upon. Note that the 7-ft. 4-in. drop width being tried is at the specification minimum of one-third the transverse column spacing of 22 ft. Also observe that at the column we have a rectangular section upside down, in spite of appearances to the contrary.

PLATE 7–2.   Dome-shaped, thin-shell precase concrete atomic blast shelter.

Diagonal Tension Studies. The rest of the calculations for the concrete dimensions consist of investigations of the diagonal tension stress at sections defined by the edges of the drops and the caps, and reproportioning as found necessary. They must be large enough for the total panel shear outside their limiting sections to be a safe one, as suggested by the illustrations on Sheet 3/7. Here for the first time the student is asked to visualize diagonal tension in a panel-sized slab supported at its center by a single column and carrying a uniformly distributed loading, in umbrella-fashion. The section defined by the edge of the dropped panel is studied in the first sketch. Only the loading outside the base of the inverted frustum of the pyramid defined by the potential 45° cracks pictured is considered to cause diagonal tension in the 10½-in. thickness. The *b* of the diagonal tension formula is the whole perimeter of the base of the pyramid. If this drop were made smaller, *b* would be smaller, but *V* and *v* would increase.

A similar study must always be made at the section defined by the edge of the column capital, where the thickness is greater. Here the geometrical figure to be visualized is an inverted cone, but the method is the same.

To avoid needless additional weight, caps and drops should be made as small as possible and the earlier calculations correspondingly revised.

FLAT–SLAB CONCRETE PROBLEMS

Problem 7–9. (*Individual*) *Design of Flat-Slab Floor Concrete.* Take your individually assigned building and loading, and the ACI *n* = 10 concrete and specification.

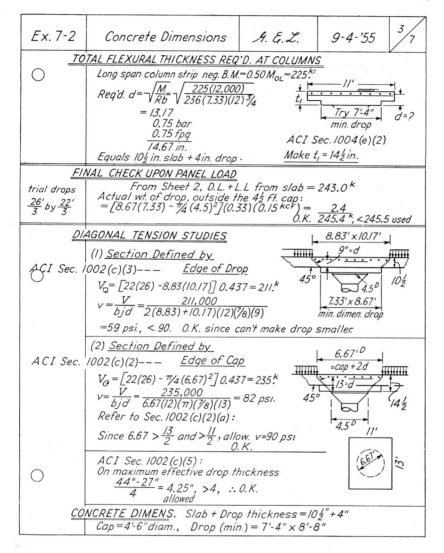

| Ex. 7-2 | Concrete Dimensions | *A. E. L.* | 9-4-'55 | 3/7 |

TOTAL FLEXURAL THICKNESS REQ'D. AT COLUMNS

○ Long span column strip neg. $B.M. = 0.50 M_{OL} = 225^{k'}$

$$Req'd. \ d = \sqrt{\frac{M}{Rb}} = \sqrt{\frac{225(12,000)}{236(7.33)(12)\cdot\frac{3}{4}}}$$

$$= 13.17$$

$$\frac{0.75 \ bar}{0.75 \ fpq} \over 14.67 \ in.$$

Equals $10\frac{1}{2}$ in. slab + 4 in. drop.

Try $7'-4''$ min. drop

$d = ?$

ACI Sec. 1004(e)(2)
Make $t_1 = 14\frac{1}{2}$ in.

FINAL CHECK UPON PANEL LOAD

trial drops
$\frac{26'}{3}$ by $\frac{22'}{3}$

From Sheet 2, $D.L. + L.L$ from slab = 243.0^k
Actual wt. of drop, outside the $4\frac{1}{2}$ ft. cap:
$$= [8.67(7.33) - \frac{\pi}{4}(4.5)^2](0.33)(0.15^{kcf}) = \frac{2.4}{245.4^k, <245.5 \ used}$$
$O.K.$

DIAGONAL TENSION STUDIES

$8.83' \times 10.17'$

(1) *Section Defined by*
ACI Sec. 1002(c)(3) ---   *Edge of Drop*

$$V_Q = [22(26) - 8.83(10.17)] \ 0.437 = 211^k$$

$$v = \frac{V}{bjd} = \frac{211,000}{2(8.83) + 10.17)(12)(\frac{7}{8})(9)}$$

$$= 59 \ psi, \ < 90. \quad O.K. \ since \ can't \ make \ drop \ smaller.$$

$9'' = d$
$45°$
4.5^D
$10\frac{1}{2}$
$7.33' \times 8.67'$
min. dimen. drop

(2) *Section Defined by*
ACI Sec. 1002(c)(2) ---   *Edge of Cap*

$$V_Q = [22(26) - \frac{\pi}{4}(6.67)^2] \ 0.437 = 235^k$$

$$v = \frac{V}{bjd} = \frac{235,000}{6.67(12)(\pi)(\frac{7}{8})(13)} = 82 \ psi.$$

Refer to Sec. 1002(c)(2)(a):

Since $6.67 > \frac{13}{2}$ and $> \frac{11}{2}$, allow. $v = 90 \ psi$
$O.K.$

$6.67'^D$
$= cap + 2d$
$13 = d$
$45°$
4.5^D
$11'$
$14\frac{1}{2}$
6.67
$13'$

ACI Sec. 1002(c)(5):
On maximum effective drop thickness
$$\frac{44'' - 27''}{4} = 4.25'', \ >4, \ \therefore O.K.$$
allowed

CONCRETE DIMENS. Slab + Drop thickness = $10\frac{1}{2}'' + 4''$
Cap = $4'-6''$ diam., Drop (min.) = $7'-4'' \times 8'-8''$

Include a clear "Data & Spec." statement of the problem, together with a scale plan and elevation sketch of the structure. Contemplate Type ——— end supports and Type ——— side supports for the edges of the strips, as assigned by the instructor. Provide dropped panels.

Perform your first trial concrete designing following the old rules for size of caps and drops, expecting to adjust them later to meet the code requirements, particularly with respect to diagonal tension stress thereat.

Design the slab and dropped panel thicknesses by half-inches, capitals by half-feet of diameter and dropped panels by feet and even inches.

Make a *clear* and *complete* sectional final design sketch at an interior column, showing all concrete dimensions decided upon, to the scale 1½ in. = 1 ft.

Name	Case	Panels, in ft.	Live Load, in psf	Name	Case	Panels, in ft.	Live Load, in psf
	a	18.6 × 22.5	195		h	16.0 × 19.0	305
	b	22.5 × 27.0	105		i	21.4 × 25.7	115
	c	19.2 × 23.0	175		j	23.0 × 27.6	100
	d	18.0 × 21.6	210		k	17.6 × 21.0	215
	e	20.0 × 24.0	150		l	19.6 × 23.4	160
	f	17.0 × 20.4	250		m	16.6 × 20.0	260
	g	20.8 × 25.0	130		n	15.6 × 18.8	335

Problem 7–10. Re-perform the concrete designing for the structure of Example 7–2 if dropped panels are not to be used. Compare your concrete yardage with that of Example 7–2, and comment.

PLATE 7–3. Shearhead reinforcement for flat-plate floors. The dropped panels and column capitals of flat-slab floor construction may be dispensed with by providing a cage of **shearhead** reinforcement about the column heads. Note that the inclined bars run substantially perpendicular to the directions of the potential diagonal tension cracks pictured on Calculation Sheet 3/7.

Such construction is known as **flat-plate** floor. It approaches the ideal, since its use decreases story heights and results in a perfectly plane ceiling surface which simplifies the duct and piped services.

The above model was made by the Bethlehem Steel Company.

7–16. Designing the Flat-Slab Steel. Two examples of routine designing for flexural steel content appear on Calculation Sheet 4/7 as items (1) and (3), namely, the calculation of the top and bottom reinforcement for a typical long-span column strip. The calculations for the rest of the sections are shown in condensed tabular form on Sheet 5/7.

The full width of strips is taken in designing the steel, except for the negative reinforcement of the column strips, where b is limited to the width of the dropped panel. For orientation refer early to the final design sketch of Calculation Sheet 6/7.

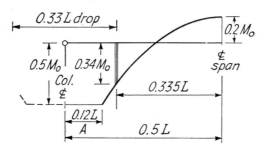

FIG. 7–5. Bending moment at edge of drop in typical interior panel, after DiStasio.

Flexure at the Edge of the Dropped Panel. Although earlier editions of the Code required that reinforcement should be provided to resist the bending stresses at all sections, they did not direct attention to sections other than the positive moment section at midspan and the negative moment section over the line of column centers.

In Fig. 7–5, let us consider the typical interior span and supports of a column strip, as DiStasio did. The moments at midspan and at the supports are, from the tabulated coefficients of the Code, $0.20M_o$ and $0.50M_o$, respectively. Since the *elastic method* considers the maximum negative moment to exist over a carefully defined distance $2A$ [Sec. 1002(b)], which is somewhat greater than the diameter of the column capital, consider the distance A to be 0.12 L. If now a minimum dropped panel of 0.33 L be considered, the moment at the edge thereof will be found, by offsets from the tangent to the parabolic moment diagram, to be $0.34M_o$. This is 68 per cent of the negative moment over the columns, and 170 per cent of the positive moment at midspan, where the same $10\frac{1}{2}$-in. slab thickness prevails!

In study (2), on Calculation Sheet 4/7, this $0.34 M_o$ negative moment was used to calculate the area of negative reinforcement required at the edge of the drop. It proved to be just slightly less than that already computed in study (1) for the section over the columns. Thus we see

PLATE 7–4. Long span ribbed-type flat-slab construction. The columns are on 50 by 51½ ft. centers. Note that instead of using dropped panels, the recesses near the columns were simply filled in, thus providing diagonal tension resistance.

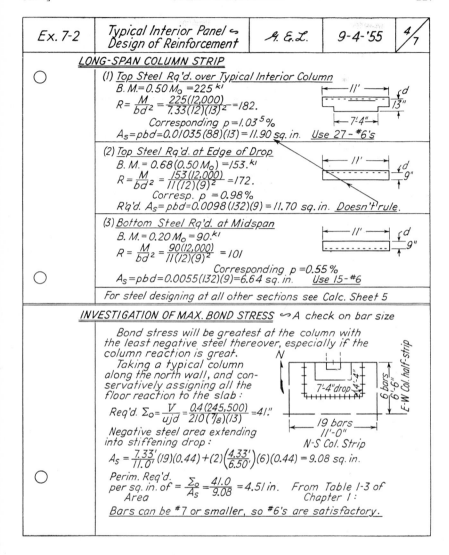

Ex. 7-2	Typical Interior Panel ↪ Design of Reinforcement	$\mathcal{A}. \mathcal{E}. \mathcal{L}.$	9-4-'55	4/7

LONG-SPAN COLUMN STRIP

(1) *Top Steel Rq'd. over Typical Interior Column*

$B.M. = 0.50 M_o = 225^{ki}$

$R = \dfrac{M}{bd^2} = \dfrac{225(12,000)}{7.33(12)(13)^2} = 182.$

Corresponding $p = 1.03^5 \%$

$A_s = pbd = 0.01035(88)(13) = 11.90$ sq. in.   *Use 27 - #6's*

(2) *Top Steel Rq'd. at Edge of Drop*

$B.M. = 0.68(0.50 M_o) = 153.^{ki}$

$R = \dfrac{M}{bd^2} = \dfrac{153(12,000)}{11(12)(9)^2} = 172.$

Corresp. $p = 0.98 \%$

R'q'd. $A_s = pbd = 0.0098(132)(9) = 11.70$ sq. in.   *Doesn't rule.*

(3) *Bottom Steel Rq'd. at Midspan*

$B.M. = 0.20 M_o = 90.^{ki}$

$R = \dfrac{M}{bd^2} = \dfrac{90(12,000)}{11(12)(9)^2} = 101$

Corresponding $p = 0.55 \%$

$A_s = pbd = 0.0055(132)(9) = 6.64$ sq. in.   *Use 15 - #6*

For steel designing at all other sections see Calc. Sheet 5

INVESTIGATION OF MAX. BOND STRESS ↪ A check on bar size

Bond stress will be greatest at the column with the least negative steel thereover, especially if the column reaction is great.

Taking a typical column along the north wall, and conservatively assigning all the floor reaction to the slab:

Req'd. $\Sigma_o = \dfrac{V}{ujd} = \dfrac{0.4(245,500)}{210(7/8)(13)} = 41.''$

Negative steel area extending into stiffening drop:

$A_s = \dfrac{7.33'}{11.0'}(19)(0.44) + (2)\left(\dfrac{4.33'}{6.50'}\right)(6)(0.44) = 9.08$ sq. in.

Perim. Req'd. per sq. in. of Area $= \dfrac{\Sigma_o}{A_s} = \dfrac{41.0}{9.08} = 4.51$ in.   From Table 1-3 of Chapter 1:

Bars can be #7 or smaller, so #6's are satisfactory.

that *the t_2 formula* used in Calculation Sheet 1/7 to compute the required slab thickness at midspan *was actually devised to call for enough slab thickness at the edge of the drop so that the negative steel provided over the column where the thickness is greater would usually also safely reinforce the section at the edge of the drop.*

In checking *exterior* spans, the same 68 per cent coefficient may be applied to the greater negative moment of $0.56 M_o$ there existing.

| Ex. 7-2 | Tabular Designing of Flat Slab Reinforcement | J. E. L. | 9-4-'55 | 5/7 |

Type B end supports and Type 3 side supports for edges of strips. $M_{oL} = 450.^{kl}$ $7\frac{1}{2}''$ drop dimen. $M_{oB} = 362.^{kl}$ $8\frac{2}{3}''$ drop dimen.

Slab Type	Strip	Bar Loca.	26-ft. Span Reinf. in N-S Strips 11 ft. Wide							22-ft. Span Reinf. in E-W Strips 13 ft. Wide						
			B.M. Coeff. of Mo	B.M. kl	Actual d in.	R	p %	Per Strip As	Per Strip Bar Choice	B.M. Coeff. of Mo	kl	Actual d in.	R	p %	Per Strip As	Bar Choice
Typ. Inter. Panels & Supports	Col.	Top	-0.50†	225	13.0	182.	1.035	11.90	27-#6	-0.50†	181.	13.0	124	0.69	9.33	21-#6
		Bot.	+0.20	90.0	9.0	101	0.55	6.54	15-#6	+0.20	72.4	9.0	68.8	0.37	5.20	12-#6
	Mid.	Top	-0.15	67.5	9.0	75.8	0.42	4.99	12-#6	-0.15	54.3	9.0	51.5	0.27	3.79	9-#6
		Bot.	+0.15	67.5	9.0	75.8	0.42	4.99	12-#6	+0.15	54.3	9.0	51.5	0.27	3.79	9-#6
North Exter. Panels & Supports	Col.	Inter. Top	-0.56†	252	13.0	203	1.17	13.40	31-#6	Same as for Typical Interior Panel Column Strip						
		Bot.	+0.24	108	9.0	121	0.67	7.93	18-#6							
		Ext. Top	-0.36†	162	13.0	131	0.73	8.36	19-#6							
	Mid.	Inter. Top	-0.17	76.5	9.0	86	0.47	5.59	13-#6	Same as for Typical Interior Panel Middle Strip						
		Bot.	+0.20	90.0	9.0	101	0.56	6.63	15-#6							
		Ext. Top	-0.20	90.0	9.0	101	0.56	6.63	15-#6							
Supports	□Wall	Top	-0.13†	58.5	13.0	94.4	0.52	2.97	7-#6							
		Bot.	+0.05	22.5	9.0	50.5	0.27	1.60	4-#6							
West Exter. Panels & Supports	Col.	Inter. Top	Same as for Typical Interior Panel Column Strip							-0.56†	203	13.0	139	0.775	10.50	24-#6
		Bot.								+0.24	87	9.0	82.6	0.45	6.32	15-#6
		Ext. Top								-0.36†	130.4	13.0	88.8	0.49	6.61	15-#6
	Mid.	Inter. Top	Same as for Typical Interior Panel Middle Strip							-0.17	61.5	9.0	58.5	0.315	4.41	10-#6
		Bot.								+0.20	72.4	9.0	68.8	0.37	5.21	12-#6
		Ext. Top								-0.20	72.4	9.0	68.8	0.37	5.21	12-#6
Supports	□Wall	Top								-0.13†	47.1	13.0	64.4	0.35	2.40	6-#6
		Bot.								+0.05	18.1	9.0	34.5	0.25*	1.76	4-#6

† An alternate calculation at the edge of the drop, using 68% as much B.M., called for less reinforcement, in this case

* Specified minimum. See ACI Sec. 702 (e)(2)

□ Half-strip

Tabular Designing of Reinforcement. Referring to Calculation Sheet 5/7, the upper right-hand portion of the table shows the calculation of the steel for the typical short-span strips, using the smaller M_o value.

Most of the work centers about the exterior panels where the particular end and side conditions of the strips call for special moment coefficients.

Reinforcement of Exterior Panels. As shown in the table of ACI Sec. 1004(f), a choice of deep marginal beams will mean Type B *end support* for the strips perpendicular thereto, and probably Type 3 *side support* for the half-strip parallel thereto. Concentrating upon the North Exterior Panels of the tabulation, we see that both the column and middle N–S strips thereof must be studied at three sections, namely, the negative moment section just north of the interior column, the midspan positive moment section and the negative moment section at the north exterior wall. Note that the interior moment section required 31–#6 bars, the most heavily reinforced point in the floor system. Refer also to the final design sketch of Calculation Sheet 6/7.

In this case, the half-strips parallel to and immediately adjacent to the north wall required only a minimum amount of reinforcement because the marginal beam, acting as a side support, will be assigned a large share of the panel floor load.

Due to lack of information upon the type and weight of the exterior wall also to be carried by such beams, they will not be designed here, though preliminary calculations indicate about a 9 to 10-in. width.

Maximum Bond Stress. Since exterior columns tend to have a relatively small amount of top steel thereover, a (rough) bond stress check upon the bar size earlier selected should be made thereat. This was done in the lower portion of Calculation Sheet 4/7 in a manner similar to the around-the-column diagonal tension studies of Sheet 3/7. Note that the edge of the stiffening dropped panel was considered the supporting element, and that only the bars crossing it entered the calculation. Since the column is at the end of a long N–S continuous system its load was considered to be closely 0.4 of the panel load.

A similar check was made about a *typical interior* column. The result was that #8 bars or smaller could be used, as was expected for this less critical situation.

The decreased allowable bond stress of $0.07f'_c$ used in both cases should be taken because the concrete shrinkage phenomenon dictates that the placing of the column concrete should be temporarily discontinued at the base of the capital. This means that there will be more than 12 in. of plastic concrete below the top bars in question after placing has been resumed, and that the footnote to the allowable stresses table of ACI Sec. 305 applies.

Openings in Flat Slabs. One of the few disadvantages of flat slab construction is the difficulty in designing around holes in such floors. Consequently, if a floor is to have a good many openings, some other type of construction involving girders and numerous beams should be considered, as they can serve to reinforce the boundaries of the openings.

Holes not over 2 ft. in diameter in the flat slab itself can be dealt with by simply spreading the reinforcement around them.

7–17. Arrangement of the Reinforcement. The designing of the reinforcement for continuous slabs involves the consideration of the following six items:

(1) The required steel area.
(2) The required bar perimeter.
(3) The location of the contraflexure points.
(4) The points where bars are to be bent up.
(5) The portion of the bottom steel to be bent up.
(6) The terminations, or endings, of the bars.

We are now principally concerned with the latter four items. The steel arrangement finally chosen is shown in the design sketch on Calculation Sheet 6/7. For quick reference, the number of bars required at each *design section* of the panel strips has been conveniently placed in a small square, all taken from Calculation Sheet 5/7. Some ingenuity is necessary in arranging the steel from panel to panel. Since more is needed over the columns than at midspan, more than half must be bent up, or short top bars provided, or both. It is very helpful at the outset to draw the boundary lines of the panel strips through the quarter points of all spans and to regard them as the locations of the contraflexure points, at which the steel may be bent up.

The 1956 ACI regulations for flat-slab bar bendings and endings have been incorporated into Fig. 7–6, assuming that dropped panels are involved. It is believed to be self-explanatory.

Contrary to the former practice of hooking all top bars at the extreme ends of a floor system, the present practice is to provide *full anchorage*, measured from the inside face of the marginal beam or wall. This can usually be achieved without hooking, though some bending is often required, as pictured in Fig. 7–6. For our 3000-lb. concrete, either 17 or 24 diam. of anchorage will be required, depending upon how great a height of concrete is to stand plastic below the horizontal portion of the bar. Refer to the table of ACI Sec. 305.

7–18. Quantity Comparison of the Three Types of Floor Designs. Table 7–2 shows clearly that for the span and loading condition taken, flat-slab construction, in comparison with the other two types of floors studied, is decidedly the most economical of steel. This is partly the

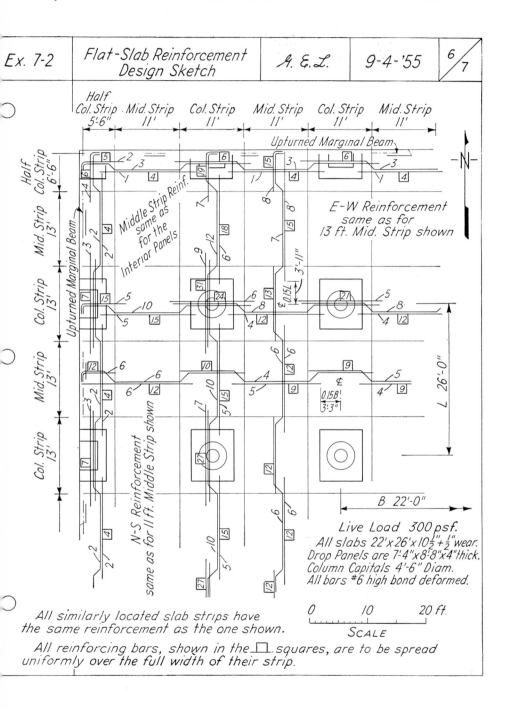

Ex. 7-2 — Flat-Slab Reinforcement Design Sketch — *A. E. L.* — 9-4-'55 — 6/7

Live Load 300 psf.
All slabs 22'x26'x10½"+½"wear.
Drop Panels are 7'-4"x8'-8"x4"thick.
Column Capitals 4'-6" Diam.
All bars #6 high bond deformed.

0   10   20 ft.
SCALE

All similarly located slab strips have the same reinforcement as the one shown.

All reinforcing bars, shown in the ⊡ squares, are to be spread uniformly over the full width of their strip.

result of having the greater slab thickness required by the present ACI Code, which caused the flat-slab construction to require the *most* concrete. This cost is considerably offset by the much simpler formwork of

TABLE 7–2

SUMMARY AND COMPARISON OF ESTIMATED QUANTITIES OF CONCRETE AND STEEL REQUIRED FOR A TYPICAL INTERIOR 22 × 26-FT. PANEL OF FLOOR UNDER 300-PSF LIVE LOAD

Item	One-Way Slab plus Beams and Girders	Two-Way Slab plus Girders	Flat-Slab Construction
References:	Example 6–1	Example 7–1	Example 7–2
CONCRETE (cu. yd.)			
Slab*	7.03	13.20	18.50
Beams (stems)	5.60	—	—
Girders (stems)	2.53	5.06	—
Drop Panel	—	—	0.74
Column Capital †	—	—	0.40
	15.16	18.26	19.64
Less volume of reinf. steel	−0.28	−0.34	−0.19
Net (cu. yd.)	14.88	17.92	19.45
REINFORCING STEEL (lb.)			
Slab: flexure	907	2785	2460
temp.	121	—	—
Beams: flexure	1645	—	—
stirrups	23	—	—
Girders: flexure	787	1442	—
stirrups	180	315	—
Net (lb.)	3663	4542	2460

* Exclusive of ½-in. wearing surface.
† The portion beyond the limits of the column proper.

flat-slab construction. The two-way system, due to its long spans and expensive simplifying approximations, has more steel in its slab than there is in the whole flat-slab construction. The strictly column concrete was eliminated from the study in all cases.

7–19. Multistory Column Design. In buildings, column designing begins with the evaluation of the roof loads per column and progresses downward to the footings, accepting the floor loads on the way. Roof loads are relatively light, so a different type of construction is often used at that level. In the case at hand, a thinner flat slab was designed, assuming a 40 psf snow load within the 3½-ft. parapet walls, plus the usual 20 psf live load. The roof covering was taken at 6 psf. On Cal-

Story	Source of Load	Axial Loads – in kips			Unbal. Floor Jt. Mom. –in k₁	e –in.	Column selected Ref. Ex. 4-5	Concrete Ag –sq.in.	p –%	fa/Fa	Bending I uncrack transf. –in.⁴	fb/Fb	Sum of Stress Ratios
		D.L.	L.L.	N total									
	Roof Slab & tower	50.0	34.3		⅓ share of,								
	Drop	2.4											
	3' Cap	0.4											
4th	Total @ Col.top	52.8	34.3	87.1	22.3	3.07	16"diam 6-#6 bars spirals 3/8φ @1¾ c.c.	201	1.31	0.43	3613	0.44	0.87 = best possible
	Est. Col. wt.	2.2			(14.0)								
	Total @ Col.base	55.0	34.3										
	4th Fl. Slab	75.0	170.5*										
	Drop	3.2											
	4½ Cap	2.0											
3rd	Total @ Col. top	135.2	204.8	340.0	97.0	3.42	24"diam 12-#11 bars spirals 3/8φ@2"c.c.	452	4.14	0.50	22340	0.46	0.96
	Est. Col. wt.	4.4			(39.0)								
	Total @ Col. base	139.6	204.8										
	3rd Fl. Slab †	75.0	136.5†										
	Drop	3.2											
	Cap	1.9											
2nd	Total @ Col. top	219.7	341.3	561.0	72.0	1.54	28"diam 10-#11 bars spirals 3/8φ@2"c.c.	616	2.53	0.77	39460	0.23	1.00
	Total @ Col. base	( )	( )										
	etc.						etc.						

▲ Intermediate grade L.L. @ 100%
* L.L. @ 100%

□ – Hard grade vertical bars at 50,000 psi.y.p. used in the columns.
† – L.L. of 80% of 170.5ᵏ applied, following Art. 6-2.

Multistory Interior Column

R — All drops 7'-4" by 8'-8" — 16"D — 10.3' — 3' diam — 3½" 9½"
4 — All 1½" — 10½" 2½+½ — 4 — 10½+½
3 — 24"D — 9.4' — All 4'-6"diam unless otherwise noted — All 12' — 10½+½
2 — 28"D — 9.25' — 4 — 10½+½

culation Sheet 7/7, a 6½-in. slab with 3½-in. drops was taken, and a very small capital resulted.

It is best to keep the vertical steel content of columns below 2 to 2½ per cent whenever possible. This will avoid spacing difficulties at the splices, which are made just above each floor. Although a maximum of 8 per cent is permitted in spiral columns, such a quantity cannot be gotten into a single ring of bars.

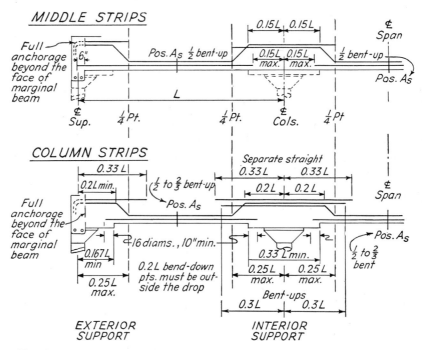

FIG. 7–6. Guide for bar bendings and endings when dropped panels are used. From 1956 ACI Sec. and Table 1004(g).

Round columns should be designed to even whole inches of diameter to suit the steel forms used. An even number of vertical bars should be taken. In the larger columns the bar centers diameter will usually turn out about 5 in. smaller than the diameter of the column (ACI Sec. 507). To prevent excessive offsetting of the bars at splices, avoid, where possible, more than a 6-in. increase in column diameter per story. Refer to the *ACI Manual of Standard Practice for Detailing Reinforced Concrete Structures.*

7–20. Interior Column Designing. In Calculation Sheet 7/7 the dead and live loads shown are slightly greater than heretofore used because they are based upon the *whole* area of the panel, rather than the portion outside the column capitals.

The panel moment, M_o, of the empirical method of flat-slab design was purposely[A,B] set large enough to allow for the expected increase under partial live loading, so far as *floor* designing is concerned. For flat-slab *column designing*, the 1956 ACI Code, Sec. 1004(b)(2), requires that interior columns be proportioned to resist their axial load plus a live* load panel moment at the floor joint of $\frac{1}{40}W_LL$ from one adjacent panel of live loading W_L, in proportion to their respective stiffnesses. For example, the third story column is to be designed for

$$\frac{I_3/h_3}{(I_3/h_3) + (I_4/h_4)} = \frac{22{,}340/9.4}{(22{,}340/9.4) + (3613/10.3)} = 87.5\%$$

of the moment at the floor joint, so:

$$M_3 = 0.875[(\tfrac{1}{40})170.5](26) = 97. \text{ kip-ft.}$$

Upon examining the moment column of the tabulation one sees that the moment at the top of any chosen column is much greater than at the bottom, while the axial loads differ only slightly in the reverse sense, so the upper end is always the more critical.

For the special case of the top of the column supporting the roof:

$$M_4 = \tfrac{1}{40}(34.3)(26) = 22.3 \text{ kip-ft.}$$

The last six columns of Calculation Sheet 7/7 show in each case the *interaction* stress investigation of the column finally selected. The designing operation was performed as in Example 4–5 of Art. 4–14, but was greatly facilitated by early reference to the column tables of pages 235 and 317 of the 1952 *Design Handbook* of the Concrete Reinforcing Steel Institute.

Column Live Load Reduction. Since the second-story column carries two *floors* of live load, reference to the table of Art. 6–2 showed that it is permissible to design it for only 90 per cent of the live load of two full floors. As the fourth-floor load had already been put into the tabulation at the full value of 170.5 kips, only 80 per cent of the third-floor load was compensatingly included. The first-story column load is subject to a greater reduction in the same manner. Since no new situation will arise, the work was discontinued at this point.

Comments. Had the floor been of the slab, beam, and girder type, as in Chapter 6, the moments at the ends of the columns might have been gotten by the *cut-out moment distribution* procedure demonstrated therein, and the story-to-story column designing otherwise performed as in Sheet 7/7 herein. Observe also that as the axial load becomes great in the lower stories the bending moment is of lesser relative importance.

---

* For exterior columns use live load plus dead load, and change the coefficient from $\frac{1}{40}$ to $\frac{1}{30}$.

(Courtesy Inland Steel Co.)

PLATE 7-5. Flat-slab reinforcing steel in place, ready for the concreting operation. Note the spiral column reinforcement and the form for the column capital. Small plain rod *high chairs* support the

Note that hard grade vertical steel is an economy in columns, as stronger concrete would also be.

A practice of holding column outside dimensions constant throughout more than one story has developed, but it seldom avoids the splicing of bars at each floor level. For typical illustrations of splicing see Dwg. 25 of the ACI *Manual of Standard Practice for Detailing Concrete Structures.*

7-21. Exterior Column Designing. The respects in which exterior column designing differs from that of interior ones will be pointed out and a procedure outlined, but a numerical example will not be presented.

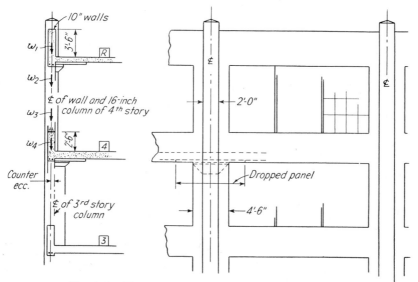

Fig. 7-7. Exterior column wall loads and eccentricities.

The principal difference is in the details of finding the loads and bending moments upon the exterior column. The typical *additional* loads are the *wall loads* due to the dead weight of the roof parapet, the spandrel (marginal) beams, the bits of exterior wall and the weight of the windows, as shown by the arrows in Fig. 7-7. These four items often have centers of gravity externally eccentric to the central axis of the column in question and thus produce reverse moments which tend to erase some of the unbalanced floor-joint moment with which the student is already familiar.

The columns themselves are built rectangular, the capitals being portions of inverted pyramids of the same lateral dimension as the diameter of the corresponding interior capitals. If exposed, as in Fig. 7-7, the columns should present the same face width from top to bottom of the structure, and project beyond the walls 2 or 3 in. for best appear-

PLATE 7-6. *Column head* diagonal tension reinforcement for flat-slab construction, as devised by Mr. Walter H. Wheeler, consulting engineer of Minneapolis. It eliminates the necessity for column capitals and dropped panels, and makes possible a perfectly smooth ceiling. Structural steel or reinforced concrete columns are used.

ance. Being laterally tied columns, the factor 0.8 must be applied in their strength calculations. All such exposed columns should have an additional half-inch of cover for the reinforcement, namely, the 2 in. mentioned in ACI Code Sec. 507.

Axial Loading. The live-load item to be added at each floor will have a value not over half of the corresponding typical interior column item, because only the outer half-panel is tributary.

When a column of assumed dimensions is being tried for *axial strength*, its floor live load is added to the additional wall loads mentioned above, and to the familiar dead load of all slabs, drops, caps, and columns carried to get N, the design axial load, from which the stress ratio f_a/F_a is computed, as formerly.

Bending Action. The *unbalanced floor joint moment* to be computed will be much greater than the 111-kip-ft. value used at the interior columns of the example. This is because (a) the *dead* load of the exterior floor panel is unbalanced and must here be included in the bending formula along with the live load, and (b) the coefficient of the formula is to be increased from $\frac{1}{40}$ to $\frac{1}{30}$. At this point the reader is reminded that a single *full* panel of floor load is taken to compute the floor *joint* moment. This moment is subject to being decreased somewhat by the moment of the wall loads now to be discussed.

As one proceeds downward in the building, the sectional depth of exterior columns increases, as shown exaggeratedly in Fig. 7–7, causing them to project farther into the structure, as do their central axes. This displacement is the principal source of the development of the helpful *reverse moments*, each of which is the product of the weight of an item of wall above the level in question multiplied by its eccentricity with respect to the central (bending) axis of the column being designed.

The algebraic sum of the unbalanced *floor* moment and the *wall* reverse moments gives the net moment, which is to be divided between the column ends above and below the floor joint in proportion to the column stiffnesses. The bending stress ratio f_b/F_b may then be computed and added to the axial stress ratio, as formerly.

Comment. It is sometimes practicable to locate exterior columns several feet inside the exterior wall, so that the reverse moment of the overhanging portion will practically erase the large unbalanced floor-joint moment, and so permit the exterior columns to be the same size and shape as the interior ones. Refer to photographic Plate 6–2 of Chapter 6.

7–22. Summary of Flat-Slab Designing. Flat-slab floor construction consists of continuous slabs supported on columns with enlarged heads called capitals, or *caps*. The slab is often thickened at the column to form a dropped panel, or *drop*.

When (a) the floor is continuous for at least three panels in each direction, (b) the ratio of length to width of panel does not exceed 1.33, (c) the successive span lengths in each direction differ from the longer by not more than 20 per cent, and (d) the structure is not over 125 ft. high, the Code moment coefficients may be used in designing.

Reinforced in both directions, flat slabs develop a two-way flexural resistance both in compression and tension, which makes them quite efficient.

The slab must be designed thick enough to meet flexural strength requirements at all sections, including those at the edges of the dropped panel.

The slab plus drop thickness must be enough to resist safely the diagonal tension which surrounds the columns, usually without the use of stirrups.[D]

The variation in concrete compressive stress across the width of floor strips is offset, in computing slab thickness, by using only three-fourths of the actual width in the beam formula. This greater slab thickness also helps to prevent excessive deflection.

The reinforcing bar size must be chosen small enough to keep bond stresses within the allowable. They tend to be high at the column heads, and particularly so at exterior ones.

Bar arrangements should usually include bent-up as well as straight bars, all of whose lengths and bend-up points have been set with quarter-point contraflexure in mind.

All top bars must be fully anchored at the edges of the floor system, by bending if necessary. The standard hook, as such, is no longer required.

The design live load for multistory columns is subject to reduction in the lower stories, depending upon the improbability of all floors being fully loaded at the same instant.

The possible unbalanced moment at an interior floor joint must be safely resisted by the columns immediately above and below it in the ratio of their stiffnesses.

Exterior columns are subject to additional bending moments due to the eccentricity of wall loads with respect to the column axis. They usually tend to decrease the large dead plus live floor panel moment to which such columns are subject.

BIBLIOGRAPHY

A) WESTERGAARD, H. M., and SLATER, W. A. Moments and Stresses in Slabs, *Proc. American Concrete Institute*, 1921, Vol. 17, p. 415 ff.

B) WESTERGAARD, H. M. Formulas for the Design of Rectangular Slabs and Supporting Girders, *Proc. American Concrete Institute*, 1926, Vol. 22, p. 26.

C) SEELY, FRED B. *Resistance of Materials.* New York John Wiley & Sons, pp. 349–53.

D) Shearhead Reinforcement for Flat Plate Floors, *Modern Developments in Reinforced Concrete*, 1948, No. 22, published by the Portland Cement Association, Chicago.

E) DISTASIO, JOSEPH, SR., and VAN BUREN, MAURICE P. An analysis of the 1956 ACI Code formulae for the design of girderless floors. Scheduled for publication by the American Concrete Institute.

FLAT–SLAB QUESTIONS

1. Define the terms capital, drop, M_o, column strip, middle strip, marginal beam.

2. What several limitations are there upon the use of the Code moment coefficients for flat slab design?

3. Do flat slabs or two-way slabs carry a greater bending moment in the shorter direction, or do both?

4. What are the two principal steps in the design of a flat-slab floor?

5. In flat-slab design, what portions of the whole floor panel load is considered (a) to bend the slab, (b) to shear the slab, (c) to cause bond stress?

6. Why is only three-fourths of the width of the strip or dropped panel used in the flexure formula to set slab thickness? What width is used when designing the steel?

7. Tell in detail how to examine a flat slab floor design for unit diagonal tension stress.

8. As now being designed, is there a possibility of a column strip being unsafe in flexure at intermediate points other than the edge of the dropped panel? Explain.

9. Tell in detail how to determine the load and bending moment for the design of an interior column of a flat slab or other rigid frame type of building.

10. Explain why rigid frame columns carrying only a roof construction have to be so large.

11. Enumerate the detailed respects in which the designing of an exterior column for a rigid frame building differs from that of an interior one.

FLAT–SLAB AND COLUMN PROBLEMS

Problem 7–11. (*Individual*) *Design of Flat-Slab Floor Steel.* Design the reinforcement for your flat-slab floor, the concrete dimensions of which were worked out in Problem 7–9. Work up the typical interior panel and the corresponding adjacent west exterior panel reinforcement, including that at the wall. Take high bond deformed bars.

Tabulate your calculations as in Calculation Sheet 5/7.

Demonstrate the correctness of your work by computing the area of steel required at the edge of one dropped panel, as the author did in Calculation Sheet 4/7.

Make a scale layout similar to that on Calculation Sheet 6/7, *complete* for over two panel widths north and south, and for full two-and-a-half panel widths east and west, in order to show your intended bar arrangement plan fully. The steel design of the north exterior panels is not required.

Draw the bend-up points and the bar *endings* clearly and carefully.

Identify all strips, put their widths on the drawing, as well as all the other types of information shown on Sheet 6/7.

Problem 7–12. On Calculation Sheet 4/7, consider the negative moment section of the long-span column strip: $d = 13$ in., req'd. $A_s = 11.90$ sq. in.

Using the beam chart, show how to *investigate* this section to find f_s and f_c maximum.

Problem 7–13. This problem is the same as Example 7–2 except that the live load per square foot of floor is only 100 psf. Design the concrete and steel for a typical interior panel. Tabulate a comparison of quantities with those of Problem 7–6, a two-way design for 100-psi live load, if available, or comment at length upon your findings.

Problem 7–14. Referring to Calculation Sheet 7/7, design the typical interior column for the first story.

Problem 7–15. Design the exterior columns for the fourth and third stories of the west wall of the building of Example 7–2. Take the roof live load at 20 psf and snow at 40 psf. For the other loads and dimensions refer to Fig. 7–7, Art. 7–21, Calculation Sheet 7/7, or the instructor.

CHAPTER 8

FOOTINGS

8–0. Introduction. From an engineering standpoint, a structure consists of the **superstructure** and the substructure or **foundation.** The former is the portion which is entirely above the ground surface, while

Dr. A N. Talbot, 1857–1942, Professor of Municipal and Sanitary Engineering, University of Illinois. Active in the formation of the Engineering Experiment Station at Illinois, he began a comprehensive experimental investigation of reinforced concrete in 1903, the results of which were the foundation of the early knowledge of the subject.

The findings of his tests on footings, which established the diagonal cracking concept of their action, were highly significant.

the latter is partly above and partly below ground. The function of the foundation is to transmit the superstructure loads safely to the ground without causing undue settlement thereof.

Since foundations must not be subject to destruction by rot, insects, or borers, concrete is now almost universally used. The upper part consists of a *foundation wall* or a column-like *pedestal;* the flat lower portion, resting directly on earth, is called the **footing**. The function of the latter is **to distribute a concentrated load** *to the ground at a safe unit pressure called the* **bearing value** *or "bearing power."*

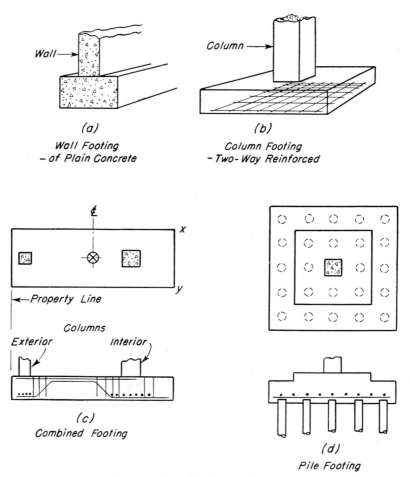

Fɪɢ. 8–1(a) to (d). Types of footing.

When a structure is to be built upon sound rock, no footing or excavation is necessary. The great majority of structures rest upon earth, which varies greatly in bearing value. In the northern United States proper, the bases of footings must be located from 3 to 5 ft. below the exposed ground surface to prevent their dislocation by frost action.

Additional excavation is often necessary in order to get down to firm bearing. Other factors being equal, the deeper a stratum, the greater its safe bearing value, since all strata have been naturally compacted by the weight of the overburden.

Figure 8–1 illustrates the five most common types of footings. They are shown in the order of their suitability to progressively poorer ground conditions. For light loads and good soil bearing values, a plain concrete

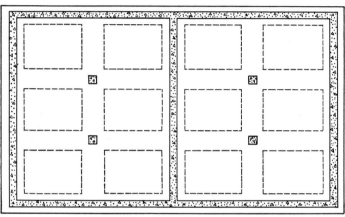

Sec. X-X

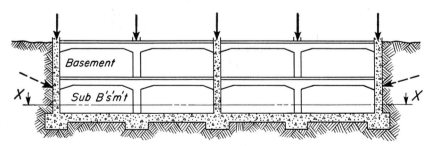

Fig. 8–1(e). Rigid frame foundation.

wall footing, (a), serves very well. The reinforced concrete *two-way,* or **column footing,** (b), is common for supporting interior columns of either steel or concrete. A *pedestal,* Fig. 8–16, serves to spread the load coming upon the footing and to take up the variation in footing elevation over the building site. **Combined footings,** (c) in Fig. 8–1, become necessary adjacent to property lines, or whenever footings tend to overlap. If the position of end *xy* is restricted also, or if the exterior column carries the heavier load, a trapezoidal shape becomes necessary. A **pile footing,** (d), is a footing whose load is transferred to firm earth or rock at a lower level by means of piles. A **rigid frame foundation,** as at (e), is a large, well-braced, boxlike structure of reinforced concrete designed to support a whole building on soil of low bearing value and also to resist earth and water pressure. The removal of enough earth to offset the weight of the structure is a feature of such designs. It is fundamentally a boat.

8–1. The Action of Earth Under Load. Since all ground settles more or less when load is applied, it should be considered as a spongelike mass which compresses as the load squeezes the water out. At one end of the scale of soil classification we find **clay,** which consists of very small soil particles with correspondingly small diameter void channels between them. Such a soil usually has a large percentage of water-filled voids from which the water cannot readily escape because of the constricted channels. Consequently, clay soils settle slowly, but for a very long time, and therefore a great deal. A low **bearing value** is assigned to soft clay, as shown in Table 8–(1).

TABLE 8–1

Tentative Safe Soil Bearing Values of the Boston Building Code

Material	Tons per sq. ft.
Rock (variable)	100 to 35
Shale or hardpan	10
Gravel or sand-gravel mixture	
compact	5
loose	4
Sand	
coarse and loose, or fine and compact	3
fine and loose	1
Clay	
hard	6
medium	4
soft	1

Sand, which consists of comparatively large (rock) particles, is at the other end of the scale. (Most common soils fall between the above mentioned extremes.) Large particles mean large diameter void channels, or pipes, from which water escapes easily under the pressure of the load. Therefore a sandy soil settles very quickly. Unless it is very loose at the outset, the total settlement to be expected is very small compared to that of clay.

Gravel, which may be thought of as an extremely coarse sand, makes an excellent foundation. It must, however, be confined, just like sand. It is literally a rock pile.

Shale is a clay which has been compressed by nature to the state of a weak rock. Some shales disintegrate rather quickly upon exposure to the air.

In the absence of data from *borings* taken at the building site, and comprehensive *soil tests*, including particle size analysis, load tests, consolidation and shear tests on undisturbed samples, the accompanying table of conservative safe bearing values may be used (Table 8–1).

Each footing should be proportioned for a uniform distribution of soil pressure if possible. Furthermore, the whole group of footings for a given structure should have relative bearing areas conducive to uniform settlement throughout. Unequal settlements cause cracking and even failure of structures.

8–2. Footing Calculations. It is customary to consider a footing rigid, and the supporting earth elastic. This means that the centrally loaded footing of Fig. 8–2 is assumed to be supported by a uniform soil pressure, even though, due to bending, the pressure may actually be smaller at the edges. If the load is applied eccentrically, but within the middle third of the width, a straight line variation of earth pressure is considered to exist across the width of the footing. (Compare with reinforced concrete columns, Chapter 4, under direct load and bending.) If the load, or **resultant force,** is outside the middle third, the pressure will be greatest along the side nearest the force and will decrease to zero at some undetermined point within the footing width. Obviously, tension cannot exist unless the footing is a pile footing.

Since a plastic mass of concrete conforms perfectly to the irregularities of the ground, the weight of the footing itself is considered to be non-existent so far as forces tending to shear or bend the footing are concerned. The decreased value of earth pressure obtained by deducting the footing dead-load pressure from the total pressure is called the **net footing pressure.** It is used in computing footing strength, but the total pressure is taken when referring to that which reposes upon the earth itself.

Although the weight of a normal backfill over a footing would appear further to decrease the shear and bending in the footing (cantilever), and increase the total pressure underneath, its effects are usually disregarded because of the probable **arching** of the backfill as the footing settles.

8–3. Plain Concrete Footings. When the loads are comparatively light and the ground conditions good, or if steel is scarce, plain concrete footings may be designed. The bending stresses in such footings are computed in the same manner as for homogeneous cantilever beams, but the shear stresses are studied somewhat differently. The lowest 2 in. of concrete tend to be of inferior quality and may be disregarded

in strength calculations, as will be seen.   (Under the Joint Committee
Specifications they *must* be disregarded.)

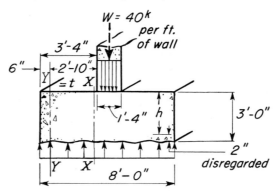

Fig. 8–2.   Plain concrete wall footing.

EXAMPLE 8–1

Investigation of a Plain Concrete Wall Footing.   **Given the unreinforced footing of Fig. 8–2, carrying a 16-in. concrete wall weighing
40 kips per ft.   The concrete is 2500 lb., ACI Specification: $f'_c = 2500$,
allowable $f_t = 0.03f'_c = 75$ psi, average vertical shear, $v = 0.02f'_c =
50$ psi, per Sec. 1207(b).**

**Assuming that the maximum safe soil bearing value is 3 tons per
sq. ft., investigate the safety of the footing.   Take the weight of plain
concrete at 145 pcf (pounds per cubic foot).**

Solution: (Taking a one-foot length of wall, b)

(a) *Soil Bearing Pressure:*

$$\tfrac{40}{8} + 3(0.145) = 5.44 \text{ ksf (kips per square foot)}$$
$$< 6.0, \textit{ therefore safe in soil bearing.}$$

(b) *Plain Concrete Bending:* At Sec. X–X, ACI Code, Sec. 1204.

$$\text{B. M.} = \frac{40}{8}(3.33)[20] = 333 \text{ k-in.}$$

$$\text{Section modulus, } Z = \frac{bh^2}{6} = \frac{12(34)^2}{6} = 2320 \text{ in.}^3$$

$$\text{Unit bending stress, } f_t = \frac{M}{Z} = \frac{333(1000)}{2320} = 143 \text{ psi}$$

$$> 75 \text{ psi.} \quad \textit{Unsafe}.$$

(c) *Plain Concrete Shear:* At Sec. Y–Y, per ACI Secs. 1205(a) and 1207(b).

$$\text{Residual } V = \frac{40}{8}\left(\frac{6}{12}\right) = 2.5 \text{ kips}$$

$$\text{Residual } v = \frac{V}{bh} = \frac{2500}{12(34)} = 6.1 \text{ psi, avg.}$$

$$< 50 \text{ psi, } \textit{safe in vertical shear.}$$

Comment. Plain concrete footings were formerly studied for an *average* vertical, or "punching shear," at the vertical section at the face of the wall in the same manner as in homogeneous cantilevers of other materials. The allowable average punching shear stress was usually $0.06f'_c$ or 150 psi for 2500-lb. concrete. By this former method, V would have been 16.7 kips in our case, and $v = \dfrac{16,700}{12(34)} = 41$ psi, which being less than 150 psi, would have been considered safe.

The close student of mechanics will recall that the *maximum* vertical (or horizontal) unit shearing stress would be $\frac{3}{2}$ of the above value.

The odd practice of studying a section located a distance from the wall equal to the depth of the footing has been carried over from *reinforced* concrete footing technology, wherein it has a real meaning, as will be seen later. When such a section of a *plain* concrete beam is studied, one should recognize that only the *residual* portion of the whole shear which is more than h inch outside the face of the wall is being computed and referred to an allowable shearing unit stress of only one-third the former value, which governed at the face of the wall.

The term *punching shear* is not even mentioned in current codes.

PLAIN CONCRETE WALL FOOTING
INVESTIGATION PROBLEMS

Problem 8–1. Find the soil bearing pressure, f_t and v in the footing of Example 8–1 if the load w is 25 kips per ft. and the wall thickness is 20 in.

Ans. 3.56 *ksf*, $f_t = 81$ *psi*, $v = 2.5$ *psi.*

Problem 8–2. Calculate for the footing of Example 8–1 the maximum tensile and shearing stress values, and their directions, by Mohr's circle construction or combined stress formulas:

(a) At 33 in. from the top of the footing,

(b) At the neutral axis, 17 in. down,

(c) At the bottom fiber.

Problem 8–3. Find the soil pressures beneath the footing of Example 8–1 if the load w is 22 kips per ft. and acts 2 in. eccentric to the middle of the footing.

Hint: Use $w/A \pm Mc/I$ as in column calculations.

Ans. 3.53 *ksf max. and* 2.85 *ksf min.*

8–4. Design of Plain Concrete Footings. A *design* procedure is illustrated in Example 8–2. The dead load of the footing may be estimated or completely ignored in the first trial design. The outside dimensions should be set in feet and whole inches, as may be seen on Dwgs. 23 and 24 of the previously mentioned ACI *Manual of Standard Practice.* An examination of the calculations will reveal that flexure will dictate the footing thickness, except when safe soil values are quite high.

A trial width having been computed in (a), the tentative flexural design proceeds in (b), following the computation of the tentative *net pressure* causing bending. The 3 ft. 10 in. total thickness found enables one to recalculate flexure in (c), using an accurate value of footing dead load to reproportion the width and revise the net pressure.

In (d) the design was checked for residual vertical shear.

EXAMPLE 8–2

Design of a Plain Concrete Wall Footing. Given the same wall load, safe soil value, and class of concrete as in Example 8–1, namely: $w = 40$

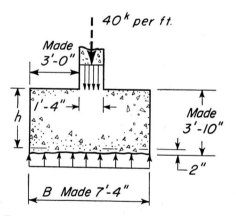

Fig. 8–3. Plain concrete wall footing design.

kips per ft., soil at 3 tons per sq. ft. and the ACI Specification: 2500-lb. concrete, with allowable stresses of $f_t = 75$ psi, and average $v = 50$ psi.

Required to properly proportion the footing for the conditions given.

Solution:

(a) *Footing Width.* Estimating the footing weight at 8 per cent of the superimposed load (later corrected):

$$\text{Required width, } B = \frac{1.08(40)}{6} = 7.2 \text{ ft.}$$

Take a 7 ft. 2 in. trial width.

(b) *Flexural Design.*

$$\text{Tentative net footing pressure} = \frac{40}{7.17} = 5.57 \text{ ksf.}$$

$$\text{B. M. at face of wall} = 5.57 \left(\frac{35}{12}\right)(17.5) = 285 \text{ kip-in.}$$

$$\text{Req'd. sec. mod.,} \quad \frac{bh^2}{6} = \frac{12h^2}{6} = \frac{M}{f_t} = \frac{285(1000)}{75}$$

Req'd. $h = 43.5$ in.,

Try 3 ft. 10 in. total thickness.

(c) *Flexure Recalculation.* (D.L. now 0.555 ksf)

$$\text{Req'd. } B = \frac{40 + 0.555B}{6} = 7.33$$

Make B = 7 ft. 4 in.

$$\text{Revised net pressure} = \frac{40}{7.33} = 5.45 \text{ ksf}$$

$$\text{B. M.} = 5.45(3)18 = 294 \text{ kip-in.}$$

$$\text{Req'd. } Z = \frac{M}{f_t} = \frac{294(1000)}{75} = \frac{12h^2}{6}$$

Req'd. $h = 44$ in.,

which is consistent with the 3 ft. 10 in. total thickness last taken.

(d) *Check for Shear.* ACI Sec. 1207(b).

Since a shear section at a distance of 44 in. from the face of the wall is outside the limits of the footing, $v = 0$, and the footing is safe.

Make footing 7 ft. 4 in. wide by 3 ft. 10 in. total thickness.

8–5. Stepped Footings. Footings are sometimes stepped or sloped in order to save concrete, or, more commonly, to clear an obstruction, as suggested by Fig. 8–4. It will be apparent from (a) that the bending moment at intermediate points along *OH* will be proportional to the square of the distance from the outer edge. Furthermore, if the upper corner of the footing were cut off down to the dashed line, the section moduli of the remaining portion would vary in the same manner, thus leaving f_t at the safe allowable value at all sections. Since the dashed line is inclined at more than 45° to the horizontal, vertical shear is not a factor. (Why?)

A small flaw exists in the above reasoning in that the net footing design pressure is no longer uniformly distributed, due to the removal of dead load.

Stepped footings must be checked for strength at every offset plane. It will be evident from Fig. 8–4(a) that, after observing the 8-in. minimum edge thickness of ACI Code, Sec. 1209(b), either the stepped form

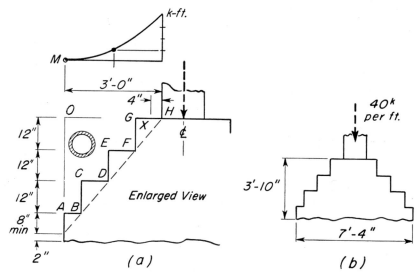

Fig. 8–4. Permissible stepping of a wall footing.

AGCDEFGH or sloped variations thereof may be adopted so long as a 4-in. minimum shelf *XH* is retained to provide a support for the wall forms. Provision also must be made to place the whole footing in one continuous operation. (Why?)

PLAIN CONCRETE–WALL FOOTING DESIGN PROBLEMS

Problem 8–4. Redesign the footing of Example 8–2, taking a safe soil value of 6 tons per sq. ft.

Ans. Make 3 ft. 5 in. wide by 2 ft. 1 in. total thickness.

Problem 8–5. Design a plain concrete wall footing for a 20-in. concrete wall carrying 60 kips per lin. ft., and 2 tons psf safe soil pressure. Use ACI 2000-lb. concrete and allowables. Comment upon your design.

Problem 8–6. Accurately redesign the footing of Example 8–2 by stepping it at the levels indicated in Fig. 8–4(a). As always, make a final design sketch to scale and show all dimensions.

Problem 8–7. (*Individual*) Given a superimposed wall load of 60 kips per lin. ft. of 20-in. wall. The safe soil bearing value is 4, 5, 6, 7, 8, 9, 10, 11, or 12 tons per sq. ft., as individually assigned. Take ACI 3000-lb. concrete and specification: $n = 10$, allowable flexural $f_t = 90$ psi, allowable (residual) average vertical shearing stress $= 60$ psi.

It is required to design the footing to the *nearest safe whole inch* of outside dimension. Take the weight of plain concrete at 145 pcf.

Provide two inches of thickness more than called for by theory, and *show it with the other dimensions* on the final design sketch. Refer to Art. 8–3.

More than one trial will usually be necessary to bring the calculations consistent with the dimensions decided upon.

If the 45°ACI shear section falls outside the limits of the footing, investigate the vertical shear unit stress at the face of the wall, and see that the former punching shear allowable of $0.06f'_c$ is not exceeded.

8–6. The Design of Reinforced Concrete Footings. For the heavier loads, massive plain concrete footings are avoided by reinforcing the concrete. Such a footing is illustrated in Fig. 8–5(a) to the same scale as the plain concrete footing previously designed for the same load in Fig. 8–3.

Diagonal tension largely governs the thickness of reinforced concrete footings. Formerly they were proportioned by the "punching shear" concept, involving a vertical shearing, as in punching holes in structural steel plate. The present practice conforms to the results of Dr. Talbot's tests[A] at the University of Illinois, published in 1913, which showed that reinforced concrete footings tend to fail in diagonal tension across the 45° lines shown in the figure, and that the maximum value thereof is to be computed at Section Y–Y, at a distance d from the face of the wall, column, or pedestal. Stirrups in wall footings are avoided by designing to a safe low value of v equal to $0.03f'_c$.

The flexure of footings under (rigid) concrete walls was found in Talbot's tests to be such that the bending moment may be computed at the face of the wall, rather than at the center thereof.

Bond stress is quite important. It is computed at the face of the concrete wall, column, or pedestal, as is flexure. The ACI Code formerly required that all footing steel be hooked, since the bond stresses tend to be high. With the advent of the high bond type of bar (ASTM A305), hooks were shown by test to be superfluous, so they are no longer demanded, except on plain (obsolete) bars.

A good design procedure, illustrated in Example 8–3, is first to establish the outside dimensions of the footing by (a) using the safe soil bearing value to get the required width, and (b) using the allowable diagonal tension stress to find the required thickness. Next (c) calculate the thickness required for flexure, and the necessary steel content, A_s. Finally, (d) select *bar size* from a systematic study of bar perimeter required for safe bond stress.

In reinforced concrete *footing design* the precise value of j should be used in diagonal tension and bond calculations when it differs appreci-

ably from the flat value of 7/8 used heretofore. Refer to the upper
portion of the beam charts of Appendix A.

EXAMPLE 8–3

Design of a Reinforced Concrete Wall Footing. Given the same
wall load, safe soil value, and class of concrete as in Example 8–1,
namely $w = 40$ kips per ft., a safe soil bearing value of 3 tons per sq. ft.,
ACI 2500-lb. concrete and specification: 20,000–1125–12, $v = 75$, and
$u = 250$ psi for high bond deformed bars in one-way footings. Secure
3 in. cover for the bars.

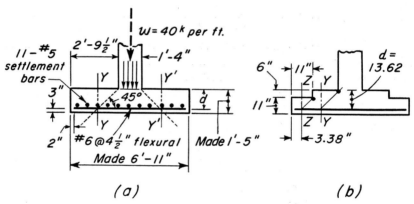

FIG. 8–5. Reinforced concrete wall footing design.

(A) Required to proportion a reinforced concrete footing, and to
tabulate a comparison of its size with the plain concrete footings of
Figs. 8–3 and 8–4.

Solution: (Refer to Fig. 8–5)

(a) *Footing Width.* Estimating the footing weight at 4 per cent of the
superimposed load:

$$\text{Required width, } B = \frac{40(1.04)}{6} = 6.92 \text{ ft.}$$

Take a trial width of 6 ft. 11 in.

(b) *Diagonal Tension.* Referring to Dr. Talbot's tests[A] and ACI Code,
Sec. 1205, design at Section Y–Y:

$$\text{Tentative net footing pressure} = \frac{40}{6.92} = 5.78 \text{ ksf.}$$

$$\text{Req'd. } d = \frac{V}{vbj} = \frac{5780(33\tfrac{1}{2} - d)}{75(12)(\tfrac{7}{8})(12)} = 12.70 \text{ in.}$$

Trying #6 bars:

$$12.7 + 0.38 + 3.00 = 16.08 \text{ in.}$$

Ref. ACI Code, Sec. 507(a).   *Try 1 ft. 5 in. total thickness.*

(c) *Flexure Designing.*

$$\tfrac{1}{2}f_c b(kd)[jd] = \text{B. M.}$$

$$563(12)(.0403)(0.866)d^2 = \frac{5780(33.5)(16.75)}{12}$$

Req'd. $d = 10.7$ in., <12.70,

Therefore, diagonal tension governs the thickness. *Make thickness 1 ft. 5 in.*

Assuming #6 bars, actual $d = 17 - 3.38 = 13.62$ in.

(a') *Width Recalculation.*
A 1-ft., 5-in. thickness makes a dead load of 0.21 ksf.

$$\text{Req'd. } B = \frac{40 + 0.21B}{6} = 6.91 \text{ ft.}$$

Make width 6 ft. 11 in. as before.

Net footing pressure stands at 5.78 ksf.

(c') *Flexure Steel.*

$$R = \frac{M}{bd^2} = \frac{5780(33.5)(16.75)}{12(13.62)^2(12)} = 121.$$

Find $p = 0.68\%$.

Required $A_s = pbd = 0.0068(12)(13.62) = 1.11$ sq. in. per ft. of wall.

(d) *Perimeter Required for Bond.*

$$\text{Required } \Sigma_o = \frac{V}{ujd} = \frac{5780(33.5)}{250(\tfrac{7}{8})(13.62)(12)} = 5.41 \text{ in. per ft. of wall.}$$

For proper bar *size* refer to Chapter 1, Table 1–3:

$$\text{Perimeter req'd. per sq. in. of area} = \frac{5.41}{1.11} = 4.87,$$

Use #6 bars.

Bar Spacing:

$$\frac{0.44(12)}{1.11} = 4.75 \text{ in.}$$

Use #6 high bond bars at $4\tfrac{1}{2}$ in. c. to c.

By ACI Code, Sec. 505(a):

$$\text{Maximum aggregate size} = \frac{3.75}{1.33} = 2.82 \text{ in.}$$

Say $1\tfrac{1}{2}$ in. aggregate.

(B) Determine whether it will be safe to "step" the above footing as shown in Fig. 8–5(b). Refer to the ACI Code, Secs. 1203 and 1209(a). Include the results in the tabular comparison of quantities.

Solution:

Diagonal Tension check at Sec. Z–Z, distant 7.62 in. from the face of the proposed stepping:

$$v = \frac{V}{bjd} = \frac{5780(3.38)}{12(\frac{7}{8})(7.62)(12)} = 20 \text{ psi}$$

$$< 75, \text{ satisfactory.}$$

Flexure check at face of step:

$$R = \frac{M}{bd^2} = \frac{5780(11)[5.5]}{(12)(7.62)^2(12)} = 42.$$

$$p = \frac{0.44}{4.5(7.62)} = 1.29\%$$

Found f_c and f_s quite low, satisfactory in flexure.

Bond check at face of step:

$$u = \frac{V}{\Sigma_o jd} = \frac{5780(11)}{\frac{12}{4.5}(\frac{3}{4})(\pi)(\frac{7}{8})(7.62)(12)} = 126 \text{ psi.} = <250, \text{ satisfactory.}$$

Therefore the proposed stepping is safe. However, the small saving in concrete in this case would be more than offset by the extra forming cost.

Final Comments. The concrete in the frustum between Secs. $Y–Y$ and $Y'–Y'$ acts mainly in compression, as distinguished from the diagonal tension action outside thereof. Between Y and Y' the horizontal frictional forces developed between the swelling concrete and the soil appear to be large enough to prevent the formation of tensile cracks.

A 3-in. minimum of protection is required between the ground of the *footing bed* and the flexure steel. For *formed* surfaces, such as at the sides of the footing, the minimum is 2 in. Refer to ACI Sec. 507(a) and to Fig. 8–5(a).

To arrive at the proper bar size, form the habit of computing the required amount of bar perimeter per square inch of bar area, and refer to the Perimeter/Area column of Table 1–3 of Chapter 1.

The occasional tendency for bond requirements to demand a number of small bars means that they must sometimes be arranged in two layers to ensure proper placing of the concrete.

Tremendous savings of concrete can accrue from using steel in footings, as is evident from Table 8–2.

TABLE 8–2

QUANTITY COMPARISON OF 40-KIP WALL FOOTING DESIGNS

Material per Foot of Wall	Plain Concrete Footings		Reinforced Concrete Footings	
	Rectangular Fig. 8–3	Stepped Fig. 8–4	Rectangular Fig. 8–5(a)	Stepped Fig. 8–5(b)
Concrete (cu. ft.)	28.1	20.1	9.8	8.9
Steel, flexural (lb.)	0	0	26.3	26.3

Settlement Reinforcement. Some reinforcement should usually be placed longitudinally of the wall to enable the structure to bridge soft spots in the foundation soil. A minimum of 0.3 per cent thereof[D] called for 11–#5 bars, or the equivalent, as shown in Fig. 8–5(a).

CONCENTRIC R/C WALL FOOTING PROBLEMS

Problem 8–8. Investigate the footing design of Example 8–3(a), assuming that the soil pressure varies parabolically to zero at the edges, as for loose sandy soil.

Problem 8–9. Redesign the reinforced concrete wall footing of Example 8–3 for a wall thickness of 24 in. Make a tabular comparison of the quantities of steel and concrete required in the two cases, and comment.

Problem 8–10. Redesign the reinforced concrete wall footing of Example 8–3 for soil bearing values of 6 and $1\frac{1}{2}$ tons per sq. ft. Study in each case the d's required for diagonal tension and flexure, and plot a curve of d_v/d_f versus soil bearing value to determine at what soil value the required depths are equal.

Problem 8–11. (*Individual*) Given the same 20-in. wall thickness, 60-kip wall load, 3000-lb. class of concrete, and safe soil bearing values of 4, 5, 6, 7, 8, 9, 10, 11, or 12 tsf, as individually assigned in Prob. 8–7.

The pertinent ACI allowable stress values are 20,000–1350–10, $v = 75$, $u = 300$ psi for the high bond bars to be used. Assume 1-in. aggregate size.

It is required to design a R/C wall footing to the nearest safe whole inch of outside dimension. The bars are to be spaced by half-inches, observing the min. spacing of ACI Sec. 505. See also Sec. 507(a). The minimum bar size is #4. Take the weight of *reinforced* concrete at 150 pcf. Refer to the table in ACI Sec. 305(a).

8–7. Nonuniform Soil Bearing. Frequently, in designing, there is more than one loading situation to be considered, in which case the footing design becomes a compromise resulting from *designing* for one situation and *investigating* it for other loading conditions. These latter situations generally cause nonuniform pressures upon the soil which must be evaluated and mitigated as much as possible. In all such cases the maximum pressure should be kept well below the uniformly loaded allowable soil pressure. The following Example 8–4 illustrates the two most common cases of investigation.

EXAMPLE 8–4

Investigations of Soil Pressures under an Eccentrically Loaded Footing. **Given** the 7-ft. wall footing pictured in Fig. 8–6.

Required to find the maximum soil pressure if the *superimposed* loading is:

(A) **Wall load 20 kips, wall moment 35 k-ft. clockwise.**

(B) **Wall load 20 kips, wall moment 60 k-ft. clockwise.**

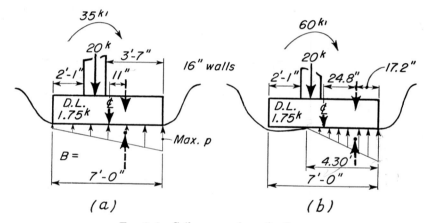

FIG. 8–6. Soil pressure investigations.

Solution (A): [Fig. 8–6(a)]. ΣM about the centerline of the footing, at the ground level, to find the position of the resultant force:

$$
\begin{array}{rcr}
1.75 \times & 0 = & 0 \\
20.00 \times (-9) = & -180 \\
12(35) = & +420 \\
\hline
21.75 \text{ k} & & 240 \text{ k-in.}
\end{array}
$$

$$\frac{240}{21.75} = 11 \text{ in. from the center}$$

$$< \frac{84}{6} \text{ or 14 in., therefore no uplift.}$$

As for columns:

$$\frac{w}{A} = \frac{21.75}{7} \qquad\qquad = 3.11 \text{ ksf}$$

$$I = \frac{bt^3}{12} = \frac{(1)(7)^3}{12} = 28.6 \text{ ft.}^4$$

$$\frac{Mc}{I} = \frac{20(3.5)}{28.6} = 2.45$$

$$Max.\ p = \overline{5.56}\ ksf = 2.78\ tsf.$$

Method:

1. Working at the ground level, locate the position of the resultant downward vertical force with reference to the kern limit of the footing width. If it falls within the kern, proceed as follows:

   a. Find the direct pressure by dividing the total vertical load by the area of the footing.

   b. Find the pressure distribution due to the moment of all the applied forces about the center of gravity of the base, using Mc/I as in columns, taking the width of the footing, B, as t, the depth of the imaginary column.

   c. Add the (a) and (b) results to get the combined soil pressure.

2. *If the resultant vertical force lies outside the kern limit of the footing,* there will be uplift. The combined soil pressure diagram will then be triangular, with its centroid directly beneath the resultant vertical force.

Solution (B): ΣM about the centerline of the footing to find the position of the resultant force:

$$
\begin{array}{rl}
1.75 \times & 0 = \quad 0 \\
20.00 \times & (-9) = -180 \\
& 12(60) = +720 \\
\hline
21.75\ k & \qquad 540\ k\text{-in.}
\end{array}
$$

$$\frac{540}{21.75} = 24.8 \text{ in. from center}$$

$$24.8 > \frac{84}{6}, \textit{ therefore, there is uplift along the left side.}$$

Referring to Fig. 8–6(b), the resultant ground reaction must be 17.2 in. from the right side.

Assuming the customary straight-line variation of pressure, and knowing that the centroid of a triangle is at one-third the distance from its base, the pressure must vary from a maximum to zero at $\dfrac{3(17.2)}{12} = 4.30$ ft. from the right side.

$$Max.\ p = \frac{21.75}{0.5(4.30)} = 10.1\ ksf = 5.05\ tsf \qquad\qquad Ans.$$

ECCENTRIC WALL FOOTING INVESTIGATION PROBLEM

Problem 8–12. Find the maximum soil pressure under the footing of Example 8–4 if:

(a) The load is 17 kips and the bending moment 42 kip-ft. clockwise.

(b) The load is 30 kips and the bending moment 32 kip-ft. counterclockwise.

(c) The loading consists only of a 35-kip wall load.

8–8. The Design of Eccentric Footings. Even when there is a moment at the base of the wall in addition to the direct vertical load, as in retaining walls and fixed-ended rigid frames, it is often possible to design a practical footing that bears uniformly upon the ground by offsetting it with respect to the wall or column. As shown in Fig. 8–7, let B be the required footing width as set by the uniform allowable soil-bearing

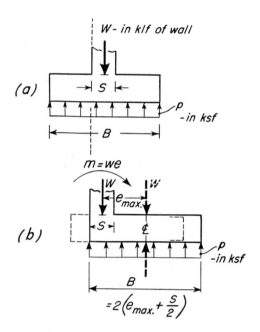

Fig. 8–7. Locating a footing eccentrically.

pressure, p, when loading w only is acting, as at (a). If a moment, m, is added, compute $e = m/w$, **the position of the resultant force,** and center the footing upon it as shown by the solid lines in (b) for the limiting case. If the moment is smaller, the footing will be less eccentric, as shown dotted. If the moment is greater than m, the footing will partially pass from under the wall unless B is arbitrarily increased.

In rigid frame buildings the bending moment at the base of exterior columns is likely to be in the direction which demands that the footing project outward considerably, as in Fig. 8–8(a). If the column abuts the property line, the footing cannot project, so a *combined footing* such as that shown in Fig. 8–13 of Art. 8–11 must be designed.

Example 8–5 illustrates how a uniform soil pressure can be achieved at the base of a fixed-ended rigid frame by designing an outwardly projecting eccentric footing.

EXAMPLE 8–5

Design of an Eccentric Reinforced Concrete (Wall-type) Footing for a Rigid Frame. **Given** the same 40-kip wall load of Example 8–3, but combined with a bending moment of 30 kip-ft. from the rigid frame action shown in Fig. 8–8(a) and (b).

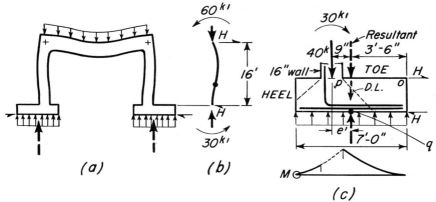

Fig. 8–8. Rigid frame footing design.

Required to design the footing for a uniform soil pressure of 3 tons per sq. ft., if uniformity is possible. Use 3000-lb. concrete. Specification: 20,000–1350–10, $v = 75$, $u = 300$ psi for deformed bars.

Solution:

(a) *Trial Footing Width*, as in Example 8–3, $= \dfrac{40(1.04)}{6} = 6.93$ ft. $=$

$$Try\ 7\ ft.\ 0\ in.$$

(a') *Offsetting of Footing.* Try for a uniform soil pressure. From Fig. 8–8(b) the shear force H at the top of the footing will be $\dfrac{60 + 30}{16} = 5.63$ kips, which produces additional moment upon the *base* plane of the footing.

Let e' be the required offsetting of the centroid of the footing with respect to the position of the 40-kip load. Then make a summation of the moments of all forces about the base point q at the centroid of the footing, estimating the footing thickness at 20 in.:

$$\overset{21}{40e' + \text{D.L.}[0] - 5.63[\cancel{20}] - 30(12) \equiv 0}$$

$$e' = \overset{11.95}{\cancel{11.82}}\ in.$$

Now $42 + \overset{11.95}{\cancel{11.82}} - 8 = \overset{45.95}{\cancel{45.82}}$ in. for *op.*

$$\cancel{Try}\ 3\ ft.\ 10\ in.\ toe.$$

TOE SIDE

(b) *Diagonal Tension.*

$$\text{Tentative net footing pressure} = \frac{40}{7.0} = 5.713 \text{ ksf.}$$

$$\text{Req'd. } d = \frac{V}{vjb} = \frac{5713(46 - d)}{75(\frac{7}{8})(12)(12)},$$

$$= 17.33 \text{ in.}$$

$$17.33 + 0.44 + 3.00 = 20.77 \text{ in.}$$

Try footing thickness at 1 ft. 9 in.

A corresponding recalculation through item (a') above yielded the marking up shown.

$$\text{Total soil pressure} = \frac{40 + 7(1.75)(0.15)}{7(2)} = 2.98 \text{ tsf.}$$

$<3.00, \therefore O.K.$

Maintain 7 ft. 0 in. footing width.
Maintain 3 ft. 10 in. toe.

(c) *Flexure Designing (toe side).*

$$\text{Req'd. } d = \sqrt{\frac{M}{Rb}} = \sqrt{\frac{5713(45.95)[22.98]}{12(236)(12)}} = 13.31 \text{ in.}$$

<17.33 *above.*

Therefore diagonal tension governs.

Make total thickness 1 ft. 9 in.

Assuming #7 bars, $d = 21 - 0.44 - 3.00 = 17.56$ in., and

$$v = \frac{17.33}{17.56}(75) = 74 \text{ psi., O.K.}$$

$$\text{Actual } R = \frac{M}{bd^2} = \frac{5713(46)[23]}{12(17.56)^2(12)} = 135.$$

Find $p = 0.75\%$.

$$\text{Req'd. } A_s = pbd = 0.0075(12)(17.56) = 1.58 \text{ sq. in. per ft. of wall.}$$

(d) *Perimeter Req'd. for Bond.* *(Toe Side)*

$$\Sigma_o = \frac{V}{ujd} = \frac{5713(46)}{300(\frac{7}{8})(17.56)(12)} = 4.74 \text{ in. per ft. of wall.}$$

For proper bar size refer to Chapter 1, Table 1–3:

$$\text{Perimeter required per sq. in. of area} = \frac{4.74}{1.58} = 3.0.$$

Can use #10 bars, or smaller.

Bar Spacing:

$$\frac{1.27(12)}{1.58} = 9.65 \text{ in.}$$

Can use #10 bars @ 9½ in., or #7's at 4½ in., c. to c.

HEEL SIDE

(e) *Flexure Design at Heel.*

$$R = \frac{M}{bd^2} = \frac{5713(22)[11]}{12(17.56)^2(12)} = 31,$$

Find p = $<0.20\%$.

By ACI Sec. 702(e)(2) we must use a min. of 0.25 per cent.

Spec. $A_s = pbd = 0.0025(12)(17.56) = 0.527$ sq. in. per ft.

This is exactly one-third of the required toe steel content.

(f) *Perimeter Req'd. for Bond (Heel Side).*

$$\Sigma_o = \frac{V}{ujd} = \frac{5713(22)}{300(0.93)(17.56)(12)} = 2.14 \text{ in. per ft. of wall.}$$

Perim. req'd. per sq. in. of area $= \dfrac{2.14}{0.527} = 4.06$ in.

From Table 1–3,   *Use #7 bars throughout the footing.*

Max. bar spacing $= \dfrac{0.60}{0.0025(17.56)} = 13.7$-in. sp'c'g.

In heel use #7 bars @ $1' - 1\frac{1}{2}''$ c. to c.

Each such bar is to alternate with bent pairs in the toe side.

8–9. Comments upon the Eccentric Footing Designing. The same four previously used design steps (a), (b), (c), and (d) were first taken in studying the *toe* side of the footing. Upon considering the *heel* for both flexure and bond it was found that bond was the critical factor, since smaller (#7) bars were required in that side. Fortunately, the area of steel required in the toe was exactly three times that needed in the heel. This meant that #7 bars could be used economically throughout. Therefore two out of every three toe bars were bent upward to act as wall dowels; the third became heel reinforcement.

The horizontal thrust, H in Fig. 8–8, of 5.63 kips is assumed to be safely resisted by the ground friction developed by the 41.84-kip vertical pressure. In case there is doubt, a trench may be cleanly excavated in the footing bed, and a *shear lug* of concrete placed, as shown dotted in Fig. 8–9. It is also possible to lay tie rods in a trench between the two footings and do the first backfilling with concrete to protect the steel.

In no case should the backfill along the side of the footing be relied upon to resist the horizontal thrust.

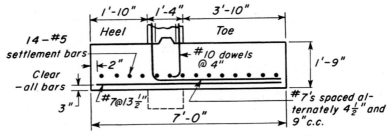

Fig. 8–9. Final design sketch. (Example 8–5.)

The design sketch also shows the endings of the steel from the wall above. This steel was calculated by the method illustrated in Example 4–7 for column-like members subject to heavy bending.

ECCENTRIC WALL FOOTING DESIGN PROBLEM

Problem 8–13. Redesign the eccentric wall footing of Example 8–5 for 75 kip-ft. of bending moment instead of 30 kip-ft. Incorporate a step in the footing along the toe side. Refer to Fig. 8–5(b). Be sure that the reduced section at the step is safe.

8–10. The Design of Two-Way Reinforced Concrete Footings. Professor Richart's Tests. A footing supporting a concentrated load, such as a column, should be square (or round), or substantially so. Such footings are ordinarily reinforced in both directions for two-way strength, and are known as **two-way footings, column footings,** or **isolated footings.**

During the forty-five years since Talbot's footing tests[A] were made, concrete strengths have increased greatly, stronger steels have been used, and new patterns of deformed bars with greater bond strength have appeared. Consequently in 1944 Professor Frank E. Richart, of the University of Illinois, undertook a new series of footing tests in cooperation with the American Iron and Steel Institute. The results, reported[B] in 1949, include:

1. Evidence that the full statical bending moment and shear should be used in two-way footing bending and bond calculations, and not 85 per cent thereof, as permitted by current codes. [Ref. ACI Code, Sec. 1204(e).]

2. Data indicating that the current design practice with respect to diagonal tension is too optimistic; that the critical section should probably be set closer to the column or wall. (Not evident from Fig. 8–10.)

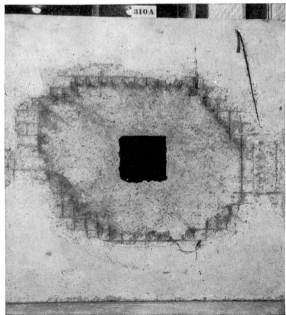

FIG. 8–10.　Typical Richart Series two-way test footing after failure.　The bars were cut to permit separation of the two parts.　The square block is a stub column poured integrally with the footing.

3. Data showing that the anchorage and bond value of certain new types of deformed bars is not appreciably increased by hooking the ends.

Items (1) and (3) above have been tentatively embraced by the author[1] in Example 8–6 and elsewhere. With respect to Item (2) and others not mentioned here,[B] future developments are awaited.

Example 8–6 and Fig. 8–11 illustrate the designing of a two-way footing for a 400-kip load. The work proceeds through the same four items of study, (a) through (d), as for one-way footings. A pyramidal frustum of concrete, with a base d inches outside the limits of the column, defines a compression region outside of which the soil pressure is considered to produce 45° diagonal tension, which is assumed to be a maximum all around the base of the frustum. Bending and bond stresses are computed at the face of the column [ACI Code, Secs. 1204(b) and 1205(c)], as formerly.

The depth downward to the point of contact between the crossed-bar groups is used as an average d throughout.

In two-way footings, 75 psi is the maximum unit diagonal tension stress, v, permitted by the ACI Code (Sec. 809).

In two-way footings, the flexural tension normal to a particular bar weakens, somewhat, the bond of the concrete thereto. Consequently, the bond stress allowed in two-way footings is only 80 per cent of that for one-way ones, namely $0.08f'_c$.

EXAMPLE 8–6

Design of a Square Two-Way R/C Column Footing. **Given** a 22 by 22-in. tied column with 12–#9 high bond deformed bars of 50,000 psi Y.P., carrying 400 kips.

Required to design the corresponding ACI two-way footing for a 3-ton per sq. ft. safe soil value, taking ACI 2500-lb. concrete and specification: 20,000–1125–12, $v = 75$, $u = 200$ psi for the high bond bars to be used.

Solution: Referring to Fig. 8–12 and estimating the footing weight at 6 per cent of the column load:

---

[1] No doubt many will prefer to await general acceptance of Richart's report and formal recodification before abandoning the permissive 85% coefficient. On the other hand, it can be demonstrated easily that the true moment coefficient which might be applied to the moments as computed by ACI Sec. 1204(a) to arrive at the moment tributary to each face of the column or pedestal *varies between the limits of* 100% *and* 67%. At the outermost step of a footing the use of 85% can be on the danger side, so its virtue for *general* use is questionable anyway.

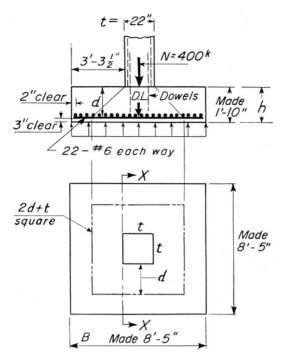

Fig. 8–11.   Two-way footing design.

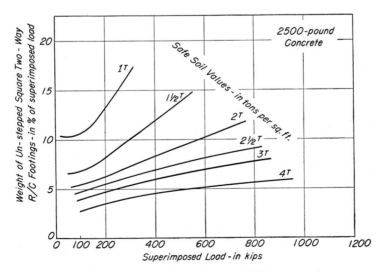

Fig. 8–12.   Chart for estimating weights of ACI two-way footings.

(a) *Footing Area.*

$$\text{Trial} = \frac{1.06(400)}{6} = 70.7 \text{ sq. ft.} \qquad \textit{Try 8 ft., 5 in. square.}$$

$$\text{Tentative net pressure, } p, = \frac{400}{(8.42)^2} = 5.65 \text{ ksf.}$$

(b) *Design for Diagonal Tension* using the shear outside the pyramid of base $2d + t$ in Fig. 8–11. Refer to ACI Code, Sec. 1205(a) and (b) or Dr. Talbot's tests:

From $\qquad\qquad\qquad v = \dfrac{V}{b'jd}, \qquad d = \dfrac{V}{vjb'}.$

But $\qquad\qquad\qquad b' = 4(2d + t),$

and $\qquad\qquad\qquad V = p[B^2 - (2d + t)^2].$

Therefore $\quad$ Req'd. $d = \dfrac{p[B^2 - (2d + t)^2]}{vj(8d + 4t)}$

$$= \frac{5650[(101)^2 - (2d + 22)^2]}{144(75)(0.90)(8d + 88)} = 17.60 \text{ in.}$$

(This value of j used corresponds to the steel percentage finally provided.)

(c) *Designing for Bending* using the whole cantilever bending moment upon Sec. X–X as indicated by Professor Richart's tests of 1948, instead of 85 per cent as *permitted* by ACI Code, Sec. 1204(e):

$$\text{B. M.} = \frac{wL^2}{2} = \frac{5.65(101)(39.5)^2}{2(12)(12)^2} = 258 \text{ k-ft.}$$

$$\text{Req'd. } d = \sqrt{\frac{M}{Rb}} = \sqrt{\frac{258(12,000)}{197(101)}} = 12.46 \text{ in.}$$

But h will be set by diagonal tension at $17.60 + 0.75 + 3.00 = 21.35$.

Make footing 22 in. thick.

Now trying #6 bars, $d = 18.25$ in., and the flexural $b = B = 101$ in.:

$$R = \frac{M}{bd^2} = \frac{258(12,000)}{101(18.25)^2} = 92.$$

Corresponding $p = 0.52\%$,

Req'd. $A_s = 0.0052(101)(18.25) = 9.56$ sq. in.

(d) *Designing for Bond* using the shear at Sec. X–X, ACI Code, Sec. 1205(c):

$$\underset{\text{req'd}}{\Sigma_o} = \frac{V}{ujd} = \frac{5650(101)(39.5)}{200(0.90)(18.25)(144)} = 47.6 \text{ in.}$$

Required perimeter/area $= \dfrac{47.6}{9.56} = 4.97.$ (From Table 1–3.)

Use #6 bars or smaller.

Recalculation with corrected dead load:

$$\text{D.L.} = 1.83(8.42)^2(0.15) = \begin{array}{r} 19.5 \text{ kips.} \\ \underline{400.0} \\ 419.5 \end{array}$$

Required $B = \sqrt{\dfrac{419.5}{6}} = 8.36$ ft.

Keep footing 8 ft. 5 in. square.

Checking diagonal tension:

$$v = \frac{5650[(101)^2 - (58.5)^2]}{144(234)(0.90)(18.25)} = 69 \text{ psi,} \qquad <75, \; satisfactory.$$

Since B. M. is unchanged, $A_s = 9.56$ sq. in.

Use 22–#6 bars in each direction.

Check for bond:

$$u = \frac{V}{\Sigma_o jd} = \frac{5650(101)(39.5)}{22(\frac{3}{4})(\pi)(0.90)(18.25)(144)} = 184 \text{ psi,}$$

$$<200, \; satisfactory.$$

Transfer of Steel Stress from Base of Column (Bar Splicing). Referring to ACI Code, Secs. 1103(c)(1) and 1206(c) and (d), conveniently try 12–#9 bar dowels, the same as the column bars, extending them $20(1.13) = 23$ in. *upward* into the 3000-lb. concrete of the column.

Downward into the footing, Sec. 1206(d), requires that the dowels be embedded far enough to "develop their full working value" at a safe bond stress.

Taking the column design steel stress of $0.8(0.4)(50,000) = 16,000$ psi, as in Chapter 4, and trying a 19-in. maximum possible embedment:

$$u = \frac{A_s f_s}{\Sigma_o a} = \frac{1.00(16,000)}{1.13(\pi)(19)} = 237 \text{ psi}$$

$$<250, \; \therefore \; O.K.$$

TWO–WAY FOOTINGS PRACTICE PROBLEMS

Problem 8–14. *(Individual) Design of Square R/C Column Footings.* Given the cases tabulated below and deformed bars. Take ACI 3000-lb. concrete and specification, including $v = 75$ and u at 240 psi. Allow 3 in. clear damp proofing. Select the thinnest footing meeting all requirements.

Required to design the footing:

Case	Safe Soil Bearing Value (t/sq. ft.)	Superimposed Concentric Load (kips)	Square Column Size, t (in.)
a		110	12
b		50	10
c	1.50	330	16
d		190	15
e		380	16
f		270	16
g		210	14
h		490	17
i	2.50	90	10
j		330	16
k		560	18
l		610	18
m		50	10
n		250	16
o	2.00	470	16
p		130	12
q		525	18
r		370	16
s		350	14
t		130	12
u	4.00	790	21
v		900	22
w		570	18
x		1060	26
y		430	16
z		250	14
a'	3.00	80	10
b'		610	20
c'		800	22
d'		760	20

Problem 8–15. Redesign (a) the two-way footing of Example 8–6, or (b) the individualized one designed in Problem 8–14 (whichever is assigned by the instructor) using 85 per cent of the full static moment and shear in the flexure and bond calculations, respectively. Refer to ACI Specs. 1204(e) and 1205(c), (d) and (e).

Make a comparative study of the quantities of steel and concrete required in the two cases, and comment.

8–11. Combined Footings. A footing which carries two or more columns is called a *combined footing*. Such an arrangement should be considered whenever the load from a column cannot be spread uniformly over the footing soil. A common case is that of an exterior building column which abuts the property line. Refer to Figs. 8–1(c) and 8–14.

When the adjacent interior column has been embraced, the position of the resultant of the two column loads is computed and the combined footing is centered upon it. Usually the exterior column carries the smaller load, so the footing can be rectangular. (Why?) However, if there is any restriction upon the length of the footing, it cannot be made rectangular. (Again why?)

After the center of the footing has been located, the required area is easily found by dividing the total load by the safe soil value, from which the required rectangular footing width follows.

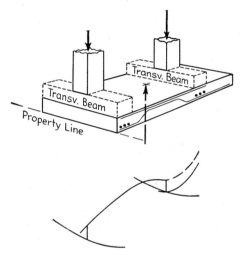

Fig. 8–13. Conception of combined footing forces and deformations.

Figure 8–13 illustrates the concept of combined footings which is directly applicable to the designing to be performed in Example 8–7. By turning the book upside down one sees that the structure consists of a uniformly loaded simple span slab with an overhang. The column forces are distributed across the slab by *transverse beams*, which are shown in phantom because they often do not exist in reality except for the **transverse reinforcement** finally provided. The work consists principally in computing and arranging the *longitudinal reinforcement*, as may be seen from Fig. 8–15.

EXAMPLE 8–7

Design of a Combined Footing. *Given* an 18 by 18 in. exterior column abutting a property line and carrying 200 kips, and the 22 by 22 in. 400-kip interior column of Example 8–6 centered 15 ft. away, as shown in Fig. 8–14.

Required to design the necessary combined footing for a 3-ton per sq. ft. safe soil value, taking high bond deformed bars, ACI 2500-lb. concrete and specification, including $v = 75$ (200 with stirrups) and u normally 250 psi. For top bars $u = 175$. In localities that are two-way reinforced, $u = 200$ psi.

Solution: (See Art. 8–12 for further discussion.)

(a) *Footing Area.*

<table>
<tr><td>Estimated
footing weight</td><td align="right">200 kips
400
40</td></tr>
<tr><td></td><td align="right">6)640 kips</td></tr>
<tr><td>Required area =</td><td align="right">106.7 sq. ft.</td></tr>
</table>

For uniform soil pressure the center of the footing must coincide with the resultant column load. Referring to the lower view of Fig. 8–14, the center must be 10.75 ft. from the left end of the footing:

Make footing 2(10.75)
= 21 ft. 6 in. *long.*

Required width:

$$b = \frac{106.7}{21.5} = 4.96 \text{ ft.}$$

Make footing 5 ft. 0 in. *wide.*

Net design pressure:

$$p = \frac{600}{5(21.5)} = 5.57 \text{ ksf}$$

$$w = 5(5.57) = 27.85 \text{ klf}$$

(b) *Longitudinal Design.* See the moment diagram, Figs. 8–14 and 8–15.

Flexure:

$$\text{Req'd. } d = \sqrt{\frac{M}{Rb}} = \sqrt{\frac{568,000}{197(5)}} = 24 \text{ in.}$$

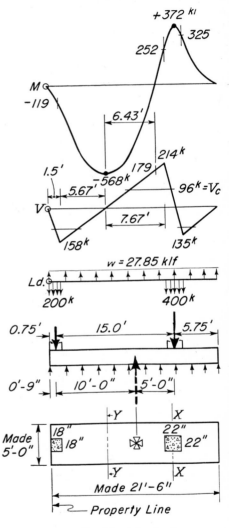

FIG. 8–14. Combined footing forces.

Diagonal Tension:

$$\text{Req'd. } d = \frac{V}{vjb} = \frac{214{,}000}{200(\frac{7}{8})(60)} = 20.4 \text{ in.}$$

With d made 24 in., $v_{\max} = 170$ psi.

Assuming two layers of #6 bars, $1\frac{1}{2}$ in. between layers, #4 stirrups and 3-in. dampproofing:

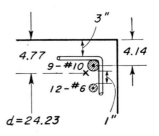

@ Sec. X–X (Bot.)

Make $D = 29$ in.

Bottom Steel at Sec. X–X, Figs. 8–14 and 8–15:

$$R = \frac{372(12{,}000)}{60(24.0)^2} = 129, \qquad p = 0.73\%$$

Req'd. $A_s = 10.5$

$$\text{Req'd. } \Sigma_o = \frac{214{,}000}{200(\frac{7}{8})(24.0)} = 50.9 \text{ in.}$$

$$\text{Req'd. } \frac{\Sigma_o}{A_s} = \frac{50.9}{10.5} = 4.84 \qquad \textit{Take \#6 bars or smaller.}$$

29.00 in.
-0.75
-0.75
-0.50
-3.00
$d = 24.00$

Use 24–#6 bars at the section. Bend up 12 for use at Sec. Y–Y.

Top Steel at Sec. Y–Y, Figs. 8–14 and 8–15:

$$R = \frac{568(12{,}000)}{60(24.23)^2} = 193$$

$$p = 1.12\%, \qquad A_s = 16.30$$

At contraflex:

$$\text{Req'd. } \Sigma_o = \frac{179{,}000}{175(\frac{7}{8})(24.23)} = 48.2 \text{ in.}$$

4.77   3″   4.14

9 – #10

12 – #6

$d = 24.23$ 1″

@ Sec. Y–Y (Top)

	Area	Perimeter
Required	16.30	48.2
Value of #6's bent up	5.28 (12 bars)	14.2 = 6 bars at contrafl.
Still needed	11.02 sq. in.	34.0 in.

Use 9–#10 straight and 12–#6 bent.

Web reinforcement:

Multiple **U**-stirrups have been provided in three localities, as defined by the V-diagram, with concrete alone taking 75 psi. $V_c = 96$ kips.

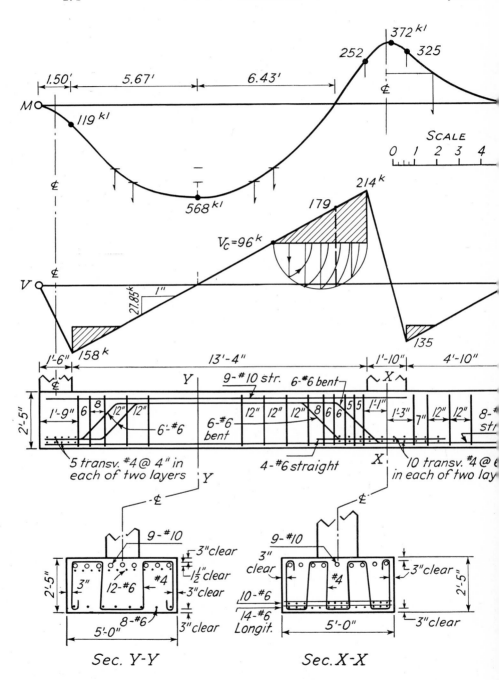

Fig. 8–15. Design sketch of the combined footing.

(c) *Transverse Design*. Refer to lower portion of Fig. 8–13 for concept.

400-kip "beam" under 22-in. interior column: 29.00 in.

$$w = \frac{400}{5} = 80 \text{ klf of 5-ft. beam}$$

                                                                  -0.87
                                                                  -0.50ϕ
                                                                  -0.75

$$M = \frac{80(1.59)^2}{2} = 101 \text{ kip-ft.}$$

                                                                  -0.50
                                                                  -3.00

Refer to sketch of Sec. *X–X:* $\overline{23.38}$

$$\text{Approx. } A_s = \frac{101(12,000)}{20,000(\frac{7}{8})(23.38)} = 2.96 \text{ sq. in.}$$

$$\text{Req'd. } \Sigma_o = \frac{80(1.59)1000}{200(\frac{7}{8})(23.38)} = 31.1$$

$$\frac{31.1}{2.96} = 10.5 \qquad\qquad\qquad\qquad \textit{Avoid \#3 bars.}$$

Use 10–#4 bars at 6 in. c. to c., in each of two layers, symmetrically located underneath the 400-kip interior column.

Diagonal Tension: 22.0
Refer to latter part of text, Art. 8–12:   23.+

$$v_{\max.} = \frac{80(1.59)1000}{74(\frac{7}{8})(23.38)} = 84$$

                                                                  23.+
                                                                  6.
                                                                  $\overline{b = 74.+}$

> 75, *so use a few stirrups.*

200-kip "beam" under 18-in. exterior column:
Similarly, its req'd. $A_s = 1.78$ sq. in., $\Sigma_o = 13.5$ in., calc. $b = 45$ in., actual $v = 75$ psi, no stirrups required.
                    Use 5–#4 bars @ 4 in. c. to c. in each of two layers.

8–12. Combined Footing Designing. In Example 8–7, the dimensions of the base of the footing were established in item (a) as aforementioned, and load, shear, and moment diagrams drawn in Fig. 8–14.

The Structural Concept. From the very beginning one must visualize the deformed *shape* of the structure, and the localities where flexural steel will be needed. The solid curved lines of the lower view in Fig. 8–13 show the behavior of typical top and bottom reinforcing bars. Note the two-way action underneath the interior column.

The Required Thickness was set in item (b) by the stirrup beam demand for a d of 24 in. Had this footing been proportioned to eliminate the necessity for stirrups, it would have had to be a great deal thicker.

The Designing of combined footings is not separately covered in the ACI Code, so general principles were followed. Since they are never of a compact shape like those tested by Talbot and later by Richart, it is customary conservatively to compute the diagonal tension at the faces of the columns as in one-way structures (wall footings excepted), instead of at a distance d therefrom. The Joint Committee Report, Sec. 868, is fairly specific on this subject.

Flexure Reinforcement was designed in item (b) at the two principal sections, X–X and Y–Y, and proportioned elsewhere by reference to the bending moment diagram, all of which is shown to large scale in Fig. 8–15. Since bond requirements usually demand that a relatively large number of bars be used, it is best to plan for two layers of bars, as in this case, to ensure that they will be far enough apart for good concrete placing. Note also that at Sec X–X the decreased allowable bond stress of 200 psi had to be used because the flexure tensile reinforcement is working heavily in both horizontal directions in that locality.

Bond Stress also influenced the choice of bar size in the top of the footing at Sec. Y–Y. The greatest beam shear in this steel is at the contraflexure point, about one foot to the left of the face of the interior column. The allowable u was only 175 psi because the bars were top bars.

Uncertain Ground Conditions inherent in footing design and the possibility of variation in the column loads suggested the continuation of a portion of the bottom reinforcement at Sec. X–X through the negative moment Sec. Y–Y, and on to the exterior column.

The 400-*kip Transverse "Beam"* flexure steel areas were computed in item (c) rather casually because it was early discovered that excess area would have to be provided anyway in order to meet the (cantilever) bond stress requirements without using impracticably small bars.

Regarding a check upon diagonal tension, the ACI Code sheds no light as to what width b shall be used in transverse "beams" such as these, which are indistinguishable from the footing slab itself. The Joint Committee Report, Sec. 868, makes the statement that: "The transverse reinforcement . . . should be placed uniformly within a band having a width not greater than the width of the column plus twice the effective depth of the footing." This *band* philosophy was here adapted to computing a b by adding one bar space to the above stipulated width, as may be seen for the 400-kip beam. In the case of the 200-kip beam, the dissymmetry was recognized in establishing the 45-in. value. Such nicety with respect to these "beams" is hardly justifiable, except to make the reader conscious of the importance of providing some transverse reinforcement.

COMBINED FOOTING PROBLEMS

Problem 8–16. Given an 18 by 18 in. exterior column carrying 250 kips which clears a property line 6 in., and a 22 by 22 in. 450-kip interior column centered 18 ft. away.

Required to design the necessary combined footing for a 4-ton per sq. ft. safe soil value, taking ACI 3000-lb. concrete and specification and high bond deformed bars.

Problem 8–17. Given an exterior column abutting a property line and an interior column centered 16 ft., 6 in. away, each of which is 20 in. square and carries 400 kips.

Required to design quickly a combined footing for a 4-ton per sq. ft. safe soil value, taking ACI 2500-lb. concrete and high bond deformed bars.

8–13. Adjustment of Footing Areas for Equal Settlement. It is well known that all structures founded on soil settle more or less, sometimes for long periods. The structural engineer undertakes to minimize the effects thereof by proportioning the areas of the individual footings of the site so that the amount of settlement will be equal at all columns or walls. There will then be no appreciable relative vertical dislocation of portions of the structure or unanticipated stresses which cause unsightly cracking and sometimes structural failure.

Although the rate and amount of settlement depend upon the type of soil, they also depend upon the use to which the structure is put. Formerly, settlement was said to be due only to the dead load of the structure because it is the only load that is always present. The auditorium of a college building may be filled for only a few hours per week or month. Such a loading contributes very little to the settlement. On the other hand, the live load content of a storage building or room acts continuously over long periods and certainly has its effect.

A common practice is to include the live load but to discount it on a time basis when adjusting footing areas. The percentage of the yearly time that the live load is present is used to compute a decreased value of live load which is considered to be permanent, and to have the same effect on settlement[2] as the full live load applied intermittently, as illustrated in the accompanying example, taking simply a three-column group.

EXAMPLE 8–8

Given the dead and live loads on the columns of a structure, together with the minimum footing area for each based upon a Table 8–1 (Boston) safe soil bearing value of 3 tons per sq. ft. for a granular ma-

---

[2] The circumstances under which this method may be questioned are taken up in the *Discussion* following the example.

terial under the total load, as shown in the table below. The percentage
of the time that each column carries its full live load is also given. The
dead load shown includes the estimated weights of the footings themselves.

Required to adjust the footing areas for equal settlements under the
equivalent long-time loading.

Data and Solution:

Line	Item	Column A	Column B	Column C
1	Dead load	130 kips	100 kips	150 kips
2	Live load, full*	200	310	180
3	D.L. + full L.L.	330 kips	410 kips	330 kips
4	Min. footing area, from 3 tsf safe soil value	55 sq. ft.	68.2 sq. ft.	55 sq. ft.
5	Live load duration percentage	20%	40%	75%
6	Decreased L.L. value	40 kips	124 kips	135 kips
7	D.L. + decreased L.L.	170 kips	224 kips	285 kips
8	−corresponding soil pressure	3.08 ksf	3.28 ksf	5.17 ksf
9	−corresponding soil pressure ratios	1.00	1.06	1.68
10	Adjusted footing areas—*Ans.*	55 sq. ft.	72.6 sq. ft.	92.5 sq. ft.
	CHECK			
11	D.L. + full L.L. pressure	6.0 ksf—max	5.64 ksf	3.57 ksf

Discussion of the Adjustment of Footing Areas. Lines (1) to (5) inclusive present the given data, including a set of minimum footing areas
which are necessary to carry the dead plus full live load on each column.
All areas except one are due to be increased as they are adjusted so that
there will be equal lesser pressures and settlements under dead load plus
the decreased live load. Line (7) shows the decreased total loads considered to be productive of settlement. In line (8) we find the corresponding soil pressures, assuming that the areas of line (4) still exist.
The ratios of line (9) show the extent of the inequality of these pressures,
taking the lightest footing pressure as a base. The original footing areas
of line (4) were then increased, using the ratios of line (9) to yield the
desired adjusted areas of line (10).

Line (11) is a check upon the work, and also shows the footing base
pressures corresponding to the dead plus full* live load.

The above method has been criticized from a soil mechanics standpoint,
since under a given unit pressure, the larger of two footings will have a deeper
bulb of pressure, and thus compress a greater depth of soil, resulting in more
settlement.

* Or a reduced probable live load if several stories are involved. See Art. 6–2.

Dr. Paul Andersen[E] has presented a *size formula* for making this further correction. It, or some similar correction, should be applied when the footing areas are widely different. Dr. Donald W. Taylor[F] also has shown that the use of the uncorrected method leads to relatively large settlements in the central portions of a structure.

FOOTING AREAS PROBLEMS

Problem 8–18. Given the dead and live loads on the six columns of a structure, together with live load duration percentages, as shown in the accompanying table.

Column No.	1	2	3	4	5	6
D.L. (kips)	100	150	125	80	120	90
Full L.L. (kips)	200	175	300	180	320	120
L.L. Duration (per cent)	50	20	60	40	80	30

The safe maximum soil bearing value is 4 tons per sq. ft. An estimate of the weight of the footings is included in the dead loads tabulated.

Required to compute and adjust the footing areas for equal settlement:
(a) Using the live load duration percentages, as in Example 8–8,
(b) Using dead load plus one half live load throughout,
(c) Using dead load only.

Make a tabular comparison of the three sets of areas, and discuss.

8–14. Ground Slope and Pedestals. On a building site, the bases of the footings often cannot all be set a constant distance below the ground surface, as set by northern climates, because to do so would mean that lateral earth pressure from an upper footing might act to dislodge a lower one. Such a situation arose in Fig. 8–16 wherein the footing for Column *B* had to be set deeply to keep within the 1 on 4 safe slope ($\tan^{-1} 0.25$) as set by the *angle of repose*[3] of the soil. A column-like member called a **pedestal,** or pier, was used to reach above the ground surface.

Pedestals are used to take up the difference in the elevations of footings over a site and to distribute the column load over an area advantageous for the design of the footing, especially when steel columns are used. The pedestals of Fig. 8–16 are for the three columns and footings discussed in the preceding article.

The cross-sectional areas of pedestals are governed by the allowable compressive stress of $0.25f'_c$ [ACI Code, Sec. 1207(a), for plain concrete

---

[3] As mentioned by Krynine[C] the angle of repose is smaller than the soil mechanics *angle of internal friction,* ϕ, whose tangent varies from about 0.58 to 0.70 for sands in the loose and dense states, respectively. The angle of repose of sand may be taken the same as ϕ for the loose state.

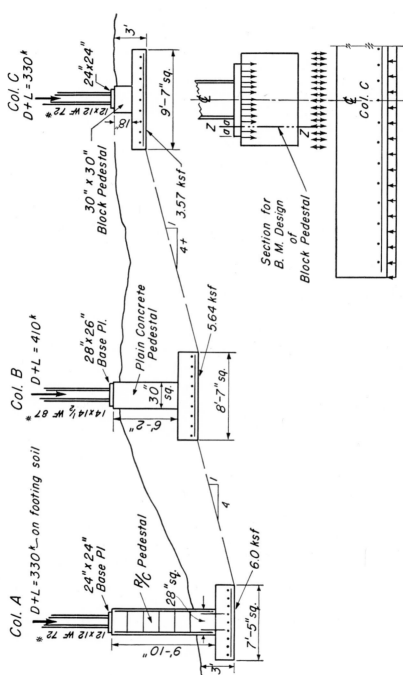

Fig. 8–16.   A site plan using three types of pedestals.

pedestals], or arbitrarily by the size of the column base plate, or by the desirability of distributing the footing load more widely.

If the ratio of height to least lateral dimension exceeds three, the member is technically not a pedestal [ACI Code, Sec. 104(a)]. It must be reinforced as a column, such as that for Column A of the figure.

If a pedestal has very little height, such as that for Column C, it is more like a block, and has been called a **block pedestal.** Such a member may be more a beam than a column and should be so computed. The enlarged view at Column C shows the section Z–Z specified for a study of bending in ACI Code, Secs. 1207(b) and 1204(b)(3), and the assumed uniform pressures involved. Of course, if the block concrete is placed integrally with the footing slab, then the block is part of a stepped footing and should be so computed.

8–15. Pile and Mat Footings. These types of footings are needed when the soil bearing values are poor to very poor. Their design is beyond the present scope of this text, but will be found in a number of standard works[D] on reinforced concrete design, including *Substructure Analysis and Design,* by Paul Andersen, 2nd ed. (New York: The Ronald Press Company, 1956).

8–16. Summary of Footing Design. Structurally, footings are inverted cantilever beams loaded with the distributed upward pressure of the ground, less the dead load pressure of the footing itself.

The common assumption that the ground pressure is uniformly distributed is a safe one for footing design except for unusual cases wherein the pressure may be greatest toward the edges of the footing. Normally, the deformation of the footing and the ground tends to decrease the pressure in the outer portions.

The outside dimensions of footings are dictated by the allowable bearing pressure upon the ground and the necessity for having enough depth, or thickness, safely to resist bending and the diagonal tension resulting from vertical shear.

Plain concrete footings serve well when loads are light and ground conditions excellent, but for the reverse conditions they must be very thick, requiring too much concrete and sometimes an excessive amount of excavation. In this connection compare the sizes of four footings, all designed for the same conditions, namely Figs. 8–3, 8–4(b), 8–5(a) and 8–5(b).

The vertical (punching) shear method of reinforced concrete footing design has long since been abandoned in favor of the recognition of the limiting 45° frustum observed in Talbot's tests. On the other hand, *bending* and *bond* stresses must be calculated at the face of the column or pedestal.

Bond stresses in footings are kept low by using the smaller bars, which have a great deal of perimeter per square inch of cross-sectional area.

To design a concentric reinforced concrete footing (a) use the safe soil values to get the required area, (b) calculate the thickness, d_v, required to resist diagonal tension safely, (c) compute the thickness, d_f, required for flexure, and (d) choose the bar *size* to suit the bond requirement.

Eccentric footings should also be designed to deliver a uniformly distributed pressure to the soil whenever possible by offsetting the footing with respect to the column or wall.

The soil pressure under eccentrically loaded footings may be *investigated*, employing the $(N/A) + (Mc/I)$ column expression, using the width of the footing as the *depth* in the expression for moment of inertia. If uplift develops on one side, the method must be abandoned.

In designing eccentric footings, first draw the position of the resultant vertical force, then build the footing around it.

The two-way action of the reinforcement in column footings means that the adhesion of the concrete to the bars of one direction tends to be weakened by the concrete tension at right angles thereto. Consequently the allowable bond stress has been set at 80 per cent of the one-way value.

Combined footings supporting two or more columns are often necessary at property lines in order to maintain a uniform soil pressure in cases where there is no room for the spread of a single footing.

BIBLIOGRAPHY

A) TALBOT, ARTHUR N. Reinforced Concrete Wall Footings and Column Footings, *Bulletin* No. 67, *University of Illinois Engineering Experiment Station*, 1913.
B) RICHART, FRANK E. Reinforced Concrete Wall and Column Footings, Parts I and II, *Proc. American Concrete Institute*, 1949, Vol. 45, pp. 97, 237.
C) KRYNINE, DIMITRI P. *Soil Mechanics*. 2d ed. New York: McGraw-Hill Book Co., Inc., p. 307.
D) PECK, HANSON, and THORNBURN. *Foundation Engineering*. 1st ed. New York: John Wiley & Sons, Inc., 1953, pp. 313 and 319.
E) ANDERSEN, PAUL. *Substructure Analysis and Design*. 2d ed. New York: The Ronald Press Co., 1956, p. 101.
F) TAYLOR, DONALD W. *Fundamentals of Soil Mechanics*. 1st ed. New York: John Wiley & Sons, Inc., 1948, Art. 19–34.

QUESTIONS

1. Define the terms superstructure, pedestal, footing, and foundation.

2. Classify footing types and state the field of each.

3. Discuss the physical properties of four common earth materials, especially their action under load. Assign safe bearing values to each.

4. Tell how to design a plain concrete wall footing, discussing each step.

5. Explain how plain and reinforced concrete flexural members differ in their action when subjected to transverse shear.

6. Distinguish structurally between a stepped footing, such as in Fig. 8–5(b), and a footing surmounted by a block pedestal, such as in Fig. 8–16, Column *C*.

7. Discuss the four essential items of procedure in designing a reinforced concrete footing.

8. Is there one correct size of reinforcing bar for every footing, or several? Explain.

9. In cantilevered reinforced concrete beams it is customary to compute the unit diagonal tension at the face of the column, but in reinforced concrete footings a section at *d* distance is studied. How do you reconcile the two practices?

10. In designing an eccentric footing for direct load and bending moment, what force relationship should be computed at the outset?

11. What is meant by the moment of inertia of a footing? How is it used, and why?

12. Why is a lowered value of allowable unit bond stress used in two-way footings, and also in flat slabs?

13. If a column or wall has bending therein, must the footing necessarily bear nonuniformly upon the ground? Explain.

14. Tell how to investigate the pressure variation under an eccentrically loaded footing.

15. It has been asserted that if plain bars were used in footings, instead of deformed ones, "there will have to be more of them, which increases the steel tonnage." Explain thoroughly.

16. Demonstrate a general method for finding the correct size and shape of combined footings. In which cases are trapezoidal shapes needed?

CONTINUATION PROBLEMS

Problem 8–19. Redesign the square two-way footing of Example 8–6 or Problem 8–14 (as assigned by the instructor) to be of rectangular shape, two and one-half times as long as wide. Refer to ACI Sec. 1204(g).

Problem 8–20. Redesign the footing of Example 8–7 to have no stirrups. Make a comparative study of the quantities of steel and concrete required in the two cases, and discuss.

Problem 8–21. Proportion the base dimensions of the footing of Fig. 8–14, Example 8–7, if the 22-in. column and its load abuts the property line and the 18-in. column is the interior one.

Problem 8–22. Redesign an assigned square two-way footing of Problem 8–14 if the resultant superimposed column load is eccentric an amount $t/2$, the half-dimension of the column.

What new situations arose, and how were they met?

CHAPTER 9

RETAINING WALLS

9–1. Introduction. The function of a retaining wall is to confine a mass of earth or other bulk materials.

Retaining walls are of two general types, *gravity* and *cantilever*. A gravity wall, illustrated in Fig. 9–1(a), is usually built of plain concrete, though sometimes of stone masonry. It depends principally upon its

Dr. Karl Terzaghi, Emeritus Professor of the Practice of Civil Engineering, Harvard University, and internationally known consulting engineer. Originator and interpreter of soil mechanics theory, he developed important concepts now used to predict the action of soil masses under load, and devised techniques for applying them to the design and construction of earth dams, retaining walls, and foundations.

Dr. Terzaghi is the author of five textbooks in his field and has received four major scientific citations, including the Brown Medal of the Franklin Institute.

weight for stability. Cantilever walls, shown throughout the rest of the illustration, achieve stability largely by having their rear portions tucked underneath the adjacent backfill. Thus the weight of a portion of the soil mass is used to help confine the whole in place. Cantilever walls consist of relatively slender elements well reinforced with steel. When such a wall is relatively high, the vertical *stem* and horizontal *base* portions are connected by ribs, making a *counterforted wall* when the ribs are hidden within the backfill, as at (c), or a *buttressed wall* if exposed in front of it, as shown at (d). *Bridge abutments* at (e) not only support the structure but also confine the approach fills and serve as a form of retaining wall.

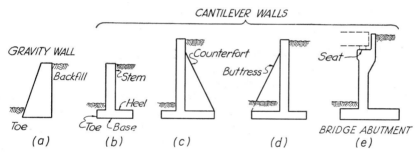

FIG. 9–1. Types of retaining walls.

9–2. Forces upon Retaining Walls. The designing of a retaining wall involves the determining of the earth pressure upon the back thereof and proportioning the wall for strength as well as for stability against overturning and sliding, while guarding against excessive settlement.

The pressure upon walls varies widely depending upon a number of factors, including the type of backfill soil, its seasonal condition, the drainage thereof, the possibility of an overloading of the surface of the backfill, and others. However, if the soil is a well-drained sandy or gravelly one, the methods of computing earth pressure illustrated in this chapter are applicable, and conservative.[1]

The effects of some of the above mentioned variable factors have been taken up briefly and evaluated in Appendix F. Others are beyond the scope of this text. A young engineer who encounters soil conditions appreciably different from those discussed in this chapter should, if he has had the benefit of formal training in *soil mechanics*, refer to the most

---

[1] In this chapter the author has undertaken to apply the findings of the new science of *soil mechanics* to modernized designing of retaining walls without placing an undue burden upon those who have never studied the subject. A few soil mechanics terms and topics are used in connection with the illustrative "Examples," and others less pertinent will be found in Appendices F and G.

recent literature[A,B,C] of the field before proceeding with his designing. Otherwise, he should consult a specialist. Great strides have been made in this new science, but certain topics, such as the design pressure of a *clay* backfill, are still controversial. Meanwhile this material should never be used if at all avoidable. Granular (sandy) soils are assumed throughout this chapter.

9–3. The Coulomb Theory of Earth Pressure.[2]

This well-established theory, developed over 180 years ago by C. A. Coulomb, a French army engineer, asserts that a dry sandy backfill tends to fail by the incipient slippage of a wedge thereof down a steeply inclined plane, called the *failure plane,* as the wall moves outward slightly and perhaps tilts a bit, as pictured in Fig. 9–2. The wedge comes into equilibrium under three forces W, P_A and R—namely, the weight of the wedge, the resistance of the wall and the resultant upward earth force, respectively— all of which must intersect in a point.

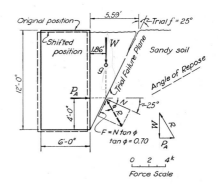

The incipient movement along the failure plane mobilizes a frictional force, $F = N \tan \phi$, where N is the intergranular pressure normal to

FIG. 9–2. Forces on a sliding wedge of sandy soil behind a gravity type of retaining wall; after Coulomb. (Wall friction disregarded.)

the plane, and ϕ is the angle of friction, as in physics and mechanics. This friction between grains is called the *internal friction.* The resultant of forces N and F defines the resultant R. In Fig. 9–2, the third-point position of the point of intersection of the three forces is consistent with an assumed hydrostatic pressure variation along the failure plane and the back of the wall.

In the following example, illustrating the Coulomb theory, the variable friction between the fill and the wall has conservatively been disregarded.

EXAMPLE 9–1

Gravity Retaining Wall Forces According to Coulomb. **Given a rectangular plain concrete gravity-type retaining wall supporting a level backfill, as shown in Fig. 9–2.**

---

[2] Current developments suggest the use of the Coulomb method, and its graphic counterpart the Culmann method, for determining earth pressures generally.

The Terzaghi and Peck semiempirical chart method may be used for relatively

It is desired to find the forces upon the sliding wedge of earth and upon the wall by the Coulomb theory of earth pressure.

The fill material is dry sand weighing 100 pcf; angle of internal friction, $\phi = 35°$; angle of repose, 30°. Take the weight of (plain) concrete at 145 pcf.

Required:

(a) Assuming that sliding is about to take place along the 25° trial failure plane, find by fundamental mechanics the magnitude, position, and direction of the earth force P_A per foot of wall. Disregard possible wall friction.

Solution: (All forces are per lineal foot of wall.)

The earth load, W, will act vertically downward at g, the centroid of the wedge, which is located at one-third of the distance from each side to the opposite vertex:[3]

$$W = \frac{12}{2}(5.59)(0.10) = 3.35 \text{ kips}$$

Making the customary assumption of hydrostatic variation of the pressure against the wall, the wall force, P_A, will act horizontally at one-third the distance up the wall.

From mechanics, the equilibrant earth force, R, must pass through the point of intersection of the forces W and P_A, as shown. It is the resultant of the total normal force, N, over the whole failure plane *and* the internal frictional force, $F = 0.70N$ acting parallel thereto:

$$\tan 35° = 0.700, \quad \sin = 0.574, \quad \cos = 0.819$$

$$\sin 25° = 0.423, \quad \cos = 0.906$$

Writing P_A, W, and R force components along the 25° trial failure plane:

$$P_A \sin 25° + R \sin \phi - W \cos 25° = 0 \tag{1}$$

While perpendicular to the plane we have:

$$P_A \cos 25° - R \cos \phi + W \sin 25° = 0 \tag{2}$$

Solving Eqs. (1) and (2) simultaneously:

$$P_A = 1.94 \text{ kips}$$

Also

$$R = 3.87, \quad N = 0.819R = 3.17, \quad \text{and} \quad F = 0.7N = 2.22 \text{ kips.}$$

---

low walls and for quick preliminary earth pressure calculations for walls of any height.

The well-known simple and rapid Rankine method may well be used, instead of the semiempirical method, by those who still prefer it. Refer to Appendix F, Part (a), Formula 1.

[3] The point is also at the intersection of *median* lines, drawn to each vertex from the midpoint of each side.

Comments. Obviously, the backfill which lies below the **angle of repose** shown in the figure does not contribute to the pressure upon a wall. This fact should always be kept in mind no matter what method of earth pressure calculation is used.

The angle of repose for loose dry sand is approximately equal to ϕ. For uniformly graded round-grain sands, ϕ will vary from about 28°, determined from a loose-state heap, to about 35° for the dense state.

When the friction between the wall and the sand is considered, the force P_A pictured in Fig. 9-2 will be inclined upward, making an angle ϕ' with a normal to the wall surface, as defined by the frictional coefficient between sand and concrete. (See also Fig. 9-3.) In such cases it is probably best to reconcile the point of intersection of the three forces by moving the earth force R upward along the failure plane.

For the wall pressure P_A to have the low value computed above, it is necessary that the retaining wall be free to move (act) outward slightly under the pressure of the sand.[B] This situation is known as the (wall) **active case.**

If the wall is immovable, due to being connected to some larger structure, there can be no downward slipping of the sand, and because there is no motion, the helpful frictional force F cannot develop. The wall force P_A then has to be much larger in order to support the wedge of sand. This situation is known as the (wall) **at rest case,** evaluated in Appendix F [Case (c)].

Except by chance, the 25° failure plane assumed in Example 9-1 will not result in the maximum value of P_A for the active case. Other planes should also be studied, as outlined in the accompanying problems.

EARTH PRESSURE PRACTICE PROBLEMS
(*Sandy or Gravelly Soil*)

Problem 9-1. Referring to Example 9-1 and Fig. 9-2, take an assumed sliding wedge failure angle of $f = 32°$ and recompute the Coulomb wall pressure, P_A. Then check independently by graphics, taking the scale 1 in. = 4 ft.
Partial Ans. $P_A = 1.91$ *kips*

Problem 9-2. Same as Problem 9-1 except that $f = 20°$. Also plot all three of the values of P that have been found and deduce the maximum P by drawing a smooth curve through the points.
Ans. $P_A = 1.83$ *kips.* *Maximum* $P_A = 1.95$ *kips,* *when f makes 27° 30′ with the vertical.*

Problem 9-3. (a) Taking a coefficient of friction between the sand and the concrete of the wall of 0.45, recompute P_A of Example 9-1 considering wall friction.

(b) Recompute P_A for another assumed failure plane, and finally deduce the maximum P_A from a graph.

(c) Compare this maximum value of P_A with that found in Problem 9–2 and discuss.

9–4. Earth Pressure by the Culmann Construction. When the ground surface of the backfill behind a retaining wall is sloping or irregular, the back surface of the wall inclined, the backfill carries a succession of concentrated loads, wall friction is to be considered, or any combination of the above conditions exists, the Culmann graphical method is the best and most convenient for determining the pressure upon a wall. It is actually a graphical Coulomb[4] solution which is arranged for convenient repeated trials to find the maximum value of the pressure.

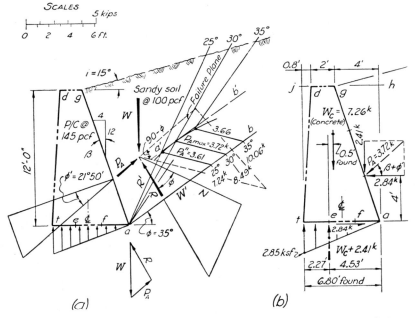

FIG. 9–3. Design of a gravity type of retaining wall, illustrating the Culmann construction. Wall friction considered.

Figure 9–3 shows the results of proportioning the *base width* and *inclination of the front face* of a 12-ft. gravity wall for a triangular distribution of upward pressure at the base, using the Culmann construction to find the failure plane of the sliding wedge of earth, and the value of the active earth pressure force P_A per foot of wall. All the essential data are shown on the drawings.

---

[4] For the Coulomb *formulas*, see Appendix F.

Construction (For a more extended treatment, refer to Bibliography item F.)

In Fig. 9–3(a) the given backfill slope angle i and the batter angle β were accurately constructed. The position and direction of the earth pressure force P_A was next laid down by deflecting it from the normal to the wall an amount ϕ'. (Trigonometric tangents are the most convenient for such work.) Taking next a first trial *failure plane* of 25° with the vertical, the normal N was constructed through the intersection of forces P_A and W, and the corresponding resultant force R was positioned therefrom, using the internal friction angle ϕ, as shown.

Obviously the value of P_A for the 25° failure angle could have been determined graphically by laying off the computed value of W to scale as the third side of a force triangle with sides P_A and R, but *Culmann rotated all three forces through the clockwise angle* 90°–ϕ *so that, with repeated trials for the failure plane, R would lie within the trial failure plane, W would always lie along the line ab, and the maximum value of P_A would be evident by drawing a line* **a′b′** *parallel to ab.* The symbols W', P'_A and R' have been used in Fig. 9–3(a) to indicate the rotated positions of the forces for the 25° failure trail, from which the 3.61-kip value of P_A was scaled.

Successive trials of 30° and 35° failure planes were made by computing the correspondingly greater values of W from the larger triangular backfill area, laying them off from a and drawing the closing P line to the failure plane under consideration. The 30° plane proved to yield the maximum P_A of 3.72 kips.

9–5. The Stability Requirements. A good retaining wall must first of all be *stable;* that is, it must stay put. In this respect it should be proportioned to resist safely three possible destructive movements. This work is called the *stability designing.* There must be:

1. Adequate *resisting moment* about the toe to resist the *overturning moment* of the lateral pressure of the backfill,
2. Enough base width to distribute the load to the foundation soil without causing *excessive settlement*, and
3. Sufficient frictional resistance along the plane of the base to resist safely the *sliding* tendency.

Resistance to overturning may be studied readily by constructing the *resultant force line* and extending it to the horizontal plane of the base, as shown in Fig. 9–4. The resultant of the lateral pressure P_A and the vertical gravity force W_c, representing the weight of the wall, is kj. From mechanics, its extension must fall within the middle third of the base if there is to be no uplift at the heel, and on the center of the base for the base pressure to be uniformly distributed, i.e., no tendency for unequal settlement. The ratio of *the resisting moment* of the weight of the retaining wall about the toe of the wall, t, together with that of any (inert) soil that may be resting thereon, *to* the overturning moment of the resultant lateral pressure of the fill is termed the *factor of safety against over-*

turning. Its value should not be less than about 2.0, depending upon the specifications or the engineer's judgment.

Settlement is usually guarded against by ensuring that the vertical pressure at the base, particularly the toe, does not exceed an allowed value, such as the common safe footing values shown in Table 8–1 of Chapter 8. If the foundation soil is clayey, this practice is hardly satisfactory, since the clay consolidates as its entrapped moisture is very slowly squeezed out by the pressure of the wall, causing unsightly settlement.

Resistance to sliding is computed by multiplying the total vertical pressure upon the base by the appropriate coefficient of friction between the concrete and the foundation soil. The ratio of this sliding resistance to the horizontal component of the earth pressure against the wall is called the *factor of safety against sliding.* It should not be less than 1.5.

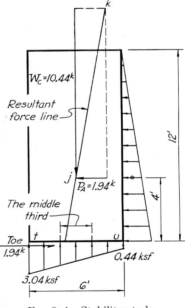

EXAMPLE 9–2

Stability of a Retaining Wall. Given the gravity wall studied in Example 9–1 and reproduced as Fig. 9–4.

Required:

(a) To show graphically the forces acting upon the wall and to construct the path of the resultant force through the plane of the base.

Solution: The gravity force,

$$W_c = 6(12)(0.145) = 10.44 \text{ kips.}$$

The resultant of W and P_A is the force kj which strikes the base at about three-fourths of the distance outward to the *edge of the middle third* of the base,

Fig. 9–4. Stability study.

so there will be no uplift. (Refer to Article 4–10, and Fig. 8–6 of Example 8–4 in Chapter 8.)

(b) Calculate the factors of safety against (1) overturning, (2) sliding, and (3) the vertical soil pressures at both edges of the base. Take 0.4 as the coefficient of friction at the base.

Solution:

(1) The factor of safety against overturning is the ratio, about the toe point, t, of the moment of the gravity forces *to* the moment of the earth pres-

sure forces:

$$\text{F.O.S.} = \frac{10.44[3]}{1.94[4]} = 4.04 \qquad \textit{Against overturning.}$$

(2) The factor of safety against sliding is the ratio of the potential resistance to sliding *to* the (earth) force tending to produce sliding:

$$\text{F.O.S.} = \frac{0.4(10.44)}{1.94} = 2.16 \qquad \textit{Against sliding.}$$

(3) The vertical soil pressures at both edges of the base may be computed as for footings: (Refer to Example 8–4 of Chapter 8.)

$$\text{Direct} = \frac{W_c}{A} = \frac{10.44}{6} \qquad = 1.74 \text{ ksf}$$

$$\text{Overturning: } I = \frac{bt^3}{12} = \frac{1(6)^3}{12} = 18 \text{ ft.}^4$$

$$\frac{Mc}{I} = \frac{1.94[4]3}{18} \qquad = 1.30$$

$$Max. = 3.04 \text{ ksf} = 1.52 \text{ tsf}$$
$$Min. = 0.44 \text{ ksf} = 0.22 \text{ tsf}$$

Comments. If a downward **wall friction** force is developed upon the wall as the backfill moves downward, additional resistance to overturning will be created. On the other hand, if the wall also settles, such friction can be nullified, or even reversed in direction.

STABILITY PRACTICE PROBLEM

Problem 9–4. Taking the gravity wall and fill material of Fig. 9–3, and the forces there shown, calculate for the maximum P_A condition the factors of safety against overturning and against sliding, considering a base sliding coefficient of 0.45. Check also the corresponding vertical soil pressures at both edges of the base.

9–6. The Strength Requirements. Although retaining walls of all types must meet the stability requirements, only the slender-membered cantilever ones require attention to strength: namely, the designing of three reinforced concrete cantilevers, the *stem*, *heel*, and *toe*. They must be proportioned for bending and diagonal tension, and the reinforcement checked for bond stress and anchorage as in other structures. This work will be illustrated in the succeeding Example 9–3.

9–7. Choice of Earth Pressure Methods. In addition to the four variables mentioned in Art. 9–2, at least five more factors affect the pressure upon retaining walls; namely, the degree of care exercised in backfilling, the possible fixity of the wall, vibration (of sandy soil), the

type of foundation soil, and the level of the water table. Some of these
are taken up briefly in Appendix F. Nevertheless, Terzaghi and Peck[A]
have summarized their masterly discussion as follows:

In connection with the design of retaining walls, the planning of adequate
drainage provisions and a careful consideration of the foundation conditions
are more important than a correct evaluation of the earth pressure. The
pressure exerted by the backfill can be estimated either on the basis of semiempirical rules or else by means of earth-pressure theory. The first method

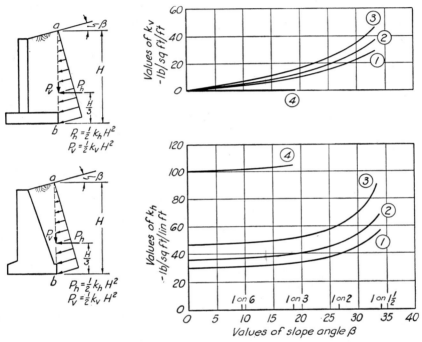

Fig. 9–5. *Chart*[5] *for estimating pressure of backfill* against retaining walls supporting *backfills with plane surface.* Use of chart limited to walls not over about 20 ft.
high.
(1) Backfill of coarse-grained soil without admixture of fine particles, very per-
meable, as clean sand or gravel.
(2) Backfill of coarse-grained soil of low permeability due to admixture of particles
of silt size.
(3) Backfill of fine silty sand, granular materials with conspicuous clay content,
and residual soil with stones.
(4) Backfill of very soft or soft clay, organic silt, or silty clay.

has the same drawbacks as the evaluation of the safe load on piles by means
of pile formulas. Some walls designed according to this method are excessively safe, others are barely stable, and occasionally a wall fails. Nevertheless,
for routine jobs the first method is cheaper and preferable. The second

[5]Included in the AREA Specifications.

method requires that the backfill and the drainage system be constructed in strict compliance with the conditions imposed by the theory. The time and labor involved in this process are not justified, unless the retaining wall constitutes a prominent part of an individual job or has a height exceeding about 20 feet.[6]

The American Railway Engineering Association's 1953 *Specifications for Design of Retaining Walls and Abutments*, Section C, Article 2, third paragraph thereof, suggests the use of Rankine or Coulomb-type earth pressure calculations [Appendix F, Case (a)], but for walls not over 20 ft. high, these specifications permit the use of *semiempirical charts*,[7] such as the accompanying Fig. 9–5.

Since the AREA specification referred to was formulated quite recently, and since it encourages practical usage of the findings of soil mechanics, we will follow it in designing a 16-ft. cantilever retaining wall, using the Terzaghi and Peck chart for the earth pressure. Subsequently, the results of an investigation of the design by the Culmann graphical Coulomb method will be presented.

EXAMPLE 9–3

The Design of a Cantilever Retaining Wall. It is desired to design a cantilever retaining wall of 16-ft. total height for Cooper's E–72 railway loading.[D] The 1953 AREA specification for retaining-wall design will be followed, taking AREA Type No. 1 backfill and foundation soil properties.

For concrete and steel, the ACI Code, 3000-lb. concrete and high bond intermediate grade reinforcing bars will be taken.

See the accompanying Calculation Sheet 1 for additional starting information.

Solution: Refer to the several succeeding calculation sheets.

Retaining Wall Designing

9–8. The Proportioning of a Cantilever Retaining Wall. (Author's Method.) In Calculation Sheets 1 and 2, the earth pressure forces shown were gotten from the empirical charts previously mentioned. The railway equipment load was converted to an equivalent additional height of backfill, and the additional lateral pressure of this *surcharge* found. (If unfamiliar, refer to Appendix F.)

---

[6] Reprinted with permission from Terzaghi and Peck's *Soil Mechanics in Engineering Practice* (New York: John Wiley & Sons, Inc., 1948).

[7] Reprinted by permission from Peck, Hanson, and Thornburn's *Foundation Engineering* (New York: John Wiley & Sons, Inc., 1953).

Ex. 9-3	Design of a Cantilever Retaining Wall	H.E.L.	7-21-54	1/8

DATA & SPECS

○ **Rail Loading:** Take 72,000 lb. axles at 5 ft. c-c on track and cross-section sketched on Calc. Sheet 2.

See Appendix G for '53 A.R.E.A. Specification

Backfill and Base Soil: The earth pressure will not be increased for impact or vibration per A.R.E.A., Secs. C1 & 2, third paragraph of each.
Consider water table at 15 ft. below foundation bed.

Sec. C2 Take A.R.E.A. Type I soil: $\gamma = 105$ pcf, $\phi = 33°42'$, tan. = 0.667.

Sec. D2 Coeff. of base-to-ground friction = 0.55,
Take sliding F. of S. = 1.5, O.T.M. F. of S. = 2.00 (added)

Sec. D3 Safe bearing capacity = 1.7 tsf (at F. of S. of 2.0)

and its Fig. 2 Get foundation bed 4 ft. below final grade (frost).

Concrete & Steel: Take A.C.I. Code, 3,000 lb. concrete and high bond deformed bars. Per J.C. Spec., Sec. 877, provide 3 in. cover for reinforcement where concrete is in contact with the soil, 2 in. over all exposed surfaces. Take $1\frac{1}{2}$ in. max. aggregate size.

Sec. F1 Heel stresses must not exceed $1\frac{1}{2}$ times allowable when foundation reaction is considered absent.

○ *Sec. F1* Not less than 0.25 sq. in. temperature reinforcement in stem per foot of height.

"OLD RULES" - for proportions:

Sec. D1 "Get resultant force within the middle third of the base.
"Center the stem over the resultant force.
"Ten-inch min. stem top thickness (concrete placing)
"Try a base-of-stem thickness of $\frac{1}{6}$ to $\frac{1}{8}$ of the width of the base.
"Try a base thickness the same as the base-of-stem.

EARTH PRESSURE CALCULATIONS.

Use Terzaghi & Peck's empirical chart data for Type I soil: Refer to textbook Fig. 9-5.
For horizontal backfill, $k_v = 0$ and $P_v = 0$, $k_h = 31$.

$$P_h = \frac{1}{2} k_h H^2 = \frac{31}{2} \times \frac{(17)^2}{1000} = 4.48 \text{ kips}$$

○ *Sec. C1* Equivalent soil head = $\frac{72000}{5(14)(105)} = 9.8$ ft.

Surcharge lateral pressure = 31(9.8) = 304 psf.

The design rule stated in Sheet 2 was utilized to get a trial base width, B, by taking moments of all forces to the rear of the front edge of the base of the stem. To do this, the desired position of the vertical component of the upward resultant reaction was set at e, just inside the edge of the middle third[8] of the base, $0.66B$ from the rear edge in this case. The thickness of the base of the stem was then estimated at $0.14B$ and *centered* over the resultant force. The thickness of the base slab was taken the same as the base of the stem. Moments of the overturning and approximate[9] resisting forces *about e*, the resultant force point, yielded a trial base width of 11 ft. 3 in., which did not require revision later, in this instance.

The required base-of-stem thickness was next calculated in Sheet 3 because it is often the critical one. The resulting 18.8 in. demand proved consistent with the $0.14B$ early assumed. The thickness of the base of the wall was then tentatively taken at 19 in. also, awaiting calculation thereof.[10]

Throughout this portion of the work one undertakes to settle *only* the *concrete* dimensions, namely the *outline* of the structure, leaving spaces on his sheets for the later computation of the reinforcement needed, as was done in this case.

9–9. The Checks upon Stability. In the lower half of Sheet 3 and the upper half of Sheet 4 the very important matter of *stability* could be accurately studied because the dimensions of the retaining wall had become established.

Overturning must always be studied in tabular form, keeping the vertical *resisting* forces separate from the horizontal *overturning* forces. It is also a good plan to isolate and identify the surcharge forces because they are transient ones and are sometimes excluded, as was done at the top of Sheet 4.

Of course, there are other combinations of loadings and manners of application, as well as different methods of getting the forces, but the two possibilities considered usually "bracket" the common cases.

Sliding of the wall upon the foundation soil is a possibility involving only the horizontal and vertical forces, not moments of forces. In this case, the structure would probably prove safe without a base shear key if more vertical load were on the structure, increasing the sliding resistance. Such a condition would exist if the surcharge extended to the

---

[8] For the poorer foundation soils, set the desired location of the reaction close to the *center* of the base, thus predetermining a substantially uniform pressure.

[9] In this approximate method, the moment of the disregarded toe portion is substantially offset by conveniently considering the concrete of the stem and heel portions no heavier than the soil.

[10] If the front face of the stem has batter, any slight tilting of the wall will never be noticed.

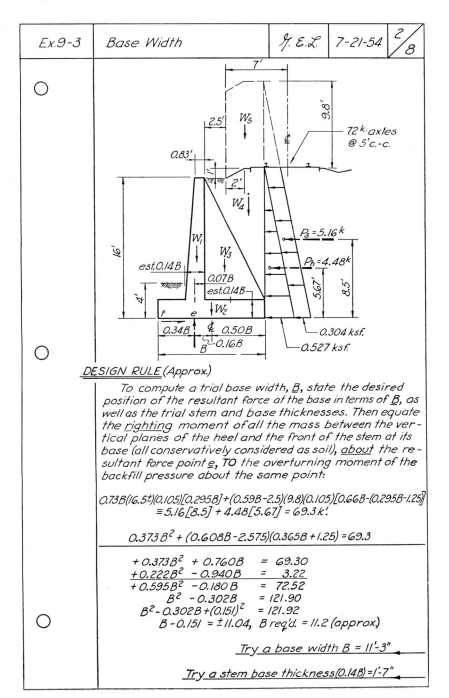

| Ex.9-3 | Base Width | | $\mathscr{Y}.\mathscr{E}.\mathscr{L}$ | 7-21-54 | 2/8 |

<u>DESIGN RULE</u> (Approx.)

To compute a trial base width, <u>B</u>, state the desired
position of the resultant force at the base in terms of <u>B</u>, as
well as the trial stem and base thicknesses. Then equate
the <u>righting</u> moment of all the mass between the vertical planes of the heel and the front of the stem at its
base (all conservatively considered as soil), <u>about</u> the resultant force point <u>e</u>, TO the overturning moment of the
backfill pressure about the same point:

$$0.73B(16.5^{\pm})(0.105)[0.295B] + (0.59B-2.5)(9.8)(0.105)[0.66B-(0.295B-1.25)]$$
$$\equiv 5.16[8.5] + 4.48[5.67] = 69.3k!$$

$$0.373B^2 + (0.608B-2.575)(0.365B+1.25) = 69.3$$

$$\begin{aligned} +0.373B^2 &+ 0.760B &= 69.30 \\ \underline{+0.222B^2} &\underline{- 0.940B} &= \underline{3.22} \\ +0.595B^2 &- 0.180B &= 72.52 \\ B^2 &- 0.302B &= 121.90 \\ B^2 - 0.302B &+ (0.151)^2 &= 121.92 \\ B - 0.151 &= \pm 11.04, \quad &B\ req'd. = 11.2\ (approx.) \end{aligned}$$

<u>Try a base width B = 11'-3"</u>

<u>Try a stem base thickness (0.14B) = 1'-7"</u>

Ex. 9-3	Stability etc.	𝓗.𝓔.𝓛	7-21-54	3/8

STEM STRENGTH — 1'-7" stem & base being tried

○

17.00
1.58
15.42

3.69
4.69   3⟌15.42'
8.38   5.14

19.0
36.2
55.2

$Shear\ Force = \left(\dfrac{15.42}{17.0}\right)^2 (4.48) + \dfrac{15.42}{17.0}(5.16) = 8.38^k\ max.$

$D.T.\ \underline{d}\ req'd. = \dfrac{V}{bjv} = \dfrac{8380}{12(7/8)(90)} = 8.86''$

$B.M._{max.} = 3.69\ [5.14] + 4.69\ [7.71] = 55.2^{k'}$

$Flex.\ d\ req'd. = \sqrt{\dfrac{M}{Rb}} = \sqrt{\dfrac{55.2\,(12000)}{236\,(12)}} = 15.30''$

                                         0.50 bar rad.
                                         3.00 cover
Make base of stem 1'-7," trying #8 bars   18.80"
                        —//—   —//—   —//—

See Calc. Sh. 6 (Later)
for arrange- $R = \dfrac{M}{bd^2} = \dfrac{55.2\,(12000)}{12(15.50)^2} = 230,$ $p = 1.34\%$
ment of stem   Req'd $A_s/l'' = 0.207^{□''}$
steel   Bond Stress   Equals #8's @ 3.82" max.

                $u = \dfrac{8380}{12/382\,(\pi)(7/8)(15.50)} = 63\ psi,\ OK$

○   Req'd Anchorage - A.C.I. Sec. 1103(c), Splices in Vertical
                          Reinforcement, requires 20 diams.

STABILITY   —Assuming a 1'-7" base slab.

(a) Against Overturning: ΣM about bot. toe pt. t

Vertical Forces	Kips	Arm	Moment
			—Clockwise
$W_1 = 1.21(14.42)(0.15) = $	2.62	3.98'	10.43 k'
$W_2 = 1.58(11.25)(0.15) = $	2.67	5.62	15.00
$W_3 = 6.67(14.42)(0.105) \div 2 = $	5.05	6.81	34.40
$W_4 = 6.67(15.42)(0.105) \div 2 = $	5.40	9.03	48.75
	15.74		108.58

Surcharge
$W_5 = 4.17(9.8)(0.105) = $ 4.29   9.17   39.40 k'
                        $\Sigma V = 20.03^k$ $\Sigma M_R = 147.98\ ^{k'}$

Horizontal Forces			Counter-clockwise
$P_h \quad = $	4.48	5.67	25.4
P_s (surcharge) =	5.16	8.50	43.9
$\Sigma H = 9.64\ ^k$			O.T.M. = 69.3 $^{k'}$

○

Ex.9-3	Stability, Toe	𝒴.ℰ.ℒ.	7-21-54	4/8

Overturning Moms. about Toe — to locate resultant force:

All forces acting:

$$x = \frac{147.98 - 69.30}{20.03} = 3.93', \text{ or } 1.70' \text{ to left of } \cancel{\xi},$$
$$= 0.17' \text{ inside kern, O.K.}$$

$$F. \text{ of } S. = \frac{147.98}{69.30} = 2.13, > 2.0, \therefore O.K.$$

2 ⌐11.25'
3 ⌐5.63
　1.87

5.63	5.63
3.93	5.28
1.70	0.35
5.63	108.58
5.28	25.40
0.35	83.18

If surcharge absent:

$$x = \frac{108.58 - 25.4}{15.74} = 5.28', \text{ or } 0.35' \text{ to left of } \cancel{\xi}, O.K.$$

$$F. \text{ of } S. = \frac{108.58}{25.4} = 4.27, \ O.K.$$

Sec. D2

(b) Against Sliding　　　　　　　　　A.R.E.A. coeff. = 0.55

— All forces acting:

$$F. \text{ of } S. = \frac{0.55(20.03)}{9.64} = 1.14, < 1.5, \text{ inadequate.}$$

Surcharge absent: $F. \text{ of } S. = \dfrac{0.55(15.74)}{4.48} = 1.93$

Must design a base shear key. See later work.

(c) Toe Pressure — All forces acting.

$$\frac{N}{A} = \frac{20.03}{11.25} = 1.78$$

$$I = \frac{(11.25)^3}{12} = 119$$

$$\frac{Mc}{I} = \frac{20.03(1.70)(5.63)}{119} = \underset{3.39 \ ksf.}{1.61}$$

3.0'　1.58'　6.67'　　11.25'

1.58 · 3.15 · 2.29 · 2.16 · 2.08 · 6.96' · 0.17

1.58(0.15) = 0.24 ksf base D.L.

A.R.E.A. Sec. D3 and its Fig. 2

≤ 1.7 tsf allowed, O.K.　End of Stability Studies.

TOE STRENGTH

　3.15
　2.29
2 ⌐5.44
　2.72

Diagonal Tension

$$d \text{ req'd.} = \frac{V}{v j b} = \frac{2.72(3)(1000)}{90(7/8)(12)} = 8.6''$$

　3.15
　1.14 +
　4.29 +

Bending

$$B.M. = \{1.575[2] + 1.145[1]\}(3) = 12.9 \ k!$$

$$d \text{ req'd.} = \sqrt{\frac{M}{Rb}} = \sqrt{\frac{12.9(12000)}{236(12)}} = 7.4''$$

(Later) — Having taken 1'-7" base thickness, and #8 bars:

Ref. A.C.I. Sec. 702(e)(2)

$$R = \frac{M}{bd^2} = \frac{12.9(12000)}{12(15.5)^2} = 53.7, \ p = 0.29\%$$

Req'd. $A_s / 1'' = 0.045,^{\square''}$ equals #8 bars @ 17.5" c-c. max.

rear face of the stem, or if the heel portion were lengthened to "gather" more earth (gravity) load.

Toe Pressure is some measure of the tendency of a retaining wall to settle at the toe and is almost independent of whatever the overturning moment factor of safety, computed earlier, may be. In the present case the calculated maximum unit toe pressure was slightly less than the allowable of 1.7 tons per sq. ft. for our granular soil. Oftentimes, with poorer foundation soils, this is the critical point in the stability calculations. When the toe stress turns out excessive, it can be brought under control rather easily by lengthening the toe portion, which decreases the eccentricity of the resultant ground reaction with respect to the centerline of the base, and incidentally, widens the base. The overturning calculation, as in Sheet 3, is then easily corrected because all the original vertical forces have had their moment arms lengthened by the amount of the widening. Reiterating: the resultant forces will be found to be relatively much nearer the center of the enlarged base, which results in a *much* smaller Mc/I component of toe pressure.

Omission of Vertical Forces. The overburden directly over the toe is always disregarded, except when it is paved. Neither is the soil directly in front thereof (Fig. 9–6) relied upon to resist sliding. Both these earth masses tend to shrink away from the wall.

As in the case of surcharge, the vertical component of inclined backfill pressure, or a portion thereof, is sometimes omitted from calculations when it is conservative to do so; particularly if there is some possibility of settlement of the wall relative to the backfill.

STABILITY PRACTICE PROBLEM

Problem 9–5. Calculate how wide the base of the retaining wall should be in order to bring the toe stress down to 1.25 tons per sq. ft.

Instructor: See also stability investigation Problem 9–8 at the end of the chapter.

9–10. The Reinforcement. The strength design of the stem[11] and toe in Sheets 3 and 4 presented no new problems. Attention is called to the practice of deducting the dead load of the toe when proportioning it and its reinforcement, as in footing design.

The Heel Strength computations on Sheet 5 pose two new practices. The cantilever bending moment was properly computed about a *support point* $3\frac{1}{2}$ in. inside the stem, where its main reinforcement is centered, as shown in Sheet 6. Also, alternate situations were considered in finding the design shear and bending moment forces. As usually computed

---

[11] A possible improvement would be to make the base of the stem thicker than required for a balanced section, resulting in wider bar spacings.

Ex.9.3	Toe, Heel		$\mathcal{Y.E.L.}$	7-21-54	$\dfrac{5}{8}$

○ Toe (Later) concluded   Taking #8 bars

$$Bond, \mu = \frac{2.72(3)(1000)}{12/17.5(\pi)(7/8)(15.5)} = 280 \; psi. < 300, \therefore O.K.$$

Anchorage ~ req'd:

For horizontal portion $\dfrac{fs}{4\mu} d' = \dfrac{20000}{4(300)} d' = 17 \; diams.$

For vert. stem splice portion, A.C.I. Sec.1103(c), 20 diams. min.

HEEL STRENGTH

Forces – downward		Kips	Arm*	Moment*
$W_3 = 3.33(14.42)(0.105)$	=	5.05	2.52	12.72^k
$W_4 = 3.34(15.42)(0.105)$	=	5.40	4.74	25.60
D.L. = 1.58(6.96)(0.15)	=	1.65	3.48	5.74
SURCHARGE		12.10		44.06
$W_5 = 4.17(9.8)(0.105)$		4.29	4.88	20.95
		16.39		65.01

$\frac{2}{3}$ thereof = 10.92 $\frac{2}{3}$ = 43.34

See Sheet 4 ___Upward

6.96 (1.08)	=	- 7.52	2.32	- 17.45
6.96 (0.085)	=	- 0.59	4.64	- 2.74
	Total = 8.28^k down		Total = 44.82$^{k't}_c$	

*About stem reinf. resistance point, 3½" inward

A.R.E.A. Sec. F1 possibility of no ground reaction rules.

○ 3 | 6.96
       2.32
     × 2
     ——
     4.64

Bending

$$d \; req'd. = \sqrt{\frac{M}{Rb}} = \sqrt{\frac{44.82(12000)}{236(12)}} = 13.76''$$

9.17
4.29
4.88

6.67
 .29
——
6.96

                                        0.50 bar rad.
                                        3.00 cover
          Req'd. thickness = 17.26", rules

Diag. Tension

$$d \; req'd. = \frac{V}{vjb} = \frac{10920}{90(7/8)(12)} = 11.56''$$

Arbitrarily make heel 1'-7" and take #8 bars.

(Later)

$$R = \frac{44.82(12000)}{12(15.5)^2} = 186, \quad p = 1.07\%, \; A_s/_{1''} = 0.166^{\square''}$$

                        Use #8's @ 4½" or less.

Bond Stress

$$\mu = \frac{10920}{12/4.5(\pi)(7/8)(15.50)} = 96 \; psi, < 210, O.K.$$

Req'd. Anchorage ~ of top bars, A.C.I. Sec.& Table 305(a)

○

$$a = \frac{fs}{4\mu} d' = \frac{20000}{4(210)} d' = 24 \, d' = 24'' \; beyond$$

                        the intersection* with
                        the stem steel.

they are (from Sheet 5) 8.28 kips and 44.82 kip-ft. However, Appendix G, AREA Sec. F 1, last paragraph, requires that the allowable unit stresses shall not be exceeded more than 50 per cent if uplift should occur and the upward ground reaction disappear. Accordingly, on Sheet 5, when the "upward" items are disregarded, the design forces become 16.39 kips and 65.01 kip-ft. In the tabulation, directly below these values, two-thirds of each has been set down for direct comparison with the original values ("Total"). Note that in this case the original total moment predominated, and was used in designing the reinforcement, but that the reverse situation prevailed with respect to shear. Also observe that the dead load of the heel itself was purposely included, since it contributes to the tension in the top when there is uplift. Otherwise not.

As is usually the case, the required heel thickness set the minimum thickness of base slab.

The required steel area per inch of width, the tentatively chosen bar size, and the corresponding required embedment required for anchorage were computed for all three of the cantilever elements, for convenient reference in later selecting the final arrangement of the reinforcement.

9–11. Bar Arrangement. In Sheet 6, the stem reinforcement dominated the arrangement of the rest of the steel.

In construction, the base slab (with key) is first placed and allowed to set. The stem forms are then built upon it. The longest stem bars are then set upon the base concrete and laterally secured to the stem forms. They are spliced into the base concrete by straight vertical dowels previously embedded therein, or by bent-up extensions of the toe steel, as in this case. Refer to the central portion of Sheet 6.

The stem bar size finally selected was one which, at the top of the wall, could work at some wide spacing divisible by four, and which did not exceed the $3t$ maximum spacing permitted by ACI Sec. 702(e)(3), namely, 30 in. As shown on Sheet 6, a spacing decreasing from 16 in. down to 4 in. was used, with three out of every four bars being #8's, the fourth a #9, the lengths thereof varying according to the accompanying diagram of steel area required at each level.

The bars extending only 5 ft. 5 in. above the base were considered to be short enough to support themselves, so the base concrete was cast around them.

Splicing of Stem Steel. Portions of ACI Chapter 11, *Reinforced Concrete Columns and Walls*, are applicable to the design of the stem. Therein, Sec. 1103(c), *Splices in vertical reinforcement*, requires 20 diam. of lap for bond splices. Because of the great importance of the connection between stem and base, 24 diam. were conservatively provided.

Since a base shear key was needed, it was located so that it served as an anchorage block for the straight splicing dowels, which also reinforce it for bending!

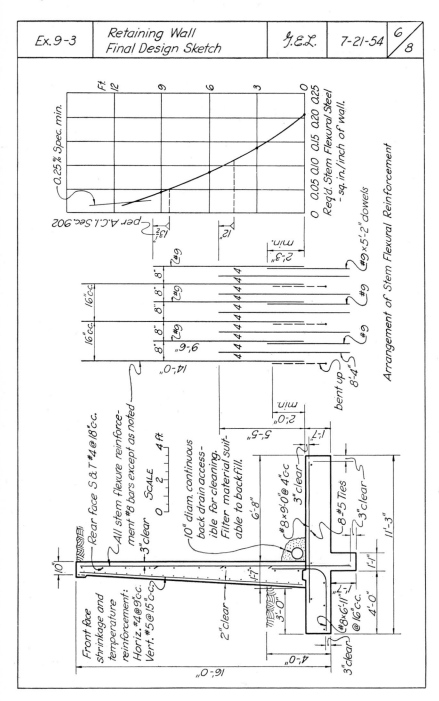

Ex. 9-3 | Retaining Wall Final Design Sketch | J.E.L. | 7-21-54 | 6/8

The toe steel size was chosen for a 16-in. spacing so that its bent-up ends could serve as splice material for one-fourth of the stem bars. The heel steel was arbitrarily spaced at 4 in. c. to c. so as to avoid any interference with the rest of the reinforcement.

9–12. Design of Base Shear Key. Calculation Sheet 7 presents the latest recommended practice.[E] Refer especially to Fig. 9–6, noting that reliance is placed upon the passive resistance of the earth below the toe point.

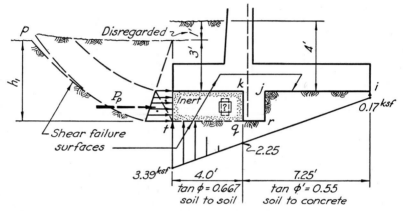

Fig. 9–6. Passive resistance and shearing action at base shear key.

Base shear keys have sometimes been proportioned for the passive resistance computable at the face of the key, kq, from the base pressure. To so act, the wall would have to lift itself, according to the pictured deformation of the unit cube. This will not happen if failure can occur more easily along $ptqrji$.

Note that no reliance whatever is being placed upon the upper foot of the toe fill, or upon the *lateral* strength of the earth in front of the toe.

For the key to be effective, the trench must be cleanly cut and the shoulder at kq firm and free of root holes. If such is not the case, the unsound portion may be removed, a form placed, and the earth replaced by thorough compaction of thin layers. If the earth is not cohesive enough to compact properly, it should be stabilized by the addition of not over 10 per cent of clay. After drying, the form is removed and the concrete of the key placed integrally with the base concrete.

BASE SLIDING PRACTICE PROBLEMS

Problem 9–6. For the retaining wall of Example 9–3 above, calculate the required depth of base shear key if the passive resistance computable at the

| Ex.9-3 | Keys | | $\mathscr{H}.\mathscr{E}.\mathscr{L}.$ | 7-23-54 | 7/8 |

DESIGN OF SHEAR KEYS

Stem Key

This is closely a case of pure shear, for which an allowable of at least $0.08\,f_c'$ may be taken: *(Table 1-2, Chapter 1)*

$$V_{max} = \frac{8380}{6.5(12)} = 108 \text{ psi}, < 240, \therefore O.K.$$

Base Shear Key   Ref. "Sliding" on Sheet 4, and Fig. 9-6.

At incipient leftward sliding of the retaining wall, the value of a key will depend upon how much passive resistance, P_p, can be developed below the toe as a potential failure surface develops. For this purpose, the weight of the upper foot of toe fill earth has conservatively been disregarded.

From fundamentals, or Appendix F, Cases (a) and (d), the *active* hydrostatic pressure ratio is:

$\phi = 33°42'$

$$C_A = \frac{1}{C_p} = tan^2[45° - \phi/2] = tan^2\ 28°\text{-}9' = 0.286$$

45° 0'
16° 51'
28° 9'

Taking h_1 as in Fig. 9-6, the passive resistance will be:

$$P_p = \frac{\gamma h^2}{2C_A} = \frac{0.105}{2(0.286)}\ [h_1^2 - (3)^2] = 0.183 h_1^2 - 1.65 \text{ k/ft}.$$

At incipient sliding failure:

$$P_p + tan\ \phi\ W_{toe} + tan\ \phi' W_{heel} = \Sigma H\ (F.\ of\ S.)$$

From bottom of Sheet 3.

$$0.183 h_1^2 - 1.65 + 0.667(3.39 + 2.25)\left(\frac{4}{2}\right) + 0.55(2.25 + 0.17)\left(\frac{7.25}{2}\right) = 9.64(1.5)$$

Req'd. $h_1 = 4.54'$, req'd. key depth = 1.54', *make 1'-7."*

Refer to Sheet 6. Study has shown that the existing large dowel bars will safely reinforce the key for bending if its horizontal dimension be only 7 inches. Conveniently make it at least 12 in. and cleanly trim the trench to undisturbed surfaces.

face of the key from the foundation pressure were relied upon for the additional shearing resistance needed. Comment upon your result.

Problem 9–7. For the retaining wall of Example 9–3, endeavor to get along without a base shear key by making the heel (and base) longer, and discuss your findings.

9–13. Shrinkage and Temperature Reinforcement. This reinforcement is needed to control expansion and contraction perpendicular to the direction of the flexure steel in structures that are extensive in that direction. Refer to Calculation Sheet 8.

For the stem portion, ACI Sec. 1111(h) for the walls of buildings was followed, since there is no section on retaining walls. It requires a minimum of 0.25 per cent of horizontal reinforcement, spaced at not over 18 in. About two-thirds of it is ordinarily located near the exposed front face.

The above requirement exceeds that of AREA Sec. F 1, which calls for a minimum of 0.25 sq. in. per ft. of wall height.

Vertically, the ACI-required 0.15 per cent was provided near the front surface. The rear one is taken care of by the flexure reinforcement.

The base slab is primarily a buried footing which is little subject to temperature or moisture variations. About 0.1 per cent of reinforcement was provided longitudinally of the structure to serve principally as *ties* for the flexure bars. As much as 0.3 per cent is *sometimes* provided to reinforce the base against possible soft spots in the foundation soil.

Expansion Joints. Keyed *expansion joints* should be located about 80 ft. apart or more, depending upon the climate. At intermediate 20-ft. intervals, weakened plane *contraction* joints should also be provided.

9–14. Drainage Features. The *continuous back drain* covered with filter material, pictured on Calculation Sheet 6, is satisfactory for chart-designed walls up to 20 ft. high. An alternate scheme is the provision of *weep holes*[12] through the lower portion of the stem. They are less satisfactory because (a) they cannot be gotten low enough to drain the full height of the backfill, (b) they tend to become clogged with snow, ice, and debris, and (c) the emerging water tends to soften the foundation soil at the critical toe point.

Retaining walls higher than 20 ft. not only require the determination of the earth pressure forces by accepted soil mechanics theory, but also "that the backfill and drainage system be constructed in strict compliance with the conditions imposed by the theory" (Ref. Art. 9–7). Their drainage should include such features as a sloped impermeable top layer of backfill, a vertical gravel (French) drain[12] covering the entire back surface of the stem (or wall) and/or an inclined drainage layer conforming roughly to the backfill failure plane. Refer to Chapter VIII of Bibliography Reference A, this chapter.

---

[12] The Terzaghi and Peck design charts of Fig. 9–5 include an allowance for the increase in backfill pressure due to the imperfect drainage features of low retaining walls.

Ex. 9 -3	S. & T. Reinf.		𝓨. 𝓔. 𝓛	7-24-54	8/8

SHRINKAGE & TEMPERATURE REINFORCEMENT

Stem — Refer to A.C.I. Sec. 1111 (h)

    Horizontally

      14' (1.2'$_{av.}$)(144)(0.0025) = 6.0 sq. in.
      In front face, 20 - #4 @ 9" c-c. = 4.0 sq. in.
      In rear face, 10 - #4 @ 18" c.-c. = 2.0

    Vertically

      In front face, #5 @ 15" c.-c.
      In rear face, the flexure reinforcement
      serves.

Base

    Provide about 0.1% as ties.
      11.25' (1.58')(144)(0.001) = 2.56 sq. in.
      8 - #5's will do.

PLATE 9–1. Front side of cantilever retaining wall on a grade. Note stepping of toe of base. Loose earth in the left foreground was later leveled transversely to become a highway subgrade.

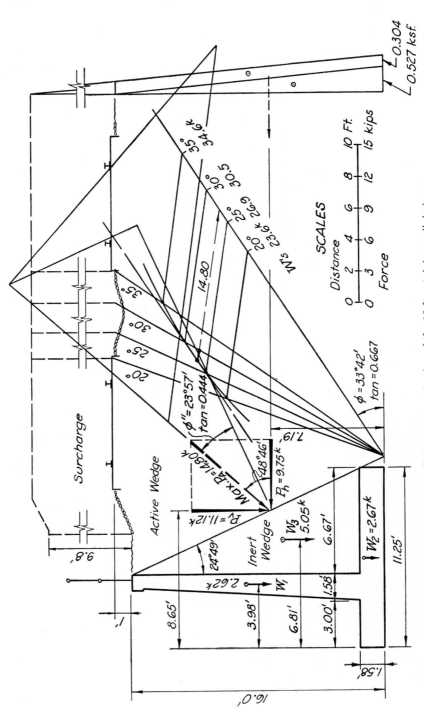

FIG. 9-7. Culmann investigation of the 16-ft. retaining wall design.

9–15. Investigation of the Stability of the Cantilever Wall Design by the Culmann Method. Since a wall 16 ft. high approaches the 20 ft. limit for determining the earth pressure forces from semiempirical charts, a Culmann investigation of the wall as designed was performed in Fig. 9–7, considering an inert wedge of earth directly behind the wall, down which a frictional coefficient, earth to earth, of $\frac{2}{3}$ tan ϕ was taken. The resulting failure plane was at about 27° with the vertical. The loads and forces involved are shown.

The corresponding stability study, Table 9–1, is the same as that of Calculation Sheet 3 of Art. 9–9, so far as the vertical forces W_1, W_2 and W_3 and their moment arms are concerned. Instead of force W_4 we now have P_v, while P_h represents the only horizontal force.

TABLE 9–1

Force		Arm about Toe Point in ft.	Moment, in kip ft.	Remarks
Designation	kips			
VERTICAL				
$W_1 + W_2 + W_3 =$	10.34	—	59.83	From Calc. Sheet 3
$P_v =$	11.12	8.65	96.30	From Fig. 9–7
$\Sigma V =$	21.46		$\Sigma M_R = $ 156.13	
HORIZONTAL				
$P_h =$	9.75	7.19	$-70.10 =$ O.T.M.	

Resultant Force at $x = \dfrac{156.13 - 70.10}{21.46} = 4.0'$, 1.63' from center of base, and within the 1.87-ft. kern limit.

Overturning F. of S. $= 156.13/70.10 = 2.23$, O.K.

Sliding F. of S. $= \dfrac{0.55(21.46)}{9.75} = 1.21, <1.5$, needs key.

Upon calculating the maximum toe pressure by $N/A + Mc/I$, as in Calculation Sheet 4, N/A proved to be 1.91, and Mc/I was 1.66 ksf, making a total of 3.57 ksf, or 1.79 tsf versus the 1.7 tsf value allowed.

Final Comment. The preceding investigation indicates that the expeditious semiempirical chart method is satisfactory for designing cantilever walls. Walls higher than the 20-ft. limit imposed usually have to be of the counterfort type anyway.

9–16. Counterfort Retaining Walls. The high cantilever type of walls are most economically proportioned if the stem and heel are tied together at intervals by ribs called **counterforts,** as illustrated in Fig. 9–1. Both stem and heel are designed as continuous slabs extending longitudinally of the wall. Their bending moments and thicknesses are thereby much decreased, but this saving is partially offset by the cost of the counterforts. The *buttress* type of wall, also pictured, is a variation thereof. For the designing of these walls, see *Reinforced Concrete Structures* by Dean Peabody, Jr., published by John Wiley and Sons, Inc., New York.

9–17. Summary of Retaining-Wall Design. Structurally, a cantilever retaining wall is a vertical cantilever anchored to a footing. Such walls are relatively light, so the weight of the front portion of the backfill is much relied upon for their stability.

The process of determining the dimensions of the members is a simple one, but the great differences in the pressures exerted by the various soils, together with the vagaries of weather conditions, combine to make an accurate determination of the forces acting an impossibility.

One of the most enlightening approaches to retaining-wall design is that of Coulomb, who many years ago visualized a sliding wedge of granular soil, the weight of which was partially supported by an inclined upward ground force, and, more importantly, by the lateral resistance of the wall.

From an engineering standpoint *internal friction* is probably the most essential attribute of a granular soil, since it is responsible for the *shear resistance*, the most important strength property. All the usual methods of retaining-wall design rely upon the presence of an active internal friction between the soil grains. When it does not exist, the wall must be a great deal larger and stronger. Refer to Appendix F.

PLATE 9–2. Workmen setting and tying the stem reinforcement for a cantilever retaining wall. Note the horizontal shrinkage and temperature steel.

To determine the trial dimensions needed in the initial stages of the *designing* process, employ the Terzaghi and Peck semiempirical charts, the simplified Coulomb formula of Equation 1, Appendix F, or the Rankine formula to approximate the earth pressure. High or complexly loaded walls should be designed, or at least checked, by the Culmann graphics or some other acceptable trial wedge procedure.

A retaining wall may fail in one of four ways; namely, by sliding, overturning, settlement, or by breaking apart. Such fracturing can be due to overstress in bending, shear or diagonal tension, bond or anchorage.

Tilting and settlement of a retaining wall on granular soil is forestalled by proportioning it so that (1) the resultant foundation reaction is within the middle third of the base, and (2) the allowable foundation pressure is not exceeded. For poorer soils the foundation reaction should be near the center of the base.

When attempting to laterally deform a soil mass against gravity forces, its high *passive resistance* is encountered. This property is used advantageously in designing abutments and base shear keys.

BIBLIOGRAPHY

A) TERZAGHI, KARL, and PECK, RALPH B. *Soil Mechanics in Engineering Practice.* New York John Wiley & Sons, Inc., 1948. Chap. VIII.

B) TAYLOR, DONALD W. *Fundamentals of Soil Mechanics.* New York: John Wiley & Sons, Inc., 1948. Chap. XVII.

C) PECK, HANSON, and THORNBURN. *Foundation Engineering.* New York John Wiley & Sons, Inc., 1953. Chaps. XI, XV, XXII, etc.

D) WILBUR, JOHN B., and NORRIS, CHAS. H. *Elementary Structural Analysis.* New York: McGraw-Hill Book Co., Inc., 1948. Chap. I.

E) FISHER, G. P., and MAINS, R. M. Sliding Stability of Retaining Walls, *Civil Engineering,* July, 1952, p. 54.

F) ANDERSEN, PAUL. *Substructure Analysis and Design.* New York: The Ronald Press Company, 1956. Chap. I, p. 16.

QUESTIONS

1. Define a retaining wall. Distinguish between the five types. Indicate under what circumstances each should be used.

2. Name and discuss the many factors that affect the forces which come upon retaining walls.

3. State the Coulomb theory of earth pressure.

4. How, if any, does the internal friction within a bulk material differ from the external friction between two objects? Is it possible to have internal friction without any externally applied normal force? Explain.

5. Taking a level backfill of sand, what portion of it presses against a wall? Is the angle ϕ a factor? Explain.

6. Enumerate all the factors which influence the presence or absence of friction between a wall and a backfill. What usually is the effect of disregarding it?

7. Enumerate the ways in which a retaining wall might fail. State reasonable specification requirements to prevent each.

8. Name six factors which tend to increase the pressure upon a retaining wall above that as usually computed, and tell how each is dealt with.

9. Define the hydrostatic pressure ratio. Explain whether it can ever exceed unity. What is the hydrostatic pressure ratio of mercury?

10. State clearly how to compute the factors of safety against sliding, overturning, and soil bearing failure.

11. If a retaining wall is securely fastened to some other large structure at its ends, will it require more material or less material than in the usual case? Explain.

12. To what extent will muddy water press more heavily upon a wall than clean water? Illustrate with a numerical example. Is the method the same for a saturated backfill?

13. Who is generally credited with devising the graphic method of determining pressures on retaining walls? In the process, why are the forces rotated through a particular angle? Is the rotation necessary?

14. How may the required base width of a gravity wall be determined systematically?

15. Explain passive resistance. What is the fundamental difference in action along the failure plane as between active and passive cases? What use is made of the principle in designing?

16. What is the advantage in having a foundation bed consist of undisturbed earth? Is it impossible to produce equal or greater strength by compaction of loose material? Explain.

17. Tell in detail how to find the required outside dimensions of a cantilever retaining wall.

18. Which is better: to have a uniform foundation pressure at the allowable bearing value, or widely varying edge pressures both of which are appreciably below the allowable value?

19. What precautions need to be observed in designing the reinforcement for retaining walls? Which reinforcement is likely to be overlooked in designing?

20. Which end of the base slab would you lengthen if (a) the toe pressure is too great? (b) the sliding factor of safety is too low? Explain.

21. Of what two items does the shearing resistance of a soil consist? What are the characteristics of sandy versus clayey soils in this respect? How may it be determined fairly accurately without special equipment (a) for clayey soil? (b) for sandy soil?

PROBLEMS

Problem 9–8. For the retaining wall of Fig. 9–8 make a complete stability investigation, including a diagram of foundation pressure. Use the Terzaghi and Peck earth pressure chart. Follow the AREA Code and prepare a brief report of your findings.

(a) Taking AREA Type 1 backfill and foundation soil.

(b) Taking AREA Type 2 backfill and foundation soil.

Problem 9–9. Additionally for the retaining wall of Fig. 9–8, make a complete strength investigation, including the base shear key and all bar anchorages. Take 2500-lb. concrete and the ACI Code for its allowable stresses. The reinforcement is intermediate grade, high bond, deformed bars. Follow the AREA Code for the retaining wall requirements and prepare a brief report of your findings:

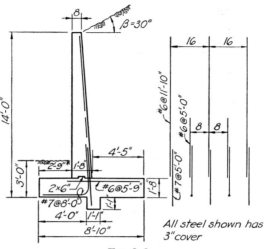

FIG. 9–8.

(a) Taking AREA Type 1 backfill and foundation soil.
(b) Taking AREA Type 2 backfill and foundation soil.

Problem 9–10. (a) Design a cantilever retaining wall of 20-ft. total depth for Cooper's E–70 railway loading. Take AREA Type 2 backfill and foundation soil properties and follow this retaining wall specification throughout.

For concrete and steel take the ACI Code, 3750-lb. concrete and high bond, intermediate grade, reinforcing bars.

For any additional starting information consult the instructor.

(b) Make an independent check upon the stability of the retaining wall by the best available method.

Problem 9–11. Given the reinforced concrete box culvert of Fig. 9–9. Investigate the safety thereof considering it as a rigid frame subject to 300 psf highway vehicle surcharge loading, the overburden and the lateral pressure of the earth.

Take AREA Type 2 soil and specification.

Take ACI 3000-lb. concrete and specification, also high bond deformed bars.

Consult the instructor for any additional starting information needed.

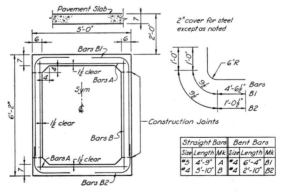

FIG. 9–9.

Problem 9–12. (*Individual*) *Determination of the Concrete Dimensions of a Cantilever Retaining Wall.*

Given: AREA Type 1 soil and specification, and a backfill slope of 33° 42′ (no surcharge). For concrete take ACI 3000-lb. concrete and specification, and high bond deformed bars. The aggregate maximum size is 1½ in.

Required: Taking your assigned total height and the Peck charts for earth pressure, follow the old rules and the general procedure of the calculation-sheet pages of the chapter.

Further, in order to meet the quite conservative value of maximum toe pressure dictated by Fig. 2 of the AREA Specification, design to have the resultant vertical earth force at 0.15B from the center of the base for the first trial, and not over 0.167B for the final position.

In addition, ensure that your design has satisfactory stability whether or not the vertical component of earth pressure, P_v, acts. The probabilities are that a greater base width, B, will be required when P_v is absent. Therefore:

1. In your first calculation for required B, stem thickness and toe pressure, consider P_v absent.

2. Check the structure evolved in (1) above with P_v present, and revamp if necessary.

If a toe pressure proves too great, refer to Art. 9–9 for guidance. To avoid

Group	Total Height of Wall
	18 ft.
	15 ft.
	13 ft. 6 in.
	12 ft.

wastefully wide base slabs see that the overturning moment factor of safety does not exceed 2.2 under the controlling loading condition.

If the stem thickness required for strength differs by more than 2 in. from that originally taken, recalculate the required B dimension, as on Sheet 2/8.

Finally draw an end view sketch of your wall at the left end of a sheet, as in Sheet 6/8, to the scale $1'' = 4'$.

Problem 9–13. (*Individual*) *Design of the Reinforcement for the Cantilever Retaining Wall of Problem 9–12.*

Given the cantilever retaining wall with an inclined backfill surface, the concrete dimensions of which were designed in the preceding problem for Type 1 soil, following the 1953 AREA Retaining Wall Spec., and the ACI Code for concrete design.

Required to design the steel for the structure, following the ACI Code and Chapter 9 of the textbook. The aggregate maximum size is 1½ in.

Systematically arrange your calculations, taking up the stem, toe, heel, and base shear key in order, and making the following subheadings:

1. *List* your shear and moment forces (from the preceding problem).
2. Study diagonal tension and shear, including the stem key designing.
3. Study bending.
4. Study bond.

5. Study anchorage (including also that of the dowel bars).

Indicate in each case what steps you have taken to ensure a safe design, whether or not P_v is acting.

Also calculate the shrinkage and temperature reinforcement, following the Chapter 9 work, and locate it properly.

Finally make a *final design sketch* to the scale $1'' = 4'$ (40 scale) showing the (a) position, (b) bar size number, (c) length, and (d) spacing of all steel. Include the two stem steel diagrams, as in Sheet 6/8 of Chapter 9, *in projection therewith, and on the same sheet*, neatly pasting on more paper if necessary.

Indicate the clear distance of all flexure steel from the face of the concrete, or cover with a general note. The shrinkage and temperature steel is to be identified as such.

Also be sure to include all the concrete dimensions, the class of the concrete, and the type of soil on the drawing.

CHAPTER 10

CREEP OF CONCRETE

10–1. Terms and Definitions. As mentioned in Art. 1–14, loaded concrete, like other building materials, immediately develops an *elastic deformation* proportional to the magnitude of the load. In addition, it continues to deform with lapse of time, albeit at a gradually decreasing

J. R. Shank, Research Professor of Structural Engineering, The Ohio State University, an early experimenter in creep and inelasticity. After careful analysis of all available world data, he evolved creep formulas for American engineers, and showed by numerical examples their application to everyday design of reinforced concrete members.

His paper, *The Mechanics of Plastic Flow of Concrete*, won him the Wason Medal of the American Concrete Institute.

rate, until the action finally ceases. Because this latter continuing deformation did not at first appear to be proportional to the magnitude of the applied load or stress, early investigators called it *plastic deformation*. The term *plastic flow* also was used for many years to designate this unusual property of concrete.

316

In recent years it has been shown experimentally[A] that the delayed deformation which takes place within the lower half of the stress-strain diagram for concrete (Fig. 10–1) is nearly proportional to the loading,[B] and is best called **creep** deformation. Therefore this lower portion of the diagram may, without serious error, be called the *elastic range* of the material. The sum of the elastic and creep unit deformations is sometimes used to compute an elapsed time modulus of elasticity, E_{ct}, called the *sustained modulus*, for the particular concrete age and loading duration involved. The subscript t is used to indicate that *time* is a factor therein.

Thus *creep* of concrete is the delayed, or *time-dependent*, portion of the total unit deformation, or *strain*, resulting from stress within the proportional elastic range of the material. It may become considerably greater than the instantaneous, or immediate, elastic unit deformation. It is partially[1] recoverable, depending upon the duration of the load.

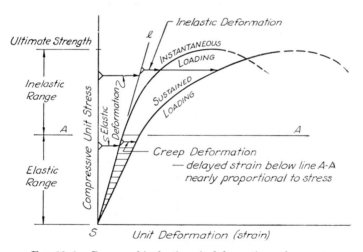

F IG. 10–1.   Creep and inelastic unit deformations of concrete.

In the upper half of the stress-strain diagram of Fig. 10–1, a small increment of stress quickly produces a disproportionately large increment of strain, which is nonlinear in nature and largely *independent of time*, now called **inelastic** deformation. Obviously this is the region of large stress adjustments due to slippage between particles as the ultimate strength is reached at the highest point of the curve. This stage is usually followed by a destructive breakdown, which occurs so quickly that there is a falling off of the test machine load. Little is known about the shape of the downturning portion of the curve, though it may have

---

[1] It is almost wholly recoverable if the duration of the loading approaches zero.

important practical significance.   Refer to Art. 12–1.   In today's concrete nomenclature the term *inelastic range* is applied to this locality of large deformations which develop rapidly within the upper region of stress approaching failure.   They cause stress redistributions, are nonlinear in nature, and nonrecoverable upon removal of the load.

10–2. Creep Diagrams and Elasticity. Figure 10–2 shows some typical creep data curves.[2]   Specimen A was loaded to 1500 psi at 28 days.   Specimens B and C were loaded to 750 psi at the 28-day age. C was unloaded 62 days later and its *creep strain recovery* observed.

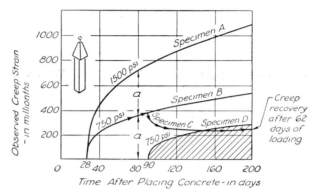

Fig. 10–2.   The time element in creep and creep recovery (sustained stress and stress removal).

Specimen D was first loaded to 750 psi at the 90-day age.   Note that the creep ordinates of specimens A and B that were loaded at the 28-day age for 172 days were proportional to the imposed stresses, thus justifying the linear relationship depicted in the lower portion of Fig. 10–1.

To simplify the presentation, the *elastic strain*, 250 millionths in the 750-psi specimens, was omitted from the lower portion of the figure, leaving only the creep.

Elastic materials return to their original form instantaneously when all load is removed, so they are said to *recover*.   In the case of concrete the effect of the *duration* of the load must be recognized in discussing recovery, since the *rate* of both creep and *creep recovery* is much slower at the later load-removal ages.   Note in the lower portion of Fig. 10–2 the relatively small creep that occurred in specimen D when the 750-psi stress was applied at the 90-day age.   On the other hand, consider

---

[2] Students of soil mechanics and foundations will recognize the similarity of the shape of typical creep-time curves to that of consolidation-time graphs of data from soil settlement tests made under constant load.

specimen C, which was loaded at the 28-day age and *unloaded* at the 90-day one. The effect of this operation may be visualized by conceiving the 28-day *compressive* load to remain on, applying an equal additional *tensile* one at the 90-day age and adding the two effects. This has been done geometrically in the figure by subtracting each specimen D creep-time ordinate from the corresponding specimen B one. The arrows indicate that the creep became considerably less after the unloading, but the large remainder accounts for the common unqualified statement that concrete structures do not recover well.

10–3. Effect of Impulsive Loads versus Dead Load. By transferring our attention from the 90-day age to the 28-day one, Figure 10–2 will show that had the 750-psi load been removed immediately after being applied, instead of 62 days later, the specimen would have fully recovered, since there can be no creep without a lapse of time. This means that the design *live loads* of fast-moving vehicles, if applied without impact and *quickly removed*, seldom cause large permanent strains in well-cured concrete members.

On the other hand, the *dead load* of a member, relatively large in concrete structures, is applied only once; it is never removed in service. It usually comes upon the structure at the early age of form removal, and so adds a great deal of creep strain to the elastic strain.

It should by now be apparent that the prediction of the deformation or deflection of concrete members is not a simple matter. It involves other variables yet to be discussed. To make even an estimate of the expected deformation one needs the whole *stress history* of the member. Formulas for estimating creep effects will be presented in succeeding articles.

Concrete is different from the other structural engineering materials. As Dr. Freyssinet has said:

Concrete is far more like a living tissue. Like the latter, it is affected by any external action—variation of pressure, temperature, or humidity—and since part of the effect is irreversible there remains a part which is never completely effaced. Thus it has a memory, and I think that the memory—even in its highest manifestations—is no more than a hysteresis phenomenon as in the case of cement. It has its age; when the circulation canals have reduced their sections to the extreme, its properties approach those of true solids. It has its sleep, for its activity may be slowed down or stopped by lack of water, and restarted by wetting.

Of all its similarities to a human being, that which interests us most is its faculty of healing its wounds, and its ability to overcome causes of failure.

10–4. Historical. At this point the experimental researches into creep and inelasticity that resulted in the findings which contributed most to the present state of the art will be very briefly reviewed.

It is probable that the phenomenon of creep had been observed before 1907 when Hatt* of Purdue University reported that the results of a series of deflection tests of beams . . . show a sort of plasticity in concrete by which it yields under the action of a load applied for a long time.

In 1915, McMillan, then at Minnesota, performed a similar series involving beams and slabs, observing in addition the changes in fiber strain. These observations called attention to the need for separating shrinkage and creep deformations.

Goldbeck and Smith, in 1916, found that creep was rapid at first, then slowed progressively. They observed also that when a long-sustained load was removed the creep recovery was relatively small.

Lord, in 1917, confirmed earlier reports and emphasized that concrete shrinkage decreases the tensile stress in flexure steel. Further, that creep tends to decrease the negative bending resistance over the supports in continuous flat-slab construction, thus increasing the deflections in regions of positive bending moment.

Investigations of creep were begun at The Ohio State University by Shank[C,D] in 1919. Experimentation both in sustained stress and sustained strain was conducted over a period of several years, under a variety of conditions. A formula for creep was developed therefrom and examples of applications to column and beam designing were presented.

In 1927, Faber of England, an eminent authority on mechanics, published the results of his tests and presented a design theory in which the effects of shrinkage and creep were incorporated by recognizing the change, with time, of the modulus of elasticity of the concrete.

A very comprehensive series of tests[E] is that of R. E. Davis of California, beginning about 1927. The tests were made under controlled conditions of temperature and humidity. Previously, experimenters had been eliminating the effects of temperature, humidity, and shrinkage variations by the use of identical unloaded companion specimens.

In 1930, Glanville of England reported[F] a similar comprehensive set of tests and derived therefrom the theoretical mechanics of creep.

More recently, Whitney,[G] and also Straub,[H] have shown how creep and inelasticity reduce secondary stresses in arch structures; and McHenry[A] and others have demonstrated that, in the working range, creep strain is nearly proportional to the elastic strain.

During 1947 and 1952 Washa[I] and Fluck[J] reported upon long-time deflection tests of slabs, singly reinforced beams and doubly reinforced beams, both sealed and air cured. Concrete strengths, span/depth ratios and steel percentages were varied. Separate elastic, creep, and shrinkage-warpage deflection data were secured in each case. Compressive reinforcement was found highly efficient for minimizing creep deflection.

10–5. The Nature of Creep.[C] The hydration of portland cement proceeds with the formation of a jelly-like *gel* around each particle.

---

* To conserve space full names and titles are not given. Most of the work mentioned has been reported in American Concrete Institute Proceedings.

It continues until the entire particle has finally been completely hydrated. The time required varies greatly, depending upon the size of the cement particles, the availability of sufficient water and the influence of retarders; it is believed by some that the gel in time changes to crystalline forms.

Creep is due to compression of the gel by load. It may be due partly to an actual loss of water volume forced toward the outside surface through capillary channels, since the rate of creep is faster in a dry curing atmosphere. A specimen that was thoroughly dried in an oven, then varnished to keep moisture out, when finally loaded had practically no creep until the hygroscopic moisture from the air penetrated the varnish to satisfy the thirst of the gel. When all specimens were initially in moisture balance, those in dry atmospheres crept much more than those in wet ones, which suggests that capillarity may be an important factor.

The *rate* of creep is greater for a small member, of low strength concrete, of high water/cement ratio, high cement factor and large slump, when hand placed, cured in a dry atmosphere, then loaded at an early age, considering the other influences constant in each instance. The rate is greatest immediately after load application, but decreases quite fast, asymptotically.

For cured-in-air concretes, about one-fourth of the total creep takes place during the first 14 days of loading, one-half during the first 3 months and three-fourths during the first year. Concrete loaded at the four-year age creeps very little, so it recovers almost completely after being unloaded. It is believed that it reaches this stable state due to solidification of the gels.

10–6. The Formula for Creep under Sustained Stress. Although good expressions have been devised by Straub, Thomas, and others for predicting the ordinates, δ_t, of a creep-time curve of concrete, as in Fig. 10–2, only Professor Shank's[C,D] will be briefly illustrated here, namely:

$$\delta_t = C \sqrt[r]{t} \qquad (10\text{–}1)$$

wherein δ_t = *specific creep*, the *time*-dependent unit creep strain of concrete, per psi of sustained axial stress, in millionths,

$\quad\quad$ C = a coefficient deduced from tests, also expressed in millionths—it is the first day's creep strain under a stress of unity,

$\quad\quad$ r = a root deduced from tests,

$\quad\quad$ t = time, the duration of the loading, in days.

For *ordinary strength concretes*, i.e., in the 2500- to 3750-lb. range, made with standard portland cement and good limestone aggregates, loaded in air at the 28-day age, Shank recommended

$$\delta_t = 0.13 \sqrt[3]{t} \qquad (10\text{–}2)$$

This formula is considered satisfactory up to one year of loading. For longer periods, apply the following multipliers to the value of δ_t at one year:

Number of Years Loaded	Multiplier
1	1.00
2	1.17
3	1.26
4	1.30
5 or more	1.33

If ordinary standard portland cement concrete is loaded at ages other than the 28-day one, Shank modifies C in Formula 10–1 to:

$$C = \frac{0.500}{\sqrt[2.5]{a}}$$

wherein a is the age when loaded, in days.

The following table has been prepared from Shank's recommendations of 1935, assuming good limestone aggregate concrete loaded in air:

Class of Concrete	Age When Loaded in Air —days	Coefficient C	
		Standard Portland Cement	High Early Strength Portland Cement
For ordinary strength concretes: $f'_c = 2500$ to 3750 psi.	3	—	0.15
	7	0.23	0.10
	14	0.17	0.07
	28	0.13	0.05
	60	0.10	0.034

For higher strength (rich mix) standard portland cement concretes in the 4000- to 5000-psi range, the data are scarce. Using silica aggregates, Shank found C's around 0.085 when loaded in air at the 28-day age.

For different aggregates, cements, ages when loaded, and curing studied by Shank, see page 51 of item D of the Bibliography.

Creep in Axially Loaded Members

EXAMPLE 10–1

Given a 3000-lb. standard portland cement unreinforced stone-concrete pier loaded in air to 700 psi at the 14-day age. It is required to compute the unit creep strain after two years of loading. Calculate also the instantaneous elastic strain, and compare.

Solution: Referring to the formulas and tables of Art. 10–6:

Basically, $\delta_t = C\sqrt[3]{t}$

$$\delta_t = 1.17(0.17)\sqrt[3]{365} = 1.42 \text{ millionths per psi.}$$

So,   700-psi unit creep strain $= 700(1.42 \times 10^{-6}) = 0.00099$ in./in.

and   Corresp. elastic strain $= \dfrac{f_c}{E_c} = \dfrac{700}{3,000,000} = 0.00023$ in./in.,

so the creep strain is over four times the elastic in this case.

CREEP PRACTICE PROBLEMS

Problem 10–1. A 3500-lb. high early strength portland cement stone-concrete pedestal is loaded to 800 psi at the 3-day age. Compute the unit creep strain after one and five years of loading. Calculate the elastic strain also.   *Partial Ans. 0.00086 in./in., at one year*
0.00114 in./in., at five years

Problem 10–2. A 3000-lb. standard portland cement stone-concrete pier 30-ft. high is loaded in air to 900 psi at the 14-day age, and unloaded at the 60-day age. Compute the creep strain in inches at the 90-day age. Refer to Fig. 10–2.   *Ans. 0.133 in.*

Problem 10–3. Same as Problem 10–2 except that the pier is reloaded at the 90-day age. Compute the creep strain at the one-year age.

10–7. The Mechanics of Creep in Axially Loaded R/C Columns under Sustained Load.[3] In Chapter 4 on columns we saw that tests have shown that wherever steel and concrete must *share* a compressive load, as in columns and in doubly reinforced beams, the concrete, due to creep, gradually divests itself of part of its elastic share of the load and transfers it to the steel. Further, that the ACI formula for designing axially loaded columns, deduced somewhat empirically from the test data, is made up of independent expressions for the resistance of the steel and of the concrete which disregard n, the modular ratio.

The profession is indebted to Dr. W. H. Glanville of England for developing the fundamental mechanics[F] of stress distribution in columns, recognizing creep. He began with the idea that the increase in steel elastic strain due to creep must equal the creep strain of the concrete plus the decrease in concrete elastic strain. In general form this was expressed as:

$$\frac{\Delta f_s}{E_s} = f_c \, \Delta \delta_t + \frac{\Delta f_c}{E_c}$$

---

[3] To THE INSTRUCTOR: Articles 10–7 and 10–8 on creep in columns may be omitted without loss of continuity.

Also that the increase of load on the steel must equal the decrease in load upon the concrete:

$$\Delta f_s \, A_s \; = \; -\Delta f_c \, A_c$$

PLATE 10–1. Reinforced concrete aircraft hangar near Rome, Italy. The three main arch ribs, integral with six buttresses (four of which are shown), were cast in place.

The diagonal ribs of the lamella type of framing consist of many individual pre-cast trusses about 3 ft. deep by 10 ft. long. They were joined at their intersections by welding the projecting reinforcing bars and then concreting the intersection in place. Ref. *Proc. of the ACI*, Vol. 49, 1953. Pier Luigi Nervi, structural engineer.

Solving the above two equations and passing to the limit, he got the differential equation:

$$\frac{df_c}{f_c} \; = \; -\,\frac{d\delta_t}{b}$$

in which $b = A_c/A_s E_s + 1/E_c$.

Upon integration thereof, and noting that when δ_t was zero f_c had its initial value f_{ci}, he found:

$$f_{ct} = \frac{f_{ci}}{e^{\delta_t/b}} \quad -----\text{Glanville}$$

(In the above particular expressions δ_t is creep strain per psi of concrete unit stress in decimal form, not millionths as heretofore.)

In his bulletin,[D] Professor Shank assumed the American notation, inserted his basic expression for creep (Formula 10–1), and by a different approach arrived at a formula which gives the same result as Glanville's:

$$f_{ct} = \frac{f_{ci}}{e^{\left[\frac{pE_sC\sqrt[r]{t}}{p(n-1)+1}\right]}} \qquad (10\text{–}3)$$

$$e = 2.7183$$
$$\log_{10} e = 0.4343$$

The computation of f_{st} follows easily from the areas involved.

EXAMPLE 10–2

Given the 20-in. diam. spiral column with 12 sq. in. of longitudinal steel as designed for 400 kips in Example 4–1 of Chapter 4, following Formula 11 of ACI Code Sec. 1103.

It is required to find the stresses in the concrete and steel according to Shank, if the column is loaded in air at the 7-day age and for 125 days thereafter. Consider that good natural stone and high early strength portland cement have been used to make 3000-lb. concrete, $n = 10$.

Solution:

The initial *elastic* concrete stress, f_{ci}, would be $\dfrac{400,000}{314.2 + 9(12)} = 946.$ *psi c*

The corresponding steel stress $f_{si} = 10(946)$ $= 9460.$ *psi c*

From Art. 10–6:

$$C = 0.10, \qquad r = 3, \qquad t = 125$$

Also $\qquad p = \dfrac{12}{314.2} = 0.0382, \qquad \text{or} \qquad 3.82\%$

Following Formula 10–3:

$$f_{ct} = \frac{f_{ci}}{e^{\left[\frac{pE_sC\sqrt[r]{t}}{p(n-1)+1}\right]}}$$

$$pE_sC\sqrt[7]{t} = 0.0382(30)(0.10)\sqrt[3]{125} = 0.573$$

$$p(n-1)+1 = 0.0382(9) + 1.0 = 1.344$$

$$\frac{pE_sC\sqrt[7]{t}}{p(n-1)+1} = \frac{0.573}{1.344} = 0.426$$

$\log_{10}$ of denominator $= 0.426(0.4343) = 0.185$

Denominator $= 1.531$

After creep for 125 days:

$$f_{ct} = \frac{946}{1.531} = 618 \text{ psi compressive}$$

Compare with 675 psi used in designing by ACI Sec. 1103.

$$f_{st} = \frac{400{,}000 - 618(314.2 - 12)}{12} = 17{,}760 \text{ psi compressive}$$

Compare with 16,000 psi used in designing by Formula 11 of ACI Sec. 1103.

Comment. Note that the value of concrete unit stress after creep, $f_{ct} = 618$, is about two-thirds of the elastic value, $f_{ci} = 946$, and not far from the 675-psi value used in designing by the Code. Thus *column Formula 4–1 of Chapter 4, evolved from many tests of columns, is consistent with Shank's findings and with Dr. Glanville's formula which was developed by pure mathematics.*

COLUMN CREEP PRACTICE PROBLEMS

Problem 10–4. Compute the stresses in the round column of Example 10–2 when it is five years old.   *Ans.* $f_{ct} = 421.$ *psi c*
$$f_{st} = 22{,}750 \text{ psi c}$$

Problem 10–5. Compute the stresses in the tied column of Example 4–2 of Chapter 4 when it is five years old. Assume standard portland cement and good stone, loaded at the 28-day age.

Compare the resulting stresses with the stresses of the original designing in Chapter 4. Make a similar comparison taking the results of Problem 10–4.

Prepare a neat and properly headed table consisting of all eight stresses.

Is there a greater divergence of the five-year stresses from the originally computed ones in the case of the tied column? Explain why.

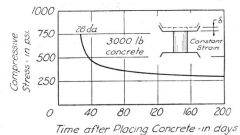

10–8. Decrease in Axial Concrete Stress Due to Creep under Sustained Strain.[3] In Fig. 10–2 the axial stress was applied and maintained con-

Fig. 10–3. Decrease of concrete axial compressive stress in a restrained specimen, due to creep (sustained strain).

stant over a time interval, resulting in a strain increase called creep, namely, the case of creep under *sustained stress.* Contrariwise, in Fig. 10–3 a safe strain was induced and maintained constant, resulting in a (creeping) stress decrease under the *sustained strain.* This latter case represents the situation which develops in continuous structures, wherein the ends of members become subjected to end rotations or displacements imposed by the connecting members, external fixity, shrinkage or temperature change.

When the elastic stress and deformation in a given member becomes high in relation to that in the adjacent members, the developing creep and/or inelastic deformation brings about a marked decrease in the original stress, as shown in Fig. 10–3. Although the stress in an adjacent member, or in a different portion of the same member, may be increased somewhat, nevertheless the over-all effect often is a beneficial *smoothing out* of the stress pattern throughout the structure. Thus, creep often has a benign influence upon (continuous) concrete structures, in the same manner that the ductility of structural steel sometimes facilitates beneficial stress adjustments in steel structures.

Referring again to Fig. 10–3, Mr. Chas. S. Whitney[G] set up the differential equations for the rate of creep and for the rate of elastic strain recovery, which must, of course, be equal in magnitude. By integration thereof he found that:

$$f_{ct} = \frac{f_{ci}}{e^{E_c C \sqrt[r]{t}}} \qquad \textit{Column under sustained strain} \qquad (10\text{–}4)$$

$$e = 2.718$$
$$\log_{10} e = 0.4343$$

wherein f_{ct} is the decreased concrete unit stress after t days of creep from the initial value f_{ci}, and C and r are as in Art. 10–6.

A study of his derivation[G] will show that when a *strain* is maintained, the presence or absence of reinforcement has no effect upon the concrete stress after creep. The member may be either a heavily reinforced column or a plain concrete pier. If steel is present, its initially induced elastic stress will be unaffected by the creep of the concrete, since the bar length will remain unchanged. However, if the external load and stress is maintained, as contemplated by Formula 10–3, the steel stress may be more than doubled due to the long-time shortening of the concrete due to creep, and shrinkage, as suggested by the result obtained in Example 10–2.

Creep in Flexural Members

10–9. Compression Stresses in and Deflection of Reinforced Concrete Beams under Sustained (Long-Time) Loading. Here we principally wish to make a reasonably accurate prediction of the elastic plus creep deflection of R/C beams under long-continued loads which cause stresses in the "Elastic Range" of performance depicted earlier in Fig. 10–1. The current trend toward longer spans is making it imperative that beam and slab constructions be designed to meet the rather strict test deflection limitations of 1956 ACI Sec. 203.

Our ability to predict R/C beam deflections, as originally presented in the United States by Shank,[D] has lately been strengthened by a simplified application of the common (elastic) deflection formulas developed by the author from studies of Professors Washa and Fluck's recent beam creep deflection tests, first reported in 1947 and 1952.

The formulas for the *elastic* deflection, y, of beams all have the product EI in the denominator thereof, the one for a uniformly loaded simple span being $y = 5wL^4/384EI$. It has been found that the large *creep* deflection will also be embraced if:

(a) The *sustained* modulus of elasticity, E_{ct}, computed after a loading duration t, and

(b) The sustained moment of inertia, I_{ct}, computed from the assumedly cracked[4] transformed section after the time t, are used.

EXAMPLE 10–3

Singly Reinforced Beam Investigation. **Given the Washa and Fluck test beams B-3 and B-6 of Bibliography, Reference J, and pictured in Fig. 10–4. Assuming ACI 3500-lb. concrete and specification, the beams**

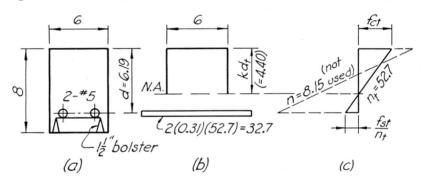

Fig. 10–4. Beam investigation for stress and deflection, after creep.

were designed in the usual manner for a total load of 107 plf over a 20-ft. simple span. The ones tested, actually of 3680-lb. strength, were loaded at the 14-day age for 2½ years. Standard portland cement and good stone aggregates were used.

It is required to compute (a) the compressive unit stress and (b) the deflection after the 2½ years by Shank's creep method. Also to compare the computed deflection with that observed by Washa and Fluck.

Solution: Referring to Formula 10–1 and Table 10–1:

Axial creep strain

$$\delta_t = 1.22(0.17)\sqrt[3]{365} = 1.485 \text{ millionths, per psi}$$

---

[4] If the loading is so light that the beam or slab will not hair-crack, more concrete area should be taken.[D]

Axial elastic strain

$$= \frac{1 \text{ psi}}{3,680,000} \qquad = \underline{0.272}$$

$$\text{Total} = 1.757$$

Note that for this concrete and early loading the creep strain is about 5½ times the elastic.

Sustained modulus

$$E_{ct} = \frac{1 \text{ psi}}{1.757 \times 10^{-6}} \qquad = 569,000 \text{ psi,}$$

$$n_t = \frac{E_s}{E_{ct}} = \frac{30,000,000}{569,000} = 52.7$$

(a) To find the decreased value of max. f_c after creep, calculate the N.A., I and Mc/I:

Get k for such unusual values of n from Plate V of Appendix A or from Formula 1 on the first page thereof:

$$pn = \frac{2(0.31)(52.7)}{6(6.19)} = 0.88, \qquad \text{find } k = 0.712, \qquad kd = 4.40 \text{ in.}$$

Get I_{ct}:
$$6(4.40)^3 \div 3 = 171.0$$
$$32.7(1.79)^2 = \underline{104.2}$$
$$I_{ct} = 275.2$$

$$M = \frac{wL^2}{8} = \frac{107(20)^2}{8} = 5350. \text{ ft.-lb.}$$

$$\text{Max. } f_{ct} = \frac{Mc}{I} = \frac{5350(12)(4.40)}{275.2} = 1030. \text{ psi,}$$

$$< 1610 \text{ of the elastic designing.}$$

(b) For predicting long-time deflection, take the conventional formula:

$$y = \frac{5wL^4}{384E_{ct}I_{ct}} = \frac{5(107)(20)^4(12)^4}{384(12)(569,000)(275.2)} \qquad = 2.46 \text{ in.} \longleftarrow \\ \qquad\qquad \text{elastic} + \text{creep.}$$

(c) *Washa's deflection test data:*

Tests B-3 and 6, p. 98 of Ref. J:

Observed immed. elastic deflection	= 1.04 in.
Observed shrinkage* + creep deflection = 2.36	
Deduced creep deflection	$= \dfrac{2.36}{1.55} = \underline{1.52 \text{ in.}}$
Observed elastic + creep deflection	= 2.56 in. $\longleftarrow$

compare

---

* The average "shrinkage" deflection of the 3750-lb. A, B, and C flexural specimens of the 1947 report, pp. 253–255 of Bibliography Reference I, was 55 per cent of the creep deflection, but apparently included some "other effects." See also subsequent Chapter 11 of this textbook, and page 106 of its Bibliography, Ref. L.

Comments. The accompanying tabulation of stresses and deflections calculated by three different methods should be studied. The 1610-psi concrete stress value is close to the $0.45f'_c$ design allowable, which the

TABLE 10-1

COMPARISON OF CREEP STRESS AND DEFLECTION VALUES
SINGLY REINFORCED 6 BY 8 IN. BEAM WITH 2-#5 BARS DESIGN-LOADED AT
14 DA. FOR $2\frac{1}{2}$ YEARS

The Actual f'_c of 3680 psi was used	Calculated Stresses and Deflections Transformed Cracked Sections Were Taken			Avg. Test Deflection Observed by Washa & Fluck
	Sustained Modulus Methods		By the Common Elastic Method (Creep Disregarded)	
	By Shank's Creep Method	By the $\frac{1}{4}E_c$ Creep Approximation		
Results:			$(n = 8.15)$	
f_c	1,030	1,122	1,610	—
f_s	21,800	21,200	19,250	—
—psi				
DEFLECTION:				
Elastic	—	—	—	1.04
Creep	—	—	—	1.52
TOTAL	2.46	—	0.13	2.56
—inches				

compare

ACI deliberately set high to allow for later decrease due to creep. It appears that 0.3 to $0.33f'_c$ would be a proper allowable concrete unit stress for singly reinforced beams *when creep methods are used.*

In the $\frac{1}{4}E_c$ *approximation,* used by McMillan[K] as early as 1915, $4n$ is used in transforming all sections, and the stresses are then computed as if creep were nonexistent.

For calculating deflections we ought to use E_{ct} to find the deflection due to the permanent loads, such as dead load, and the much greater common value, E_c, for that due to transient loads. In such cases, the dead load deflection will usually prove to be much the larger item.

In the above example the dead and live loads were not separately designated. Therefore the deflection found should be thought of as representing a case where both loadings were on for the whole period.

BEAM CREEP PRACTICE PROBLEMS

Problem 10–6. Verify the stresses in and the deflection of the beam of Example 10–3, disregarding creep. What fraction of the whole deflection is the elastic?

Problem 10–7. Investigate the long-time stresses in, and deflection of, the sample (asterisk), slab of Problem 2–11 of Chapter 2 if it is loaded at the 21-day age and for 4 years thereafter. Assume standard portland cement and good stone aggregates.

(a) By the $\frac{1}{4}E_c$ approximation

(b) By Shank's method.

10–10. Creep of Doubly Reinforced Beams. Since the large creep deflection of beams is due to the continued compressing of the concrete of the compression side, it may be effectively decreased by the addition of compression reinforcement. This case differs from the preceding example only in that there is also top steel to be transformed into a strip of equivalent concrete and included in neutral axis and moment of inertia calculations.

EXAMPLE 10–4

Doubly Reinforced Beam Investigation. **Given the same beam and loading conditions as studied in Example 10–3 except that 2–#5 compression bars have been added, as Washa and Fluck did in their B-1 and B-4 test beams of Bibliography Reference J. Consider the bars centered 1.81 in. from the top.**

It is required to compute the stresses and the deflection by Shank's creep method, and to compare it with the test data.

Intermediate Results: $E_{ct} = 569,000$, $n = 52.7$, $kd = 3.46$, $I_{ct} = 414$. See Table 10–2 for the remaining data.

Comments. In the accompanying Table 10–2, the compressive stresses found in Col. (2) by Shank's method may be compared with those gotten by three other methods, including the ACI $2n$ approximation used as a check method in earlier chapters of this textbook.

Note that the stresses of the $\frac{1}{4}E_c$ approximation of Col. 3 agree well with Shank's method as a standard.

The methods of Columns (4) and (5) disregard the effect of creep upon f_c values, giving top fiber stresses that are fictitiously *high*. On the other hand, they give compressive steel stresses which are far too *low*. For the usual conditions, *the $\frac{1}{4}E_c$ method* (or $4n$ method) is recommended as an excellent quick stress approximation.

Studies made of *balanced* doubly reinforced beam designs indicate that the allowable concrete stress should be limited to about $0.25f'_c$ when good methods recognizing creep are used.

A study of Columns (2) and (6) in comparison with Table 10–1 shows that the arbitrary introduction of the same amount of reinforcement

TABLE 10–2

COMPARISON OF CREEP STRESS AND DEFLECTION VALUES
DOUBLY REINFORCED 6 BY 8 IN. BEAM WITH 2–#5 BARS IN TOP AND IN BOTTOM,
DESIGN-LOADED AT 14 DA. FOR $2\frac{1}{2}$ YEARS

The Actual f'_c of 3680 psi Was Used	Calculated Stresses and Deflections Transformed Cracked Sections Were Taken				Avg. Test Deflection Observed by Washa & Fluck
	Sustained Modulus Methods		By the ACI $2n$ Creep Stress Approximation —Sec. 706(b)	By the Common Elastic Method (Creep Disregarded) $n = 8.15$	
	By Shank's Creep Method	By the $\frac{1}{4}E_c$ Creep Stress Approximation			
COLUMN (1)	(2)	(3)	(4)	(5)	(6)
f_c	536	733	1420	1492	
f_s comp.	13,480	10,540	4760	2875	
f_s tens.	22,300	21,700	19,800	19,600	
DEFLECTION: Elastic	—	—	—	—	0.92
Creep	—	—	—	—	0.70
TOTAL —inches	1.64	—	—	0.10	1.62

compare

into the top of the beam as exists in the bottom approximately *halves* the f_c stress, and correspondingly the deflection due to creep (1030 vs. 536 psi, and 1.52 vs. 0.70 inches).

DOUBLY REINFORCED BEAM CREEP PRACTICE PROBLEMS

Problem 10–8. Verify the findings of the solution of Example 10–4 which appear in Col. (2) of Table 10–2, and elsewhere.

Problem 10–9. Reinvestigate the creep stresses and deflection of the beam of Example 10–4, assuming the same span and loading, but that the added reinforcement is placed in the bottom instead of in the top. Take a total bottom steel content of exactly 1.24 sq. in. at the same 6.19-in. distance from the top. Make a tabular comparison of your findings with those of Example 10–4 and comment.

10–11. Prediction of Long-Time Slab or Beam Deflections from 24-hr. Experimental Data. The creep of concrete takes place at a gradually decreasing rate, following a power curve variation, Fig. 10–2, which has been well established by several investigators from many experimental data. Table 10–3 prepared from Shank's creep formula shows, for example, that 10.5 per cent of the total creep takes place during the first 24 hr. of loading. Such relationships can be used to predict deflections at much later ages *provided that the conditions prevailing during the short-time period of observation are typical of the service period.*

TABLE 10–3

PERCENTAGE EARLY CREEP OF CONCRETE

$\delta_t \smile \sqrt[3]{t}$ UP TO 1 YEAR

DEDUCED FROM EXPERIMENTAL DATA

For cured-in-air portland cement concretes* and at whatever age first loaded
—after Shank

Duration of the Loading	Creep in Percentage of Long-Time Total
1.15 min.	1.0
2	1.2
10 min.	2.2
1 hr.	3.7
6	6.6
12 hr.	7.4
1 day	10.5
3	15.1
7	20.0
14	25.0
28 days	32.0
2 months	41.0
3	46.0
6	59.5
9 months	68.0
1 year	75.0
2	88.0
3	95.0
4	98.0
5 years or more	100.0

* Except granite aggregate concretes. Refer to Shank's bulletin, Bibliography item D.

EXAMPLE 10–5

A slab weighing 50 plf deflected 0.30 in. immediately due to the application of the design live loading of 80 plf, and 0.07 in.† more within 24 hr. Predict the long-time total elastic plus creep deflection due to dead plus uninterrupted live loading.

---

† Normally, a member will have supported its dead load for some time before the test load is applied, so little dead load creep will occur during the 24 hr. Its value may be deduced from Art. 10–6 as a percentage of the live load creep and deducted, when appreciable.

Solution:

   Live load deflection

   Elastic   = 0.30 in.

   $\text{Creep}\left(\dfrac{0.07}{0.105}\right)$ = 0.67 in.

               Total   = 0.97* in.

   Dead load deflection

   $\text{Elastic} + \text{creep} = \dfrac{50}{80}(0.97) = 0.61$ in.

   Long-time total deflection = 1.58 in.   *Ans.*

10–12. Creep in Combined Stress Members under Sustained Load.
These members, such as columns subject to ordinary bending, when
calculated as in Example 4–3 using the *interaction* relation of 1956 ACI
Sec. 1109(a) and the corresponding allowable axial and bending stresses
thereof, turn out to have about the same safe load rating as one would
get by following the refined creep methods and recommendations of
Examples 10–3 and 10–4. This is because creep was allowed for in
setting up the axially loaded column Formula 4–2 of Art. 4–5, and in
permitting the bending stresses in potentially cracked columns to be
calculated as if they were uncracked [ACI Sec. 1109(a)]. The creep
method itself is therefore hardly needed except as a verifying exercise
which begins with the calculation of the small sustained modulus of
elasticity E_{ct}, and the enlarged modular ratio n_t.

10–13. The Inelastic Range. All this chapter has been devoted to
creep, which occurs in the lower (elastic range) portion of Fig. 10–1,
the stress-strain diagram for concrete. Within it lies the region of safe
working stresses in which Shank and others did most of their experimentation. All the investigational and designing methods that have
thus far been presented in this book are intended for use only in the
elastic range, though they are sometimes mistakenly applied to the prediction of *ultimate strength*, the highest point of the *inelastic range*.
Such techniques will be taken up in Chapter 12 on "Ultimate Strength
Design."

   Two recent developments have made it necessary for concrete structural engineers to be able to predict the ultimate strength of reinforced
concrete beams with a fair degree of accuracy, namely (a) the use of
widely different factors of safety for dead load versus live load and
(b) the advent of prestressed beams, both of which are taken up in
Chapters 12 and 13, respectively.

---

* Subject to being decreased if the live loading is intermittent.

PLATE 10–2.   Use of a lifting cradle to set precast channel-slab roof panels.

10–14. Summary of Creep of Concrete. Creep is now defined as *the delayed portion of the total unit deformation resulting from stress within the proportional elastic range of the material.* It is mostly or partially recoverable, depending upon the duration of the load.

The hydration of portland cement develops a gel around each particle. Creep is due to compression of the gel and is greatest in a dry-curing atmosphere. Low-strength concretes creep more than high-strength ones. Creep practically ceases after five years.

Creep-time data for the first year of loading are well represented by power curves. For ordinary strength portland cement concretes made from good natural stone and loaded in air, Shank found the curve to be a third-power one.

When concrete is loaded at later ages, the creep is much less. By conceiving such loading to be applied in reverse sense (e.g., tensile instead of compressive) at the later age, the effect of removing the same load applied earlier can be followed. Refer to Figure 10–2.

The compressive stresses in reinforced concrete members after creep under sustained load may be found by computing a decreased value of E_c from the sum of the creep and instantaneous elastic strains, and using it to make conventional beam stress calculations. In the absence of creep data, $\frac{1}{4}E_c$ may be assumed for loading durations of a year or more. The term *sustained modulus of elasticity, E_{ct},* is applied to such decreased values.

Because of the great influence of the time element, live loads cause a great deal less creep than dead, since the former seldom act for prolonged periods. To predict the deflection of reinforced concrete beams, the full value of E_c may be used to get the live load deflection, but for the dead load deflection the much smaller elapsed time *sustained modulus, E_{ct},* should be taken.

When a sustained strain is maintained upon a concrete member, instead of a sustained stress, creep causes a decrease in concrete stress. This is the beneficial *relief of stress* which often takes place in the restrained members of continuous structures.

Formulas have been presented for computing the effect of creep upon the stresses in reinforced concrete columns and beams under sustained load. They show the tendency for such concrete unit stresses to be considerably less than those obtainable by conventional *elastic* methods.

In columns and doubly reinforced beams, wherein the compressive steel and concrete *share* in the resistance to compressive force or load, creep was found to cause a two- to fourfold increase of the common elastically computed compressive steel stress, or even more. Such steel must be well held in place by spirals, ties or stirrups.

The term *inelasticity*, as now applied to concrete, refers exclusively to the large *nonlinear* deformations which develop rapidly within the upper range of the stress-strain diagram as the ultimate strength is approached, and which are nonrecoverable. Because inelasticity causes wide deviations of beam stresses from the traditional straight-line variation, the *ultimate strength* of beams must be predicted by *ultimate strength methods*.

BIBLIOGRAPHY

A) McHenry, Douglas. A New Aspect of Creep in Concrete and Its Application to Design, *Proc. American Society for Testing Materials*, 1943, Vol. 43, p. 1069.

B) *Concrete Manual.* 5th ed. U.S. Department of the Interior, Denver, Colorado, 1951, p. 31.

C) Shank, J. R. The Mechanics of Plastic Flow of Concrete, *Proc. American Concrete Institute*, 1936, Vol. 32, p. 149.

D) Shank, J. R. The Plastic Flow of Concrete, *Ohio State University Engineering Experiment Station Bulletin* No. 91, 1935.

E) Davis, Raymond E. A Summary of Investigations of Volume Changes in Cements, Mortars and Concretes Produced by Causes other than Stress, *Proc. American Society for Testing Materials*, 1930, Vol. 30, Part 1, p. 688.

F) Glanville, W. H. The Creep or Flow of Concrete Under Load, Studies in Reinforced Concrete III, *Dept. of Scientific and Industrial Research Technical Paper* No. 12, 1930, Building Research Station, Garston, Herts., England.

G) Whitney, Chas. S. Plain and Reinforced Concrete Arches, *Proc. American Concrete Institute*, 1932, Vol. 28, p. 479.

H) Straub, L. G. Plastic Flow in Concrete Arches, *Trans. ASCE*, 1931, Vol. 95, p. 613.

I) Washa, Geo. W. Plastic Flow of Thin Reinforced Concrete Slabs, *Proc. American Concrete Institute*, 1948, Vol. 44, p. 237.

J) Washa, Geo. W., and Fluck, P. G. Effect of Compressive Reinforcement on the Plastic Flow of Reinforced Concrete Beams, *Proc. American Concrete Institute*, 1953, Vol. 49, p. 89.

K) McMillan, F. R. Discussion of the paper by A. C. Janni: Method of Designing Reinforced Concrete Slabs, *Trans. ASCE*, 1916, Vol. 80, p. 1738.

CREEP AND INELASTICITY QUESTIONS

1. Define elasticity, creep and inelasticity, distinguishing between them.

2. Sketch the stress-strain curves of concrete, subdividing and identifying all major divisions thereof.

3. Define the instantaneous, secant, initial, tangent, and sustained moduli of elasticity. Refer to Chapter 1.

4. What is the characteristic shape of creep-time curves? Delineate a creep recovery-time curve and tell how they may be deduced without experimentation.

5. Describe the nature of creep. Enumerate the factors which affect it, stating whether they increase or decrease it.

6. Enumerate all the advantages and disadvantages of the creep phenomenon.

7. Why should high early strength portland cement concrete creep less than standard portland cement concrete if they are loaded at the same age?

8. Explain the stages of interaction between the steel and concrete of a spiral column from no load to ultimate failure. Refer to Chapter 4.

9. Describe two methods for predicting the compressive stress in a singly reinforced concrete beam after creep has taken place.

10. In doubly reinforced beams, which stresses are most inaccurate if calculated by the conventional method? Explain how this situation arises.

11. Explain the deficiencies of the ACI $2n$ approximation to the final compressive stress in doubly reinforced beams.

12. In strength computations for columns subject to bending, why does ACI Code Section 1109(a) permit one to disregard the cracking thereof?

13. Explain the inelastic property of concrete as presently defined, and tell why it is becoming of increasing importance. Are stress diagrams and strain diagrams always identical? Explain.

CONTINUATION PROBLEMS

Problem 10–10. A plain concrete pier of ordinary portland cement concrete was first safely loaded in air at the 30-day age for a period of 30 days. It was then alternately unloaded and loaded at 30-day intervals until the 150-day age.

Compute the ratio of the creep at the 150-day age to what it would have been had the load never been removed. Make a scale creep-time diagram of the 120-days of movements involved in the two cases.

Problem 10–11. If the column of Example 10–2 is 15 ft. high, calculate the long-time shortening thereof, considering creep. What then will be the steel and concrete unit stresses?

Problem 10–12. Investigate the stresses at the end of the typical interior girder of Calculation Sheet 10/11 of Chapter 6, after ten years of loading. Assume standard portland cement, good stone, and fully loaded at the 60-day age.

(a) By the $\frac{1}{4}E_c$ method, referring to the *Comments* at the end of Example 10–3.

(b) By Shank's creep method.

Make a tabular comparison of your results with the answers given to Problem 6–12, and comment thereon.

CHAPTER 11

CONCRETE SHRINKAGE
AND TEMPERATURE CHANGE

11–1. Introduction. In this chapter we are concerned with the time-dependent deformations and stresses which may develop in the members of concrete structures due to influences other than externally

George W. Washa, Professor of Mechanics, University of Wisconsin, and active in concrete research.

The results of his comprehensive series of tests to determine the shrinkage and creep deformations and deflections of flexural members met a long-felt need for such information. The creep tests data from doubly reinforced beams (with P. G. Fluck) were also quite significant of their action.

His paper, *Comparison of the Physical and Mechanical Properties of Hand Rodded and Vibrated Concrete Made with Different Cements,* won him the Wason (research) Medal of the American Concrete Institute.

applied loads. These factors are **shrinkage,** or expansion, resulting from changes in moisture content and similar movements caused by **temperature change.**[1]

---

[1] The general term *volume change* is often used to refer to the following four phenomena as a group: namely, creep, shrinkage, temperature change effects, and possible chemical disintegration.

Although these topics are controversial due to the multiplicity of variables often involved, an effort will be made to develop them, and to evaluate quantitatively the stress-strain effects which may be expected in the simplified cases presented.

Axial Shrinkage

11–2. Effect of Change in Moisture Content. Concrete shrinks[A] with loss of moisture and expands with gain thereof. It also contracts somewhat due to the chemical reactions of hardening. Most of the original shrinkage takes place during the curing period of the first few months, and is known as *drying shrinkage*. It coincides with the period of most active creep, to which shrinkage is inextricably related.

Excessive shrinkage is a serious concern of the engineer. It is often traceable to such factors as poor aggregates, poor proportioning, neglected curing, or a particular source of cement. Moreover, the external restraints which often develop therewith cause tensile stresses in the concrete which sometimes result in cracking. Oft-repeated shrinkage and expansions gradually tend to cause a breakdown of the internal structure of the hardened cement-water paste and its bond to the aggregate particles, resulting in disintegration of the concrete. The engineer decreases shrinkage and expansion somewhat by introducing *shrinkage reinforcement*, and he provides suitable *joints*, contraction and/or expansion, which are designed to adjust to the expected movements. Refer to Figs. 11–5 and 11–6.

A well-proportioned mix of concrete is a cohesive plastic mass that is fully saturated with water. As the cement sets, it takes up water, or *hydrates*. Additional water, called *curing water*, must be furnished to ensure complete hydration. If such is adequately provided the concrete mass will expand slightly, and little if any shrinkage[2] will occur so long as the wet curing is maintained. Schorer's formula[B] for predicting the unrestrained shrinkage unit deformation,[3] δ_f, called the *free shrinkage coefficient, is:*

$$\delta_f = \frac{0.125(0.90 - h)}{100} \tag{11–1}$$

wherein h is the relative humidity of the surrounding atmosphere, expressed as a decimal.

---

[2] Concrete does not exhibit drying shrinkage while still plastic, except that the water which may rise to the surface during the first hour or so after placing (due to being displaced by the settling of the aggregate) may be allowed to evaporate before it sinks again to feed the hydration of the cement, thus decreasing the volume of the mass.

[3] Throughout this chapter, δ is the unit deformation, or strain, due to shrinkage.

For a fully saturated curing condition (fog or water) $h = 1.00$, and $\delta_f = -0.000125$, namely, expansion.

When curing is omitted or withdrawn, assuming an average relative humidity of 50 per cent ($h = 0.50$), δ_f turns out $+0.0005$, which is the well-established[c] average value of total free shrinkage; namely, from the quite wet to the completely dried-out condition. Most of it can be recovered (erased) by a thorough rewetting.

Note that the above value of total shrinkage is equivalent to an $83°$ temperature drop, assuming a thermal coefficient, $\propto$, of 0.000006.

It has been found that shrinkage is approximately proportional to the paste content, $c + w$, per unit volume of concrete; and that the water is responsible for about 80 per cent of the shrinkage. "Thus any factor which increases the water requirement of the paste, such as wetter consistencies, finer sands or smaller coarse aggregates, will increase the shrinkage."[A] Furthermore, although rich concrete tends to shrink more than lean, it may be very little more, provided the consistency is no wetter. For pre-tensioning the reinforcement of prestressed concrete beams, fairly accurate estimates of the amount of concrete shrinkage expected are needed in order to properly allow for the corresponding loss of steel prestress. Refer to Chapter 13.

The shrinkage of concrete is advantageous in one respect: It causes the concrete to grip the steel tightly, thus decreasing the possibility of bar slippage.

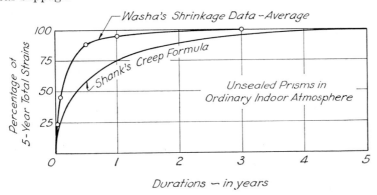

FIG. 11–1. Typical accumulations of shrinkage and creep.

11–3. Calculation of Shrinkage Stresses. Shrinkage stresses are caused by *external* or *internal* restraints upon the free contraction of the concrete. If the shrinkage strain can be estimated, the axial stress due to the shrinkage can be computed by multiplying the strain by the sustained modulus of elasticity, E_{ct}, used in the creep calculations of Chapter 10.

The marked similarity of the time-dependent actions of shrinkage and creep is shown in Fig. 11–1. Since most of the shrinkage takes place during the first few months, when the effective modulus of elasticity (elastic plus creep) still is relatively large, high shrinkage stresses of the order of δE_c can develop in a restrained member. As time passes, creep causes the effective modulus to decrease to E_{ct}, a very much smaller value, while δ increases only moderately to δ_f, the maximum value; so the shrinkage tensile stress decreases. This accounts for the common observation that creep *relieves* shrinkage and temperature stresses.

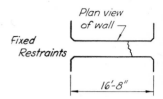

Fig. 11–2. Externally restrained wall.

EXAMPLE 11–1

***External Restraint.* Consider a new plain concrete wall extending between two large fixed concrete masses 16 ft. 8 in. apart. The wall is integral therewith, and fully restrained thereby, as indicated in Fig. 11–2.**

What shrinkage stress will develop if the wall dries out completely?

Take ACI 3000-lb. concrete, with a five-year sustained modulus[4] of elasticity, E_{ct}, of only 400,000 psi.

Solution: Shrinkage unit stress equals shrinkage unit strain times the sustained modulus of elasticity:

Five-year shrinkage stress $f_t = \delta_f E_{ct} = 0.0005(400,000) = 200$ psi, tensile

Comment: At an earlier age when the modulus was larger, the stress might well have reached 300 psi, causing cracking of the concrete. Such a crack could be expected to become $0.0005(16.7)(12) = 0.10$ in. wide.

The free shrinkage of concrete can be decreased somewhat by providing properly located *shrinkage reinforcement* therein, *in the direction of the expected contraction.* Such steel knits a member together, but becomes compressed because of its bond to the contracting concrete, and induces a small corresponding tension into the concrete. Thus the potential free shrinkage of the concrete is decreased slightly by the opposing *internal restraint* of the reinforcement. The problem is to find the internal *shrinkage force, P,* acting between the steel and the concrete, from which the shrinkage stresses and the shrinkage deformation are easily computed.

---

[4] Since shrinkage develops after moist curing is withdrawn, that age can be taken as the *age when loaded* with shrinkage stress, for purposes of calculating an E_{ct} for shrinkage calculations.

EXAMPLE 11–2

Internal Restraint. Given the same **16 ft. 8 in.** wall of Example **11–1**, except that it is now reinforced with two **#4** horizontal bars at **5-in.** intervals of its height, as indicated in Fig. **11–3(b)**.

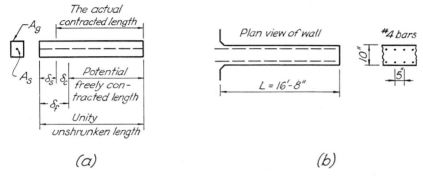

(a)   (b)

Fig. 11–3.   Internally restrained shrinkage.

It is required to calculate the shrinkage stresses at the age of six months. Also to calculate the restrained shrinkage strain and compare it with the free shrinkage strain found in Example 11–1. Take the same 3000-lb. concrete, $\delta_f = 0.0005$ and a six-month $E_{ct} = 1,000,000$ psi, $n_t = 30$. For clarity, visualize the steel as unbonded to the concrete except at the ends of the member, and opposing the shrinkage contraction of the concrete.

Derivation of the Axial Shrinkage Formula:
Employing the notation of Fig. 11–3(a):

$$\delta_s + \delta_c = \delta_f \qquad (11\text{–}2)$$

Let P be the total force compressing the steel and tensioning the concrete.[D]

Then $\qquad \delta_s = \dfrac{P}{A_s E_s} \qquad$ and $\qquad \delta_c = \dfrac{P}{A_c E_{ct}}$

Also $\qquad A_s = p_s A_g \qquad$ and $\qquad A_c = (1 - p_s)A_g,$

wherein A_g is gross concrete area.
Substituting in Eq. 11–2, and rearranging:

$$P = \delta_f E_s A_g \left[\frac{p_s(1 - p_s)}{1 + (n_t - 1)p_s} \right] \qquad Axial\ Shrinkage \qquad (11\text{–}3)$$

wherein p_s is the steel ratio stated with respect to A_g, as for shrinkage or temperature change calculations.

Knowing P, the shrinkage stresses and the deformation follow easily.

Solution:

Conveniently take $A_g = 50$ sq. in., and $A_s = 0.40$ sq. in.

Then
$$p_s = \frac{A_s}{A_g} = \frac{0.40}{50} = 0.8\%$$

$$P = 0.0005(30 \times 10^6)(50)\left[\frac{0.008(0.992)}{1 + 29(0.008)}\right] = 4825 \text{ lb.}$$

$$f_s \text{ (due to shrinkage)} = \frac{P}{A_s} = \frac{4825}{0.40} = 12{,}060. \text{ psi compressive}$$

$$f_c \text{ (due to shrinkage)} = \frac{P}{A_c} = \frac{4825}{0.992(50)} = 97. \text{ psi tensile}$$

$$\text{Total shrinkage strain} = L\delta_s = \frac{PL}{A_s E_s} = \frac{4825(200)}{0.4(30 \times 10^6)} = 0.080 \text{ in.}$$

Comment. Having noted that the free shrinkage of 0.10 in. has been decreased only 20 per cent by the introduction of 0.8 per cent of shrinkage reinforcement, an examination of the algebraic expressions shows that no greater quantity of steel will *eliminate* the shrinkage of the wall, so a *contraction joint* must be provided. Refer to Art. 11–8.

Temperature Change

11–4. Resemblance of Temperature Change to Shrinkage.[A] As indicated briefly in Art. 1–17 of Chapter 1, the thermal coefficient of expansion of concrete, α, has an average value of about six millionths per Fahrenheit degree of temperature change, but varies between four and seven millionths depending upon the kind of aggregate used.[E] Since the corresponding value for steel is 0.0000065, the justification for reinforced concrete construction is obvious. For outdoor concrete in severe climates the importance of careful aggregate selection with respect to the thermal property is very great, since bar slippage cannot be allowed to occur.

During the early part of the curing period the temperature of concrete rises well above its temperature at the time of placing, due to the heat generated by the chemical action of hydration. Within the *mass concrete* of large dams much heat is so evolved at interior points, far from any exterior cooling surface. Elaborate measures, including the embedding of refrigeration pipe systems, have often been taken to prevent excessive temperature rise.[E]

In winter a progressive cooling and contraction occurs which tends to be highly detrimental because the temperature stresses then induced

in the outside surfaces of the concrete are tensile. Thus a 10-degree fall
in temperature can produce as critical a strain as a 100-degree summertime rise. Refer to Table 1–2 of Chapter 1. *So far as temperature
change alone is concerned,* it is advantageous to place concrete in cool
weather, so that the fall to the wintertime low will be much less than the
rise to the summertime high.

Repeated cycles of *sudden change* in temperature are the most
detrimental to concrete because the temperature differential so created
between its interior and the exterior surface causes large temperature
stresses. Although they disappear as soon as the temperature has again
become uniform throughout, the member will have contracted (or
expanded) accordingly.

Although the greatest drying *shrinkage* usually occurs early, contraction due to a fall in *temperature* may occur at any time. Because the
commonly used mathematical relationships are fundamentally the same,
it is customary in designing to assume a *combined* shrinkage plus temperature coefficient when both influences are expected to be active at the
same time. A case in point would be outdoor concrete which conceiv-
ably might become thoroughly dried out during a drouth, and then be
subjected to a sudden severe drop in temperature.

In designing, engineers generally use a lowered shrinkage coefficient
between 0.0003 and 0.00035, since in most structures complete drying out
never occurs. Similarly, for temperature change, the 0.000006 thermal
coefficient may be multiplied by one-half to two-thirds of the expected
degree change to get a temperature strain component to add to the
shrinkage strain.

Designers with unusual temperature problems should consult Bibliography References F and H.

AXIAL SHRINKAGE AND TEMPERATURE CHANGE
PRACTICE PROBLEMS

Problem 11–1. A plain concrete wall is fully restrained at both ends by
large concrete masses.

(a) Assuming that it was wet cured for the first 14 days, compute the
shrinkage tensile stress therein one year after the withdrawal of curing. Take
a five-year shrinkage strain of 0.00045 and refer to Fig. 11–1. Compute your
sustained modulus of elasticity using Shank's formula of Art. 10–6, assuming
3000-lb. standard portland cement concrete.   *Ans.* 275 *psi.*

(b) Compute the shrinkage stresses after several other assumed periods
and deduce the age at which the cracking tendency is the greatest.

Problem 11–2. A 60-ft. wall of ACI 3750-lb. standard portland cement
concrete containing 0.30 per cent of horizontal temperature reinforcement was
placed and wet cured for 28 days at 80°F. If the annual range of change to be

considered is 0° to 120°, calculate the required freedom of joint adjustment, in each direction, and the total travel to be provided for so far as temperature change is concerned. Take $\alpha = 0.0000065$ for both materials. Hint: Adapt Formula 11–3 to your purpose.

11–5. Shrinkage and Temperature Reinforcement. In wide structural elements such as walls and one-way footings, as well as in floor and roof slabs that are reinforced for flexure in only one (the spanwise) direction, shrinkage and temperature reinforcement must be provided in the direction of the width, i.e., perpendicular to the flexural span and the direction of the principal reinforcement, as illustrated in Fig. 11–4.

EXAMPLE 11–3

Shrinkage plus Temperature Stresses. **Given the floor slab of Fig. 11–4, consisting of ACI 3000-lb. concrete. Considering the design free shrinkage coefficient to be three-quarters of the 0.0005 value,**

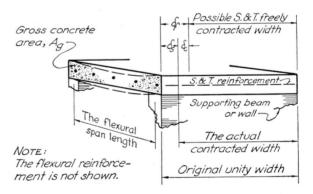

FIG. 11–4.   Idealized slab shrinkage and temperature reinforcement.

and that 50 degrees of temperature drop is also to be taken into account, compute the shrinkage plus temperature stresses if 0.2, 0.3, 1 and 4 per cent of such reinforcement, p_s, is used. Take the thermal coefficient, α, at 0.000006, and a 6-month $E_{ct} = 1,000,000.$ psi; $n_t = 30.$

Solution: Conveniently consider an A_g of 100 sq. in.

$\delta_f = 0.75(0.0005) + 50(0.000006) = 0.00067$ in./in., free S. & T. strain

$$P = \delta_f E_s A_g \left[\frac{p_s(1 - p_s)}{1 + (n_t - 1)p_s} \right] \qquad \text{(from Example 11–2)} \qquad (11\text{–}3)$$

Sample Calculation, with $p_s = 0.2\%$:

$$P = \frac{0.00067(30 \times 10^6)(100)(0.002)(0.998)}{1 + 29(0.002)} = 3800 \text{ lb.}$$

$$f_s = \frac{3800}{0.002(100)} = 19{,}000. \text{ psi, compressive.}$$

$$f_c = \frac{3800}{99.8} = 38. \text{ psi, tensile}$$

Comments. The accompanying Table 11–1 demonstrates that the small percentages of shrinkage and temperature reinforcement ordinarily used are consistent with accepted shrinkage calculations. Unfortunately, the nature of the algebraic expression is such that the calculated

TABLE 11–1

CALCULATED SHRINKAGE PLUS TEMPERATURE STRESSES, PSI

Slab Shrinkage plus Temperature Steel Content p_s, in per cent	In Steel f_s, Compressive	In Concrete f_c, Tensile	Remarks
0.2	19,000	38.	Requires #4's at 14″ in c.c. in a 7″ slab
0.3	18,450	55.	Ref. ACI Sec. 707
Column or Wall Principal Vert. Steel Content			
1.0	15,440	156.	
4.0	8,930	372.	Potential concrete tensile failure See *Comments*

steel stress hardly rises to 20,000 psi when even smaller percentages are used, so the actual content to be used must be based largely upon experience.

Note in the lower portion of the table that *symmetrical arrangements of high percentage longitudinal reinforcement*, such as in columns, tend to cause high concrete tensile stresses as contraction takes place. However, it is believed that this elastically computed condition seldom develops, due to (a) the relief of concrete stress provided by the creep of the concrete and (b) the early application of superimposed dead load to columns as construction progresses, which prevents tensile cracking. Nevertheless, columns have been known to develop such tensile cracks many years later when, due to remodeling operations, a large portion of their superimposed dead load was removed!

As shown by Pickett[H] there is a great deal more mathematics involved in precise studies of shrinkage than can be presented here. Those with highly important shrinkage problems should refer to his work.

11–6. The ACI Code Requirements for Shrinkage and Temperature Reinforcement, Section 707. The minimum S. & T. steel ratios of 0.0025 for plain bars, and 0.0020 for deformed bars as set by the ACI Code are not inconsistent with the findings of Table 11–1. The 1956 Code considerably increased the minimum S. & T. steel *content* by calling for the application of the former steel ratios to the whole thickness t of slabs, rather than to the d dimension.

The reader should remember that the Code ratios are *minimums*. In case the concrete is to be placed and cured at quite high summer temperatures, 150 per cent of the above values will be good insurance. Mr. I. E. Morris, consulting structural engineer of Atlanta, Georgia, would distinguish considerably between the degrees of exposure; for outdoor slabs of unheated structures, porches and canopies wholly exposed to the winter climate of northern United States, he considers that the Code minimum steel percentages should be fully doubled. "The added cost would be small, and will usually prove to be money well spent."

Eccentric Shrinkage (Warpage)

11–7. Effect of Concrete Shrinkage upon the Stress in the Tensile Reinforcement of Beams and Slabs. In flexural members, the effect of shrinkage is to introduce a considerable amount of compression into the flexure steel, thus greatly decreasing the design tensile stress. At the same time, the concrete of the tension side is subjected to additional tension, which causes it to crack[5] at a lighter load than if there were no shrinkage. This latter condition is accentuated because beam flexure steel is nearly always *eccentric* to the centroid of the whole concrete area; and its opposition to the shrinkage of the concrete causes shrinkage *bending* tensile stresses in the concrete in addition to the shrinkage *axial* tensile ones.

The topic of eccentric shrinkage is being introduced here partly because of its great importance in evaluating the losses of pre-tension from the reinforcement of prestressed beams, the design of which is taken up in Chapter 13. A principal objective of prestressing is to produce beams that will be crack-free under the design loading.[5]

---

[5] Numerous tests have shown that reinforced concrete beams that have been designed in the usual manner normally develop very fine "hairline" cracks before all the design load has been applied.

EXAMPLE 11-4

Prediction of the Shrinkage Warpage of a Singly Reinforced Concrete Slab, and Comparison with Test Data. Given the slab section of Fig. 11-5(a), which is from Professor Washa's creep and shrinkage series of tests begun in 1941.[1] The actual final concrete strength, f'_c, was 3090 psi, and the observed free shrinkage coefficient of companion test

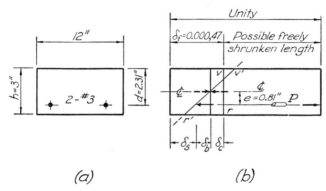

FIG. 11-5. The eccentric shrinkage of beams (warpage).

prisms was 0.00047. The slabs were made using standard portland cement. They were loaded at the 6-day age. Conveniently consider that the curing was discontinued at the same time.

It is required: (a) To calculate predicted five-year shrinkage stresses and strains and to compare them with test data. Compute and use the elapsed time *sustained modulus of elasticity.* Refer to Example 10-3 of Chapter 10 on creep.

Derivation of the Eccentric Shrinkage Formula[D]

Utilizing from Fig. 11-4 the familiar notation for the axial shrinkage unit deformations δ_s and δ_c, consider in Fig. 11-5(b) that δ_b is the additional bending unit deformation at the level of the steel due to the bending moment Pe resulting from the eccentricity of the reinforcement; so.

$$\delta_s + \delta_b + \delta_c = \delta_f \qquad (11-4)$$

As is usually conceived when dealing with eccentric loadings, two equal and opposite (dashed line) P forces have been inserted in Fig. 11-5(b) at the mid-depth of the section. One of them is considered to cause the uniform tensile axial strain in the concrete, δ_c. The other is teamed with the actual P force to produce the couple Pe which causes the bending strain δ_b.

Consider the steel bar to be unbonded to the concrete and pressing eccentrically against section $v - r$ as the concrete shrinks, causing it to get into the tilted position $v'r'$, as shown by the arrows. Then:

$$\delta_s = \frac{P}{A_s E_s}, \qquad \delta_b = \frac{Pe^2}{I_c E_{ct}}, \qquad \delta_c = \frac{P}{A_g E_{ct}}$$

wherein the concrete area, A_g, and the moment of inertia, I_c, are conveniently those of the uncracked gross[6] plain concrete section.

Substituting in Eq. 11–4 and rearranging:

$$P = \frac{\delta_f E_{ct}}{\dfrac{1}{A_g}\left(1 + \dfrac{1}{n_t p_s}\right) + \dfrac{e^2}{I_c}} \qquad \textit{Eccentric Shrinkage} \qquad (11\text{--}5)$$

wherein p_s states the flexure steel content in terms of A_g for shrinkage calculations only; and n_t and E_{ct} are elapsed time values.

Solution:

Calculating the 5-year sustained modulus of elasticity, E_{ct}, for a slab loaded at the 6-day age:

From Art. 10–6, $\delta_t = C\sqrt[r]{t}$; so,

5-yr. axial creep strain $= 1.33(0.25)\sqrt[3]{365}$ $= 2.38 \times 10^{-6}$ per psi

$$\text{Axial elastic strain} = \frac{1 \text{ psi}}{E_c} = \frac{1}{3{,}090{,}000} = \frac{0.32}{2.70}$$

$$E_{ct} = \frac{1}{2.70 \times 10^{-6}} = 370{,}000 \text{ psi}$$

For Formula 11–5:

$$p_s = \frac{A_s}{A_g} = \frac{2(0.11)}{3(12)} = 0.61\%,$$

$$I_c = \frac{bh^3}{12} = \frac{12(3)^3}{12} = 27., \qquad n_t = \frac{30{,}000{,}000}{370{,}000} = 81.1$$

Then $P = \dfrac{0.00047(370{,}000)}{\dfrac{1}{36}\left[1 + \dfrac{1}{81.1(0.0061)}\right] + \dfrac{(0.81)^2}{27}} = 1610$ lb., the shrinkage force.

Shrinkage Stresses

  Steel

$$f_{ss} = \frac{P}{A_s} = \frac{1610}{2(0.11)} \qquad\qquad = 7320 \text{ psi, compressive.}$$

---

[6] If, due to applied external loading, hair-line flexure cracks have already developed, use the remaining effective concrete area and recompute I_c and e accordingly. See Shank, Bibliography Reference J, p. 32, revised.

This shrinkage compressive stress will decrease Washa's original design tensile steel stress of 20,600 psi to 13,280 psi.

Concrete

		Concrete Unit Stress
Top Fiber		

$$\text{D.S.} \quad = \frac{P}{A_g} = \frac{1610}{3(12)} \qquad = \quad 45 \ t$$

$$\text{Bend.} \ = \frac{Pec}{I} = \frac{1610(0.81)(1.5)}{27} = \frac{72 \ c}{27} \ c = f_{cs}$$

Bottom Fiber

D.S.	= as before	45 t
Bend.	= as before	72 t
		117 t

This value is less than the 300 psi axial tensile strength of 3000-lb. concrete; and less than its 400-psi *minimum* bending modulus of rupture, as determined from the tests of 1954. (Refer to Fig. 13–12 of Chapter 13.)

Shrinkage Strains.   All are contractile.

	Calculated	Observed Test Data Washa's Warp* Slab D
Top Concrete Fiber	Strains in millionths	
$0.00047 + \dfrac{27}{370,000} =$	543	690
Steel		
$\dfrac{7320}{30,000,000} =$	244	no data
Bot. Concrete Fiber		
$0.00047 - \dfrac{117}{370,000} =$	154	220†

* To isolate the shrinkage strains, the warpage test slab was not sealed or loaded, but lay on edge, supported at the quarter points.

† The slab D observed value of 510 was inconsistent with the 220 mean value of two similar slabs but of different slumps, of which the mean *top* strain was 705.

Required: (b) **To calculate the predicted 5-year deflection of the 12.5 ft. simple span slab due to shrinkage warpage, and to compare it with test data.**

Solution:

The shrinkage moment in the slab is, from Fig. 11–5(b) and Solution (a). $Pe = 1610(0.81) = 1303$ in.-lb. over its full length.

By the moment-area law of the tangent, the midspan deflection will be the moment of the area of half the moment diagram about one end, and divided by EI:

$$\Delta = \frac{M(L/2)[L/4]}{EI} = \frac{1303(75)[37.5]}{370,000(27)} = 0.37 \text{ in.}$$

Professor Washa's observed deflection was 0.44 in.

Comment. By using the sustained modulus of elasticity and the gross plain concrete moment of inertia, the shrinkage strains and deflections of beams and slabs may be approximated, especially at the later ages. For more accurate predictions the depth of any tensile cracking[6] should be taken into account.

ECCENTRIC SHRINKAGE PRACTICE PROBLEM

Problem 11–3. Compute the shrinkage deflection of the beam of Example 10–3 of Chapter 10, add it to the elastic deflection and the creep deflection there computed to get *total 2½-year deflection*. See Bibliography Reference L, p. 106.

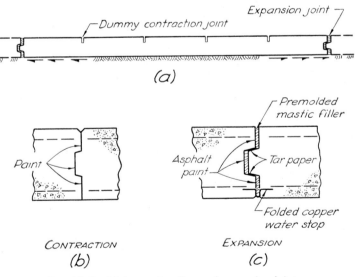

CONTRACTION
(b)

EXPANSION
(c)

FIG. 11–6. Major contraction and expansion joints.

11–8. Contraction and Expansion Joints. As indicated in earlier articles, shrinkage and temperature reinforcement decreases the free contraction or expansion of concrete members only slightly. The actual movements must be provided for by joints especially introduced for the purposes, since concrete structures are typically integral, or jointless.

Contraction Joints. The general philosophy of joint design may be illustrated by the 150-ft. section of pavement or basement floor pictured in Fig. 11–6(a). As it contracts due to drying shrinkage and/or fall in temperature, the friction of the subgrade develops the tensile forces shown, and possible tensile cracks. To prevent their being unsightly, the four weakened plane *dummy contraction joints* are formed to ensure that any possible cracks will be straight and largely hidden in the groove. Moreover, since the total contraction will be distributed among five sections, each will hardly be noticed. The interlocking of the rough surfaces at a fracture is relied upon to transmit vertical shear. The *keyed contraction joint* at (b) is much better in this respect. Care must be taken to prevent a bond between the slabs. Less shrinkage will develop if alternate slabs can first be placed and well cured. The key is sometimes replaced by plain-bar dowels about 60 diam. long, one-half

of each of which is embedded in the slab or wall first cast; the other is greased or fitted with a noncorrosive sleeve to facilitate movement. In no case should the principal slab or wall reinforcement cross the joint.

Expansion Joints. When slabs or walls *expand*, due usually to temperature rise, an *expansion joint* consisting of a relatively wide gap filled with slabs of mastic filler, as in Fig. 11–6(a) and (c), is needed at intervals of 100 to 200 ft. in buildings, assuming $\frac{1}{2}$ to 1-in. filler material. Such a joint can also function as a contraction joint. If a wall must be completely watertight, the folded sheet copper *water stop* pictured in (c) can accommodate to the movement and also help hold the mastic in place. Refer also to Fig. 11–7.

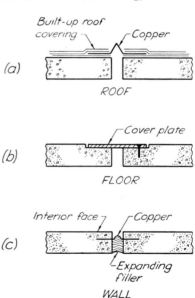

FIG. 11–7. Joints in buildings.

Temperature Change Demands. As stated previously, most of the concrete shrinkage takes place at an early age, but temperature change continues indefinitely. Sudden weather changes are the most detrimental. Concrete foundations, being buried in the ground, expand and contract very little. Brick masonry building walls bearing thereon can usually accommodate to them, but a long exposed concrete wall, with twice as great a thermal coefficient, cannot. Therefore, in concrete structures, vertical joints should make a complete separation all the way to the ground, and preferably be not over 100 ft. apart for average exposures. Joints should be provided between wings and the parent structure, and at the beginnings of extensions.

Wide Ranges of Temperature Change. The usual winter to summer temperature range visualized is 100°F. But roofs pass through a wider range than most walls, so there tends to be relative movement between them. In summer the range will be even greater between the inside and outside of cold storage plants and similar installations. The amount of thermal movement is easily estimated and must be accommodated.

General. The range of travel needed at a given joint can be lessened by more judicious locating of S. & T. reinforcement. Although theory says in Table 11–1 that it is possible to *cause* cracking by having too much reinforcement, this condition almost never occurs. Extra bars should be provided around large openings in floors and walls to offset concrete's tensile weakness thereabout. More effective moist curing of the concrete enables it to develop greater tensile strength before shrinkage and temperature strains accumulate.

11–9. Summary of Shrinkage and Temperature Change. With lapse of time the dimensions of extensive concrete members may change without the application of any external force, due to shrinkage or a change in temperature.

The initial shrinkage of concrete accompanies the drying which occurs when moist curing is withdrawn, and finally reaches a maximum value of about one in two thousand. After such a member has been expanded by a thorough rewetting, it will again shrink, but to a lesser extent.

Since steel and concrete must expand and contract the same amount in order to adhere permanently, the thermal coefficient of expansion of cured concrete should approach steel's value of 0.000,006,5 per degree Fahrenheit. Suitable aggregates are an important factor.

As moisture or heat enters or leaves a concrete member, unequal strains develop as between the outer shell and the inner portion, due to the time required for complete penetration. These differential strains cause internal stress, the magnitude of which would be great were it not for the mitigating effect of shear deformation between layers, and the creep property of the concrete.

In slabs and walls, the destructive effect of repeated cycles of contraction and expansion may be greatly reduced by providing suitable amounts of shrinkage-temperature steel in the directions not already reinforced for the purpose of carrying the design loads. The movements will thereby be somewhat decreased; but long members still must be provided with joints which can adjust to them.

In singly reinforced beams, due to the eccentricity of the flexure reinforcement, shrinkage is accompanied by a warpage of the beam as the compressed steel minimizes the contraction of the tension side. The design tensile stress in the reinforcement is thereby appreciably decreased; but the adjacent concrete is subjected to shrinkage tension, which causes hair-line tensile cracks to develop at lighter loads than would otherwise be the case.

Since shrinkage and temperature effects are more or less *time-dependent*, estimates of the magnitudes of the corresponding stresses and deformations should be made, utilizing a *sustained* modulus of elasticity of the concrete, which has been computed for the period of time involved, as in the creep calculations of Chapter 10.

In designing prestressed beams, one must be able to closely estimate the shrinkage, creep, and elastic deformations of the concrete of the tension side in order to predict the magnitude of the losses of steel prestress due thereto.

BIBLIOGRAPHY

A) Volume Changes of Concrete. *Modern Developments in Reinforced Concrete*, No. 18, published by the Structural Bureau, Portland Cement Association, Chicago.

B) SCHORER, HERMAN. Prestressed Concrete, Design Principles and Reinforcing Units, *Proc. American Concrete Institute*, 1943, Vol. 39, pp. 493 and 501.

C) McMILLAN, F. R. Discussion of a paper by A. C. Janni, Method of Designing Reinforced Concrete Slabs, *Trans. Am. Soc. C.E.*, 1916, Vol. 80. Discussion beginning on p. 1738.

D) SHANK, J. R. The Mechanics of Plastic Flow of Concrete, *Proc. American Concrete Institute*, 1935, Vol. 32, p. 149.

E) DAVIS, RAYMOND E. A Summary of Investigations of Volume Changes in Cements, Mortars and Concretes Produced by Causes other than Stress, *Proc. American Society for Testing Materials*, 1930, Vol. 30, Part 1, p. 668.

F) RAWHOUSER, CLARENCE. Cracking and Temperature Control of Mass Concrete, *Proc. American Concrete Institute*, 1945, Vol. 41, p. 305.

G) WHITNEY, CHAS. S. Plain and Reinforced Concrete Arches, *Proc. American Concrete Institute*, 1932, Vol. 28, p. 479.

H) PICKETT, GERALD. Shrinkage Stresses in Concrete, *Proc. American Concrete Institute*, 1946, Vol. 42, pp. 165, 361, and particularly p. 375.

I) WASHA, GEORGE W. Plastic Flow of Thin Reinforced Concrete Slabs, *Proc. American Concrete Institute*, 1948, Vol. 44, p. 237.

J) SHANK, J. R. The Plastic Flow of Concrete, *Ohio State University Engineering Experiment Station Bulletin*, No. 91, 1935.

K) The booklet *Concrete Bridge Details* published by the Portland Cement Association, Chicago.

L) WASHA, GEORGE W., and FLUCK, P. G. Effect of Compressive Reinforcement on the Plastic Flow of Reinforced Concrete Beams, *Proc. American Concrete Institute*, 1953, Vol. 49, p. 89.

SHRINKAGE AND TEMPERATURE CHANGE QUESTIONS

1. Distinguish clearly between shrinkage and creep in the most important fundamental respect by defining each carefully.

2. If a shrinkage crack develops, it is usually at a relatively early age. Explain.

3. Distinguish clearly between external and internal restraints upon contraction and expansion. Are they both undesirable? Explain.

4. Why are shrinkage and expansion sometimes destructive? Enumerate and explain what preventive measures may be taken.

5. What property of concrete sometimes prevents shrinkage and temperature stresses from becoming excessive? Describe how and when this is possible.

6. Sketch the localities of a concrete test cylinder which becomes stressed (a) in tension and (b) in compression under each of the following:

drying   external cooling

external heat   rewetting

heat of hydration

7. Will strain gage readings taken upon the flexure reinforcement of a simple span beam before and after loading reveal the true tensile stress therein? Explain. Suggest a much better technique.

8. Derive a fundamental formula for the force induced in temperature steel. State your notation clearly.

9. Is it possible for an excessive amount of shrinkage and temperature steel to be positively detrimental as well as wasteful? Demonstrate how.

10. Distinguish between axial and eccentric shrinkage. In what type of designing does the amount of the latter become quite important?

11. Discuss at length the effects of temperature change upon concrete structures and what measures can be taken to mitigate or eliminate them.

12. Outline, in order, the steps necessary to predict by calculation the shrinkage deflection (warpage) of a singly reinforced concrete slab. How could you check your results experimentally?

CONTINUATION PROBLEM

Problem 11–4. *Shrinkage Warpage of a Doubly Reinforced Concrete Slab.* Recalculate the five-year shrinkage stresses, strains and midspan deflection of the slab of Example 11–4, if compressive reinforcement, centered 0.69 in. from the top, is added, as follows:

(a) One-half of the tensile A_s, namely, one #3 bar.

(b) Equal to the tensile A_s, namely, two #3 bars.

Make a tabular comparison of your results with those of Example 11–3, and comment.

CHAPTER 12

ULTIMATE STRENGTH DESIGN

12–1. Introduction. In the preceding chapters allowable working stresses were used to design at the safe *working strength* level, which,

Charles S. Whitney, Consulting Engineer, Ammann and Whitney, New York and Milwaukee. Long active in improvements in reinforced concrete design, including his method of arch design and concrete shell roof construction, he was awarded the Wason Medal of the American Concrete Institute for his committee chairmanship report, *Plain and Reinforced Concrete Arches*. In 1950 Mr. Whitney also received from the Institute the Alfred E. Lindau Award "in recognition of his many contributions to reinforced concrete design practice."

His introduction to American engineers in 1937 of the *stress block* method of ultimate strength design greatly stimulated interest in the subject.

for concrete, is in the lower half of the stress-strain diagram, Fig. 12–1(a), called the *elastic range*, where stress is substantially proportional to strain.

An exception was the design of axially loaded columns, wherein the elastic modular ratio, n, is no longer used as equivalent to the ratio of steel to concrete unit stresses, f_s/f_c, though the work was performed at the working stress level.

Over twenty years ago it was clearly demonstrated that a more realistic and economical design could be produced for columns by applying a factor of safety to the ultimate strength, as experimentally determined, or predicted by an *ultimate strength* calculation which disregarded n.

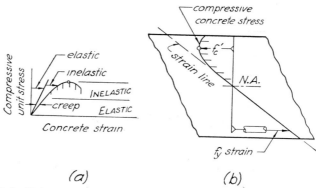

FIG. 12–1. Relationship of concrete stress-strain diagram (a) to concrete flexural stress distribution; (b) in a balanced ultimate strength beam at failure.

In ultimate strength *beam* designing, to which this chapter is principally devoted, the engineer first magnifies the service load bending moment by a *load factor* to get the ultimate design moment. He then furnishes sufficient steel and concrete to provide independently, at their failure strengths, the desired ultimate resisting moment.

For concrete, his attention is focused upon the upper portion of the *inelastic range* of the stress-strain diagram, as pictured in Figs. 10–1 and 12–1(a). In the case of the steel, the yield point is the useful limit of its strength in a beam. Note that the upper portion of Fig. 12–1(b) is the curve of (a) rotated through 90°; and that the concrete stresses in the upper fibers fall short of the corresponding strain-line values.

As one takes up the subject of the inelasticity of beams it *is quite important to recognize that the traditional straight-line variation of flexural unit stress,* so much used in elastic calculations, *does not exist in the inelastic range.* It *is* true that there is a straight-line variation of *strain* throughout both ranges, as has been demonstrated many times by taking *strain* gage readings during testing. But the *stress* variation in the inelastic range is some kind of curve which is not easily determined experimentally, since there are very few research devices which may be said to measure *stress* that is not proportional to strain.

12-2. Failure of Reinforced Concrete Beams. Primary failure of reinforced concrete beams in flexure occurs when either the concrete of the compression side initially factures near f'_c, the test cylinder ultimate compressive strength, or the steel gradually reaches f_y, its tensile yield point strength. In this latter case the beam does not collapse, but tensile cracks develop and later open so widely due to the yielding that deflection becomes excessive. Its practical usefulness having been badly impaired thereby, the beam is said to have failed. *Secondary* failure via the concrete will be discussed in Art. 12-7.

So-called "balanced beams," as commonly designed by the straight-line theory of bending, nearly always fail by yielding of the tensile steel. This indicates that there is a greater reserve of compressive strength in the concrete than is suggested by the ratio of the ACI design safety factors of $40,000/20,000 = 2$ for steel, versus $f'_c/0.45f'_c = 2.22$ for the concrete. The actual factor for the concrete of beams has been nearer $3\frac{1}{3}$, since, due to the *creep* property taken up in Chapter 10, the true working load extreme fiber stress is seldom over two-thirds of the value computable by the usual straight-line elastic method. Nevertheless, it is generally agreed that the concrete factor of safety should always be the higher because it is a brittle type of material which gives little or no warning of approaching failure.

12-3. Methods of Predicting the Ultimate Strength of Reinforced Concrete Beams. Although in years past other ultimate strength methods have been used, only three will be mentioned herein. They have these characteristics in common:

1. All are somewhat empirical—having been developed from studies of failure test data.
2. All recognize that the extreme compressive fiber *stress* in the concrete at failure is a great deal less than the usual elastic *strain* calculation would indicate, due to creep and inelasticity.
3. At the failure load, the variation in the compressive unit stress in the concrete, no longer linear, is assumed.
4. The neutral axis for bending is located, using the accepted straight-line variation of flexural *strains*, if at all.
5. The percentage of flexure steel required for *balanced design*, as dictated by ultimate strength calculations, is greater than that required by the straight-line safe working load method.

For reasons to be discussed later, only Whitney's method will be taken up at length.

12-4. Whitney's Stress Block Method.[A] This method, first presented in 1937, and more completely in 1940, has the great advantage of simplicity. Moreover, its remarkable correlation, in Fig. 12-2, with the results of tests on many beams, both under-reinforced and over-

reinforced, attests to its accuracy. By plotting the failure bending
moment divided by bd^2 and further by f'_c, rectangular test beams of
various sizes and concrete strengths were put upon the same strength

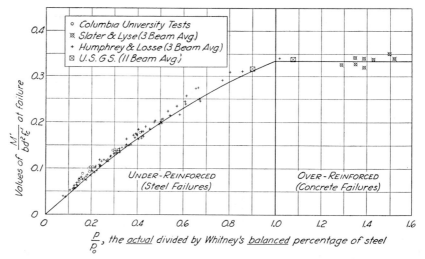

FIG. 12–2. Whitney's calculated ultimate strengths of rectangular concrete
beams compared with the results of 309 tests. Ref. *Trans. ASCE* 1940, p. 1763.

basis. Along the horizontal axis, the p/p_o relation creates a distinct
separation between under-reinforced and over-reinforced cases. Whitney's balanced steel ratio, p_o, turns out to be 4.28 per cent for a typical
combination of 3750-lb. concrete and 40,000 psi yield point steel.

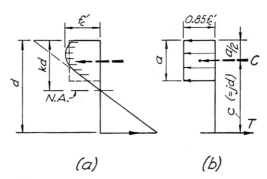

FIG. 12–3. Whitney's compressive stress block.

In Fig. 12–3(a), Whitney pictured a probable compressive stress
distribution at failure, similar in shape to the stress-strain curve of
Fig. 12–1(a). He next proceeded to devise, at (b), a convenient office
method for approximating the internal resisting moment of the beam.

For one side of the "stress block" he took $0.85f'_c$ as the stress intensity, and conveniently the same as the failure value[1] found in the ACI tests of axially loaded columns, Art. 4–4 of Chapter 4.

Singly Reinforced Beams

12–5. Whitney's Balanced Beam Designing. By studying the failure bending moments of the rectangular beams of the Slater and Lyse[B] series of tests, all of which were concrete failures, and eliminating a few inconsistent ones, an average maximum value of stress block depth, a, in Fig. 12–3(b) of $0.537d$ was deduced; it is here designated as a_o, the depth of the stress block[2] for Whitney's *balanced* singly reinforced rectangular beams.

In designing, no neutral axis or n value is used, as will be seen.

EXAMPLE 12–1

Design of a Balanced Ultimate Strength Rectangular Beam. **Given an ultimate strength specification of f_y = 40,000, and f'_c = 3,000, and an ultimate strength bending moment of 106 kip-ft. It is required to design a rectangular beam 8 in. wide by Whitney's ultimate strength method, and to compare the resulting section with that of Example 2–4 (and Table 2–1) of Chapter 2, which was designed for the corresponding 50.4 kip-ft. of *working strength* bending moment (Art. 12–10).**

Solution: With only one of the three quantities b, d and A_s already set, the beam can be a balanced one.[3] (See Fig. 12–3.)

$$M' = C'jd = C'a_o = 0.85f'_c(0.537d)(8)[d - 0.268d] = 106(12,000)$$

Substituting 3000 for f'_c we find:

Required d = 12.60 in.

$$\text{Since } T' = C' = \frac{M'}{jd} = \frac{1,272,000}{0.732(12.60)} = 138,000 \text{ lb.:}$$

$$\text{Req'd. } A_s = \frac{138,000}{40,000} = 3.45 \text{ sq. in.}$$

Make d = 12.60 in. and use 2-#9 and 2-#8 bars.

---

[1] It is also true that full-sized members (in comparison with 6 by 12 in. cylinders) are (a) slenderer and (b) are unrestrained laterally by the friction of a test machine head and base. They fail at compressive stresses somewhat less than the f'_c of standard cylinders.

[2] Note that a and a_o are not neutral axis distances. Whitney does not compute it.

[3] Superscript primes (') are being used throughout this chapter to indicate ultimate values.

Comparison. In Example 2–4 the dimensions required for the corresponding working strength design were: $b = 8$ in., $d = 17.9$ in., $A_s = 1.95$ sq. in. Balanced ultimate strength designs require less concrete but more steel.

Drill Problem 12–1. Substitute the algebraic symbols in the numerical solution of Example 12–1, and derive the expression for the failure moment:

$$M'_c = C'c = \text{closely } \frac{f'_c}{3} bd^2 \qquad \text{\textit{Whitney's[4] balanced, or over-reinforced, rectan-}}$$
$$\text{\textit{gular beams}} \quad (12\text{–}1)$$

and use the formula to check Example 12–1.

12–6. The Balanced Beam Steel Ratios of Whitney and the ACI.
In the preceding example the balanced steel content required was, by A_s/bd, equal to $3.45/[8(12.60)] = 3.42\%$.

The Whitney balanced steel ratio may be calculated for any combination of concrete and steel strengths by equating T' to C' in a balanced beam:

$$p_o bd(f_y) \equiv 0.537 d(b)(0.85 f'_c)$$

$$p_o = 0.456 \frac{f'_c}{f_y} \qquad \text{\textit{(Whitney balance—in decimal form)}} \qquad (12\text{–}2)$$

Such beams are designed to be balanced at *failure*, so a concrete failure is as likely as a steel one. Since concrete failures are sudden, and therefore undesirable, beams that are somewhat under-reinforced are usually designed, so that failure will be via the steel. The ASCE–ACI Joint Committee limits p to $0.40f'_c/f_y$ in their Formula 2. Since it is $0.40/0.456$ or fully $\frac{7}{8}$ of Whitney's balanced content, many engineers consider that the limit should be still lower, especially in view of economy.[4]

12–7. Failure Action of Under-Reinforced Beams.
When a beam is under-reinforced, *primary failure* will be due to yielding of the steel, as illustrated in Fig. 12–4(a). Note that the concrete stress at the top fiber is less than the $0.85f'_c$ failure value.

At (b), under a small increase in load, the tensile steel crack next opens considerably due to the pictured *inelastic strain* occurring in the yielded steel. This causes the *strain neutral axis* and the centroid for C' to move upward. Since $T' = f_y A_s$, C' also must be fully as great as before. But it is distributed over a smaller concrete area, so the top fiber stress soon reaches the failure value $0.85f'_c$, which constitutes the *secondary failure*. At this stage[4] the ultimate resisting moment of the beam has increased somewhat, due to the increase in jd.

---

[4] The ACI maximum stress block depth is only $0.47d$, which results in a maximum M'_c value of only $0.306f'_c bd^2$.

In (c) an effort has been made to follow the effect of progressive crushing of the upper concrete fibers as the steel *continues* to elongate inelastically. The continued rise of the strain neutral axis, in combination with the destruction of the uppermost fibers of concrete results in

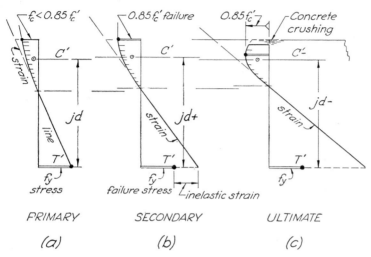

FIG. 12–4.   The three failure stages of an under-reinforced beam.

decreased compression area, decreased compressive resistance, $C'-$, and decreased couple arm $jd-$. The internal resisting moment having thus decreased appreciably below the applied bending moment, *ultimate failure* ensues.

Thus, *whether a beam is over-reinforced or under-reinforced, the concrete stress block unit stress at the ultimate bending moment is to be taken at the* $0.85f'_c$ *failure value.* Sufficient block depth, a, is then taken so that the failing strength of the concrete will match the yield point strength of the steel used.

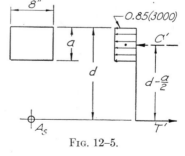

FIG. 12–5.

EXAMPLE 12–2

Design of an Under-Reinforced Ultimate Strength Rectangular Beam. **Given the same ultimate strength specification of 40,000 and 3000 psi, and the 106 kip-ft. ultimate bending moment of the preceding Example 12–1. It is required to design a rectangular beam 8 in. w..'e with 2.5 per cent of steel. Refer to Figure 12–5.**

Solution: Find the relationship of the unknowns a and d by equating C' to T':

$$0.85(3000)(8)(a) = pbdf_y = 0.025(8)(d)(40,000)$$

So the req'd. $a = 0.392d$

Then $M'_s = T'jd = 0.025(8)(d)(40,000)[d - 0.196d] = 106(12,000)$.

Req'd. $d = 14.08$ in., $A_s = pbd = 0.025(8)(14.08) = 2.82$ sq. in.

Make d at least 14.08 *in. and use* 1–#10 *and* 1–#11 *bar.*

Comment. Investigations to find the maximum safe resisting moment of sections are conducted in the same general manner.

Also note in the accompanying Table 12–1 the difference in the sizes and steel contents of beams designed for the same live load by several methods.

12–8. The Under-Reinforced Beam Formula. If the algebraic symbols of Example 12–2 are taken, and the expression $C' = T'$ used

TABLE 12–1

Comparison of Rectangular Beam Sections designed by the ◣ and the ◲ Methods.			
All have 40,000 Y. P. Steel and 3,000-lb. concrete, n=10, and carry the same Live Load Bending Moment.			
Calc. by ACI ◣ Safe Working Load Method	CALCULATED BY THE ◲ ULTIMATE STRENGTH METHOD		
Live Load B.M.=50^{kl} Dead Load B.M.=33.6 Design B.M.=83.6^{kl}	Live Load Ultimate B. M. = 50 × 2.4 *=120.^{kl} Dead Load Ultimate B. M. = 25 × 1.2 * = 30 Design Ultimate B. M. =150.^{kl} **		
ACI ◣ BAL. BEAM	UNDER-REINFORCED ‡	ACI MAX. STEEL %	WHITNEY'S BAL. %
10" 20.6 2.84$^{a''}$ p =1.38%	10" 15.0 3.80$^{a''}$ p =2.53%	10" 14.1 4.24$^{a''}$ p =3.0%	10" 13.4 4.56$^{a''}$ p =3.42%
Gradual failures via the steel			Sudden failure via concrete

*These are *load factors.* Refer to the latter part of Art. 12-10.
**For "ACI MAX. STEEL %" case. The other 3 cases involve the somewhat different dead load.
‡ Whitney recommends under-reinforcement.

to evaluate a, the following much used expression for ultimate bending moment results:

$$M'_s = T'jd = A_s f_y d \left[1 - \frac{pf_y}{2(0.85)f'_c} \right]$$

Whitney's under-reinforced rectangular beams (12–3)

This formula also is general, since if p is replaced by p_o, the Whitney balanced steel content, we get $M' = (f'_c/3)bd^2$, which is Formula 12–1 for balanced or over-reinforced beams.

In Fig. 12–2, the graph of test beam strengths, the inclined line represents Formula 12–3, while the horizontal straight line is Formula 12–1.

RECTANGULAR BEAM PRACTICE PROBLEMS

Problem 12–2. The specification is 50,000 and 3750 psi. Design a balanced rectangular beam with $d = 16$ in., for an ultimate bending moment of 150 kip ft.

Partial answer: Required b = 5.61 in.

Problem 12–3. Redesign the beam of Problem 12–2 for 2.0 per cent of steel. The d still is 16 in.

(a) Using the formula.

(b) Without the formula.

Ans. Required b = 8.33 in.; A_s = 2.67 sq. in.

(c) Make scale sketches of the beams designed in Problems 12–2 and 12–3, and comment.

Problem 12–4. Given a rectangular beam of 3750-lb. concrete, 10 in. wide by 20 in. deep to the center of 4–#10 bars of 50,000-psi yield point steel.

(a) Find its ultimate bending moment.

Suggestion: First find whether the beam is under- or over-reinforced.

Ans. 341. kip ft.

(b) Alternately show how to solve without knowing which type of beam it is.

Problem 12–5. Given an ultimate design specification of 50,000 and 4000 psi. Calculate the required b, d and A_s for an ultimate strength beam with b equal to $d/2$. The ultimate B.M. is 100 k-ft. Take ACI max. steel content.

12–9. Ultimate Strength T-Beams and Otherwise. It will be recalled that when dealing with beams of T-shape using the *working strength* methods of Chapter 2, it was necessary to determine at the outset whether or not the working stress neutral axis fell within or beneath the flange portion.

In designing T-shaped beams by Whitney's ultimate strength method, the differentiation is made by reference to the depth, a, of the compressive strength block.

Since Formula 12–3 has general application to all practical rectangular beams, consider the bracketed term thereof, which expresses j for the arm, jd, of the internal couple.   Therefore, since $d - jd = a/2$, the whole stress block depth must be:

$$a = \frac{pf_y}{0.85f'_c}\,(d) = 1.18p\,\frac{f_y}{f'_c}\,(d) \text{ as usually}^5 \text{ written} \qquad (12\text{–}4)$$

When the flange thickness of a T-shaped ultimate strength beam is *greater than a*, it is computed as a rectangular beam, with the flange width taken as b; and p computed accordingly.

When the flange thickness is *less than a*, the member is technically a T-beam, and separate resisting couples must be computed for (1) the web and (2) the overhanging flange portion.

EXAMPLE 12–3

ACI T-Beam Designing. **Given an ultimate bending moment of 225 kip-ft. and the ultimate strength specification of $f_y = 40,000$, $f'_c = 3000$. It is required to design a T-shaped beam with a 6-in. flange thickness and a depth, d, of 14 in., as shown in Fig. 12–6(a).**

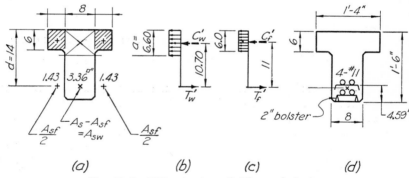

(a)   (b)   (c)   (d)

Fig. 12–6.   Ultimate strength T-beam designing.

Preliminary.   Referring to Art. 12–6, the ACI design maximum steel content for a rectangular section is:

$$p = 0.40\,\frac{f'_c}{f_y} = 0.40\left(\frac{3,000}{40,000}\right) = 3.0\% \text{ in this case.}$$

Furthermore, since the proposed 6-in. flange thickness is less than Whitney's stress block depth, $a = 1.18(0.03)\dfrac{40,000}{3,000}(14) = 6.60$ in., the beam is technically a T-beam.

---

⁵ The term $p\,\dfrac{f_y}{f'_c}$ is q in the 1956 ACI Appendix notation.

Method: Such a beam is designed by considering that the total tensile steel area, A_s, in Fig. 12–6(a), consists of two items. The first is the quantity $A_s - A_{sf} = A_{sw}$ permitted by the ACI to balance[4] the compressive strength of the upper portion of the web, as suggested by the construction at (b). The other is A_{sf}, which matches the compressive strength of the total *overhanging flange* area. The two internal couples thus created resist the design ultimate bending moment.

Solution: Taking an 8-in. stem as sufficient width to cover a two-bar arrangement, the steel area required (ACI) to balance the web portion will be:

$$A_{sw} = 0.03(8)(14) = 3.36 \text{ sq. in.}$$

Corresp. balanced

$$M'_w = A_{sw}(f_y d)\left[1 - \frac{pf_y}{1.7f'_c}\right] \qquad \text{(from Formula 12–3.)}$$

$$M'_w = \frac{3.36(40,000)(14)}{12,000}\left[1 - \frac{0.03(40,000)}{1.7(3000)}\right] = 120. \text{ kip-ft.}$$

Corresp. stress block depth, a, from the "Preliminary" study above, = 6.60 in.

The remaining bending moment to be taken care of by the flange couple represented by Fig. 12–6(c) = $225 - 120 = 105.$ kip-ft.

$$\text{Req'd. flange } T'_f = \frac{105(12,000)}{14 - 3} = 114,600 \text{ lb.}$$

$$\text{Req'd. } A_{sf} = \frac{114,600}{40,000} = 2.86 \text{ sq. in.}$$

Total tensile steel required = 6.22 sq. in.

$$\text{Req'd. total flange overhang } = \frac{C'_f}{0.85f'_c(t)} = \frac{114,600}{0.85(3000)(6)} = 7.48 \text{ in.}$$

As shown in Fig. 12–6(d): *Make over-all flange width 16 in. and use 4–#11 bars.*

Comments: The above designing may be checked by Formula A4 of Sec. A-607 of the ACI Abstract of the ASCE–ACI Report.[c]

For an ultimate strength investigation of an I-shaped beam see Calc. Sheet 2/6 of Example 13–2 in Chapter 13.

T-BEAM ULTIMATE STRENGTH PROBLEMS

Take 50,000-psi steel, 3750-lb. concrete and the ACI design recommendations.

Problem 12–6. Given an ultimate bending moment of 575 kip-ft., a flange thickness of 7 in. and a d of 19 in. Design the flange width, web thickness, and steel content for a T-shaped beam with 2.5 per cent of steel assigned to the web.

Ans. Use a flange width of at least 19.4 in., and 6–#11 bars in an 11-in. web.

Problem 12–7. Given an ultimate bending moment of 400 kip-ft. Design a true T-beam with an 8-in. flange thickness. Deduce all needed dimensions.

12–10. Load Factors for Ultimate Strength Design. *A load factor* is a number used to compute a multiple of the working load bending moment called the *ultimate bending moment,* which is used in ultimate strength designing.

Terminologically, a load factor should be distinguished from a *factor of safety,* which is sometimes divided into the ultimate strength of a material to find an allowable stress to use in conventional *working strength* designing.

Load factors have been used by aircraft structures engineers for many years. Only recently, with the rebirth[E] of ultimate strength design of concrete members, have present-day structural engineers begun to use them.

As stated by Lin,[F] *the primary purpose of ultimate strength design is to attain a more uniform degree of safety* when a structure is loaded to near its ultimate strength. Such balancing of hazards cannot be accomplished simply by totaling the bending moment from all the loads, and multiplying it by a single load factor. Load factors must vary for:

> Different kinds of loads.
> Different combinations of loads.
> Static, dynamic or fatigue-producing loads.
> Different types of structures.

The intelligent selection of load factors is a study in itself.[F] When faithfully carried out, the resulting ultimate strength design should contain less material in localities where the live load/dead load ratio is small, but more where the ratio is large, with an increased ultimate strength for perhaps the same total amount of material. This is because a much smaller load factor is assigned to dead load than to live.

Load factors are chosen *with regard to the maximum anticipated increases in loads.* They are the coefficients in the following expressions for U, the ultimate strength capacity of a section, as excerpted from the ASCE–ACI Report:[C]

When the effect of wind and earthquake loading can be properly neglected:

$$U = 1.2B + 2.4L \tag{I}$$

wherein B is the effect of dead load plus "strain loads" due to elastic action, creep, shrinkage and temperature change.

L is the effect of live load, plus impact if present.

It is additionally required that the following expression be observed:

$$U = K(B + L) \tag{II}$$

wherein K has the value 1.8 for beam and girder flexure, 2.00 for shear, diagonal tension and bond, as well as for columns and combined stress members.

Thus if the working dead, *et al.*, load B of a girder is 100 kip-feet, and the live load plus impact L is 300, the ultimate strength bending moment capacity to be provided must be the larger of the two values computed by Formula I:

$$U = 1.2(100) + 2.4(300) = 840 \text{ kip-ft.}$$

and by Formula II:

$$U = 1.8(100 + 300) \qquad = 720 \text{ kip-ft.}$$

Formula II governs when $L < B$.

For the load factors to use when wind or earthquake loading must be considered see the ASCE–ACI Report.[c]

12–11. Whitney's versus Other Methods. The foregoing examples have illustrated the simplicity of Whitney's method as applied to singly reinforced beams. It makes a distinct break with the *elastic theory* of bending by abandoning the conventional straight-line variation of flexure stress, the modular ratio, n, and the computing of the neutral axis. Instead, it substitutes an *inelastic* rectangular concrete stress distribution.

Of the many ultimate strength methods,[J] two which grade more or less *gradually* from the straight line to the curved concrete ultimate stress variation, as load is increased toward failure, have been plotted with Whitney's in Fig. 12–7. Dr. Vernon P. Jensen's *trapezoidal* method[I] was presented in 1943, the author's *expanding cubic* one was developed in 1952. Their structural nicety is more acceptable to mechanics-minded persons, including advanced engineering students; but they are not nearly so simple to use, nor are they appreciably more accurate *at the failure level* than Whitney's method.

12–12. Economy of Ultimate Strength Beams. In Fig. 12–7, the common ACI elastic method also was plotted, using the steel and concrete factors of safety deduced in Art. 12–2 as *load factors*. Note that all methods predict about the same strength up to the elastic *balanced beam* steel content of 1.7 per cent. Beyond it, recalling from Fig. 12–2 that the *test data* coincide well with the upper group of curves, one sees that the elastic method is ultraconservatively incorrect for predicting ultimate strengths for steel contents greater than about 2 per cent.

The ultimate strength method recognizes that considerably more compressive resistance develops in the upper portion of a beam after the extreme concrete fiber barely reaches its failure value than would exist if the distribution of the concrete stress were linear. Refer again to Art. 12–7 and the three portions of Fig. 12–4.

Since beams with more than the Whitney balanced percentage of steel
are not only quite uneconomical, but also subject to sudden failure via the
concrete, ultimate strength designing is usually most advantageous when the
steel contents are between 2 and 3 per cent. Practically, it usually is difficult
to get much more than 3 per cent into a beam.

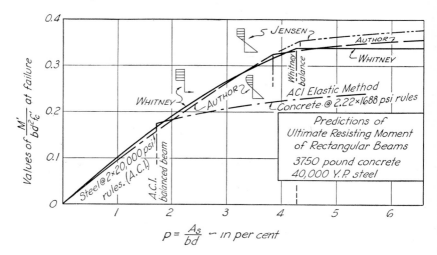

FIG. 12–7. Comparison of Jensen's and author's beam ultimate strength calculation methods with Whitney's and the ACI Code (singly reinforced beams).

By computing the ultimate strength *coefficient of resistance*, $R' = M'/bd^2$,
for beams of balanced steel contents consisting of high and low strength steels
and concretes, it may be shown that the use of high strength concrete in conjunction with ordinary strength reinforcement is not advantageous for flexure.
However, the reverse situation of ordinary strength concrete with high
strength reinforcement is advantageous because a proportionately lower
percentage of it is needed to resist the same tension. It takes up less space
and does not cost proportionately more.

Long-span construction has been considerably advanced by employing the ultimate strength method of calculation in conjunction with
high strength concrete and moderately large percentages of high strength
reinforcement, though deflections tend to become excessive, and must
be carefully checked.

Doubly Reinforced Beams

12–13. Whitney's Doubly Reinforced Beams. Whether designing
or investigating, doubly reinforced beams are calculated by considering
the total tensile steel area, A_s, to consist of two parts: one is A'_s, which
matches the same compressive steel area in the top; the other is $A_s - A'_s$,

which represents the single reinforcement balancing the compressive strength of the concrete. To prevent sudden failures, the ASCE–ACI Report[c] limits the design percentage of $A_s - A'_s$ to $0.4(f'_c/f_y)$, as in singly reinforced beams.

When investigating, the ultimate bending moment to be found will be the sum of the ultimate resisting moments of the two internal couples involved, taking all steel at its yield point stress.

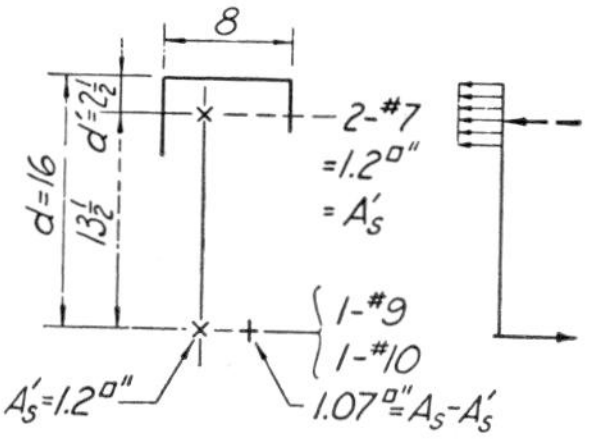

Fig. 12–8. Ultimate strength investigation of a doubly reinforced rectangular beam.

EXAMPLE 12–4

Doubly Reinforced Beam Investigation. Given $f'_c = 3000$, $f_y = 40,000$, and the doubly reinforced 8 by 16 in. beam of Table 2–1, designed for a working strength bending moment of 50.4 kip-ft. in Example 2–7 of Chapter 2. It is required to find the ultimate strength bending moment thereof. Follow ACI philosophy.

Solution: Referring to Fig. 12–8:

$$\text{ACI max. single reinf.,} \quad p - p' = 0.4\frac{f'_c}{f_y} = 0.4\left(\frac{3,000}{40,000}\right) = 3.0\%$$

Have $1.07/8(16) = 0.835\%$; therefore the beam is quite under-reinforced. Now:

$$M' = (A_s - A'_s)(f_y d)\left[1 - \frac{(p - p')f_y}{2(0.85)f'_c}\right] + A'_s f_y*(d - d') \quad (12\text{-}5)$$

$$= 1.07(40)(16)\left[1 - \frac{0.00835(40)}{1.7(3)}\right] + 1.2(40)(13.5)$$

$$M' = 640 + 648 = 1288 \text{ kip-in.} = 107.3 \text{ kip-ft.}$$

Ans.

Average load factor $= 107.3/50.4 = 2.13$.

Compare this beam with the one designed in Example 12–1.

In designing, compute from the maximum permissible amount of single reinforcement, $A_s - A'_s$, the portion of the whole required ultimate moment resistance which can be so taken care of. Then provide equal amounts of additional reinforcement in the top and bottom to resist the remaining bending moment. All steel is taken at its yield point stress.

---

* If desired, the correction for the concrete area displaced by the compressive reinforcement may be made by subtracting $0.85f'_c$ from f_y in this term only.

EXAMPLE 12–5

Doubly Reinforced Beam Designing. Given $f'_c = 3000$, $f_y = 40{,}000$, and $M' = 106$ kip-ft. as in Example 12–1. It is required to make a doubly reinforced ultimate strength design, taking $b = 8$ in., and $d' = 2\frac{1}{2}$ in.

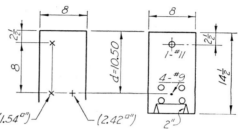

FIG. 12–9. Ultimate strength designing of a doubly reinforced rectangular beam.

Solution: Refer to Fig. 12–9. Since in Example 12–1 a d of 12.60 in. and 3.45 sq. in. of single reinforcement were required, try for a d of 10.50 in.
ACI max. single reinforcement:

$$p = \frac{0.4(3000)}{40{,}000} = 3\%$$

Corresp. required single reinf. $= 0.03(8)(10.50)$ $= 2.42$ sq. in.

Corresponding ultimate moment taken by single reinforcement:

$$106(12) = 1272 \text{ kip-in.}$$

$$M'' = (A_s - A'_s)f_y d\left[1 - \frac{(p - p')f_y}{2(0.85)f'_c}\right]$$

$$2.42(40)(10.5)\left[1 - \frac{0.03(40)}{1.7(3)}\right] = \underline{778}$$

Remaining B.M. $= 494$ kip-in.

Steel couple:

$$d - d' = 10.5 - 2.5 = 8.0 \text{ in.}$$

Req'd. $A'_s = \dfrac{M}{f_y c'} = \dfrac{494}{40(8)} = \underline{1.54}$

Total bottom steel req'd. $= 3.96$ sq. in.

Make d 10.50 in. and use 1–#11 in top and 4–#9 in bottom.

DOUBLY REINFORCED BEAM PROBLEMS

Take 4000-lb. concrete, 50,000-psi steel and the ACI ultimate strength design recommendations.

Problem 12–8. Find the ultimate strength bending moment of a rectangular beam with $b = 14$ in., $d = 28$ in., and $d' = 3$ in., if the following steel contents are used:

(a) Four #9's in the top and eight #11's in the bottom.

Ans. 883. *kip-ft.*

(b) Four #9's in the top and twelve #11's in the bottom.

Ans. 1636. *kip-ft.*

Problem 12–9. Given a beam with $b = 16$ in., $d = 30$ in., and $d' = 4$ in. It is required to calculate the necessary double reinforcement for an ultimate bending moment of 2400 kip-ft.

Ans. 8.58 *sq. in. in the top and* 23.94 *sq. in. in the bottom.*

Problem 12–10. Calculate the required b and steel areas for a doubly reinforced beam with $d = 34$ in., $d' = 4$ in., and one-fourth as much steel in the top as in the bottom. The ultimate bending moment is 2120. kip-ft.

Problem 12–11. *Ultimate Strength Investigation of a Section of I-shape Doubly Reinforced with High Tensile Strength Steel Wire.* Given the beam section of Fig. 12–10 reinforced with a total of forty #6 gage wires, each 0.192 in. in diameter, and 0.0290 sq. in. area.

The wire is of 250,000 psi ultimate strength. Since such steel has no well-defined yield point, consider it to be at 0.9 of the ultimate strength.

The concrete is ACI 3750-lb., $n = 8$.

It is required to find the ultimate bending moment of the section by Whitney's method, and to demonstrate whether or not the failure will be primarily a compressive or a tensile one.

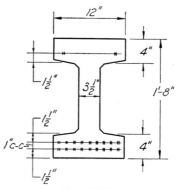

Fig. 12–10.

12–14. Ultimate Diagonal Tension and Bond Strengths. Because the studies and experimental investigations for the joint ASCE–ACI Committee on Shear and Diagonal Tension and for the ACI Committee on Bond Stress are being continued, no recommendations regarding the ultimate strength of reinforced concrete members in these two respects have yet been made by the ACI (November, 1956). The reader should consult the later technical publications for advice thereon.

Combined Stress Members

12–15. Designing for Bending plus Axial Load. Beams which additionally carry axial load and columns subjected to bending are fundamentally identical cases in the general field of *combined stress members*. That the one lies horizontally, while the other stands vertically, is actually not significant. The beams of Chapter 2 and the axially loaded columns of Chapter 4 are simply at the two extremes of the zero to infinity range of eccentricity/depth ratios of combined stress members.

This topic is of considerable importance because reinforced concrete structures, by their very nature, are rigidly connected frames in which *all* members thereof are subject to some degree of combined stressing.

For everyday designing of such members, the method which is by far the best is that involving *axial load transfer*. In it, the axial load is initially transferred to the position of the tensile reinforcement, accompanied by the corresponding bending moment easily deduced by the mechanics principle for creating equivalent force systems. Refer to Example 4–7 of Chapter 4 wherein the same method was used in designing the steel for a combined stress member by the *working strength* method, using the doubly reinforced beam designing procedure.

EXAMPLE 12–6

Ultimate Strength Designing of Unsymmetrical Reinforcement for a Combined Stress Member Subject to Heavy Bending. **Given an 18-in. square member subjected to *service* resultant axial loads of 25 kips dead, *B*, and 76 kips live, *L*, acting 9 in. outside the face thereof. Take 3000-lb. concrete and 50,000-psi yield point steel.**

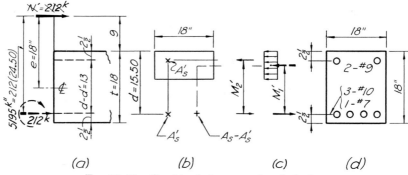

Fig. 12–11. Combined stress member designing.

It is required to design the unequal quantities of reinforcement, to be centered 2½ in. from the two bending faces.

Solution: Referring to Formula (I) of Art. 12–10 on *load* factors, the required eccentric *design ultimate load* will be:

$$U = 1.2B + 2.4L = 1.2(25) + 2.4(76) = 212 \text{ kips}$$

The corresponding ultimate moment of this load *about* the centroid of the tensile steel is, from Fig. 12–11(a), 212(24.50) = 5195 kip-in.

Refer to Fig. 12–11. Using the ACI maximum of about seven-eighths of Whitney's balanced single flexural reinforcement percentage, in order to preclude sudden compression failure:

$$p - p' = 0.4\frac{f'_c}{f_y} = 0.4\frac{(3000)}{(50,000)} = 2.4\%$$

The corresponding ACI balanced beam single reinforcement is

$$A_s - A'_s = 0.024(18)(15.5) \qquad\qquad = 6.72 \text{ sq. in.}$$

The corresponding singly reinforced ultimate resisting moment is

$$M'_1 = (A_s - A'_s)f_y d\left[1 - \frac{(p - p')f_y}{2(0.85)f'_c}\right]$$

$$\qquad\qquad\qquad\qquad\qquad\qquad 5195 \text{ (above)}$$

$$= 6.72(50)(15.5)\left[1 - \frac{0.024(50)}{1.7(3)}\right] = \underline{3980} \text{ kip-in.}$$

$$\text{Remaining } M'_2 = 1215$$

Steel couple:

$$A'_s = \frac{M'_2}{f_y(d - d')} = \frac{1215}{50(13)} \qquad\qquad = \underline{1.87}$$

$$A_s = 8.59$$

$$\text{Tensile equivalent of the 212-kip load} = \frac{212}{50} \qquad = \underline{4.24} \text{ sq. in.}$$

$$\text{Net tensile steel req'd.} = 4.35$$

$$\textit{In "bottom" use } 3\text{--}\#10 \textit{ and } 1\text{--}\#7.$$

In the compression side, adjacent to the load, as defined above by $A'_s = 1.87$ sq. in.,   *In "top" use 2--#9.*

Check upon Concrete Unit Stress:

Dealing with a one-inch unit width of the member, the depth of the stress block will be, from the above calculations:

$$a = \frac{(p - p')f_y d}{0.85f'_c} = \frac{(0.024)(50)(15.5)}{0.85(3)} = 7.28 \text{ in.}$$

Then

$$f_c = \frac{T}{ab} = \frac{6.72(50,000)}{7.28(18)} = 2550 \text{ psi} = 0.85f'_c, \qquad \text{as planned.}$$

Comment. The procedure used throughout the foregoing example is most useful for those cases of large eccentricity, wherein economy[6] usually dictates an unsymmetrical arrangement of the reinforcement.

---

[6] If the whole Whitney balanced beam steel percentage, $p_o = 0.456 (f'_c/f_y)$ had been taken initially in Example 12–6, the resulting required steel areas would have been 1.32 compressive and 4.72 sq. in. tensile. Thus the effect would be to *redistribute* steel away from the compressive side, leaving more compression upon the concrete.

Substantially the same results may be obtained using the Portland Cement Association's convenient combined stress member design chart[G] which evidently was prepared using a *plasticity ratio* philosophy, as Jensen did.[I]

It is also useful in designing *symmetrical reinforcement* for columns or combined stress members by the ultimate strength method, as will be seen in the following article.

12–16. Ultimate Strength Designing of Symmetrical Reinforcement for Columns with Bending. An examination of the computations of Example 12–6 will show that if the initial singly reinforced "beam" steel percentage is decreased from 2.4 per cent to 1.52 per cent, the corresponding ultimate resisting moment item (previously 3980 kip-in.) will become 2800 kip-in., the $A_s - A'_s$ area then being 4.24 sq. in. This area is the same as the *tensile steel equivalent* of the 212-kip compressive load; so no flexure *single* reinforcement would finally be needed in this case. The *double* reinforcement required for each face of the member would then be $(5195 - 2800)/[50(13)] = 3.68$ sq. in., or a total of 7.36 sq. in. for the section.

To design such symmetrical sections, simply *take an area of (nonexistent) single reinforcement equal to the tensile equivalent of the applied load and compute the corresponding resisting moment. Then provide enough symmetrical reinforcement to take care of the remaining moment.*

The 7.36 sq. in. *symmetrical* reinforcement area required above is greater than the 6.12 sq. in. total of *unsymmetrical* reinforcement provided in Example 12–6. However, symmetrical reinforcement generally will prove the more economical when the resultant position of the load lies within the limits of the section. Refer to Example 4–5 for the *working strength* designing of a similar 18 by 18 in. column having symmetrical reinforcement, but with less than half as much eccentricity of the loading.

12–17. Combined Stress Member Investigations. To predict the ultimate eccentric load of a combined stress member, conduct the operations of Example 12–6 or Art. 12–15 in reverse order, sometimes working algebraically for the unknown load N'. Finally state whether the failure will be via the steel or the concrete, and whether sudden or gradual.

Bibliography items C, D, and K contain lengthy formulas and some useful charts, which can speed up ultimate strength investigation or design calculations for one with a good grasp of the foregoing methods.

COMBINED STRESS MEMBER PROBLEMS

Problem 12–12. This problem is the same as Example 12–6 except that:
(a) The load is 424 kips at an e of 9 in., and
(b) The load is 106 kips at an e of 36 in.

Tabulate a comparison of the three steel contents required for tension and compression, and comment.

Problem 12–13. Perform the recalculation of Example 12–6 necessary to account for the results reported in footnote 6.

Problem 12–14. A 16 by 16 in. tied column is eccentrically loaded 4 in. outside one face thereof. It is required to calculate the necessary symmetrical reinforcement, centered $2\frac{1}{2}$ in. from the bending faces by the ultimate strength method, taking a design ultimate load $U = 1.2B + 2.4L$ as in Art. 12–10. The service loads are 26.7 kips dead, and 70 kips live. Take 3000-lb. concrete and 50,000-psi yield point steel.

Ans. 2.35 sq. in. in each bending face.

Problem 12–15. Calculate the predicted ultimate (failure) load for the symmetrically reinforced 18 by 18 in. tied column designed in Example 4–5 of Chapter 4 for an eccentric service load of 120 kips at $7\frac{1}{2}$ in. from its central axis. State the type of failure expected, and the average load factor.

Ans. When the load becomes 382 kips, expect sudden failure via the concrete. The steel stress still will be well below the yield point. Were the 382-kip load 2.4 in. more eccentric, or about half as much steel present, the failures would occur simultaneously. Average load factor = 3.18.

Axially Loaded Columns

12–18. Ultimate Strength of Axially Loaded Columns. As shown in Art. 4–4, the ultimate strength of axially loaded tied columns, and the yield point strength of all columns, may be predicted by the formula:

$$N' = 0.85f'_c(A_g - A_s) + f_y A_s$$

EXAMPLE 12–7

Predict the ultimate strength and the over-all load factor of the 19 by 20 in. tied column with 12-#10 bars designed by the ACI (creep) method for a service load of 400 kips in Example 4–2 of Chapter 4, taking $f'_c = 3000$ and $f_y = 40,000$.

Solution:

$$N' = 0.85(3)[19 \times 20 - 12(1.27)] + 40(12)(1.27) = 991. \text{ kips}$$

$$\text{Average load factor} = \frac{991}{400} = 2.48$$

Comment. The 1955 ASCE–ACI Joint Committee Report[c] recommends that the designing of all axially loaded columns shall include the consideration of a minimum eccentricity of $0.1t$ for tied columns, and $0.05t$ for spiral columns, wherein t is the depth of the section. Such work may be carried out easily in the manner outlined in Art. 12–16.

12–19. Summary of Ultimate Strength Design. Ultimate strength designing differs from the common working strength method in that the work is performed at the high point of the stress-strain diagram for the concrete, namely, at the ultimate strength of the material, which is the upper limit of its *inelastic* range.

In the case of the reinforcement, the yield point strength of the steel is considered to be the corresponding useful limit of strength.

Members are designed using the *design ultimate load*, or bending moment. It is computed by magnifying each working load by a number called a *load factor*.

Established load factors vary from 1.2 to 2.4 or more, depending upon whether the load is dead, live, or other. This enables the engineer to make more economical and better balanced designs of members and structures.

In beams, the concrete compressive *stress* distribution at ultimate load is a curved line which is concave toward the section taken. The *strain* line is linear at all loads, is tangent to the stress line at the neutral axis, and lies well outside it in the upper fibers. Refer to Figs. 12–1(b) and 12–4.

The ACI has approved the Whitney type of office method for predicting the ultimate strengths of beams. Although a rectangular compressive "stress block" is assumed, its contribution to ultimate resisting moment must be closely that of the true distribution, since many tests have demonstrated the accuracy of the method. Refer to Fig. 12–2. Recall that neither the neutral axis nor the modular ratio, n, is used.

The *balanced* percentage of reinforcement for designing beams by the *ultimate strength* method is approximately twice that required by the common straight-line variation method. This is because the steel area called for by the latter has been insufficient to develop fully the compressive strength of the concrete, and has therefore not been a truly balanced content, so far as *ultimate* strength is concerned.

To ensure against disastrous sudden failures of beams via the concrete, the ACI limits the tensile steel content to closely seven-eighths of the Whitney balanced percentage. Considerably lower steel contents may be used if desired. Refer to Fig. 12–7.

The ultimate strength bending moment of rectangular beams which are over-reinforced according to Whitney's criterion may be closely predicted by doubling the plain concrete modulus of rupture (straight-line variation) moment obtainable by using only b, d, and the full value of f'_c (concrete failures). Refer to Formula 12–1.

The formula for predicting the ultimate strength of under-reinforced beams contemplates that at ultimate failure both the steel and the concrete will be at their failing values. This is because the continued yielding elongation of the reinforcement decreases the area of concrete resisting compression until a compressive failure also occurs secondarily.

Tee-beam reinforcement may be designed by first reinforcing the *web portion* with the ACI balanced percentage of reinforcement, and then adding enough more steel area to match the required remaining ultimate strength of the *overhanging* flange portion.

Doubly reinforced rectangular beams are designed initially in the same fashion as T-beam webs. Then the remaining ultimate strength moment is taken care of by additional tensile steel, and an equal area of compressive reinforcement.

Combined stress member reinforcement may be computed as in *working load* designing (Example 4–7), by first transferring the axial load to the tensile steel location and then designing the steel as for doubly reinforced ultimate strength beams.

The method of predicting the ultimate strength of axially loaded columns was presented much earlier in Art. 4–4 of Chapter 4.

Ultimate strength design as herein considered embraces the study of sections of individual members. The progressive redistribution of moments which may take place from member to member in a continuous structure, as one section after another reaches its limiting moment, is known as *limit design*.

BIBLIOGRAPHY

A) Whitney, Charles S. Plastic Theory of Reinforced Concrete Design, *Trans. ASCE*, 1942, Vol. 107, p. 251.

B) Slater, W. A., and Lyse, Inge. Compressive Strength of Concrete in Flexure as Determined from Tests of Reinforced Beams, *Proc. American Concrete Institute*, 1930, Vol. 26, p. 831.

C) Report of the ASCE–ACI Joint Committee on Ultimate Strength Design. *Proc. ASCE*, 1955, Vol. 81, Paper No. 809.

    Also see the Appendix of The ACI Building Code, 1956 Edition, for the "Abstract" thereof.

D) Whitney, Charles S. Application of Plastic Theory to the Design of Modern Reinforced Concrete Structures, *Jour. Boston Society of Civil Engineers*, 1948, Vol. 35, No. 1, January.

E) Boase, A. J., and Morgan, C. E. Balanced Design for Reinforced Concrete, *Proc. American Concrete Institute*, 1943, Vol. 39, p. 277.

F) Lin, T. Y. Load Factors in Ultimate Design of Reinforced Concrete, *Proc. American Concrete Institute*, 1952, Vol. 48, p. 881.

G) Portland Cement Association. Ultimate Strength Theory Simplifies Combined Bending and Axial Load Design, *Modern Developments in Reinforced Concrete*, R/C No. 31, 1955.

H) Siess, Chester P. Review of Research on Ultimate Strength of Reinforced Concrete Members (excellent bibliography included), *Proc. American Concrete Institute*, 1952, Vol. 48, p. 833.

I) Jensen, Vernon P. The Plasticity Ratio of Concrete and Its Effect on the Ultimate Strength of Beams, *Proc. American Concrete Institute*, 1943, Vol. 39, p. 565.

J) HOGNESTAD, EIVIND. Fundamental Concepts in Ultimate Load Design of
Reinforced Concrete Members. *Proc. American Concrete Institute*, 1952, Vol. 48,
p. 809 and 815.

K) CORNING, LEO H., Committee Chairman. Ultimate Strength Design, a report
by ASCE–ACI Committee 327 which includes six charts for the ultimate strength
designing of columns and combined stress members. *Journal, American Concrete
Institute*, January 1956, p. 505.

QUESTIONS

1. Define: working strength design, ultimate strength design, limit design, the stress block, the trapezoidal method, the expanding cubic method and Whitney's method.

2. Distinguish between: stress and strain, under-reinforcement versus over-reinforcement, load factor and factor of safety, elastic and inelastic range, ACI balanced reinforcement and Whitney's balanced reinforcement.

3. (a) Tell how to design the following sections by the ultimate strength method:

    T-beam   Combined stress member
    Doubly-reinforced beam   Column under small bending

   (b) Tell how to investigate the above sections.

4. Trace, step by step, by several sketches, the stress and strain action of an under-reinforced singly reinforced rectangular beam from low load to ultimate load, explaining all stages of its performance.

5. Suggest how one might deal with diagonal tension and bond situations in ultimate strength method calculations.

6. Tell what limitation has been placed upon the percentage of reinforcement in designing ultimate strength beams, explaining why.

7. It has been said that the strength of a combined stress member can be increased by increasing the axial load. Is this possible? Explain.

8. What great similarity is there between the designing of T-beams and doubly-reinforced beams by the ultimate strength method?

9. Demonstrate with a numerical example how to design symmetrical reinforcement for a rectangular column subject to ordinary bending, by the ultimate strength method.

10. Comment upon and explain this statement: Whether a beam is over-reinforced or under-reinforced by the ultimate strength criterion, it will fail through crushing of the concrete if enough load is applied.

CONTINUATION PROBLEMS

Problem 12–16. Calculate the predicted ultimate strength bending moment of the Flexicore type of floor slab section of Fig. 12–12. Carefully develop your method from the philosophy behind the formulas developed in Arts. 12–5, 8, 9, and 13.   The properties of circular segments are available in Plate XI of Appendix A.   Take 3750-lb. concrete and 50,000-psi yield point steel.

Additionally state whether the failure will occur suddenly or gradually.

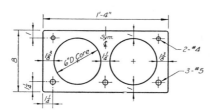

Fɪɢ. 12–12.   Flexicore type of precast floor-slab section.

Problem 12–17. Calculate the predicted ultimate eccentric load for the 16 by 30 in. *unsymmetrically* reinforced combined stress member section designed in Example 4–7 of Chapter 4 for an axial service load of 78.5 kips acting 30 in. from its geometrical axis.   Refer to Fig. 4–10.   State the type of failure expected.

CHAPTER 13

PRESTRESSED CONCRETE BEAMS[1]

13–1. Introduction. A fully prestressed beam is one into which sufficient *initial compression* has been introduced to counteract the anticipated tensile concrete stresses resulting from the service loads.

Dr. Eugene Freyssinet, distinguished French structural engineer, whose early experimentation and practical experience with prestressed concrete on important structures demonstrated the necessity for using both high quality concrete and high strength steel reinforcement in order to surmount the losses of prestress due principally to concrete shrinkage, elastic deformation, and creep.

In 1950 he was awarded the Frank P. Brown Medal of the Franklin Institute of Philadelphia "for his outstanding development of engineering and technique for prestressed concrete."

Such beams are dependably crack-free[2] in normal service. The precompression is usually accomplished by initially tensioning high strength

---

[1] In this chapter the techniques for computing the creep, shrinkage, and ultimate strengths of members, as presented in Chapters 10, 11, and 12, are applied.

[2] Numerous tests have shown that conventional reinforced concrete beams develop hair-line flexural tensile cracks before all the design safe load has been applied. The common practice of omitting the tensile concrete from bending calculations is consistent therewith.

steel bars, straight wires, or helically laid wire (*strands*) located principally within the tensile portion of the beam.

Although prestressed concrete has been used in Europe for 20 years or more, its engineered use in the United States began in 1949 with the construction of the Walnut Lane Bridge in Philadelphia. See the Frontispiece.

Strictly speaking, a prestressed concrete beam is not reinforced concrete because

1. The reinforcement need not be bonded to the concrete if securely end-anchored by mechanical means, and
2. The initially compressed concrete resists the bending tension.

Because the whole sectional area of the concrete is effectively utilized to resist the service loads, prestressed beams are of about two-thirds the size and weight of corresponding reinforced concrete ones. Furthermore, the longitudinal steel may be only one-fourth as much, though it must be of high tensile strength.

The precompressing of the concrete increases its resistance to the weather, i.e., its *durability*, because the entrance of moisture is largely prevented thereby.

Some surprising characteristics that will be revealed in designing prestressed beams are that:

1. The amount of (prestressing) steel required is not directly dictated by the load to be carried, but by the need to have enough to precompress the whole concrete sectional area to the desired degree,
2. All or most of the dead load of the beam can be carried "free" by proper designing,
3. A simple span beam that is safe in flexure at midspan may be unsafe therein at the supports,
4. When the design working load is finally applied, the then-existing unit stress in the steel is increased comparatively little above the prestress value,
5. The factor of safety under any chosen loading cannot be deduced by comparing unit stresses, but
6. The *ultimate* flexural strength is closely the same as if the beam were un-prestressed, although the crack-free safe working load is much increased.

Since the characteristics mentioned above bear little resemblance to those of other beams, it probably will be another surprise to learn that the *ultimate* strength of prestressed beams is predicted exactly as in Chapter 12 for conventional reinforced concrete beams. This is because such beams lose all their prestress in the inelastic range of high overload approaching failure. Refer to Fig. 10–1 of Chapter 10.

13–2. Concept of a Prestressed Beam. A prestressed beam is like a rectangular *plain* concrete pier, as in Fig. 13–1, eccentrically loaded with an external axial compressive force F, to which a lateral loading w has later been added without causing any crack-

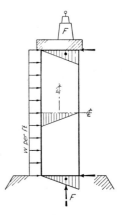

ing. The typical unit stress diagrams pictured are all compressive. By rotating the book clockwise through a right angle it will be evident that there is no tension in the bottom fiber of this "beam."

In actual prestressed beams the internal pre-tensioning steel should be regarded primarily as a convenient means of applying the compressive force F to the concrete.

13–3. The Basic Mechanics of Prestressing. As indicated in Fig. 13–2(a), one might precom-press the 5000-lb. concrete of a beam by pre-ten-sioning a centrally located rod or wire, thus in-ducing a uniform precompression (1000 psi in this case). If, thereafter, enough design live load is applied to create an additional 1000 psi of bending stress in this uncracked section, the maximum

Fig. 13–1. Action of a prestressed beam standing vertically.

combined stress will become 2000 psi compressive in the top fiber, as shown at the extreme right. Note that the triangular distribution thereof leads to zero total stress in the bottom fiber.

In (b), the capacity of the beam for carrying design live load was *doubled* simply by moving the prestressed steel downward 3 in., one-sixth of the depth, until the precompression in the top fiber of concrete became zero. The 2000-psi total stress is the same as in (a).

Now looking at Fig. 13–2(c) in a general way, we see that the dead load of the beam, heretofore disregarded, has been added to Live Loading II used in (b). Furthermore, looking at the stress diagrams at the right, we note that the middle one, representing the effect of uni-formly distributed load, has had its extreme fiber stress value increased from 2000 psi to 2810 psi, due to considering the dead load. Neverthe-less the "Total," or *combined*, stress at the extreme right is the same as in (b), namely, 2000 psi. Returning to the side view sketch of (c), we see that this astounding result has been achieved simply by moving the prestressed steel 2.43 in. farther down,[3] until $e = 5.43$ in., and at no additional cost in materials! (The values of the dead and live loading, together with the span distance, have been shown in (c) to enable the reader to check the stresses just discussed.) Due to the increased

---

[3] In shallow long-span beams and slabs all the dead load cannot be so taken care of. Part of it must be included with the live load when proportioning the member.

eccentricity of the prestressing force, the left-hand stress diagram in (c), representing prestress combined unit stress in the concrete, has become 810 psi tensile at the top, but it is immediately erased by the corresponding dead load compressive stress. This matter will be taken up again later.

The Kern Points. The student is assumed to be familiar with the fundamental mechanics of direct stress plus bending situations in rectangular sections, as reviewed in Art. 4–10 of Chapter 4 on columns and as reproduced in the accompanying Fig. 13–2(a). The key situation for our purposes is that of (b) of the figure, wherein the axial prestress force is at the lower "edge of the middle third" of the section, causing the triangular distribution of stress pictured nearby. This elevation is the *lower kern point* of the section, as defined by the centroid of the triangular stress diagram, and the corresponding (3 in.) eccentricity, e_n, of the prestress force will hereinafter be called the *normal eccentricity*.

The Dead and Live Load Ranges. The lower kern point of a prestressed section is a base elevation, *downward* from which the additional eccentricity required to offset the dead load bending moment may be laid off in designing. In the case shown in Fig. 13–2(c), the bending moment involved is $0.162(40.25)^2(12)/8 = 393$ kip-in. This, when divided by the 162-kip prestress force, gives 2.43 in. of additional downward displacement, which is known as the *dead load eccentricity*, Fig. 13–3, for the particular dead load that we have. Obviously we *could* have compensated for some maximum dead load,[3] the displacement of which would be defined by the lowermost $h/3$ measurement minus the centroidal elevation of the steel, known as the *dead load range limit*.

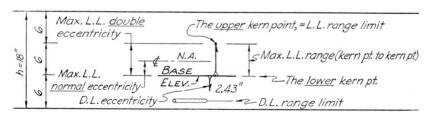

Fig. 13–3. Example of the relationship of the kern points to dead load and live load ranges and eccentricities. Beam of rectangular section.

Note in Fig. 13–2(b) that the application of the chosen live load converted the prestress stress triangle with base *downward* to an identical one with its base *upward*; and that the centroid moved upward 6 in., or $h/3$, in the process. This distance is called the *double eccentricity*, $2e_n$ of the live load. Its value should not exceed the vertical distance from the lower kern point to the upper kern point of the section, called the *live load range.* Note that the eccentricities referred to are related to the *loadings*, while the kern limits are properties of the *cross section*.

For rectangular beams the live load range is always the $h/3$ distance between kern points. It may be increased to $0.50h$ or even $0.55h$ by designing a suitable I-section, thus increasing the live load capacity without increasing the beam depth or cross-sectional area.

Live Loading versus Beam Size. Reference to the stress diagrams of Fig. 13–2(b) and (c) will show that neither the addition of the prestress force nor of the dead load increased the maximum total stress on the section. Therefore the required *concrete* dimensions of prestressed sections *may* be quickly proportioned from the live load bending moment only,[4] $(w_L L^2)/8$ in this case, so far as safe working strength is concerned.

EXAMPLE 13–1

The Design of a Pre-tensioned Concrete Slab. Given a simple span of 30 ft. and a live loading of 0.72 ksf. It is required to design the slab thickness (to some whole inch), and the pre-tensioned steel content at midspan.

Concrete Data. Take 6250-lb. concrete, $E_c = 4,500,000$, E_s for strand $= 27,000,000$, $n = 6$, allowable $f_c = 0.4f'_c = 2500$ psi in compression, zero in tension in the bottom fiber. Provide fireproofing of ¾-in. more than the ¾ in. that ACI Sec. 507(b) requires for conventional slabs. Take the weight of prestressed concrete at 147 pcf.

Steel Data. Take Roebling's uncoated stress relieved twisted steel pre-tensioning strand, ultimate tensile strength $= 250,000$ psi, design final pre-tension $= 140,000$ psi. See Appendix H for strand sizes and strengths.

Solution:[5] By the kern points method (ref. Art. 13–3 and Figs. 13–2 and 3):

(a) *Calculation of the required thickness.* (Taking $b = 12$ in.)

$$M_L = \frac{0.72(30)^2}{8} = 81.0 \text{ kip-ft.}$$

Required F force, for L.L. range $= \dfrac{M_L}{h/3} = \dfrac{81(12)}{h/3} = 2920/h$ \hfill (A)

Required force F to precompress the section, as in Fig. 13–2(b),

$$F = \frac{f_c}{2}(A_g) = \frac{2.50}{2}(12)h = 15.h \text{ kips} \hfill \text{(B)}$$

Solving Eqs. (A) and (B), req'd. $h = 13.94$ in.

Make $h = 14$ in.; corresp. L.L. stress $= 2490$ psi, Fig. 13–4(b).

Corresponding required $F = 1.25(12)(14) = 210$ kips.

---

[4] Except when the dead load is relatively large.

(b) *Dead Load Stress*

$$Z = 12(14)^2/6 = 392 \text{ in.}^3$$

$$w_D = \frac{14}{12}(0.147) = 0.171 \text{ klf}, \qquad M_D = \frac{0.171(30)^2}{8} = 19.3 \text{ kip-ft.}$$

$$f_D = \frac{M_D}{Z} = \frac{19.3(12,000)}{392} = 591. \text{ psi., [Fig. 13–4(c)].}$$

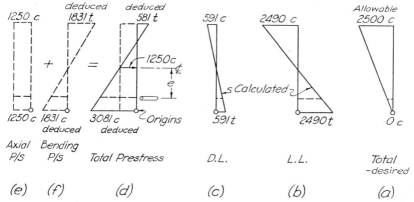

FIG. 13–4. Graphical deducing of required axial and bending prestress unit
stresses from the dead and live load stresses at midspan of the pre-tensioned slab.

(c) *Prestress Stresses*[5] [Refer to Fig. 13–4(d), (e) & (f).]

	Bottom Fiber	*Top Fiber*
Axial + bending $\equiv 3081.c*$		
Axial $= \dfrac{210,000}{12(14)} = 1250.c$		$1250.c$
P/S bending $= \overline{1831.c}$		$1831.t$
	Axial + bending $= \overline{581.t}$	

---

[5] *Corresponding Algebraic Calculation*—at midspan.
Considering compressive unit stress positive:

Top fiber: $\dfrac{F}{A} - \dfrac{Fe}{Z_t} + \dfrac{M_D}{Z_t} \equiv 0$ (general)   (1)

$\dfrac{F}{12(14)} - \dfrac{Fe}{392} + \dfrac{19.3(12)}{392} = 2500\text{–}2490 \text{ in this case}$ (1′)

Bottom fiber: $\dfrac{F}{A} + \dfrac{Fe}{Z_b} - \dfrac{M_D}{Z_b} = \dfrac{M_L}{Z_b}$ (2)

$\dfrac{F}{12(14)} + \dfrac{Fe}{392} - \dfrac{19.3(12)}{392} = \dfrac{81.0(12)}{392}$ (2′)

Solving: $F = 210 \text{ kips},$ $e = 3.41 \text{ in.},$ $\dfrac{F}{A} = 1250 \text{ psi. } c,$ $\dfrac{Fe}{Z} = 1831 \text{ psi } t/c$

* For there to be no tension finally.

(d) *Required Depth of the Steel*

Since $e = h/6$ when $Mc/I = F/A$:

$$\text{Required } \boldsymbol{e} = \frac{1831}{1250}\left(\frac{14}{6}\right) = 3.41 \text{ in. from mid-depth.}$$

(e) *Steel Selection*   (Refer to Fig. 13–5.)

$$A_s \text{ required per one-foot width} = \frac{210,000}{140,000}$$

$$= 1.50 \text{ sq. in.}$$

For available strand sizes and strengths, see App. H:

Trying two layers of ½-in. strand at 0.1438 sq. in.:

$$\text{Maximum spacing} = \frac{2(0.1438)(12)}{1.50}$$

$$= 2.30 \text{ in.}$$

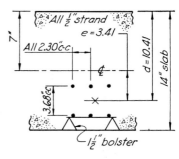

Fig. 13–5.

Use two layers of ½ in. strand at 3.68 in. c.c. vertically, and 2.30 in. c.c. horizontally. For intermediate supports take 1½ in. std. and 5.18 in. special bolsters.

13–4. Discussion of the Prestressed Slab Designing. In Example 13–1, the required 14-in. depth of the section was computed from the live loading only, as earlier directed. The live and dead load unit stresses were then easily computed and the corresponding diagrams (b) and (c) of Fig. 13–4 were constructed therefrom. Diagram (a), at the right, is the desired final stress situation. Item (d) is the corresponding diagram of required prestress deduced

Courtesy of The Reliable Electric Company

Fig. 13–6. Reusable "Steelcase Strandvise" pre-tensioning wire or strand anchor. See also Appendix H.

leftward from (a), (b), and (c). The algebraic average abscissa on (d) is the 1250 axial prestress shown at (e), which checked with the $f_c/2$ value it must have if the final distribution at (a) is to be triangular. The undesirably high stresses of diagram (d) exist only in combination with the mitigating dead load ones of diagram (c) of reversed sense, as will be discussed in a succeeding article.

The prestress bending stress of 1831 psi at (f), resulting from the still undetermined eccentricity of the prestress force, was gotten in item (c) of the calculations by simple subtraction.

In calculation item (e), the size of prestressing strand selected was the one which most nearly gave a square arrangement pattern, since the strand anchors, Fig. 13–6, ordinarily used to maintain the tension in the strand while the concrete is gaining strength, are round, and greater clearances are thereby attained.

As a matter of interest, a conventional un-prestressed slab was designed for the same span, live loading and class of concrete. It required 30 per cent more concrete, and 163 per cent more steel.

Members of solid rectangular cross section are rather disadvantageous for prestressing because the portion of the section that is within the middle third of the depth (a) contributes very little to bending strength and (b) requires additional steel to compress it. An I-section is much more suitable, as will be seen in Example 13–2, which follows Art. 13–15.

PRESTRESSING PRACTICE PROBLEMS

Problem 13–1. Design a prestressed slab for the same conditions as those of Example 13–1 except that:
(a) The span is 33 ft. and the live load 0.54 ksf,
(b) The span is 45 ft. and the live load 0.29 ksf.
Comment upon any new situations encountered and how you met them.

Problem 13–2. Verify the statement that the prestressed slab of Example 13–1 has only 77 per cent as much concrete and only 38 per cent as much steel as the corresponding conventional reinforced concrete slab.

Problem 13–3. Compute the stresses in the slab designed in Example 13–1 under the design loading, assuming that the amount of the pre-tension has decreased 142 kips. Investigate the possibility of tensile cracking of the concrete, and the extent thereof.

13–5. Further Study of the Pre-tensioned Slab Design. Referring again to Figs. 13–4 and 13–5 and the attendant calculations of the slab designing, the following additional important topics need to be introduced:

End Section Stresses. Figure 13–4(d) shows that at the ends of the beam, where the dead and live load stresses are zero, the compressive prestress in the bottom concrete is 3081 psi, or $0.49f'_c$. The tensile prestress in the top concrete is 581 psi, or about 0.90 of the 650-psi modulus of rupture[6] value, f'_{cb}, or the 625-psi ultimate axial tensile strength; which means potential cracking.

---

[6] Refer to Fig. 13–12 for an expression for the Kesler minimum moduli of rupture values.

The 140,000-psi pre-tension used in the designing is Roebling's recommended *final* prestress value (Appendix H). Before the several *losses of prestress* (soon to be taken up in detail) occurred, the *initial* prestress must have been at least 25 per cent greater, say, 175,000 psi. The corresponding concrete unit stresses then must have been $0.61f'_c$ and $1.13 \times f'_{cb}$. These elastically computed stresses are uncomfortably higher than usually permitted at the end sections, even though the instantaneous mitigating effect of concrete elastic and steel creep strains prevents their full development.

Ultimate Strength of Prestressed Flexural Members. The relationship between the ultimate load of a prestressed flexural member and its safe working load is not a linear one computable from the failure/safe working stress ratio of the materials involved. This is because one or both of the materials get into the curving *inelastic range* of performance depicted in Fig. 13–7 as beam failure is approached. The corresponding large *inelastic deformations* of the steel *erase the prestress* therein, so that shortly before failure a prestressed beam functions in the same manner as a conventional reinforced concrete beam. This means that we can predict its failure load by referring to Whitney's formulas of Art. 12–8 of Chapter 12 for rectangular beams.

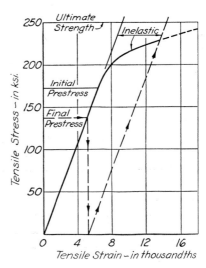

FIG. 13–7. Loss of steel prestress within the inelastic range approaching failure.

Since our prestressed slab contains high tensile steel which is thoroughly bonded to the concrete, and has no well-defined yield point,[7] the British First Report suggests that failure of the slab may be assumed to occur at the ultimate strength of the steel, f'_s; but your author conservatively prefers to predict it at $0.9f'_s$, or at the stress producing 0.002 permanent strain, when known. Then the Whitney *balanced* steel content would be:

$$p_o = 0.456 \frac{f'_c}{0.9f'_s} = \frac{0.456(6250)}{0.9(250,000)} = 1.27\%$$

The actual $p = \dfrac{1.50}{12(10.4)} = 1.20\%$

---

[7] Refer in Appendix I to the British *First Report on Prestressed Concrete*, Sec. **7**(b), the last excerpted paragraph thereof.

Therefore the slab is slightly under-reinforced, and will fail via the steel at a bending moment of:

$$M'_s = A_s(0.9 f'_s)d \left[1 - \frac{p(0.9 f'_s)}{2(0.85 f'_c)} \right]$$

$$= 1.50(225) \frac{(10.41)}{12} \left[1 - \frac{0.012(225)}{1.7(6.25)} \right] = 219 \text{ kip-ft.}$$

$$\text{The average factor of safety} = \frac{219}{81 + 19.3} = 2.18$$

The BFR, Sec. 7(b), requires 2.00.

Alternately, by Art. 12–10 of Chapter 12, the ACI requires an ultimate moment capacity of $2.4(81) + 1.2(19.3) = 217.7$ kip-ft.

Therefore the failure strength of the slab is barely satisfactory.

13–6. Types of Prestressed Beams. The accompanying table shows the two principal types of prestressed flexural members. The essential

TABLE 13–1

CLASSIFICATION OF TYPICAL PRESTRESSED BEAMS

Type of Prestressed Beam or Slab	Materials		
	Prestressing Steel		Concrete
	When Tensioned?	How Anchored?	Where Usually Cast?
Pre-tensioned	Before concrete has hardened.	*By bond*, effective principally at the ends, sometimes supplemented by mechanical devices.	*Precast* at a factory or casting bed and transported, (joists and small beams, ordinarily)
Post-tensioned	After concrete has hardened and the steel has been pulled in.	*Mechanically*, at the ends of the beam.	*In place* in the structure if large beams, or precast if small

distinction is: was the steel tensioned before or after the concrete had gained a working strength?

Pre-tensioned Beams. When the steel is to be pre-tensioned, fixed abutments, as in Fig. 13–8, are needed to resist the large pre-tensioning force. In some systems the force is resisted by heavily constructed forms. After the concrete has been placed around the tensioned steel, and has gained a satisfactory strength, the prestress is *transferred* to it as compression, by releasing the jacks or anchorage devices. The pre-tension in the steel must thereafter be maintained either (a) entirely by the *bond* to the concrete at the ends of the beam, or (b) with the aid of some mechanical device which bears upon the concrete at the ends of the beam. In all cases the steel is bonded over its full length. If this final anchorage is to be achieved by bond alone, small diameter wire, or strands up to ⅜ in. diam., must be used in order to get enough

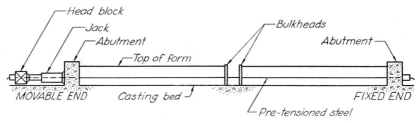

Fig. 13–8. Schematic of arrangement for multiple production of bonded pre-tensioned prestressed beams.

perimeter per square inch of cross-sectional area. Such fully bonded pre-tensioned beams are often produced end to end on a casting bed several hundred feet long, the tensioned wire being continuous, as suggested by Fig. 13–8. Such assembly line production is economical because the labor cost of pre-tensioning is spread over several beams. Pre-tensioning is also advantageous because plant labor is less expensive than field labor.

A disadvantage to pre-tensioned beams is that after records have been lost there is no way to tell how much prestress remains therein except by proof-testing to the cracking load.

Pre-tensioned beams nearly always have to be transported to their position in a structure, so some top steel is often provided to resist the tensile stresses due to the handling. It may or may not be pre-stressed.

Pre-tensioned beams are subject to considerable **loss of prestress** from progressive shortening of the member due principally to concrete shrinkage, elastic deformation, and creep. The total steel stress loss may be as much as 50,000 psi, depending upon conditions. Consequently, high tensile strength wire (Appendix H) with ultimate strengths in the 225,000 to 250,000 psi range, and proportionality limits approaching 150,000 to 180,000 psi must be used, if the final working stress pre-tension is not to fall below 100,000 to 130,000 psi, respectively. Obviously, mild steel with a proportionality limit stress of 40,000 to 60,000 psi is entirely unsuitable.

Since conditions vary considerably from case to case, the loss of prestress due to each influence should be separately computed and reconsidered from time to time, rather than assumed at some fixed percentage of the initially applied prestress.

See Example 13–2 for the designing of a bonded prestressed beam having pre-tensioned reinforcement in which the losses of prestress were initially considered.

Post-tensioned Beams. This type of prestressed beam is commonly cast with channels therein, through which the prestressing steel is finally inserted. No abutments are involved, as the steel is post-tensioned against the fully hardened concrete, and mechanically end-anchored, since there is typically no bond to the concrete.[8]

Post-tensioned beams have the advantage of being subject to less *loss of prestress* than pre-tensioned ones because (a) there is no loss due to concrete elastic deformation, (b) part of the loss due to concrete shrinkage will already have taken place before the post-tensioning, and (c) the concrete creep loss will be less because post-tensioning is usually done at a later concrete age.

An important advantage of post-tensioned beams is that, theoretically, it is possible to determine at any time the existing tension in straight reinforcement, and to adjust it if necessary.[8]

The other characteristics and advantages of post-tensioning are taken up in Art. 13–26.

13–7. Prestressed Concrete Codes. As of 1956 there still is no formally approved standard United States code or recommended practice for the design of prestressed concrete flexural members.

As stated by Professor Siess,[A] a *code* is a legal document, the purpose of which is to ensure the public safety. Its clauses "require" thus and so, without explanation. Such arbitrary requirements, if imposed during the early stages of a developing field, tend to retard further progress.

A recommended practice "recommends" procedures, stating the reasons and sometimes the sources of the data upon which they are based. It can mention the areas of uncertainty, thus stimulating research therein. Its weakness is that its use does not necessarily guarantee absolute safety.

In the United States progress toward the formulation of a standard recommended practice is well represented by:

(a) "Criteria for Prestressed Concrete Bridges," 1954, herein abbreviated as BPR. It was prepared by the U. S. Bureau of Public Roads, and is obtainable, price 15 cents, from the Superintendent of Documents, Washington, D.C., also

(b) "Preliminary Report of ASCE–ACI Joint Committee 323" (on Prestressed Concrete), 1955, herein abbreviated as *CEACI*. This proposed

---

[8] Except when post-bonded by grouting.

recommended practice, not yet in form for use, is being subjected to further study and revision, and still (1956) is not available for distribution.

In Great Britain, conservative recommended practice is represented by the

"First Report on Prestressed Concrete," 1951, herein abbreviated as BFR. It is published by The Institution of Structural Engineers, 11 Upper Belgrave St., London, SW 1, England, and obtainable therefrom at a price of 3 shillings 6 pence.

Pertinent portions thereof have been excerpted to Appendix I of this textbook.

13–8. The Loading Stages of Prestressed Beams. In prestressed designing, the loading conditions considered are called *loading stages*. At present we are concerned with two principal ones, which are, following the numbering of Sec. 7(a) of the British First Report:

Stage 1: Prestress plus dead load, the condition following the *transfer* of the prestress to the concrete.

Stage 3: Prestress plus dead load and live load, the *final condition* in service, after all losses of prestress have taken place.

Ordinarily, the dead load comes upon a beam as the prestress is transferred to it. This is because the precompressing of the lower fibers of concrete cambers the beam off its casting bed, bringing the counteractive dead loading into action.

After transfer, the concrete is considered to have tightly seized the steel. For the subsequent live loading investigations of Stage 3, and for predicting the initial (virgin) cracking load, the uncracked *transformed* section should be used, instead of the uncracked plain concrete section conveniently taken earlier in trial designing.

Figure 13–9, prepared from Fig. 13–4, shows at (b) and (c) the stresses in the pre-tensioned slab *at midspan*, under Stages 1 and 3 loadings, respectively. Note that the addition of the live load bending stresses of 2490 psi (shown in phantom) caused an inverting of the stress distribution diagram at (b) to the position at (c).

At (a) is shown the corresponding stress distribution at the end supports of the slab, which is the same for all loading situations because of the absence of dead and live load bending stresses. Recall, or note from Fig. 13–4, that it was necessary to throw the top fiber into tension under prestress only, in order to compensate for the 591-psi dead load compressive stress. Note also that the prestress values shown in Fig. 13–9(a) are rather high. Since some loss of pre-tension is presumed to have occurred already, the initial values of these stresses must have been still greater.

It will now be apparent that Example 13–1 and Figs. 13–4 and 13–9 illustrate an elementary prestress calculation which did not require an evaluation of the losses. Before taking up our next design example,

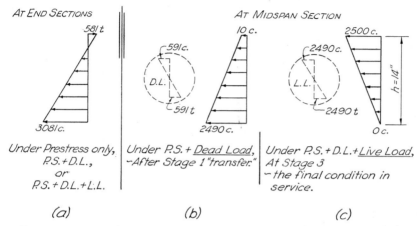

Fig. 13–9. Comparison of the concrete stresses in the pre-tensioned slab of Example 13–1, end section versus midspan section. Prepared from Fig. 13–4. Losses not involved.

these losses will be computed from fundamental considerations. Their values will then be used in Example 13–2 from the beginning of the calculations, and at every loading stage.

The Losses of Pre-Tension

13–9. Introduction. In *pre-tensioned beams*, the extent to which the end surfaces of the beam finally approach each other at the level of the centroid of the pre-tensioned reinforcement is a measure of the loss, Δf_s, of steel pre-tension due to *concrete's* properties of shrinkage, creep, and elastic deformation. The possible additional losses resulting from the individual characteristics of the *steel* are the small creep of the reinforcement and that due to the seating of mechanical end anchorages.

More insight is required to evaluate the probable losses of pre-tension for a given case than is required to design the beam! Consequently some designers conveniently assume a flat 20 per cent loss of initial pre-tension for all cases. A much better approximation would be to assume a 40,000-psi loss, since the total loss is almost independent of the amount of initial pretension in the steel, as will be seen.

13–10. The Loss Due to Shrinkage of the Concrete. As mentioned in Art. 11–4 and Example 11–3, of Chapter 11, concrete members are usually considered to be subject to a design free *axial* shrinkage of about

0.0003 of their length. In the case of a beam, the eccentricity of the reinforcement with respect to the gravity axis thereof results also in an *eccentric* shrinkage, or *warpage*, as the concrete contracts against the opposition of the steel. Consequently, the resulting shrinkage strain line is considerably inclined, and the net shrinkage coefficient *at the level of the reinforcement* turns out somewhat less than the free axial shrinkage value. Compare, from the table of Example 11–4, the value of 0.000244 with 0.00047.

In prestressed beams the difference is not so great, due principally to their much smaller steel content. Taking a design shrinkage strain of 0.00028 and an E_s for pre-tensioning strand of 27,000,000 psi, the corresponding loss of steel prestress will be:

$$\Delta f_{ss} = \delta_s E_s \qquad \text{(shrinkage loss)} \qquad (13\text{--}1)$$

Numerically:

$$\Delta f_{ss} = 0.00028(27 \times 10^6) = 7,550 \text{ psi}$$

One-third of this shrinkage loss is often considered to take place in Stage 1, at transfer. A more realistic practice, when moist curing has been maintained until transfer, is to consider that all of it occurs thereafter. Such a practice also is consistent with that of deliberately underestimating the total of the losses which occur before transfer, so that the high initial prestress in the concrete at the ends of the beam will be fully recognized.

13–11. The Loss Due to the Elasticity of the Concrete. This is a loss of steel pre-tension which occurs in Stage 1 as the prestress force is transferred to the concrete and the dead load becomes active. It is due to the elastic shortening of the concrete of the lower portion of the beam. A value may be found easily from Fig. 13–9(b) by first computing the *net* compressive stress in the concrete *at the level of the centroid of the pretensioning steel* (prestress compressive decreased by dead load tensile), and then multiplying by n, the modular ratio.

Considering the steel centroid at rh from the top of the beam:

$$\Delta f_{se} = n(r)f_c \qquad \text{(elastic loss)} \qquad (13\text{--}2)$$

Notice from Fig. 13–9(a) and (b) that, at midspan after transfer, *the tensile prestress at the top is largely offset by the compressive stress due to dead load,*[9] leaving approximately a triangular distribution at (b), so:

For our 6250-lb. concrete, $n = 6$, and $r = 0.8$:

$$\Delta f_{se} = 6(0.8)(2490) = 11,950 \text{ psi.}$$

In Stage 3, we cannot safely depend upon the tensile deformation of the live loading (such as shown in phantom in Fig. 13–9) to decrease the elastic

---

[9] Disregarding the parabolic variation of the dead load stress over the length of the beam.

losses already suffered in Stage 1, because of its transient nature. Therefore, 11,950 psi becomes the total elastic loss to be considered in this case.

If the live load is permanent, its *average* unit stress value for the whole length of the beam may be relied upon to decrease the elastic loss further.

13–12. The Loss Due to the Creep of the Concrete. Of all the losses of prestress, that due to the creep of the concrete is the greatest, and probably the most uncertain.

The concrete unit creep strains, δ_t in Formula 10–1 and Art. 10–6 of Chapter 10, now being used in calculating prestress losses, are considerably smaller than those found by Shank and others thirty or more years ago. They are based largely upon the more recent findings of English and European investigators [C,D,E] who studied the high strength concretes used in prestressed members.

By the method of Example 10–3 of Chapter 10, Shank found that for ordinary 3000-lb. standard portland cement concrete made with good natural stone aggregates and loaded at 28 days, the long-time unit creep strain, δ_t, was of the order of 1.0 millionth per psi of compressive stress; and that the long-time creep plus elastic strain could be expected to be about four times the instantaneous elastic strain. Thus, for predicting the *sustained* stresses and deflections of *conventional reinforced concrete beams* the corresponding sustained modulus of elasticity after creep might be taken at one-fourth the $1000f'_c$ instantaneous E_c value ordinarily used in computing the modular ratio, n.

For pre-tensioned beams the British First Report recommends that the long-time concrete unit axial creep strain be taken at 0.4 millionth per psi of concrete stress,[D] or at about 40 per cent of the above mentioned early value because:

(a) The 5000- to 8000-lb. concretes now used creep less,
(b) The almost universal practice of placing by vibration results in lower cement factors and correspondingly less creep,
(c) The increased concrete densities resulting from vibration, and possibly from the compacting effect of early transfer of stress thereto, decrease the creep, and
(d) The creep, related as it is to drying out, has been found to be less in full-sized members[D] and structures than in the small laboratory specimens ordinarily used in research.

It may be added that high early strength portland cement and hot moist curing, when used, both tend to decrease further the total creep below the 0.4 millionth value deducible from Professor Ross' table of Appendix I, and recommended in Sec. 7(d)(1) of the accompanying British First Report.

The urgent need for more comprehensive test data upon the creep losses of present-day high strength concretes is universally recognized

both here and abroad.   In the meantime it is convenient to remember
that since the unit elastic strain of high strength concrete is roughly
1 psi/5,000,000 psi, or 0.2 millionth, the *total* (elastic plus creep) *strain*
will be about 0.6 millionth, or *three times the elastic strain*.

Referring again to Fig. 13–9(b), the time-dependent loss of steel
pre-tension will be equal to the long-time creep strain times the modulus
of elasticity of the steel strand:

$$\Delta f_{st} = \delta_t \, r f_c E_s \qquad \text{(creep loss)} \qquad (13\text{–}3)$$

considering the steel centroid to be at a distance rh from the top of the
beam.

Since, in Fig. 13–9, the live loading is transient and is often not
first applied until some late age,[10] we cannot safely rely upon its contribution to the total tensile deformation pictured in (c) to decrease the
creep losses already accumulated under prestress plus dead loading.
Consequently, it is conservative to compute a creep loss from the
Stage 1 diagram at (b), and to consider its undiminished value as the
total creep loss.

For our case, taking $r = 0.8$:

$$\Delta f_{st} = 0.4 \times 10^{-6}(0.8)(2490)(27 \times 10^6) = 21{,}500 \text{ psi}$$

13–13. Total Losses. Note in the summary of computed losses,
Table 13–2, that for pre-tensioned beams the total loss of steel pre-tension can be about 45,000 psi, of which almost half is due to the creep of
the concrete.   Further, that the 16,000-psi loss taken after transfer is a
very minimum value gotten by considering that all the concrete shrinkage and creep losses occur later.   This is a correct procedure because it
will prevent one's early deducting of such a large share of the total loss of
steel pre-tension that high end section concrete stresses, like 581t and
3081c of Fig. 13–9(a), may be obscured.   On the other hand, the *total*
loss of steel prestress, which affects the performance in service, should
never be underestimated.

13–14. The Loss Due to the Creep of the Steel. The common
practice of initially pre-tensioning the steel strand practically to the
proportionality limit means that some permanent set or creep is likely
to develop.

In the case of Roebling's 250,000-psi stress-relieved pre-tensioning
strands, the recommended initial tensioning to 0.7 of the ultimate
strength, namely, 175,000 psi, looking toward a final tension of 0.8

---

[10] On the other hand, if the live load is applied at an early age and is relatively
permanent (the beam supporting a water storage tank, for example), credit may be
taken for the corresponding reduction in creep loss in the manner indicated for load
removal in Art. 10–2 and Fig. 10–2 of Chapter 10.

thereof, or 140,000 psi, is stated by the manufacturer to be accompanied by a maximum creep of about $2\frac{1}{4}$ per cent of the initial tensioning value or 4000 psi; which value has been included in the above mentioned table. Considerably higher values have been reported for other strands, so the matter needs close attention. In post-tensioned beams, the creep of the steel can be offset by later retensioning.

TABLE 13-2

SUMMARY OF MINIMUM LOSSES OF BEAM STEEL PRESTRESS TO TAKE IN DESIGNING
(*Following the British First Report*)

6250 psi concrete, $n = 6$ 250,000-psi strand centered
Transfer after 14-day age.   at about 0.8 beam depth.
Allowable $f'_c = 2500$ psi $E_s = 27 \times 10^6$.

Loss Due to:	Immediately after Transfer −Dead Load Carried.	Additional Loss Following Live Load Application	Min. Total Loss	
			Pre-tensioned Beams	Post-tensioned Beams
Concrete shrinkage	0* psi	7,500 psi	7,500 psi	5,000 psi ($\frac{2}{3}$)
Concrete elastic deformation	12,000	0	12,000	0
Concrete creep deformation	( )⟶ 21,500 total		21,500	16,000 ($\frac{3}{4}$)
Steel creep deformation	Roebling's uncoated stress-relieved strand 4,000	0	4,000	If reten- 0 sioned
End anchorage deformation	Likely with mechanical devices ( )	( )	( )	Also friction ( )
TOTALS —in psi of steel stress loss	16,000	29,000	45,000	21,000

* Refer to Art. 13-10.

13-15. The Nature of the Losses of Pre-tensioning. A survey of the formulas developed in the preceding article for the three principal losses of pre-tensioning (namely, those due to concrete shrinkage, elastic deformation, and creep) will reveal that *in no case are the losses directly related to the unit stress induced in the pre-tensioning reinforcement.* For well-proportioned beams built of suitable materials, the shrinkage loss is practically a constant. The elastic loss is proportional only to the relative depth of the reinforcement, since nf_c is a constant.

The creep loss *varies directly* with the *concrete* unit stress and the relative depth of the reinforcement. Also, referring to Professor Ross' table in Appendix I, it is seen to vary *inversely* (and widely so) with (a) the strength of the concrete, (b) the age of the concrete when first loaded, and (c) with the size of the beam.

The detailed study of losses of pre-tension presented in Arts. 13–9 through 13–13 was included primarily to enable the reader to compute the losses for unusual situations and to discourage the unthinking use of arbitrary values thereof. The loss values being used should be reconsidered from time to time as technology changes and better experimental data become available.

EXAMPLE 13–2

The Design of a Pre-tensioned Fully Prestressed Concrete Girder. It is desired to design an economical pre-tensioned girder of symmetrical I-shape to carry a uniformly distributed loading over a long span, as taken up in detail below.

Design Guides

The designing is to follow the ACI Code and the British First Report (our Appendices J and I, respectively) generally, especially with reference to the *flexural designing at the safe working load* level.

For the prediction of the *ultimate flexural strength* of the girder, Whitney's method of Chapter 12 will be used.

The designing of the *web reinforcement* will be carried out at the ultimate strength level, and in a manner consistent with the recommendations of the 1955 Preliminary Report of the ASCE–ACI Joint Committee on Prestressed Concrete, the only adequate advice so far available.

Loading and Span Data. The live[10a] loading is 1.4 klf over a 58-ft. simple span, center to center of 16-in. supports.

CONCRETE

The ultimate compressive strength of the concrete, f'_c, is to be 6250 psi,

$$n = \frac{E_s}{E_c} = \frac{27 \times 10^6}{4.5 \times 10^6} = 6$$

The minimum ultimate flexural strength (modulus of rupture) shall be taken as $0.08f'_c + 150$ psi. Refer to Fig. 13–12.

[10a]Herein the term "live loading" also includes any design dead load which does not get lifted at transfer.

Allowable Stresses:

> At *Stage 1*, after transfer, with the D.L. active:
> Compressive, at beam ends, $0.5f'_c$
> Tensile, temporary, at beam ends, $\frac{1}{2}$ of the modulus of rupture.
> At *Stage 3*, the service load condition, D.L. + L.L. acting:
> Compressive, at midspan, $0.4f'_c$
> Tensile, at midspan, zero.
> Shear, design trial, average over the assumedly unreinforced web, $0.05f'_c$

STEEL

For prestressing take Roebling's uncoated stress-relieved $\frac{3}{8}$-in.[N] seven-wire pre-tensioning strand at their stated 250,000 psi minimum ultimate strength, f'_s. It has no well-defined yield point, so $0.9f'_s$ will be used conservatively as f_y. Refer to Fig. 13–7, and Appendix H. Take E_s of strand at 27×10^6 psi.
Allowable Stresses:

> Max. initial pre-tension, $0.7f'_s$, Roebling.
> Max. final pre-tension, $0.56 f'_s$, Roebling.

For stirrups, at ultimate loading, use their 50,000-psi yield point. Take A-305 high bond bars, un-prestressed.
Steel Contents, for rectangular section elements:

Max. ratio $\qquad p = 0.4\dfrac{f'_c}{f_y}$ $\qquad$ [ACI Appendix, Sec. 605(c)]

Min. percentage $= 0.15\%$ $\qquad$ BFR Sec. 7(b), 5th paragraph excerpted.

Losses of Steel Pre-tension, from Table 13–2:

> *Immed. after transfer:* elastic $= 12{,}000$, steel creep $= 4000$,
> $$\text{Total} = 16{,}000 \text{ psi}$$

> *Later additional:* shrinkage at 7500, creep at 21,500,
> $$\text{Grand Total} = 45{,}000 \text{ psi}$$

INITIAL TRIAL DESIGNING

Assume a span/depth ratio between 18 and 22.
Take $0.52h$ as a trial minimum distance between kern points.
Plan for three layers of the $\frac{3}{8}$-in. strand[N] in the bottom flange. Minimum c. to c. spacing $= 4d' = 1\frac{1}{2}$ in.
Assume a #3 stirrup size.
Fireproofing: Provide a minimum of $\frac{1}{2}$ in. more protection beside and underneath prestressed reinforcement than required by the ACI Code for conventional reinforced concrete construction. That for stirrups and un-prestressed top reinforcement, if any, may be per the ACI Code.

CONCRETE DIMENSIONS

Set the total beam depth, h, in whole inches.

Design all other outside dimensions by half-inches.

Finally taper the flange thicknesses to get draft.

For the performance of the designing of Example 13–2 refer to the accompanying Calculation Sheets.

Pre-tensioned Girder Designing

13–16. The Proportioning (Designing) of the Girder. The proportioning of the outside (concrete) dimensions of prestressed girders is quite important if an efficient section is to be achieved. It is influenced by such factors as the depth/span ratio, the live/dead load ratio,[J] the critical span, the I/A ratio, and the necessity to keep the concrete area small so that the percentage of steel will be low and the ultimate strength of the girder governed by the steel content.

Somewhat opposed to the above influences is the necessity to develop a section of simple and economical shape, the minimum thicknesses of which are largely dictated by fireproofing and minimum strand spacing requirements.

Since a symmetrical I-section was called for, the earliest proportioning consisted of considering a girder depth of about one-twentieth of the span, and a probable *live load range*, kern point to kern point, of half the depth. By dividing the known live load bending moment by this distance (Figs. 13–2 and 13–3) a preliminary value of the required final prestress force, F, was obtained. It indicated that a total of about forty $\frac{3}{8}$-in. strands[N] would be required for prestressing, over thirty of which should be in the bottom flange to provide *ultimate* tensile strength for the section. The requirements for spacing and covering this steel then dictated that three layers thereof should be used (as mentioned at the top of Calculation Sheet 1) to prevent the flanges from becoming unusually wide in relation to the beam depth. A 7 by $19\frac{1}{2}$ in. flange was then tentatively adopted, as shown.

A tentative minimum web thickness was then established, as dictated by the minimum fireproofing requirements. Another guide is that the average vertical end shear therein over the full depth of the beam should not exceed 0.05 to $0.06f'_c$, assuming that web reinforcement is to be used.

Depth of the Section. At this point, it was considered that all the concrete dimensions except the total depth h were settled. The method used to determine the required thickness of the prestressed slab of Example 13–1 was again applied (Eqs. A and B), by taking trial values of h and computing (a) the force necessary to fully precompress the section to an average stress of 1250 psi, and (b) the force, acting through

| Ex. 13-2 | I. Proportioning the Trial Section for Prestress and External Loads | J.E.L. | 4-6-56 | 1/6 |

(A) MINIMUM CONCRETE DIMENSIONS

〜 As set by the necessity for properly spacing and covering the strand and stirrup steel.

Min. Flange Thickness. Preliminary estimates have indicated that 3 layers of strand will be necessary, as mentioned in the statement of this Example 13-2 under "INITIAL TRIAL DESIGN-ING." Therefore $2\frac{1}{4} + 2@\frac{1}{2} + 1\frac{3}{4}$ = a 7 in. minimum thickness.

Min. Flange Width. To cover and space an estimated 33 flange strands will require:

$$2(1\frac{1}{2} + \frac{1}{2}) + \frac{3}{8} + (\frac{33}{3} - 1)(1\frac{1}{2}) = 19\frac{3}{8}"$$

Take $19\frac{1}{2}$ in.

Min. Web Thickness.

This dimension is dictated by the necessity for covering $\frac{3}{8}"$ strands* therein: $2\times 2 + \frac{3}{8} = 4\frac{3}{8}$ in., take $4\frac{1}{2}$ in.

Now only the total depth h remains to be settled.

*The stirrups require that it be $2@1\frac{1}{2} + 3(\frac{3}{8}) = 4\frac{1}{4}"$

(B) TRIAL OF A $19\frac{1}{2}$ in. BY 36 in. SECTION

Preliminary Remarks. It was found in an earlier trial involving a total of $42 - \frac{3}{8}$ in. strands that when h was made 32 in., the F-value of 442 kips required at the assumed lower kern limit to fully pre-compress the section[xx] was closely the same as the 441 kips required at a 0.5h kern points distance to offset the L.L. bending moment (balance).

xx Refer to Eqns. (A) & (B) under "Solution" of Example 13-1, the slab designing.

However, to additionally offset the dead load bending moment, it appeared that two additional inches of depth below the neutral axis would be needed.[3] Accordingly the trial depth was changed to 36 in. (See below). Note that only plain concrete areas were conveniently considered throughout this designing operation.

Trial Live Load Unit Stress. $h = 36$ in., $L/h = 19.+$

$$M_L = \frac{w_L L^2}{8} = \frac{1.4(58)^2}{8} = 589 \text{ k-ft.}$$

$$I = \frac{19.5(36)^3 - 15(22)^3}{12} = 62,600 \text{ in}^4$$

$$S_L = \frac{M_L c}{I} = \frac{589(12,000)(18)}{62,600} = 2030 \text{ psi.}, < 2500 \text{ allowed.}$$

Trial Strand Steel. The required final pre-compression force, $F, = \frac{2.5}{2}[19.5(36) - 15(22)] = 465.$ kips the kern-to-kern distance, required to counteract the live load bending moment. When an h value of 32 in. was tried, these two forces proved to have closely equal values (about 442 kips), as indeed they must actually be.

As indicated in the lower portion of Calculation Sheet 1, a 36-in. depth was finally selected in order to provide more height in which additionally to counteract the dead load bending moment by further lowering of the centroid of the precompression force. As shown halfway down Calculation Sheet 2, all but 19 per cent thereof was so taken care of thereby.

The increase of h to 36 in. had decreased the live load stress by about 470 psi, making it available for carrying the remaining dead load.

It was then noted that for each proposed 5½ in. additional increase in web depth, the width of both flanges would have to be increased 1½ in. to admit the three additional strands required to precompress the corresponding added concrete area. The total number of strands having already been increased to 43, at the top of Calculation Sheet 2, no further increase was considered. *Every legitimate means of holding the concrete area to a minimum should be embraced* pending a final check upon all the stresses.

Loading Eccentricities versus Kern Limits. Under a corresponding heading in Calculation Sheet 2, it is shown that the live load single eccentricity of 7.60 in. is comfortably less than the estimated kern limit distance of 9.36 in.

The dead load bending moment and its desired eccentricity having been computed, the desired L.L. plus D.L. eccentricity of 11.73 in. became available. It is to be compared with the lesser *actual* eccentricity of the precompressing force F, which is at the centroid of the chosen arrangement of the prestressed strands, namely, 10.94 in. from the assumed neutral axis of the uncracked transformed section, whereby the 19 per cent deficiency of dead load eccentricity was revealed.

Ultimate Strength. Before entering upon the work of the detailed investigation of the girder design, a prediction of the approximate ultimate strength of the section should always be made. This is done partly to ensure that the desired prolonged type of failure via the steel will occur. Such work was begun at the bottom of Calculation Sheet 2. The reader is presumed to be familiar with Whitney's method thereof, as illustrated in Arts. 12–8 and 13–5.

In addition to *setting* a *maximum* permissible steel content to ensure a steel failure, the British First Report, in its Sec. 7(b), fifth excerpted paragraph, also sets a minimum one of 0.15 per cent. This is to make certain that the sudden great reduction in the section modulus of a concrete section, which accompanies deep flexural cracking of the concrete when steel contents are considerably less than 0.15 per cent, will not cause such a *shock* that the steel will thereby fracture. This matter

Ex. 13-2	Designing for Flexure	*H.E.L.*	4-6-56	2/6

Trial Strand Steel (concluded)

At 130 ksi final prestress one $\frac{3}{8}$ in. strand can carry
$130(0.0799) = 10.4$ kips.

Trial required *total* number of strands $= \frac{465}{10.4} = 44.6$

Optimistically try 33 strands in the bottom flange,
8 in the lower portion of the web, plus 2 in the top flange.

Live & Dead Ecc's. vs Kern Limits

Desired L.L. double ecc., $e_L = \frac{589(12)}{465} = 15.20''$ $\quad \left\| \quad \frac{0.52h}{2}$ est.
kern limit

Corresponding L.L. single ecc. $= \quad 7.60 \quad \left\| \quad = 9.36''$

$\qquad\qquad$ /from mid-depth\

$$w_D = \frac{372}{144}(0.147) = 0.38\text{-}k/f.$$

$$M_D = \frac{0.38(58)^2}{8} = 160 \; k\text{-}ft.$$

Desired D.L. add'n'l. ecc. $= \frac{160(12)}{465} = \underline{\quad 4.13''}$

Desired ecc. of centroid of all strands $= 11.73''$ ◄───

Actual ecc. of F, measured from the
mid-depth of the beam: From Sheet 1 sketch

$$\frac{33(14\frac{1}{4}'') + 8(6'') - 2(13\frac{1}{4}'')}{43} = \underline{\quad 11.44''}$$

Since the N.A. of the uncracked transformed section will be about 0.50" below the mid-depth:

$\qquad$ True *actual* e, from N.A. $= \underline{\quad 10.94''} $ ◄───

$\qquad$ Deficiency of D.L. ecc. $= \quad 0.79'' = 19\%$

Final Remarks.

Rather than deepen the beam 2 more
inches, increasing its cross-sectional area by 9 sq. in. and requiring more strand to pre-compress it, we are estimating
that the remaining 19% of the D.L. bending moment will not
cause an additional flexural stress greater than 470 psi, -- the
available margin evident at the bottom of Calc. Sheet 1.

$\qquad$ Make beam 1 ft. $7\frac{1}{2}$ in. by 3 ft. 0 in. and
$\qquad$ use 43 - $\frac{3}{8}$ in. strands, as shown.

Trial Prediction of Ultimate Strength

$\qquad\qquad$ Using $0.9 f_s'$ as f_y, per Art. 13-5.

The centroid of the 41 tensile strands

will be at $\frac{33(3.75'') + 8(12'')}{41} = 5.36''$ from the
$\qquad\qquad\qquad\qquad\qquad\qquad\qquad$ bottom

$$p = \frac{A_s}{bd} = \frac{41(0.0799)}{19.5(30.64)} = \quad 0.548\%, > 0.15\%$$
$\qquad\qquad\qquad\qquad\qquad\qquad$ min. of BFR Sec. 7(b)

Whitney's balanced max. $=$

$$p_0 = 0.456 \frac{f_c'}{f_y} = 0.456 \frac{6.25}{0.9(250)} = 1.27\%$$

Therefore failure will not be sudden.

8 strands ✕
33 strands ✕

PLATE 13-1. Seventy-foot box section pre-tensioned prestressed bridge beam near failure in test at Fritz Engineering Laboratory, Lehigh University. The beam was 3 ft. wide by 2 ft. 9 in. deep and contained forty-six ⅜-in. seven-wire strands with an ultimate tensile strength of 250,000 psi. It was fundamentally an I-section because of 27 by 24 in. cavities which extended over its full length, except for 2-ft. solid bulkheads at its ends and the midsection. The failure was due to excessive compression in the upper fibers of the concrete at midspan and directly under one of the load points. The steel was highly stressed, but there was no evidence of any excessive inelastic elongation, since the cracks remained quite small up to the instant of failure.

is also of importance in un-prestressed beam design. Thus, *both the maximum and the minimum permissible steel percentages exist for the same general purpose,* namely, to prevent the sudden type of ultimate failure of members which is characteristic of *concrete* fractures, whether compressive or tensile, respectively.

In this preliminary ultimate strength calculation, the depth, *a*, of the compressive stress block was assumed to lie wholly within the upper flange, and the two strands therein were conservatively disregarded.

PRESTRESSED GIRDER DESIGNING PROBLEMS

Problem 13-4. Verify numerically the statements made under (B) of Calculation Sheet 1, taking 19½-in. flanges.

Problem 13-5. Alternately re-perform the designing operations of Example 13-2, including the calculation of the trial ultimate strength:

(a) If 18-in. flanges are taken,

(b) If 21-in. flanges are taken.

Tabulate a comparison of the two designs with that of Example 13-2, with respect to required concrete and steel areas, live load concrete unit stresses, portion of the dead load carried "free," and ultimate strengths. Finally state which of the three designs you prefer, giving your reasons.

Ex. 13-2	Ultimate Bending Moment (concl.) II. Flexural Investigation	Y. E. L.	4-6-56	3/6

Trial Ultimate Strength (concluded)

From Art. 12-8:

* For a refined later calculation (1673 k-ft) see Art. 13-19.

$$M_s' = A_s f_y d\left[1 - \frac{p f_y}{2(0.85 f_c')}\right] = \frac{41(0.0799)(225)(30.64)}{12}\left[1 - \frac{0.00548(225)}{1.7(6.25)}\right] = 1663. \text{ k-ft}$$

Approx. avg. factor of safety $= \dfrac{1663}{589 + 160} = 2.22$

Satisfactory, since > 2.00 req'd by BFR Sec. 7(b).
Also since > 1605 k-ft. req'd by ACI Appendix Sec. A604(a).

(A) DETAILED FLEXURAL INVESTIGATION – uncracked transformed section.

In the Dead & Live Load Range.

Girder depth, h, = 3'-0."

Get N.A. by ΣM about $\mathcal{C}$:

Area	Arm	Moment
372.0	0	0
0.8	-13.25	-10.6
16.4	12.64	207.50
389.2		196.9 = 0.50

So N.A. is at 0.50 in. below $\mathcal{C}$.

$n-1$
$2(0.08)(5)$
$= 0.8^{a''}$ 　2 strands
$4\frac{1}{2}$
$(0.50')$
$\mathcal{C}$
N.A.
24.69
$19\frac{1}{2}$　4.75
13.25
12.64
7
$16.4^{a''}$　41 strands　1.20
$= 41(0.0799)(5)$　5.36
$n-1$　Actual centroid of precompression

Get $I_{N.A.}$:

Concrete
$19.5(36)^3 \div 12 = 75,900.$
MINUS
$15(22)^3 \div 12 = -13,300$
$\overline{\qquad 62,600.}$
$372(0.50)^2 = 93.$

Steel
$0.8(13.25)^2 = 141.$
$16.4(12.14)^2 = 2420.$
$I = 65,254.$

Actual Kern Limits

$\dfrac{F}{A} = \dfrac{Fec}{Ar^2} = 1, \quad e = k = \dfrac{r^2}{c}$

$r^2 = \dfrac{I}{A} = \dfrac{65254}{389.2} = 167.6$

Upper $= k_t = \dfrac{167.6}{18.5} = 9.06"$

Lower $= k_b = \dfrac{167.6}{17.5} = 9.58"$

Actual L.L. Range = 18.64"
= 0.518h,
Versus 0.52h used in designing.

---

(1) Concrete Stresses (Final) under Design Safe Loading, BFR Stage 3.

$F = 130^{ksi}(43)(0.0799) = 446.^k$

At Midspan (only)

		Unit Stress	
		Top (c = 18.50")	Bottom (c = 17.50")
Due to P/S	$\dfrac{F}{A} = \dfrac{446,000}{389.2} =$	1147. c	1147. c
	$\dfrac{Fec}{I} = \dfrac{446,000(10.94)(c)}{65,254} =$	1385. t	1310. c
Due to DL+LL	$\dfrac{Mc}{I} = \dfrac{(589+160)(12,000)(c)}{65,254}$	2548. c	2409. t
	Totals	2310. c	48. c
		< 2500	no tension
		∴ O.K.	O.K.

Pre-tensioned Girder Investigation

13–17. The Detailed Flexural Investigation. The sketch on Calculation Sheet 3 is that of the effective transformed uncracked section which exists in the working load range.

The calculations show that the neutral axis thereof is 0.50 in. below the mid-depth, as previously assumed. Note also that the moment of inertia proved to be only 4 per cent greater than the plain concrete one computed at the bottom of Calculation Sheet 1, which justifies the earlier use of the latter in proportioning the section.

The actual kern limits here calculated closely embrace the 0.52h assumption shown in the upper portion of Calculation Sheet 2.

Concrete Stresses at Midspan under Design Safe Loading. In (1), the computed final total unit stresses in the concrete at midspan proved to be 2310 compressive above and 48 compressive below, both appreciably within the permissible values. Consult also the corresponding stress diagrams of Fig. 13–10.

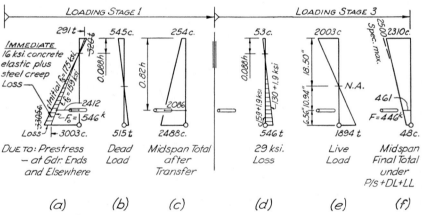

Fig. 13–10. Stress diagrams summary, investigational.

Concrete Stresses at the Girder Ends after Transfer. In (2) (a), on Calculation Sheet 4, are the calculations for the stresses in the concrete at the ends of the girder, where there are no dead load or live load stresses of opposite sense to mitigate the high prestress compressive value at the bottom fiber, or to erase the tensile one at the top. Refer also to the left side of Fig. 13–10. The magnitudes of these stresses are considered quite temporary because the 16,000 psi of prestress loss considered at this stage is an underestimate, since no portion of the shrinkage and creep losses has yet been considered. The high allowable stresses shown are tolerated only for this temporary situation.

Ex. 13-2	II. Detailed Flexural Investigation	H. E. L.	4-12-56	4/6

(2) Concrete Stresses immediately after Transfer, BFR Stage 1.

$$F_o = 159^{ksi}(43)(0.0799) = 546^k.$$

(a) At Girder Ends *

		Unit Stress	
		Top (c = 18.50")	Bottom (c = 17.50")
Due to Prestress	$\dfrac{F_o}{A} = \dfrac{546,000}{389.2} = $　 =	1400.c	1400.c
	$\dfrac{F_o ec}{I} = \dfrac{546,000(10.94)(c)}{65,254} = $	1691.t	1603.c
		291.t	3003.c
The D.L. and L.L. stresses are zero at the ends.		< 325 $= \frac{1}{2} f_{cb}$ ∴ O.K.	< 3125 $= \frac{1}{2} f'_c$ ∴ O.K.

* The stresses presented here have since been decreased due to a later thickening of the web _in this vicinity._ See Art. 13-22 and Calc. Sheet 5.

(b) At Midspan　F_o again 546^k

		Top	Bottom
	Due to axial plus eccentric prestressing (see above) -- =	291.t	3003.c
Due to D.L. picked up with the cambering.	$\dfrac{M_D c}{I} = \dfrac{160,000(12)(c)}{65,254} = $	545.c	515.t
		254.c	2488.c
		Both < 3125.c ∴ O.K.	

For the designing of the stirrup reinforcement see Calc. Sheet 5.

When the tension in the top approaches the full modulus of rupture value, f_{cb}, un-prestressed steel is sometimes added to resist it.

At *midspan,* under (2)(*b*), the concrete stresses are within the normal allowable compression due to the counteractive effect of the dead load as the girder cambers itself off the casting bed.

Initial to Final Steel Stresses. It is usually a surprise to learn that the application of the design dead and live load *increases* the tension in the prestressed steel comparatively little. The *decrease* due to the losses of prestress is a much larger item, so the final stress still is less than the initial one.

Let us determine the final stress in the steel by progressing from left to right on the stress diagrams of Fig. 13–10 and *at the level of the centroid of the steel.*

At (a) the initial 175-ksi steel pre-tension decreases almost instantaneously to 159 ksi, due to the concrete elastic plus steel creep loss of 16 ksi. Thereafter, the concrete precompression drops to 2412c. It is then immediately decreased to 2086c due to the 323t dead load stress. Since the concrete has long since *seized* the steel, the dead load has increased the steel stress by n times 323, or 1940 psi, making the total 160.9 ksi just after transfer.

At (d), the total steel stress becomes 160.9 minus 29 = 131.9 after shrinkage and creep. The live load then adds 6(1187) = 7120 psi (equals 7.1 ksi), making the final total steel stress only 139 ksi.

PRESTRESSED BEAM INVESTIGATION PROBLEM

Problem 13–6. Investigate the rectangular pre-tensioned prestressed beam of Fig. 13–11 for the pertinent concrete stresses (a) at transfer, and (b) at design safe load. Compare with the allowables, *and comment.*

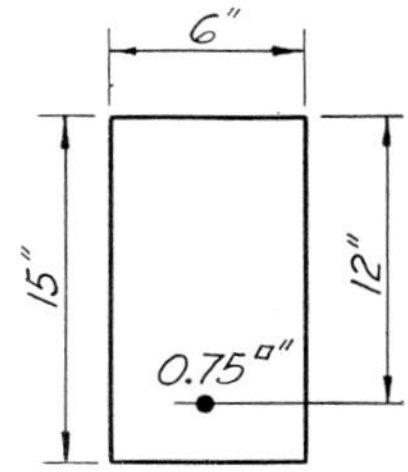

Transfer was effected at four weeks, at which time the design f'_c had been attained, though curing had been completely neglected from the beginning.

The live load is 0.40 klf over a 28-ft. simple span.

The allowables are the same as in Example 13–2, namely: $f'_c = 6250$, $n = 6$. Allowable $f_c = 0.4$ and $0.5f'_c$. Allowable $f_t = \frac{1}{2}$ the modulus of rupture in the top at the ends and zero in the bottom at midspan. Take Roebling's strand at 250,000-psi ultimate strength, 175,000-psi initial prestress.

Assume the losses to be:

FIG. 13–11. The live load is 0.40 klf over a 28-ft. simple span.

Steel creep =	4000 psi	Shrinkage	= 8000 psi
Elastic	= 12,000	Concrete creep	= 21,000

13–18. Check upon the Girder Flexural Designing by the "Prestress Formulas." In repetitive work, time will be saved by the use of the following formulas,[11] the applications of which are illustrated below.

At the supports at **transfer**

Top Fiber: Max. $f^t{}_{F_o} = \dfrac{F_o}{A'_c}\left(1 - \dfrac{e}{k_t}\right) \leqq 325$ psi tensile   (13–4)

$$= \frac{159,000(3.44)}{389.2}\left(1 - \frac{10.94}{9.06}\right) = 291.t$$

Bottom Fiber: Max. $f^b{}_{F_o} = \dfrac{F_o}{A'_c}\left(1 + \dfrac{e}{k_b}\right) \leqq 0.50f'_c$ comp.   (13–5)

$$= \frac{159,000(3.44)}{389.2}\left(1 + \frac{10.94}{9.58}\right) = 3003.c$$

At the maximum B.M. Section under Design **dead** *and* **live load**

---

[11] The notation used is that adopted by the Joint ASCE-ACI Committee. See Bibliography item (B).

Top Fiber:

$$\text{Max. } f'_{FT} = \frac{F}{A'_c}\left(1 - \frac{e}{k_t}\right) + \frac{M_{TC}c_t}{I'_c} \leqq 0.40f'_c \tag{13-6}$$

$$= \frac{130,000(3.44)}{389.2}\left(1 - \frac{10.94}{9.06}\right) + \frac{749.0(12,000)(18.50)}{65,254.}$$

$$= 2310.c$$

Bottom Fiber:

$$\text{Max. } f^b_{FT} = \frac{F}{A'_c}\left(1 + \frac{e}{k_b}\right) - \frac{M_{TC}c_b}{I'_c} \equiv 0, \text{ or compressive,} \tag{13-7}$$

$$= \frac{130,000(3.44)}{389.2}\left(1 + \frac{10.94}{9.58}\right) - \frac{749.0(12,000)(17.50)}{65,254.}$$

$$= 48.c$$

13–19. Refined Prediction of the Ultimate Strength. At this point the ultimate strength of the section, first calculated at the bottom of Calculation Sheet 2, was re-predicted by the *double couple* method used in Example 12–4, but also recognizing that the depth of part of the compressive stress area may be limited by the 7-in. thickness of the top flange. With d taken as 30.64 in., as previously, the block depth a turned out to be only 6.78 in. The steel couple moment proved to be 78 kip-ft., and that of the main couple 1595, making the total 1673 kip-ft. This meant an average factor of safety of 2.24, which is satisfactory, and closely the same as that computed earlier near the top of Calculation Sheet 3.

Problem 13–7. Verify numerically all the statements made in Art. 13–19 regarding the ultimate strength of the section designed in Example 13–2.

13–20. Resistance to Initial Cracking. Once the design live loading has been applied, the additional bending moment required to *initially* crack the beam in flexure will be:
  (a) That required to decrease the compressive stress in the bottom fiber to zero, *plus*
  (b) That required to crack the beam if it were unreinforced, i.e., the modulus of rupture bending moment.

Solution: For the girder being designed,
(a) From Fig. 13–10(f):

$$M_a = \frac{sI}{c} = \frac{48(65,254)}{17.5(12,000)} = 14.9 \text{ kip-ft.}$$

(b) From Fig. 13–12, taking a minimum value of the bending modulus of rupture of 6250-lb. concrete at $0.08f'_c + 150 = 650$ psi,

$$M_b = \frac{sI}{c} = \frac{650[19.5(36)^3 - 15(22)^3]}{18(12)(12,000)} = \underline{188.0}$$

Initial cracking moment = 202.9 kip-ft.

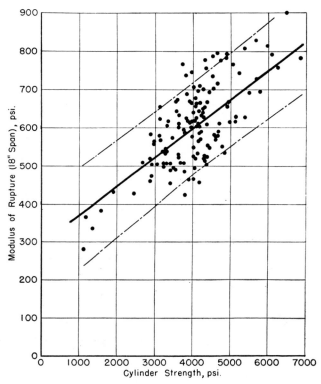

Fig. 13–12. Variation in the moduli of rupture of concrete with 6 by 12 in. cylinder compressive strength, according to Professor Kesler.[1] The minimum value, represented by the lower line, is closely:

$$f'_{cb} = 0.08f'_c + 150 \text{ psi.}$$

The corresponding D.L. + L.L. average factor of safety against *initial* cracking is, comparing bending moment values,

$$\frac{160 + 589 + 202.9}{160 + 589} = 1.27.$$

Once a girder has so cracked, the modulus of rupture strength disappears. Thereafter the factor of safety against *repeated* opening of a crack will be, in this case,

$$\frac{160 + 589 + 14.9}{160 + 589} = 1.02.$$

When greater factors of safety against cracking are desired, plan from the beginning to have a greater concrete compressive stress at the bottom fiber under the design loading by *designing* to have a more pronounced trapezoidal stress distribution in Fig. 13–10(f), instead of a nearly triangular one.

13–21. The Prediction of the Deflection of the Bonded, Pre-tensioned, Prestressed Girder. Taking the flexural deflection as δ, Fig. 13–13 shows that the long-time midspan deflection of the girder from the plane of the casting bed due to pre-tension and dead load may be approximated by moment-area prin-

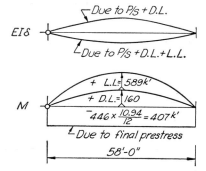

Fig. 13–13.   Pre-tensioned girder deflections.

ciples,[12] and from the sixth paragraph of Art. 13–12, as follows:

(6250-lb. concrete)

Unit elastic strain $= \dfrac{1 \text{ psi}}{E_c} = \dfrac{1}{4,500,000} \quad = 0.22 \times 10^{-6}$

Long-time unit creep strain, from Sec. 7(d)(1) of BFR $= \underline{0.40}$

Total $= \overline{0.62}$

Uncracked, the long-time total strain and deflection will be about $0.62/0.22 = 2.81$, say three times the elastic.

Due to DL and P/S:

$$EI\delta_t = 3\left\{\frac{2}{3}(160)(29)\left[\frac{5}{8} \times 29\right] - 407(29)[14.5]\right\} = -346{,}500. \text{ kip-ft.}^3$$

Taking also the 65,254 elastic I of the uncracked section:

$$\delta_t = -\frac{346{,}500(12)^3(1000)}{4{,}500{,}000(65{,}254)} = -2.0 \text{ in. (upward)}$$

Due to L.L., applied intermittently, the elastic deflection will be:

$$\delta_L = \frac{\frac{2}{3}(589)(29)[\frac{5}{8} \times 29](12)^3(1000)}{4{,}500{,}000(65{,}254)} = +1.2 \text{ in. (downward)}$$

This means that the girder would then still be cambered above the surface of the casting bed $2.0 - 1.2 = 0.8$ in.

[12] Refer to Art. 5–4 of Chapter 5.

If the L.L. becomes permanent, the long-time total deflection with respect to the surface of the casting bed will be about:

$$3(1.2) - 2.0 = 1.6 \text{ in. downward, or about } 1/435 \text{ of the span.}[13]$$

13–22. The Web Reinforcement of the Pre-tensioned Girder. It is sometimes erroneously assumed that the precompression induced in the concrete by the prestress force prevents the development of the diagonal tensile stresses associated with conventional reinforced concrete beam designing, and that, consequently, stirrups are unnecessary in a prestressed member.

The greatest error in the above assumption is that in the loading range approaching the ultimate strength of the beam the prestress disappears, due to the inelastic action of the reinforcement, as depicted in Fig. 13–7; and the beam action thereafter is that of a conventional reinforced concrete beam. If the resulting *diagonal tensile stresses* are high, some diagonal tensile reinforcement must therefore be provided to prevent a sudden and disastrous *shear* failure at a loading that is less than the flexural ultimate load.

Such web reinforcement has often been designed at the *ultimate strength level* for the whole shear at the sections, assuming the member cracked; and later checked by computing the principal tensile stresses (d'agonal) at the *safe working load level,* assuming the member uncracked, and assigning a portion thereof to the concrete as in conventional reinforced concrete beam designing.

There still is a general scarcity of data from tests of prestressed beams suffering shear-related failures. In the meantime the only clear recommended practice appears to be that contained in the (very) preliminary CEACI report of 1955, previously mentioned in Art. 13–7. It advises that prestressed concrete members be designed so that their shear-related ultimate strengths are greater than the flexural; and has set a corresponding small critical percentage of flexural tensile reinforcement, above which web reinforcement is required. Stirrups are to be proportioned at the ultimate load level for two-thirds of the shear[14] at the sections, using the common formula. They are to be provided over the whole span of the member, the maximum spacing, s, being $d/2$. This web reinforcement content, A_v/sb', must be between 1 per cent and ¼ per cent.

13–23. Stirrup Designing. In the (A) portion of Calculation Sheet 5, observe that at the predicted failure level the flexural load factor is 2.24,

---

[13] A calculation by the more precise method of Example 10–3, but considering the section uncracked because of the prestressing, will give about the same result.

[14] This shearing appears somewhat inconsistent with the practice mentioned in the early part of the third paragraph above. For an excellent discussion of the subject, consult Professor Lin, in Bibliography item J, beginning with his Art. 7–3.

| Ex.13-2 | III. Designing of Stirrup Reinforcement at Ult. Strength Level. | H.E.L. | 4-15-56 | 5/6 |

(A) ULTIMATE DIAGONAL TENSION FORCES & STRESSES.

From Art. 13-19, $\omega_{D+L}^{u} = 2.24(0.38 + 1.40) = 3.99$ klf.

- At face of 16 in. wall, $V_f^{u} = 3.99(28.33) = 113$ kips

$$v_f^{u} = \frac{V_f^{u}}{bjd} = \frac{113,000}{4.5(7/8)(30.64)} = 935 \text{ psi} = 0.15 f_c'$$

Compare with plain concrete v at safe working load :

$$v = \frac{V_f}{bh} = \frac{1.78(28.33)}{4.5(36)} = 311 \text{ psi}, = 0.05 f_c'$$

So average shear load factor $= \frac{0.15}{0.05} = 3.0$.

The superscript u is being used herein to indicate ultimate values.

See Art. 13-16, 4th paragraph.

(B) CRITICAL PERCENTAGE OF FLEXURE STEEL — causing shear-related failure :

CEACI Sec. 209.3.1.
$$p_{cr} = 0.3 \frac{f_{sp} f_c' b'}{f_y^2 b} = \frac{0.3(130)(6.25)(4.5)(100)}{[0.9(225)]^2(19.5)} = 0.11 \%$$

209.3.2 — Our girder has a p of $\frac{41(0.08)}{19.5(30.64)} = 0.55 \%$, so web reinforcement must be provided.

(C) STIRRUP DESIGNING — See Calc. Sheet 6. Take hard grade #3 stirrups.

(1) In the Subordinate Stirrup Locality defined by V_c^{u} & $\frac{d}{2}$ max. Spc'g:

Sec. 209.3.3 & 3.5
$$\text{From } s = \frac{A_v f_y jd}{2/3 V^{u}}, \quad V_c^{u} = \frac{A_v f_y jd}{2/3 s} = \frac{0.22(50)(7/8)(30.64)}{2/3(15.32)} = 28.8^k$$
@ 7.23' from ₵.

$$N_s = \frac{7.23(12)}{15.32} = 5.66 \quad \text{Use 6-#3 ¢∮ @ 14}\tfrac{1}{2}\text{", each side of ₵ of span.}$$

Corresponding $p_{min} = \frac{A_v}{bs} = \frac{0.22}{4.5(14.5)} = 0.34 \%, > 0.25, \therefore O.K.$

(2) In the 21.1 ft. Principal Stirrup Locality between V_f^{u} and V_c^{u} :

For one #3 stirrup, $sV^{u} = \frac{A_v f_y jd}{2/3} = \frac{0.22(50)(7/8)(30.64)}{2/3} = 442.^{k''}$

The width of the first stirrup region $= \frac{443}{113}$, say 4."

Sec. 209.3.4 — Corresponding $p_{max} = \frac{0.22}{4.5(4)} = 1.22 \%, > 1 \%$ max. allowed.

Therefore increase the web thickness at the face of the wall to a minimum of $\frac{1.22}{1.0}(4.5) = 5\tfrac{1}{2}$ in.

The $4\tfrac{1}{2}$ in. thickness will be satisfactory beginning where $V^{u} = \frac{4.5}{5.5}(113) = 92.4^k = $ at 5.1 ft. from the face of the support.

Then $N_p = \frac{\Sigma s V^{u}}{s V^{u}} = \frac{(113 + 28.8)(0.5)(21.1)(12)}{3/2(0.22)(50)(7/8)(15.32)} = \frac{17960}{443} = 40.5$

Use 41-#3 ¢∮

Then the total number of #3 stirrups required for one girder will be 2(41 + 6) = 94 stirrups in all.

while the shear one is 3.0. Thus diagonal tension failure should not occur if the mild steel stirrups are ultimate-strength designed at their yield-point stress for the ultimate shear force corresponding to the ultimate flexural bending moment, as we have done.

Tests have shown that the failure of un-stirruped prestressed beams is likely to be due to shear if the longitudinal steel content exceeds the small critical percentage shown in (B), as it does in this case. Stirrups were therefore provided.

First, in (C), the central locality that was to contain only the stirrups which were to be at the maximum spacing was defined spanwise. These stirrups were then located on Calculation Sheet 6.

In the principal stirrup locality abutting the ends of the girder, the calculations follow a familiar pattern, except that it was necessary to thicken the outermost portion of the girder web in order to keep the stirrup steel content below the 1 per cent maximum in this locality. As shown on Calculation Sheet 6, the outermost of these stirrups was located in the middle of its 4-in. stirrup region, while the last one was set at the $7\frac{1}{2}$ in. half-maximum stirrup space $(d/4)$ outside the inner boundary of the locality.

The effect of shear at the safe working stress level should also be examined. Presumably the prestress compression then still is present, and the beam still uncracked. Having in mind the Mohr circle construction for determining the corresponding principal tensile stresses (diagonal), special attention should be given to sections of the beam where *both* the shear and compressive stresses are high. Such situations exist in simple beams carrying heavy centrally located concentrated loads, cantilever beams, and continuous beams. Also, at any given section, the tension should be computed at the base of the web portion, as well as at the neutral axis.

13–24. Final Design Sketch of the Pre-tensioned Girder. The views in Calculation Sheet 6 call for the stirrups just computed, only the first and last one in each of the two groups having been drawn in.

Note the previously calculated thickening of the web to $5\frac{1}{2}$ in. near the ends. Such thickening might be further increased to ensure against possible horizontal tensile cracking of the web due to the expanding of the longitudinal reinforcement therein in this region of *prestress transfer bond*, to be taken up in the next article.

A few transverse ribs were sketched in to serve as stabilizers for the flanges. They are a necessity beneath concentrated loads when present.

The *shape* of the flanges was here modified to secure the draft necessary for the removal of the side forms. The one-inch fillets should relieve the tendency for stress concentrations.

13–25. Bond and Anchorage of Pre-tensioned Reinforcement. Because this field is a controversial one, its present development will

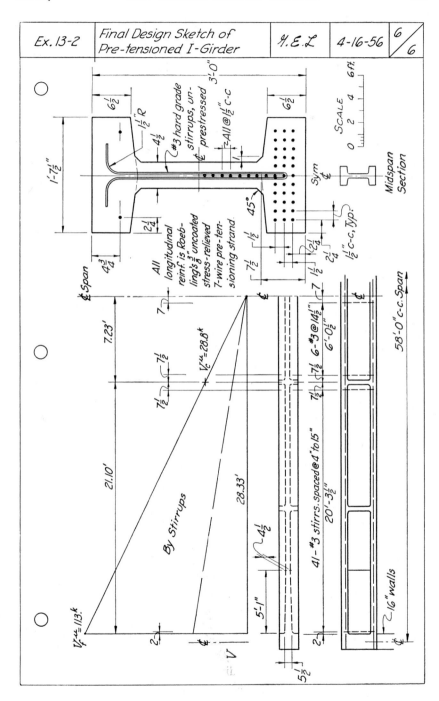

be discussed, rather than make a detailed application to the 58-ft. girder.

As in the case of flexural strength and of shear strength, different methods must be used to design the anchorage of pre-tensioned reinforcement, depending upon whether the *safe working load* range or the *ultimate strength* one is being considered. This is principally because the *rate* at which end anchorage can be developed at the supports is vastly greater at the lower level, as will be seen. Consequently, we know that a great deal more anchorage distance, or length of embedment, is needed if such a sudden type of *ultimate failure* is to be prevented, but there is uncertainty as to how much more.

In the Safe Load Range. As stated in Art. 3–11, under *Bond versus Anchorage*, bond stress, $u = V / \Sigma_o jd$, indicates the *rate* at which flexural stress gets into longitudinal reinforcement at points along the clear span of beams. In pre-tensioned beams, it is referred to as *intermediate bond*, and is seldom critically high. Safe values for it have been established from common pull-out test specimens, in which please note that due to the pull upon the reinforcing bar, its diameter *decreases* as the load is increased.

A different type of bond stress develops at the ends of pre-tensioned strands as *transfer* is effected. As the initial pre-tension in the strand of,

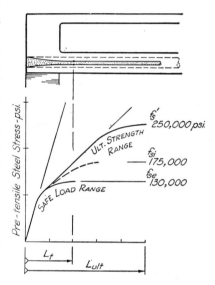

Required Anchorage Distance

Fig. 13–14. Development of anchorage of pre-tensioned reinforcement.

say, 175,000 psi decreases after transfer possibly to 130,000 psi due to early and later losses, its diameter *increases*, following Poisson's ratio. This produces a superior type of bond resistance known as *prestress transfer bond*. At the extreme ends of the strand, the diameter returns fully to its unstrained size, as shown in Fig. 13–14. The gradation to smaller diameters results in a wedgelike anchorage.

This bond resistance is principally frictional, resulting as it does from the large normal forces developed as the bar expands. The distance over which such (decreasing) expansion takes place is known as the *transfer length, L_t,* or effective length of embedment.

Hoyer[K] developed a corresponding formula for L_t which for Poisson's ratios of 0.1 for the concrete and 0.3 for the steel, $E_c = 4,500,000$ psi,

$n = 6$, initial prestress = 175,000, and a final prestress of 130,000, such as we have, gives $L_t = 6.5(d'/\mu)$, wherein d' is the diameter of his wire, and μ is the coefficient of friction between concrete and steel. Taking μ at 0.3, the required L_t becomes 22 diam. Assuming the formula applicable to 3/8-in. strand, only 8.2 in. would be required — a remarkably short distance.

Mr. R. J. Carrol, Ohio State University, in tests[L] specially devised to reveal L_t, found 7 in. necessary for 1/4-in. strand, or 28 diam.

The lower curve of Fig. 13–14, based upon tests[M] by Thorsen, indicates the relatively short transfer length L_t necessary for the safe load range when prestress transfer bond can be mobilized. Partly because the ends of strands sink inward, or slip, several hundredths of an inch at transfer, he recommends that, until better data are available, an L_t of 2 ft. be provided for developing this type of bond.

In the Ultimate Load Range. As the load is increased toward failure, not much additional prestress transfer bond can be developed between the 130,000-psi final prestress value pictured in Fig. 13–14 and the initial prestress of 175,000 psi, at which it theoretically becomes zero. For developing the additional anchorage required to prevent disastrous strand slippage in the ultimate strength range, the ordinary (pull out) bond resistance is still available, though its unit value is much smaller, as indicated by the decreased slope of the upper part of the graph.

Until more data are available, Thorsen[M] recommends that a total anchorage distance, L_{ult}, of 5 ft. be available for resisting the 250,000 psi ultimate strength of strand steel. This means that in order for the anchorage concrete to remain intact, one should be sure that no flexural cracks can occur within 5 ft. of the end of a girder. Sometimes, when concentrated loads are near, it may be necessary to cast an overhang on the member.

For the time being, conservative practice with respect to the anchorage of pre-tensioned reinforcement is well represented by the U.S. Bureau of Public Roads' prohibition[N] of single wire larger than 0.2 in., and seven-wire strand larger than 3/8 in.

Post-tensioned Beams

13–26. Post-tensioning versus Pre-tensioning. As mentioned in Art. 13–6, the concrete of post-tensioned beams is typically placed around conduits, through which the steel is later threaded, and stressed by jacking against the hardened concrete. One advantage is that since the whole elastic compressing of the concrete is eliminated, and the shrinkage and creep losses are considerably reduced, the total loss of steel tension can be approximately halved. Also, since the steel is (typically) unbonded, its tension may be adjusted at some later time if necessary.

The most important advantage of post-tensioning has been that the steel can be *draped*, as in Fig. 13–15(a), to (1) avoid tensile stress in the top concrete at end[15] sections, (2) provide diagonal tension reinforcement, and (3) avoid possible interference of the mechanical end-anchors used. Furthermore, the reinforcement need not be of small diameter, since bond is typically not relied upon for anchoring the ends. Post-tensioning is also advantageous for girders too large to be conveniently transported through traffic to the job site.

The disadvantages include possible rusting of the reinforcement (unless it is post-grouted), relatively expensive field labor must be used to position the steel and tension it, and a somewhat lower ultimate strength[16] for the member because the reinforcement is typically unbonded to the concrete at intermediate points (or only partially so).

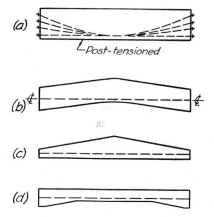

Fig. 13–15. Solutions for the problem of end-section stresses.

It should be added that some of the original differentiations between pre-tensioned and post-tensioned beams are now fast disappearing, as exemplified by the thorough post-bonding of post-tensioned reinforcement, and the post-draping of pre-tensioned strands by pushing them downward and confining them in saddles attached to the casting bed!

13–27. Mechanical End Anchorages. There are several forms of end anchorages, which are a necessity for post-tensioned beams. The wedging principle is most employed. The *Freyssinet cone*, which can accommodate up to eighteen wires, and the Magnel *sandwich plates* are examples. For excellent descriptions of these and several other makes, refer to Professor Lin's Chapter 3, our Bibliography item J.

The *Strandvise* device of Fig. 13–6 is primarily intended for use on *pre-tensioned* beams, to hold the pre-tension until *transfer*.

13–28. Summary of Prestressing Principles. In prestressed beams the concrete tensile stress is offset by a compressive prestress initially introduced by tensioning the reinforcement. Such beams are depend-

---

[15] Other solutions are represented at (b), (c), and (d).

[16] See Appendix I, Sec. 7(b), seventh excerpted paragraph.

ably crack-free under the design loading and can have large span/depth ratios without deflecting excessively.

Such members should be proportioned to have a substantially triangular distribution of pre-compressive concrete stress, with base downward. This is accomplished by arranging the prestressed reinforcement so that its centroid is in the neighborhood of the lower kern point of the (uncracked) cross section.

The later application of the gravity loads should cause a flexural stress diagram of such magnitude that, when added to the prestress stress diagram, it will produce a triangular diagram of combined compressive stress *with base upward*. This means no tension in the bottom fibers of concrete under the design safe loading.

The section of the member should be taken of sufficient depth that the product of the required prestress force, F, times the distance between the upper and lower kern points (of the section) is not less than the live load bending moment. When the dead load bending moment is relatively large, the section must be made arbitrarily deeper in order to take care of it.

The effect of the losses of steel pre-tension is to allow tensile cracking to develop. To prevent cracking, they must be computed and allowed for in the designing. The values of the principal ones are closely related to the strength and strain properties of the concrete and should not be stated as a percentage of the initial pre-tensile stress in the steel, to which they are not directly related.

As the failure load of a prestressed beam is approached, the inelastic (permanent) deformation of the reinforcement erases the prestress, allowing cracking. The beam thereafter performs as an overloaded conventional reinforced concrete beam, not only with respect to flexure, but also as to diagonal tension and anchorage. The greatly increased strengths then demanded in these latter two respects require that the provision of web reinforcement and lengths for embedment for anchorage be calculated at the flexural ultimate strength level, or above. This should forestall an undesirable sudden shear-related type of failure.

BIBLIOGRAPHY

A) SIESS, C. P. Specifications for Prestressed Concrete, *Proc. Western Conference on Prestressed Concrete*, University of California, Los Angeles, 1952, p. 133.

B) JOINT ASCE-ACI COMMITTEE 323, A. E. Cummings, Chairman. Proposed Definitions and Notations for Prestressed Concrete, *Proc. American Concrete Institute*, 1953, Vol. 49, p. 85.

C) GUYON, Y. *Prestressed Concrete.* New York John Wiley & Sons, Inc., 1953. Chap. III, *et al.*

D) ROSS, A. D. The Loss of Prestress in Concrete, *Civil Engineering and Public Works Review* (England) May 1950, Vol. 45, No. 527, p. 307.

E) THOMAS, F. G. Further Tests on Concrete Compacted on a Vibrating Table. *Journal of the Institution of Civil Engineers* (London). Vol. 8, 1937–38, pp. 554, 562, 563, 564.

F) ABELES, P. W. Prestressed Design and Construction Practices in England. *Proceedings, Western Conference on Prestressed Concrete.* University of California, Los Angeles, 1952, p. 213.

G) ABELES, P. W. Prestressed Beams with Bond, *Engineering News Record*, April 12, 1951, p. 42.

H) BAUER, EDW. E. Textbook: *Plain Concrete*, 3d ed., p. 271. New York: McGraw-Hill Book Company, Inc.

I) KESLER, CLYDE E. Statistical Relation between Cylinder, Modified Cube and Beam Strength of Plain Concrete. *Proceedings, American Society for Testing Materials*, 1954, Vol. 54, Technical Papers, p. 1178, and Fig. 4 in particular.

J) LIN, T. Y. Textbook: *Design of Prestressed Concrete Structures.* New York John Wiley & Sons, Inc. Chap. VI.

K) BILLIG, K. Textbook *Prestressed Concrete.* New York: Van Nostrand Co., 1953.

L) CARROL, R. J. Design Studies and Loading Tests of Prestressed Concrete Beams, *State of Ohio Department of Highways*, Research Report No. 4, 1954.

M) THORSEN, NIELS. Use of Large Tendons in Pre-tensioned Concrete. *Journal of the American Concrete Institute*, February, 1956, p. 649.

N) U.S. BUREAU OF PUBLIC ROADS. Criteria for Prestressed Concrete Bridges. 25 pages, 1955. Obtainable at 15 cents per copy from U.S. Government Printing Office, Washington, D.C.

O) PORTLAND CEMENT ASSOCIATION. Sound color film, 16 mm.: *America's First Prestressed Concrete Highway Bridge.* Twenty-three minutes.

QUESTIONS

1. Define prestressed concrete, pre-tensioning, post-tensioning, the transfer stage, live load range, dead load range limit, live load double eccentricity, and dead load eccentricity.

2. List five unusual characteristics of prestressed beams, as compared with conventional reinforced concrete beams.

3. Can prestressed beams always be proportioned for live load only? Explain.

4. Enumerate, in order, the steps necessary to design a pre-tensioned concrete slab. What two internal force relationships should be kept in mind at all times?

5. How can the ultimate strength of prestressed beams be predicted? Why?

6. List the losses of pre-tension. Show how to calculate each, stating typical values. Do likewise for post-tensioned beams.

7. Tell in what several respects the determination of the concrete dimensions of a pre-tensioned I-girder differs from that for a pre-tensioned slab.

8. Explain why both maximum and minimum steel percentages are set for prestressed flexural members.

9. Explain why the stresses at the end sections of prestressed beams sometimes become prohibitively high. Mention at least three ways of lowering them. Why are somewhat higher stresses permitted at such points?

10. It is sometimes said that the losses of prestress have the same effect upon the concrete stresses as the dead and live loads. Confirm or disprove, giving reference.

11. Is the working stress in pre-tensioned reinforcement equal to the initial pre-tension minus the losses? Explain.

12. Tell in detail how to predict the overload required to cause flexural cracking of pre-tensioned beams.

13. Explain under what circumstances web reinforcement is needed or not needed in prestressed beams.

14. Discuss at length the important manner in which the bonded anchorage of pre-tensioned reinforcement differs from that of conventional reinforced concrete beams.

15. State the advantages and disadvantages of pre-tensioned beams versus post-tensioned ones.

CONTINUATION PROBLEM

Problem 13–16. Retain the 36-in., $19\frac{1}{2}$-in., and $4\frac{1}{2}$-in. dimensions of the girder designed in Example 13–2, but change the inner faces of the flanges to be at a 45-degree slope to better insure against shrinkage cracking of the concrete at the junction of web and flanges. Make both flanges 3 inches thick at the edges.

Provide the same number of $\frac{3}{8}$-in. strands as originally, and space them properly. Then *investigate* this re-design to determine if its strength still is adequate.

Partial Answer: Yes.

APPENDICES

APPENDIX A

Beam Flexure Using Charts

Beam Formulas and Charts. After the fundamental methods of Chapter 2 are thoroughly understood, one needs a means for doing such work speedily. This may be accomplished by evolving general formulas for the several relationships, then constructing *charts* or *tables* therefrom which embrace the whole practical range of each function. Such aids are universally used by practicing designers.

RECTANGULAR BEAMS

Figure 1 illustrates certain items of standard notation not previously discussed.

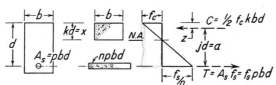

FIG. 1.   Rectangular beam notation.

The *steel ratio*, $p = A_s/bd$, is commonly expressed as a percentage. The following expressions have been derived from fundamental concepts:

Investigations.

$$k = \sqrt{2pn + (pn)^2} - pn \tag{1}$$

$$j = 1 - \frac{k}{3} \tag{2}$$

The maximum safe bending moment is given by:

Concrete side:

$$M_c = Cjd = \tfrac{1}{2}f_c kj(bd^2) = R_c(bd^2) \tag{3}$$

Steel side:

$$M_s = Tjd = f_s pj(bd^2) = R_s(bd^2) \tag{4}$$

wherein the allowable values of the unit stresses are used, and R is known as the *coefficient of resistance*.

When the applied bending moment is given, the above expressions yield the unit stresses.

427

Design (balanced).

$$k = \cfrac{1}{1 + \cfrac{f_s}{nf_c}} \tag{5}$$

$$j = 1 - \frac{k}{3} \tag{6}$$

Equating T and C from Fig. 1, and later eliminating k from Eq. 5, the ideal (balanced) steel content is:

$$p = \frac{f_c}{2f_s} k = \frac{1}{2} \cfrac{1}{\dfrac{f_s}{f_c}\left(\dfrac{f_s}{nf_c} + 1\right)} \tag{7}$$

And, as in Eqs. 3 and 4

$$bd^2 = \frac{M}{f_s pj} = \frac{M}{\frac{1}{2}f_c kj} = \frac{M}{R} \tag{8}$$

Construction of Rectangular Beam Charts. To construct a chart with R and p along its principal axes, such as Plate II for $n = 10$ concrete, first compute the coordinates of points representing *balanced designs*. They will define the intersections of the two groups of curves representing steel and concrete stresses. Taking the stresses 20,000 and 1350 for illustration:
From Eqs. 5 and 6:

$$k = \cfrac{1}{1 + \cfrac{20{,}000}{13{,}500}} = 0.403,$$

$$j = 0.866$$

From Eq. 7:

$$p = \frac{1350}{40{,}000}(0.403) = 0.0136 \text{ or } 1.36\%$$

From Eq. 8:

$$R = f_s pj = 20{,}000(0.0136)(0.866) = 235.5$$

$\left.\rule{0pt}{40pt}\right\}$ Checks

Any *intermediate* point on a stress curve may be found by choosing a value of p, and using Eqs. 1 and 2 with Eq. 3 or 4 to find the R.

Always check a few scattered points on a chart[1] before using it.

Use of Rectangular Beam Charts.[2] Refer to the singly reinforced rectangular beam examples of Chapter 2. Specification: 20,000–1350–10.

---

[1] The accompanying $n = 10$ and $n = 12$ beam charts were originally prepared by Mr. Samuel C. Pritchard in 1932 as part of his thesis.

[2] Learn to use the charts without referring to the curves of j and k.

Investigation

EXAMPLE 2-2

Given: B. M. $= 50.4$ kip-ft., $b = 8$ in., $d = 17$ in., $A_s = 2.0$ sq. in. *Find* the stresses from the $n = 10$ chart.

Solution: The coordinates of the required point are given by:

$$p = \frac{A_s}{bd} = \frac{2}{8(17)} = 1.47\%$$

$$R = \frac{M}{bd^2} = \frac{50.4(12,000)}{8(17)^2} = 262.$$

Find $f_s = 20,650$ *and* $f_c = 1470.$

EXAMPLE 2-3

Given: The beam cross section of Example 2-2 and the allowable stresses 20,000 and 1350. *Find* the maximum safe bending moment.

Solution:

$$p = \frac{2}{8(17)} = 1.47\%, \text{ as before.}$$

Find the greatest value of R such that neither allowable stress is exceeded:

$$R_{\text{safe}} = 241.$$

Then
$$M = Rbd^2 = \frac{241(8)(17)^2}{12,000} = 46.5 \text{ kip-ft.}$$

Design

EXAMPLE 2-4

Given: B. M. $= 50.4$ kip-ft., Specification: 20,000–1350–10. *Design* a balanced beam.

Solution: At the intersection of the two allowable stress curves find $R = 235.5$ and $p = 1.36\%$.

From
$$R = \frac{M}{bd^2},$$

$$bd^2 = \frac{50.4(12,000)}{235.5} = 2570.$$

If $b = 8$ in. is chosen, then $d = 17.9$ in.
Corresponding
$$A_s = pbd = 0.0136(8)(17.9) = 1.95 \text{ sq. in.}$$

EXAMPLES 2-5 and 2-6

Given: **B. M. = 50.4 kip-ft., allowables of 20,000 and 1350, and any arbitrary values of *b* and *d*. Find the steel area required.**

Solution: Say $b = 8$ in. and $d = 20$ in.:

$$R = \frac{M}{bd^2} = \frac{50.4(12,000)}{8(20)^2} = 189.$$

For safe stresses, find $p = 1.08\%$.

$$A_s = pbd = 0.0108(8)(20) = 1.73 \; sq. \; in.$$

If $b = 8$ in., and $d = 16$ in.:

$$R = 295, \quad p = 3.02\%, \quad A_s = 3.87 \; sq. \; in.$$

Note that when the chart is used it is not necessary to know whether the given space is too large or too small.

RECTANGULAR BEAM PROBLEMS

Problem 1. Perform step by step derivations of Eqs. (1) to (8) inclusive, from fundamental concepts.

Problem 2. Solve the rectangular beam problems of Chapter 2 which are marked with a star, ($\star$), using the charts.

Problem 3. (Group Problem.) Construct an $n = 7$ rectangular beam chart on $8\frac{1}{2} \times 11$ in. best coordinate tracing cloth, similar to Plate II, and using the same scales. Include steel stress curves from 12,000 to 24,000 psi at 2000-psi intervals. Concrete stress curves to go from 800 to 2200 psi at intervals of 100 psi. Cover steel contents from 0.2% to 3.0% inclusive. The instructor will indicate whether curves of k and j are to be included. Submit supporting calculations.

T-BEAMS

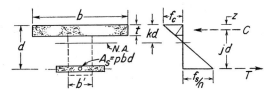

FIG. 2. T-beam notation.

Figure 2 illustrates the additional notation needed to express the T-beam formulas. Note carefully how the *steel ratio p* is always computed.

The compression in the stem has been ignored. When a preliminary study indicates that the neutral axis is within the slab the rectangular beam formulas apply.

By moments of transformed section areas:

$$kd = \frac{2ndA_s + bt^2}{2nA_s + 2bt} \tag{9}$$

or

$$k = \frac{2pn + \dfrac{t^2}{d^2}}{2pn + 2\dfrac{t}{d}} \tag{10}$$

By moments of compressive stress volumes:

$$z = \frac{3kd - 2t}{2kd - t}\left(\frac{t}{3}\right) \tag{11}$$

$$jd = d - z \tag{12}$$

Substituting in Eq. 12 the values of k and z from Eqs. 10 and 11:

$$j = \frac{6 - 6\left(\dfrac{t}{d}\right) + 2\left(\dfrac{t}{d}\right)^2 + \dfrac{\left(\dfrac{t}{d}\right)^3}{2pn}}{6 - 3\left(\dfrac{t}{d}\right)} \tag{13}$$

Also

$$\frac{f_s}{f_c} = \frac{n(1 - k)}{k} \tag{14}$$

Construction of T-Beam Charts. Since Formulas (10) and (13) for k and j are formidable, convenient charts therefor, such as Plate VII, may be prepared starting with assumed values of t/d and p. The curves for k and j must be discontinued at the point $k = t/d$, since smaller values of k would put the neutral axis within the slab portion, the beam then becoming a rectangular one. The inclusion of the f_s/f_c axis, computed from the k values by Formula (14), enables one to investigate both steel and concrete stresses from the $Tjd = M$ expression. As will be seen below, it is also possible to design balanced (rare) T-beams from the chart.

Use of T-Beam Charts. Refer to the T-beam Examples of Chapter 2. Specification: 20,000–1350–10 throughout.

Investigation

EXAMPLE 2–9(a)

Given: B. M. = 70 kip-ft. A T-shaped section with b = 40 in., d = 18 in., and A_s = 3.00 sq. in., has a slab thickness t = 6 in. *Find* the stresses from the n = 10 T-beam chart, Plate VII.

Solution: The coordinates of the required point are given by:

$$\frac{t}{d} = \frac{6}{18} = 0.33$$

$$p = \frac{A_s}{bd} = \frac{3}{40(18)} = 0.42\%$$

Since this point falls beyond the limits of the curves, the neutral axis is within the slab. Solve using the *rectangular* beam chart, as in Example 2–2.

EXAMPLE 2–9(b)

Same as (a) above except that $t = 4$ in.

Solution:

$$\frac{t}{d} = \frac{4}{18} = 0.22$$

$$p = \frac{3}{40(18)} = 0.42\%$$

Find
$$j = 0.92, \qquad \frac{f_s}{f_c} = 29.5$$

$$f_s = \frac{M}{A_s jd} = \frac{70(12,000)}{3(0.92)(18)} = 16,900$$

$$f_c = \frac{16,900}{29.5} = 570$$

EXAMPLE 2–10(a)

Same section as in Example 2–9(b), to find the maximum safe bending moment if the allowables are 20,000 and 1350.

Solution: Find $j = 0.92$ and $f_s/f_c = 29.5$, as above.

Since $29.5 > \dfrac{20,000}{1350}$, the steel will work at 20,000, and the concrete at < 1350.

$$M_{\text{safe}} = A_s f_s jd = \frac{3(20,000)(0.92)(18)}{12,000} = 82.8 \text{ kip-ft.}$$

Design

EXAMPLE 2–11

Given: B. M. = 30.2 kip-ft., Specification: 20,000–1350–10. *Required* to design a balanced T-beam.

Solution: The coordinates of the desired point are given by:

$$\frac{f_s}{f_c} = \frac{20,000}{1350} = 14.8$$

$$\frac{t}{d} \text{ chosen} = 0.21$$

Find
$$p = 1.05\%, \quad j = 0.91$$

$$A_s d = \frac{M}{f_s j} = \frac{30.2(12,000)}{20,000(0.91)} = 19.9$$

If two #8 bars are taken:

$$d = \frac{19.9}{1.58} = 12.6 \text{ in.}$$

From $A_s = pbd$:

$$b = \frac{1.58}{0.0105(12.6)} = 12.0 \text{ in.}$$

Note that other solutions are possible.

EXAMPLE 2–12

Given: Total B. M. = 26.3 kip-ft., and a 10-in. pan from Chapter 2. **F'p'f'g = 1 in., b = 25 in., slab thickness, t = 2½ in.** *Required* to design the steel.

Solution: Assuming that the bars will be of 1-in. dimension:

$$d = 11 \text{ in.}, \qquad \frac{t}{d} = \frac{2.5}{11} = 0.227$$

Since the ratio f_s/f_c is unknown,[3] select a trial value of j from the curves, based upon the known t/d value:

Trial $j = 0.905$

$$\text{Trial } A_s = \frac{M}{f_s j d} = \frac{26.3(12,000)}{20,000(0.905)(11)} = 1.58 \text{ sq. in.},$$

assuming also that the steel can work at the allowable.

The steel percentage can now be calculated from the trial steel content·

$$p = \frac{1.58}{25(11)} = 0.574\%$$

The corresponding improved value of $j = 0.91$

$$A_s = \frac{0.905}{0.910}(1.58) = 1.57 \text{ sq. in.}$$

Use two #8 bars

---

[3] The beam cannot be a balanced one, except by chance.

Checking on stresses, find the corresponding $f_s/f_c = 24$:

$$f_c = \frac{20{,}000}{24} = 830, \quad <1350. \quad \textit{Satisfactory.}$$

T–BEAM PROBLEMS

Problem 4. Perform step-by-step derivations of Formulas (9) to (14) inclusive, from fundamental concepts.

Problem 5. Solve Problems 2–15 to 2–20 inclusive of Chapter 2, and marked with a star, ($\star$), using the proper T-beam chart.

Problem 6. (Group Problem.)   Construct an $n = 7$ T-beam chart on $8\frac{1}{2} \times 11$ in. best coordinate tracing cloth, similar to Plate VII. Submit supporting calculations.

PUBLISHER's NOTE: The following beam charts, Plates I through IV, and VI through IX, have been reproduced by permission after *Principles of Reinforced Concrete Construction* by F. E. Turneaure and E. R. Mauer, published by John Wiley & Sons, Inc., 1907.

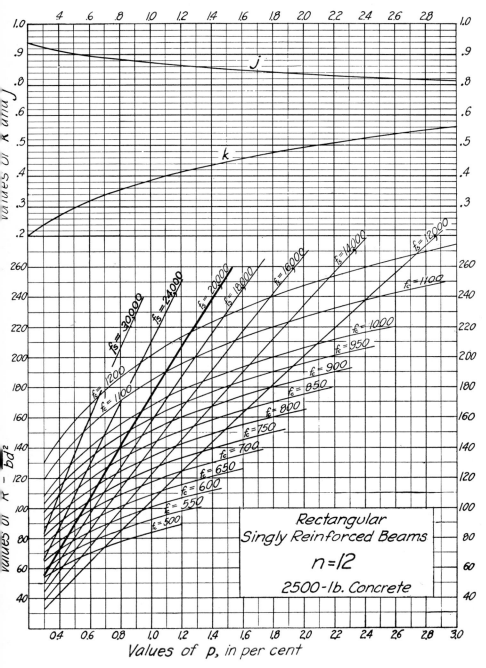

Values of K and J (vertical left axis)

Values of $K = \dfrac{M}{bd^2}$ (lower left vertical axis)

j

k

$f_s = 30000$ $f_s = 24000$ $f_s = 20000$ $f_s = 18000$ $f_s = 16000$ $f_s = 14000$ $f_s = 12000$

$f_c = 1100$
$f_c = 1200$
$f_c = 1100$
$f_c = 1000$
$f_c = 950$
$f_c = 900$
$f_c = 850$
$f_c = 800$
$f_c = 750$
$f_c = 700$
$f_c = 650$
$f_c = 600$
$f_c = 550$
$f_c = 500$

Rectangular
Singly Reinforced Beams
n = 12
2500-lb. Concrete

Values of *p,* in per cent

PLATE I

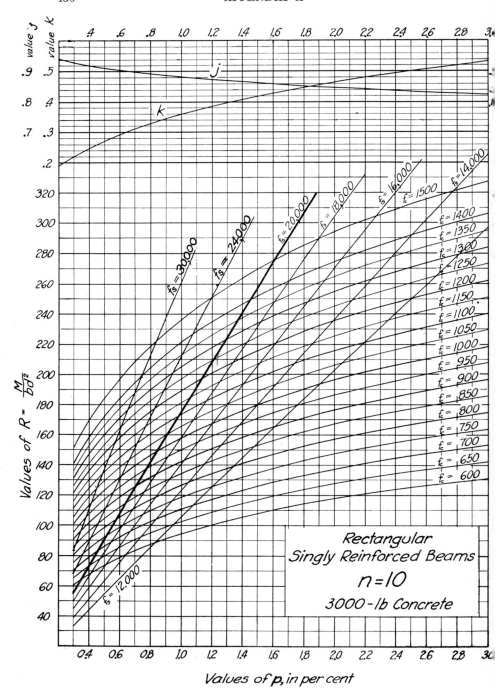

Values of $R = \dfrac{M}{bd^2}$

Values of **p**, in per cent

Rectangular
Singly Reinforced Beams
$n = 10$
3000-lb Concrete

PLATE II

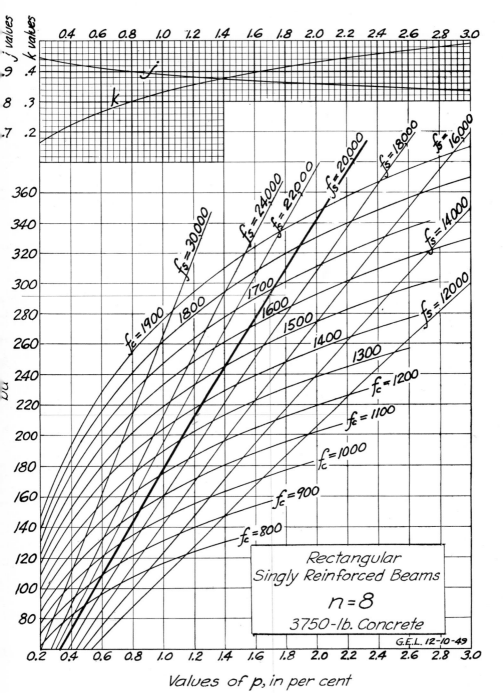

Rectangular
Singly Reinforced Beams
$n = 8$
3750-lb. Concrete

G.E.L. 12-10-49

Values of p, in per cent

PLATE III

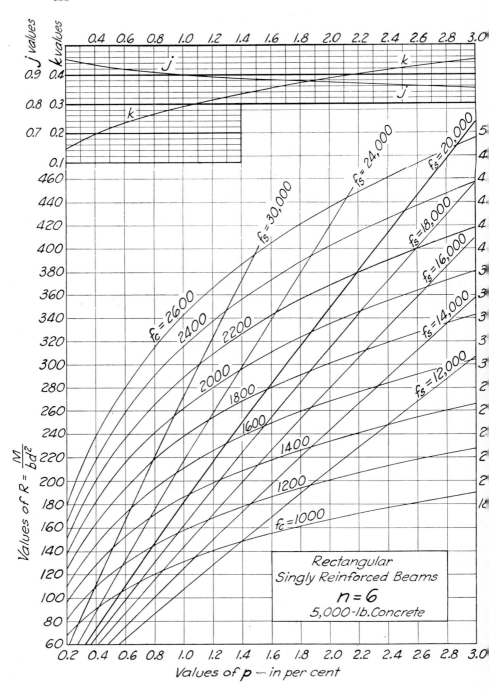

PLATE IV

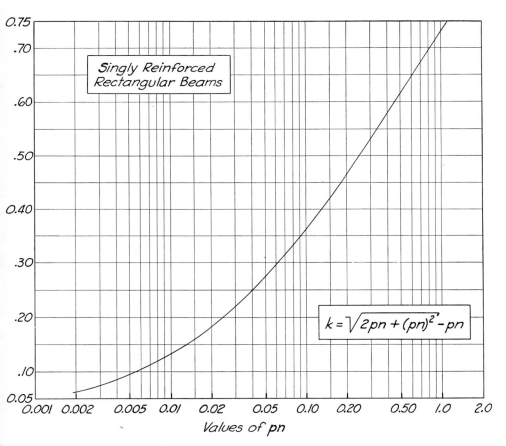

Values of *pn*

PLATE V. For finding the investigational neutral axis in ordinary singly reinforced rectangular beam culations. It is convenient when n has an odd value not contemplated by the rectangular beam charts Plates I to IV, inclusive. Also it is useful in creep type of beam investigations in which multiple ues of n, such as $4 \times 10 = 40$, are used.

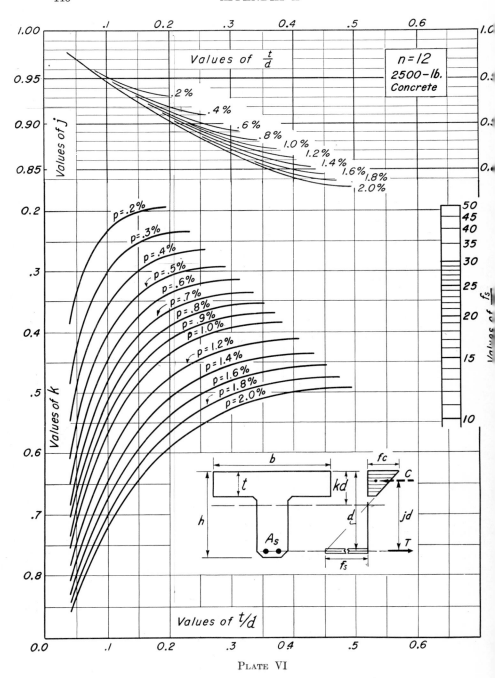

PLATE VI

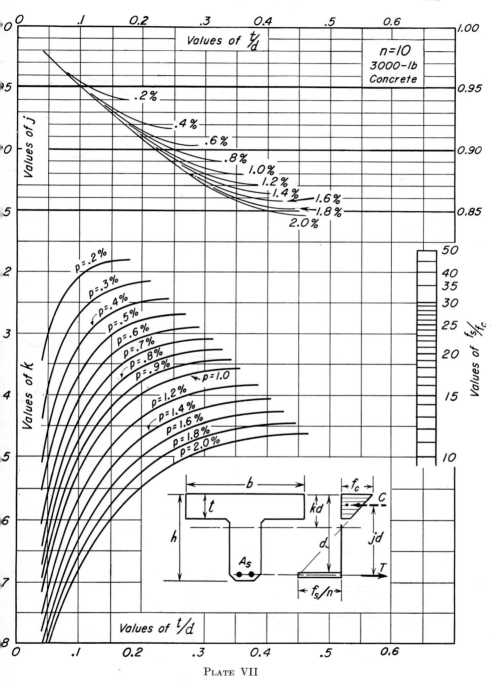

PLATE VII

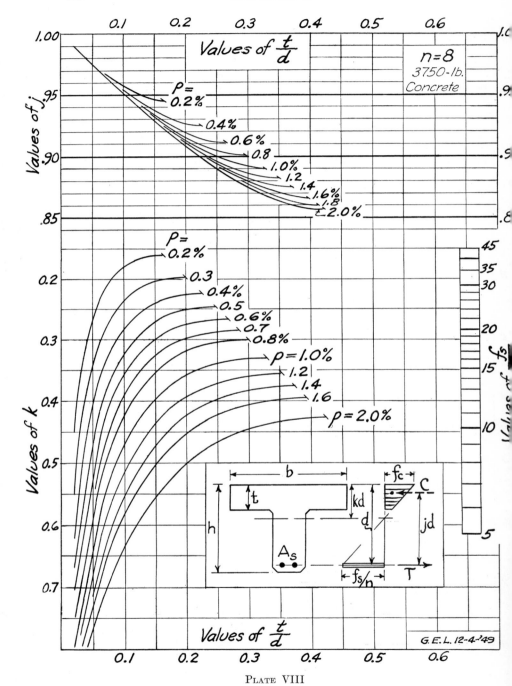

PLATE VIII

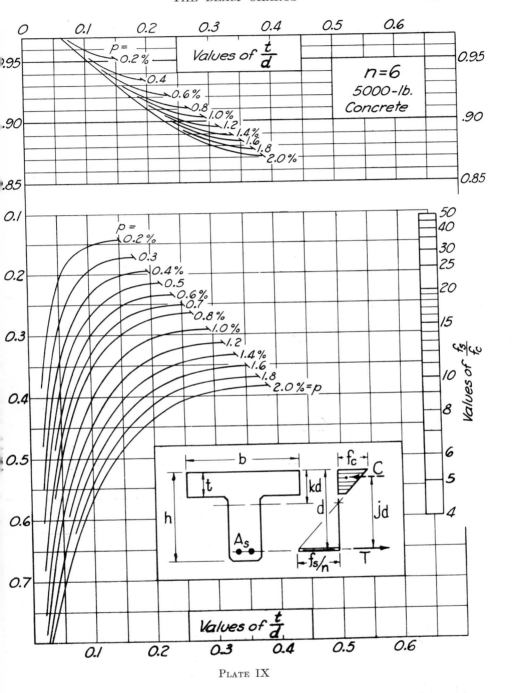

PLATE IX

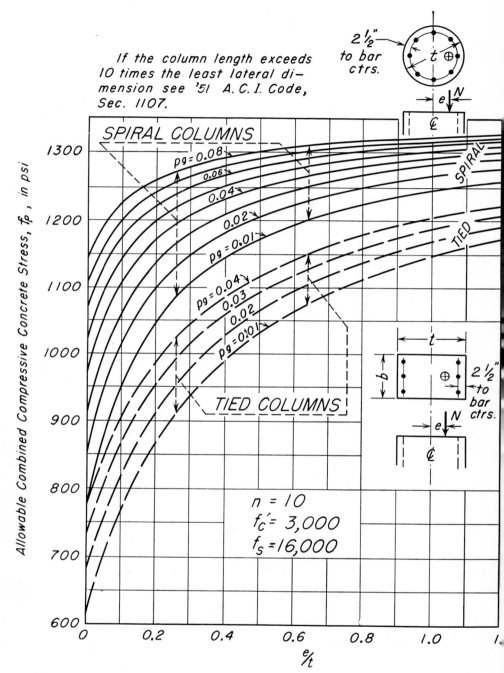

PLATE X. Allowable *combined* stresses in columns according to the previous (1951) ACI Code.

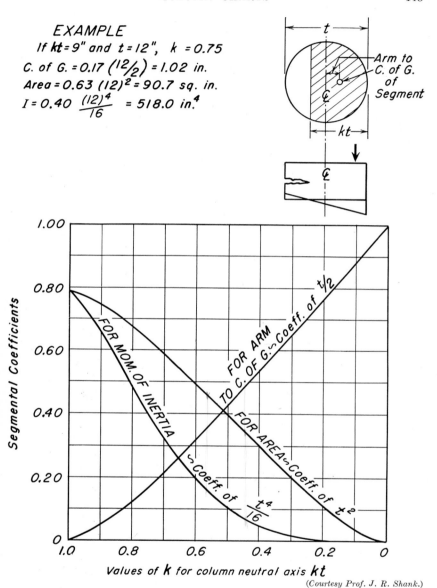

EXAMPLE

If $kt = 9"$ and $t = 12"$, $k = 0.75$

C. of G. $= 0.17 \left(\frac{12}{2}\right) = 1.02$ in.

Area $= 0.63 (12)^2 = 90.7$ sq. in.

$I = 0.40 \dfrac{(12)^4}{16} = 518.0$ in.^{4}

(*Courtesy Prof. J. R. Shank.*)

PLATE XI. Properties of segments of circular sections.

APPENDIX B

Derivation of Moment Distribution Carry-Over Factors and Stiffness Factors for Prismatic Members by the Moment Area Method

Statement of the Moment-Area Principles.[1]

(1) When a member is subjected to flexure, the change in slope of the elastic curve between any two points is equal to the area of the M/EI diagram for the portion of the member between the two points.

(2) When a member is subjected to flexure, as in Fig. 3(b), the ordinate distance of any point Q on the elastic curve, measured from a tangent drawn to the elastic curve at any other point P, is equal to the moment of the area of the M/EI diagram between the two points *about* the point Q.

Carry-Over Factor. In Fig. 3(b) it is desired to find how much moment, M_{CB}, is induced at the fixed[2] end C of a member BC when the other end is free to rotate, and subjected to a moment M_{BC}. Assume that neither end can move vertically.

By moment-area principle (2), (or Related Beam Curves Law III):

$$\frac{M_{BC}L}{2EI} \times \frac{L}{3} - \frac{M_{CB}L}{2EI} \times \frac{2L}{3} \equiv 0$$

$$M_{CB} = \frac{M_{BC}}{2}$$

Therefore carry-over factor = ½.

Stiffness Factor. In Fig. 3(b), by moment-area principle (1), (or Related Beam Curves Law II):

$$\theta_B = \frac{(M_{BC} - M_{CB})L}{2EI}$$

But
$$M_{CB} = \frac{M_{BC}}{2} \text{ (see above)}$$

so
$$\theta_B = \frac{M_{BC}L}{4EI}$$

or
$$M_{BC} = \frac{4EI\theta_B}{L}$$

---

[1] First presented in America by Professor C. E. Greene in lectures at the University of Michigan. See any modern textbook on strength of materials.

[2] In the moment distribution process all joints are considered fixed against rotation momentarily, except the one being released for moment distribution, namely, joint B in Fig. 3(b).

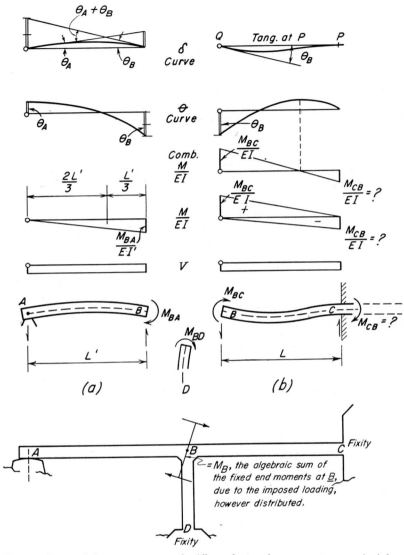

F<small>IG</small>. 3.   Determining carry-over and stiffness factors by moment-area principles.

At any given rigid joint of a structure, θ is the same for all members framing into it, and E is constant for a given material.

Therefore: M varies as I/L.

This means that in the Cross method, the unbalanced moment at a rotating joint should be distributed to the connecting prismatic members in the ratio of their I/L's.

This proves stiffness factor.

Stiffness Factor for Hinged Ended Members. If the member AB of Fig. 3(a) is hinged at end A, then the moment, theta and deflection curves will be shown. Again applying moment area principle (1):

$$\theta_A + \theta_B = \frac{M_{BA}L'}{2EI'}$$

Applying moment area principle (2) to the determination of the end ordinate tangent distances of the curve at the top of the figure, it is evident that:

$$\theta_A = \frac{\theta_B}{2}$$

Then

$$\theta_B = \frac{M_{BA}L'}{3EI'}$$

or

$$M_{BA} = \frac{3EI'\theta_B}{L'}.$$

Making a comparison with the previous fixed end case, it is seen that when the remote end of a member is hinged, only three-quarters as much moment gets distributed to the restrained end.

Time may be saved in a moment distribution analysis by using $\frac{3}{4}I/L$ as the stiffness of hinged ended members. Once the fixed end moment at the hinged end has been distributed in the first cycle there is no more work to do there, as no moments are carried over to such a joint when $\frac{3}{4}I/L$ has been used as the stiffness.

APPENDIX C

Charts for Nonprismatic Member Constants

For explanation of the use of the accompanying Plates XII, XIII, and XIV, see Chapter 5, Article 5–20. The *Handbook of Frame Constants*, published by the Portland Cement Association, contains comprehensive tables covering many similar spanwise sectional variations.

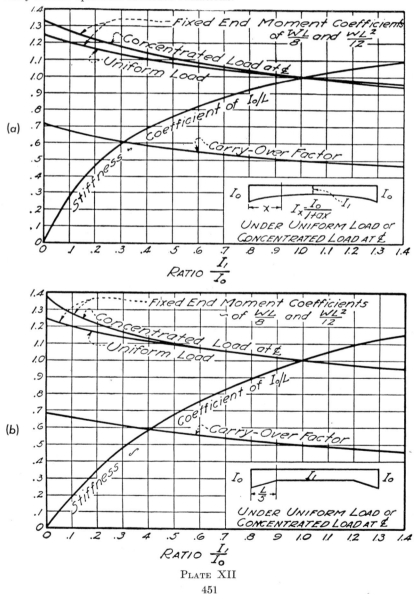

PLATE XII
451

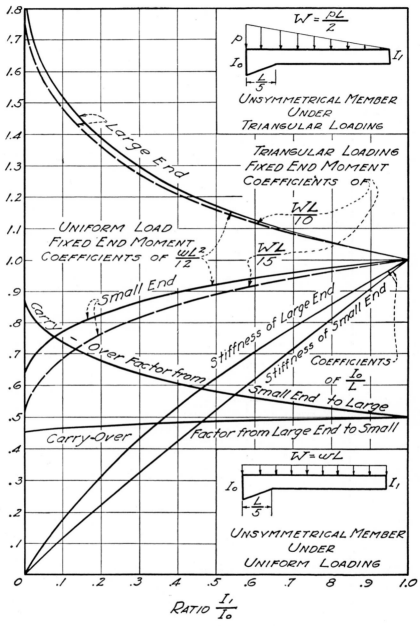

$W = \dfrac{pL}{2}$

UNSYMMETRICAL MEMBER UNDER TRIANGULAR LOADING

TRIANGULAR LOADING FIXED END MOMENT COEFFICIENTS OF

$\dfrac{WL}{10}$

$\dfrac{WL}{15}$

Large End

UNIFORM LOAD FIXED END MOMENT COEFFICIENTS OF $\dfrac{wL^2}{12}$

Small End

Carry-Over Factor from

Stiffness of Large End

Stiffness of Small End

COEFFICIENTS OF $\dfrac{I_0}{L}$

Small End to Large

Carry-Over Factor from Large End to Small

$W = wL$

UNSYMMETRICAL MEMBER UNDER UNIFORM LOADING

RATIO $\dfrac{I_1}{I_0}$

PLATE XIII

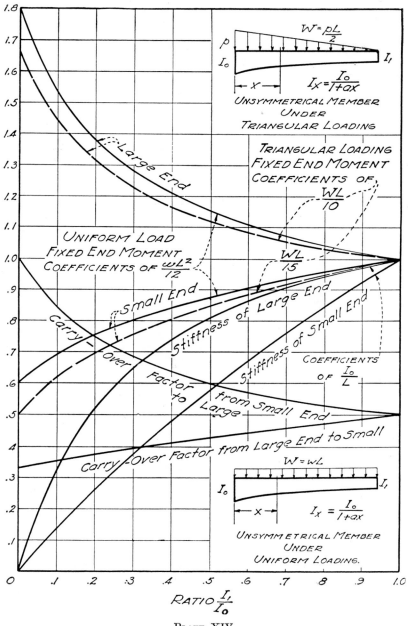

PLATE XIV

APPENDIX D

Properties of Power Curves

The accompanying expressions in Fig. 4 are useful in finding the areas and moments of areas of beam curves. They are strictly applicable only to single term equations, such as $y = 4x^3$, but they may be used without error on polynomials, such as $y = 4x^3 + 3x^2 + 2x$, *provided they are applied to each term thereof separately*, and the results later added.

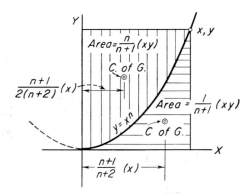

FIG. 4. Properties of power curves.

APPENDIX E

Loading Criteria for Maximum Live Load Bending Moments in Rigid Building Frames of Equal Spans and Story Heights

These loading patterns, worked out by Mr. G. E. Sutila for frames of an infinite number of equal spans and story heights, may be applied without appreciable error to regular frames of finite extent. The bending moments may then be found by the moment distribution method, or short-cut adaptations thereof, taking only a few adjacent members, as in the "Three-Zone Cut-out Method" illustrated in connection with the design of the floor girder of Chapter 6.

In each case the cross mark indicates the point at which the loading shown produces the maximum bending moment.

These loading patterns are accurate for column/girder stiffness ratios, I/L, up to 3 or 4.

In a few cases the loading pattern differs slightly, depending upon the column/girder stiffness ratio, with only a small difference in bending moment at the chosen point. Such a situation is indicated at (g) wherein dashed lines have been used to indicate the slight uncertainty as to whether those spans should be loaded.

In all cases the resulting bending moment will be well within an error of 1 per cent.

LOADING CRITERIA FOR
MAXIMUM LIVE LOAD <u>POSITIVE</u> BENDING MOMENTS
IN THE GIRDERS OF A RIGID FRAME BUILDING

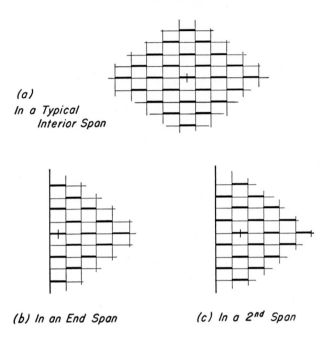

(a)
In a Typical
*   Interior Span*

(b) In an End Span   *(c) In a 2nd Span*

<u>*Note:*</u> *For the maximum bending moment in other*
spans deduce the loading pattern from Case (a)
as suggested by Cases (b) and (c)

PLATE XV

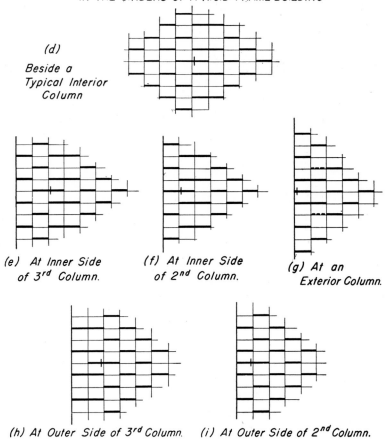

LOADING CRITERIA FOR
MAXIMUM LIVE LOAD <u>NEGATIVE</u> BENDING MOMENTS
IN THE GIRDERS OF A RIGID FRAME BUILDING

(d)

Beside a
Typical Interior
Column

(e) At Inner Side
of 3ʳᵈ Column.

(f) At Inner Side
of 2ⁿᵈ Column.

(g) At an
Exterior Column.

(h) At Outer Side of 3ʳᵈ Column.   (i) At Outer Side of 2ⁿᵈ Column.

PLATE XVI

LOADING CRITERIA FOR
MAXIMUM LIVE LOAD BENDING MOMENTS
IN THE <u>COLUMNS</u> OF A RIGID FRAME BUILDING

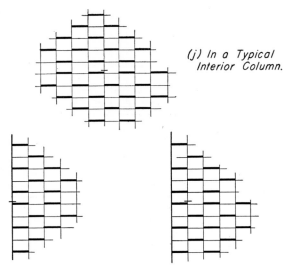

(j) In a Typical Interior Column.

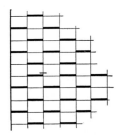

(k) In an Exterior Column.   *(l) In a Column one panel inward.*

(m) In a Column two panels inward.

PLATE XVII

APPENDIX F

The Coulomb Formulas for Earth Pressure

*(With Variations Thereof Applicable to Several Cases
Involving Greatly Increased Pressure.)*

To keep the expressions simple, so that comparisons of pressures for the several conditions can be drawn easily, these cases are limited to an assumed frictionless vertical wall supporting a level granular* backfill. For orientation, consult Chapter 9, Arts. 9–2 and 9–3, for an earlier treatment of Case (a) by components of forces.

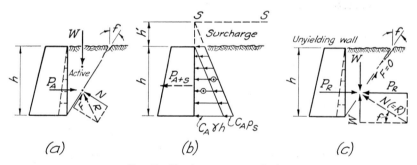

Fig. 5. Earth pressure variations.

For an excellent extended treatment involving sloping backfills and walls with friction, refer to *Substructure Analysis* and *Design*, by Paul Andersen, The Ronald Press Company, New York.

(a) *The Active Backfill Case.* Referring to Fig. 5(a),

$$W = \tfrac{1}{2}\gamma h^2 \tan f$$

wherein γ is the unit weight of the backfill material. Furthermore, by trigonometry:

$$W = N \sin f + N \cos f \tan \phi$$

$$P_A = N \cos f - N \sin f \tan \phi$$

and

$$P_A = \tfrac{1}{2}\gamma h^2 \frac{\tan f - \tan^2 f \tan \phi}{\tan f + \tan \phi}$$

---

* Except Case (*f*), wherein clay is discussed.

from which by differentiating P_A with respect to f and simplifying:

$$\text{Max. } P_A = \tfrac{1}{2}\gamma h^2 \tan^2 (45° - \phi/2) \tag{1}$$

Note: Equation 1 is the same as Rankine's (1860). He always disregarded wall friction.

Refer to Art. 9–3 of Chapter 9 for fundamental discussion of the Coulomb theory.

Problem 1. A gravity retaining wall is 12 ft. high by 6 ft. thick. The internal friction angle, ϕ, is 35°, the unit weight of the backfill, γ, is 100 pcf.

Compute the maximum intensities of both the horizontal and vertical pressures in ksf.

Ans. 0.323 *and* 1.20 *ksf, respectively.*

Definition. The hydrostatic pressure ratio, C*, is the ratio, at any chosen point, of the unit lateral earth pressure to the unit vertical pressure.* In Problem 1 it was $323/1200 = 0.27$, or only 27% of the hydrostatic pressure. Retaining walls have often been designed for an arbitrarily specified so-called *equivalent fluid pressure* of from 25 to 30 pcf.

Re-examination of Eq. 1 above will show that $C_A = \tan^2 (45° - \phi/2)$, so

$$P_A = C_A \frac{\gamma h^2}{2} \tag{2}$$

Question

Does a C-value of 1.00 mean the same pressure as an equal head of water? Explain.

(b) *The Surcharge Case.* When the surface of a backfill is *uniformly loaded,* as by being used as a storage yard, the vertical pressures within the backfill are increased by the amount of such live loading, p_s, which is called *surcharge.*

As indicated in Fig. 5(b) the surcharge load may be conceived to be replaced by an equal weight of additional earth of depth $h' = p_s/\gamma$, and the stress distribution diagram drawn from the higher level s-s.

Referring to Coulomb Eq. 1, the lateral pressure upon a surcharged wall will be

$$P_{A+S} = \left(\frac{\gamma h}{2} + p_s\right) h \tan^2 (45° - \phi/2) \tag{3}$$

or

$$P_{A+S} = C_A \left(\frac{\gamma h}{2} + p_s\right) h \tag{4}$$

The elevation of P_{A+S} may be deduced from Fig. 5(b).

Concentrated surcharge loads may be taken care of by using the Culmann method, or by converting them to equivalent uniformly distributed ones.

Refer to Example 9–3 of Chapter 9 for designing involving surcharge.

Problem 2. Take the same wall as in Problem 1 above except that the backfill will be loaded with 700 psf of surcharge. Compute the magnitude and elevation of the resultant lateral force P_{A+S}.

Ans. 4212 *lb. at* 5.06 *ft. up.*

(c) *The At Rest Case*. If a wall cannot yield, as by being securely connected to some much larger structure, the supporting frictional force, F in Fig. 5(c), cannot develop along the failure plane because of lack of movement of the sand grains. As before, $W = \frac{1}{2}\gamma h^2 \tan f$, but P_R, the *at rest* value of the earth pressure, will be, from the parallelogram of forces:

$$P_R = W \cot f = \frac{1}{2}\gamma h^2, \quad \text{the full hydrostatic pressure} \qquad (4a)$$

The corresponding C value $= 1.00$.

Note that a tremendous price would have to be paid for theoretically complete rigidity. Terzaghi found C values as high as 0.50 experimentally.

(d) *The Passive Backfill Case*. When for any reason a wall moves horizontally *toward* an earth mass, as in Fig. 6(a), rather than away from it, a large *passive resistance* is built up, which may be of the order of ten to fifteen times

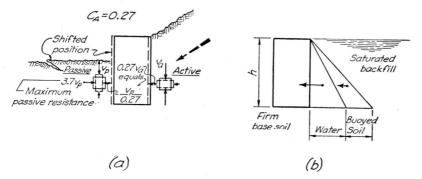

(a)   (b)

FIG. 6. Passive and saturated conditions.

the corresponding active pressure value. What happens is that the earth frictional force, F, "that always acts to oppose movement," which had an upward value in Fig. 5(a), and a zero value in Fig. 5(c), develops a downward value. Referring to the algebraic expressions of Case (a), and changing only the direction of F to work for the *minimum* value of the passive resistance:

$$P_P = \frac{1}{2}\gamma h^2 \tan^2 (45° + \phi/2) \qquad (5)$$

or, since C passive $= \dfrac{1}{C_A}$:

$$P_P = \frac{\gamma h^2}{2C_A} \qquad (6)$$

In Fig. 6(a) the deformations of unit cubes of soil and the corresponding typical unit pressures may be traced from the active toward the passive side of the wall.

Refer to the latter part of Example 9–3, Chapter 9, for application to the design of a base shear key.

Problem 3. *Given* a 12-ft. wall height of the 100 pcf sandy soil previously taken. It is *required* to compute the total passive pressure if the wall should be forced against the backfill, and the unit pressure at the base. Take $\phi = 35°$.

Ans. $P_P = 26.6$ *kips and* 4.44 *ksf.*

(Com)are 4.44 ksf with the 0.323 ksf *active* value of Problem 1.)

(*e*) *The Saturated Backfill Case.* If a granular backfill becomes fully saturated, as by clogging of the drainage system, the pressure upon a wall may increase to about three times the *active case* value for which it was designed.

The total lateral pressure will be the sum of the full hydrostatic pressure of the water of saturation, plus the earth pressure of the *buoyed* weight of the granular backfill, with ϕ unchanged. Consider the sand immersed in the all-pervading mass of water.

EXAMPLE 1

Refer to Fig. 6(b). *Given* **the 12-ft. vertical wall and level backfill of the previous discussions, consisting of 100-pcf sand filled with water of saturation. Effective angle of internal friction still 35°. Specific gravity of sand rock = 2.65. It is required to find the pressure upon the wall, assuming no wall friction, as formerly.**

Solution:	Total Pressure, kips	Equivalent Fluid Pressure, pcf
Water pressure (hydrostatic) $= \dfrac{0.0624(12)^2}{2} =$	4.50	62.4

Sand Pressure
  Principle: A solid immersed in a liquid is buoyed up to the extent of the weight of the liquid displaced.
  Solid volume of 1 cu. ft. of the sand $= \dfrac{100}{2.65(62.4)} = 0.605$ cu. ft.
  Buoyed weight of 1 cu. ft. of the sand $= 100 - 0.605(62.4) = 62.2$ pcf
  Referring to Eq. (1):

$$P_A = \tfrac{1}{2}\gamma h^2 \tan^2 [45° - \phi/2]$$
$$= \tfrac{1}{2}(0.0622)(12)^2(0.5206)^2$$

	Total Pressure, kips	Equivalent Fluid Pressure, pcf
P_A	1.21	16.8
Total lateral pressure $=$	5.71	79.2

The above results correspond to a C_A of $79.2/100.0 = 0.792$, or $0.792/0.27 = 2.93$ times the lateral pressure computed earlier for dry sandy soil.

For good granular soils, engineers often use 80 to 85 pcf to calculate the lateral pressure at possible saturation.

HYDROSTATIC PRESSURE RATIO REVIEW PROBLEM

Problem 4. Compute the maximum wall pressure in kips and the hydrostatic pressure ratio at the base for a sandy soil, sp. gravity 2.70, having an internal friction angle, ϕ, of 26°, and weighing 107 pcf, which lies in horizontal backfill against a 20-ft. vertical wall, if the soil is:

Answers

P	C

(a) Dry, and the wall can yield,
(b) Dry, and the wall cannot yield,
(c) Fully saturated,
(d) Dry, but surcharged by a 600-psf yard load,
(e) Saturated and surcharged as in (d),
(f) Saturated to a point half-way up the wall.

(f) *The Clay Backfill Case. Cohesion, Internal Friction, and Shear Resistance.* Shear resistance being a very essential engineering property of soils, little remains if for any reason it is badly impaired or absent. Figure 7 should recall the direct shear test performed in the course in soil mechanics.

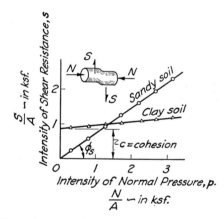

FIG. 7. Typical direct shear test data showing relative values of shear resistance.

Throughout Chapter 9 on *Retaining Walls,* an AREA Type 1 or 2 sand and gravelly soil was presumed, and ϕ, the angle of internal friction, had a large value. In clay soil ϕ_c is small—the AREA, in Sec. C2, assumes it zero. Thus, in the fundamental expression:

$$s = c + p \tan \phi$$

only c, the cohesion, or shear strength under zero normal pressure remains.

Refer to the preceding Fig. 5(a) and (c), from which it may be deduced, taking clay with $\phi = 0$, that $F = ch \sec f$. Furthermore, by a differentiation of the summation of forces along the failure plane:

$$\text{Max. } P_A = \frac{\gamma h^2}{2} - 2ch \qquad \text{(clay)} \qquad (7)$$

Clays are plastic materials, and they exhibit the property of *plastic flow*, or creep, as concrete does to a lesser degree. This means that under a constant load they continue to deform with lapse of time. Or, under a situation of constant deformation, they gradually relieve themselves of the load. Let us consider what happens when a wall is backfilled with clay. First, according to Prof. Donald W. Taylor, the wall moves from a Position 1 to a Position 2 under the full hydrostatic pressure of $\gamma h^2/2$, Formula (4). This movement develops the shearing resistance $F = 2ch$, which brings temporary relief to the wall, so it ceases to move. Next the clay *flows*, and F gradually becomes zero; meantime the original full hydrostatic pressure ($C = 1.00$) again comes upon the wall. It must then be expected to move again, say, to a Position 3.

Obviously there is little hope of such a structure remaining permanently located, unless designed for three or four times the pressure usually considered.

If involved with a clay backfill, refer to Taylor's textbook. The accompanying table should also prove helpful in evaluating the test data.

APPROXIMATE RELATIVE STRENGTH RATIOS FOR CLAY SOILS

Type of Strength	Ultimate Unit Strength	Recommended	
		Factor of Safety	Allow. Unit Stress
Unconfined compressive	1.00	—	—
Bearing capacity, confined active	3.00	3.00	1.00
Cohesion, c, intrinsic shear resistance	0.50	3.00	0.17

APPENDIX G

Excerpts from Specifications for Design of Retaining Walls and Abutments

THE 1953 AREA SPECIFICATION

Reprinted by permission of the American Railway Engineering Association
(The original numbering of the sections has been maintained)

* * *

B. INFORMATION REQUIRED

3. Loads

Loads to be superimposed either on the wall or abutment, or on the backfill, shall be indicated.

4. Character of Backfill

Backfill is defined as all material behind the wall, whether undisturbed ground or fill, that contributes to the pressure against the wall.

The backfill shall be investigated and classified with reference to the following soil types:

TYPES OF BACKFILL FOR RETAINING WALLS

Type
1. Coarse-grained soil without admixture of fine soil particles, very free-draining (clean sand, gravel or broken stone).
2. Coarse-grained soil of low permeability due to admixture of particles of silt size.
3. Fine silty sand; granular materials with conspicuous clay content; or residual soil with stones.
4. Soft or very soft clay; organic silt; or soft silty clay.
5. Medium or stiff clay that may be placed in such a way that a negligible amount of water will enter the spaces between the chunks during floods or heavy rains.

5. Character of Foundation

The character of the foundation shall be determined by means of test pits, auger borings or core borings, of a type and to an extent consistent with the magnitude of the project.

If the subsoil is essentially sandy or gravelly in character, the groundwater level shall be ascertained. In addition, the relative density of the material shall be investigated, preferably by means of penetration tests or static load tests. The penetration test shall consist of driving a sampling spoon (2-in. O.D.; 1⅜-in. I.D.) into the

465

material by means of a weight of 140 lb. falling through a distance of 30 in. The relative density is measured by the number of blows, N, required to obtain a penetration of 1 ft.

If the subsoil consists of clay, it is advisable to obtain intact specimens suitable for determination of the unconfined compressive strength. In the absence of such samples, the consistency of the clay shall be described in the following terms:

CONSISTENCY OF CLAY

Consistency	Field Identification	Ultimate Unconfined Compressive Strength Tons per Sq. Ft.
Very Soft	Easily penetrated several inches by fist	less than 0.25
Soft	Easily penetrated by thumb	0.25 to 0.50
Medium	Can be penetrated by thumb with moderate effort	0.50 to 1.0
Stiff	Readily indented by thumb but penetrated only with great effort	1.0 to 2.0
Very Stiff	Readily indented by thumbnail	2.0 to 4.0
Hard	Indented with difficulty by thumbnail	over 4.0

Where seasonal changes in the consistency of clay subsoils are likely to occur, their influence shall be taken into consideration.

Other procedures for investigating the relative density of sands or the consistency of clays may be used in place of those recommended in the preceding paragraphs, provided such procedures lead to numerical results.

C. COMPUTATION OF APPLIED FORCES

1. Loads Exclusive of Earth Pressure

In the analysis of retaining walls and abutments, due account shall be taken of all superimposed loads carried directly on them, such as building walls, columns, or bridge structures; and of all loads from surcharges caused by railroad tracks, highways or building foundations supported on the fill back of the walls.

In calculating the surcharge due to track loading, the entire load shall be taken as distributed uniformly over a width of 14 ft. for a single track or tracks spaced more than 14 ft. centers, and as distributed over 14 ft., plus the distance center to center of tracks, where tracks are spaced 14 ft. or less.

Impact shall not be considered unless the bridge bearings are supported by a structural beam, as in a spill-through abutment.

2. Computation of Backfill Pressure

Values for the unit weight, cohesion, and angle of internal friction of the backfill material shall be determined directly by means of soil tests or, if the expense of such tests is not justifiable, by means of the following table referring to the soil types defined in Sec. B, Art. 4. Unless the minimum cohesive strength of backfill material can be evaluated reliably the cohesion shall be neglected and only the internal friction considered.

Soil Type	Unit Weight Lb. per Cu. Ft.	Cohesion c Lb. per Sq. Ft.	Angle of Internal Friction Degree
1	105	0	33°42′ (38° for broken stone)
2	110	0	30°
3	125	0	28°
4	100	0	0
5	120	240	0

The magnitude, direction and point of application of the backfill pressure shall be computed on the basis of appropriate values of the unit weight, cohesion and internal friction, by means of one of the following procedures.

When the backfill is assumed to be cohesionless; when the surface of the backfill is or can be assumed to be plane; when there is no surcharge load on the surface of the backfill; or when the surcharge can be converted into an equivalent uniform earth surcharge, Rankine's or Coulomb's formulas may be used under the conditions to which each applies . . .

When the backfill cannot be considered cohesionless, when the surcharge of the backfill is irregular, or when the surcharge cannot be converted to an equivalent uniform earth surcharge, the trial wedge methods . . . may be used.

If the wall or abutment is not more than 20 ft. high and if the backfill has been classified according to Sec. B, Art. 4, the (Peck, Hanson & Thornburn) charts given in (AREA) Appendix C may be used.

If the wall or abutment is prevented from deflecting freely at its crest, as in a rigid-frame bridge or some types of U-abutments, the computed backfill pressure shall be increased 25 per cent.

In spill-through abutments, the increase of pressure against the columns due to the shearing strength of the backfill shall not be overlooked. If the space between columns is not greater than twice the width across the back of the columns, no reduction in backfill pressure shall be made on account of the openings. No more than the active earth pressure shall be considered as the resistance offered by the fill in front of the abutment. In computing the active earth pressure of this fill, the negative or descending slope of the surface shall be taken into consideration.

If local conditions do not permit the construction of drains and, consequently, water may accumulate behind the wall, the resulting additional pressure shall be taken into account.

D. STABILITY COMPUTATION

1. Point of Intersection of Resultant Force and Base

The resultant force on the base of a wall or abutment shall fall within the middle third if the structure is founded on soil, and within the middle half if founded on rock, masonry or piles. The resultant force on any horizontal section above the base of a solid gravity wall should intersect this section within its middle half. If these requirements are satisfied, safety against overturning need not be investigated.

2. Resistance Against Sliding

The factor of safety against sliding at the base of the structure is defined as the sum of the forces at or above base level available to resist horizontal movement of the structure divided by the sum of the forces at or above the same level tending to produce horizontal movement. The numerical value of this factor of safety shall be at least 1.5. If the factor of safety is inadequate, it shall be increased by increasing the width of the base, by the use of a key, by sloping the base upward from heel to toe, or by the use of batter piles.

In computing the resistance against sliding, the passive earth pressure of the soil in contact with the face of the wall shall be neglected. The frictional resistance between the wall and a non-cohesive subsoil may be taken as the normal pressure on the base times the coefficient of friction f of masonry on soil. For coarse-grained soil without silt, f may be taken as 0.55; for coarse-grained soil with silt, 0.45; for silt 0.35.

If the wall rests upon clay, the resistance against sliding shall be based upon the cohesion of the clay, which may be taken as one-half the unconfined compressive strength. If the clay is very stiff or hard the surface of the ground shall be roughened before the concrete is placed.

If the wall rests upon rock, consideration shall be given to such features of the rock structure as may constitute surfaces of weakness. For concrete on sound rock the coefficient of friction f may be taken as 0.60.

The factor of safety against sliding on other horizontal surfaces below the base shall be investigated and shall not be less than 1.5.

3. Soil Pressure

The factor of safety against a bearing capacity failure at the toe of the structure is defined as the ultimate bearing capacity of the material beneath the toe divided by the maximum pressure beneath the toe. The value of this factor of safety shall be not less than 2 if the structure rests on sand and gravel, or 3 if it rests on clay.

*   *   *

The ultimate bearing capacity of sand and gravel shall be estimated on the basis of the relative density or angle of internal friction ϕ of the material. If the relative density has been investigated by means of the penetration test described in Sec. B, Art. 5, the ultimate bearing capacity corresponding to the appropriate N value can be determined by means of the chart, Fig. 2. The same chart can be used if the value of ϕ is known. The value of N or ϕ shall be the average within the significant depth below the base of the footing. This depth may be taken as equal to the width of the base, unless the upper part of the subsoil is appreciably looser than the lower. In this event, the average value for the looser part shall be used. If groundwater level is closer to the base of the footing than a depth equal to one-half the width of the base, the ultimate bearing capacity shall be taken as one-half the value determined from the chart. For positions of the water table intermediate between the base and a depth equal to one-half the width of the base, the appropriate values may be determined by interpolation.

The ultimate bearing capacity of a clay subsoil may be considered equal to three times the average unconfined compressive strength of the clay within the significant depth below the base of the footing. This depth may be taken as equal to the width of the base unless the upper part of the subsoil is appreciably softer than the lower. In this event, the average value for the softer part shall be used. The position of the groundwater table is immaterial.

4. Settlement and Tilting

The soil pressures determined in accordance with Sec. D, Art. 3, provide for adequate safety against failure of the soil beneath the structure. If the subsoil consists of soft clay or silt it is necessary to determine the compressibility of the soil and to estimate the amount of settlement.

If the compressibility of the subsoil would lead to excessive settlement or tilting, the movement can be reduced by designing the wall so that the resultant of the forces acting at the base of the wall intersects the base near its midpoint.

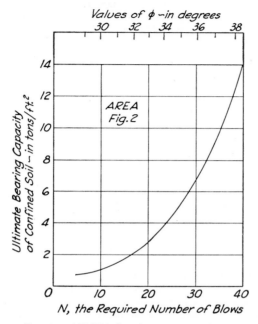

FIG. 8.   A.R.E.A. bearing capacity chart.

If the pressure on a subsoil containing fairly thick layers of soft clay or peat is increased by the weight of the backfill, the wall may tilt backward because of the compression of the clay or peat. The tilt may be estimated on the basis of a knowledge of the compressibility of the subsoil. If the tilt is likely to be excessive, it is advisable to use backfill of lightweight material, to replace the backfill by a structure, or otherwise to change the type of construction so as to avoid overloading the subsoil.

5. Progressive Creep or Movement

If the weight of the backfill is greater than one-half the ultimate bearing capacity of a clay subsoil, progressive movement of the wall or abutment is likely to occur, irrespective of the use of a key, a tilted base, or batter piles. In such cases, it is advisable to use backfill of lightweight material, to replace the backfill by a structure, or otherwise to change the type of construction so as to avoid overloading the subsoil.

E.   DESIGN OF BACKFILL

1. Drainage

The material immediately adjacent to the wall should be noncohesive and free draining. Cinders shall not be used. If a special back drain is installed, the grain size of the drain shall be coarse enough to permit free flow of water, but not so coarse that the fill material may ultimately move into it and clog it. Where economical, it is preferable that free-draining material be used within a wedge behind the wall bounded by a plane rising at 60 deg. to the horizontal. Water from the free-draining material shall be removed, preferably by horizontal drain pipes or by weep holes. Horizontal drain pipes, if used, shall be not less than 8-in. diameter and shall be installed in such a position that they will function properly. Such drains shall be accessible for cleaning. Weep holes are considered less satisfactory than horizontal drains. If used, they shall have diameters not less than 6 in. and shall be spaced not over 10 ft.

2. Compaction

The backfill shall preferably be placed in layers not to exceed 12 in. in thickness. Each layer shall be compacted before placing the next, but overcompaction shall be avoided.

No dumping of backfill material shall be permitted in such a way that the successive layers slope downward toward the wall. The layers shall be horizontal or shall slope downward away from the wall.

F. DETAILS OF DESIGN AND CONSTRUCTION

1. General

The principles of design and permissible unit stresses for walls and abutments shall conform to the (AREA) Specifications for Design of Plain and Reinforced Concrete Members, with the modifications or additions in the following paragraphs.

Retaining walls and abutments shall preferably be of the gravity or semi-gravity type. The width of the stem of a semi-gravity wall, at the level of the top of the footing, shall be at least one-fourth of its height.

The base of a retaining wall or abutment supported on soil shall be located below frost line, and in no case at a depth less than 3 ft. below the surface of the ground in front of the toe. The base shall be located below the anticipated maximum depth of scour. Where this is not practicable the base shall be supported by piles or piers.

To prevent temperature and shrinkage cracks in exposed surfaces, not less than 0.25 sq. in. of horizontal metal reinforcement per foot of height shall be provided, irrespective of the type of wall. Consideration shall be given to providing additional reinforcement above horizontal joints.

The backs of retaining walls and abutments shall be damp-proofed by an approved material.

At horizontal joints between the bases and stems of retaining walls, raised keys are considered preferable to depressed keys. The unit shearing stress at the base of such a key shall not exceed* $0.08f'_c$.

Vertical grooved lock joints shall be placed not over 60 ft. apart to care for temperature changes. They shall be protected by membrane waterproofing or non-corrosive metal water stops.

The walls above the footings shall be cast as units between expansion joints, unless construction joints are formed in accordance with the provisions of these specifications.

The heels of cantilever, counterfort and buttress retaining walls shall be proportioned for maximum resultant vertical loads, but when the foundation reaction is neglected the permissible unit stresses shall not be more than 50 per cent greater than the normal permissible stresses.

2. Cantilever Walls

The unsupported toe and heel of the base slabs shall each be considered as a cantilever beam fixed at the edge of the support.

---

* Per October, 1954, advice.

The vertical section shall be considered as a cantilever beam fixed at the top of the base.

3. Counterfort and Buttress Walls

The face walls of counterfort and buttress walls and parts of base slabs supported by the counterforts or buttresses shall be designed in accordance with the requirements for a continuous slab, AREA Specifications for Design of Plain and Reinforced Concrete Members. Due allowance shall be made for the effect of the toe moment on shears and bending moments in the heel slabs of counterfort walls.

Counterforts shall be designed in accordance with the requirements for T-beams. Stirrups shall be provided to anchor the face slabs and the heel slabs to the counterforts. These shall be proportioned to carry the end shears of the slabs. Stirrups shall be U-shaped with their legs in the counterforts, and shall extend as close to the exposed face of face walls and the bottom of base slabs as the requirements for protective covering permit. It is desirable to run reinforcing bars through the loops of the U.

Buttresses shall be designed in accordance with the requirements for rectangular beams.

* * *

(AREA's) Appendix C

Earth Pressure Charts for Walls Less than 20 ft. High

AREA's Figs. 4 and 5 may be used for estimating the backfill pressure if the backfill material has been classified in accordance with Sec. B, Art. 4.

AREA's Fig. 4 is for backfills sloping upward from the top of the wall, or for horizontal backfills. It is the same as Fig. 9–5 of Chapter 9 of this textbook.

AREA's Fig. 5 is for backfills sloping upward from the top of the wall, then changing to the horizontal. For it, refer to page 8–5–18 of the complete AREA Specification.

APPENDIX H

Courtesy of John A. Roebling's Sons Corporation

Uncoated Prestressed Concrete 7-Wire Strand for Bonded
Pre-tensioned Designs

The basic unit of Roebling 7-wire strand for pre-tensioning is uncoated prestressed concrete wire. Excellent bonding properties are afforded by these strands because of the relatively small diameter of the wires, and the mechanical bond that is provided as the concrete sets in the valleys between the outside wires.

The strands are stress-relieved to remove the internal stresses that are set up by the wire drawing and stranding operations, so that stress relaxation at the design loads is reduced to a minimum. Additional advantages of the stress-relieving process are an improvement in the bonding properties of the wire as well as in the flexibility and ease of handling the strand in the field.

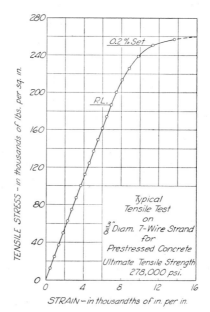

Roebling's Strand

Nominal Diameter, Inches	Area, Sq. In.	Minimum Ultimate Strength, psi
3/16	0.0214	257,000
1/4	0.0356	253,000
5/16	0.0578	251,000
3/8	0.0799	250,000
7/16	0.1089	248,000
1/2	0.1438	250,000

The average modulus of the strands in the above table is 27,000,000 psi.

473

Courtesy of Reliable Electric Company

Steelcase Strandvise

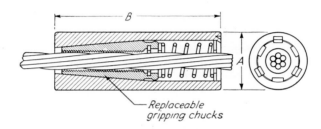

— Replaceable
gripping chucks

STEELCASE STRANDVISE

Wire Range	A	B
8 BWG. (0.144–0.165 diam.)	$\frac{5}{8}$	$2\frac{1}{8}$
6 BWG. (0.180–0.206 diam.)	$\frac{3}{4}$	$2\frac{11}{32}$
4 BWG. and $\frac{1}{4}$ (7 str.) (0.230–0.260 diam.)	$\frac{7}{8}$	$2\frac{47}{64}$
$\frac{5}{16}$ (7 str.) and rod (0.280–0.320 diam.)	$1\frac{1}{16}$	$3\frac{3}{64}$
$\frac{3}{8}$ (7-str.) and rod (0.340–0.380 diam.)	$1\frac{3}{16}$	$3\frac{29}{64}$
$\frac{7}{16}$ (7 str.) and rod (0.430–0.445 diam.)	$1\frac{1}{4}$	$3\frac{9}{16}$

APPENDIX I

Excerpts from the (British) First Report on Prestressed Concrete

Published in 1951 by *The Institution of Structural Engineers*, 11 Upper Belgrave St., London, S.W.1, England.

Reproduced by permission

Also Prof. A. D. Ross' table of concrete unit creep strain values.

* * *

7. Design considerations

(*a*) *Stages to be considered in design.* Four successive stages in construction must be taken in account in design and an appropriate factor of safety ensured at each stage. They are as follows:—

Stage 1. At transfer of prestress to the concrete, considering the maximum possible prestress and the limited concrete strength at this stage. Any relieving bending moment due to the dead weight of the beam may be taken into account, provided there is an assurance that the beam will be so handled and hoisted as to allow such bending moment to act uninterruptedly throughout the operation.

Stage 2. During any handling which does not comply with Stage 1.

Stage 3. At working load, considering the minimum possible effective prestress (after allowing appropriate losses) and the maximum permissible concrete stresses according to the age of the concrete.

Stage 4. At failure under static loading, i.e., at the maximum load that can be supported in a single loading to failure. See sub-clause (*b*) below.

(*b*) *Ultimate strength of beams in bending.* While, in ordinary reinforced concrete, working stresses give an adequate indication of safety, in prestressed concrete this is not so; it is therefore necessary to investigate the conditions of failure so as to ensure an adequate load factor or factor of safety.

Failure may be due to one or more of the following causes:—

(1) Fracture of steel in tension.
(2) Excessive elongation of steel followed by crushing of concrete.
(3) Crushing of concrete without substantial elongation of steel.
(4) Fracture of concrete in shear.
(5) Failure of anchorage or by bond slip.

Designs which would fail by causes (4) and (5) should be avoided, as failure is sudden. Failure by cause (3) is also sudden and should generally be avoided.

475

7(b) *cont'd.*

Beams in which failure occurs by either of causes (1) or (2) are called "under-reinforced" beams; beams which fail by cause (3) are called "over-reinforced" beams. In cases (1) and (2), a considerable rise of the neutral axis occurs before failure.

Where the percentage of steel is very low, failure may occur by the breaking of the wires immediately a crack is formed. Such conditions must be avoided and in general the percentage of steel related to bottom width should not be less than 0.15 for wire of an ultimate strength of 100 (long) tons/sq. in. If wire of other ultimate strength is employed the minimum percentage should be $15/t_{ult}$, the ultimate tensile strength t_{ult} being expressed in (long) tons/sq. in.

The ultimate load should be at least $2\frac{1}{2}$ times the working load (dead load plus superimposed load) where the ultimate load is calculated on the basis of failure of the concrete, and twice the working load where the ultimate load is calculated on the basis of steel fracture.

* * *

However, it is possible to calculate quite accurately the ultimate strength of under-reinforced beams with bonded wires as the tensile force in the steel at failure multiplied by the lever arm. With pre-tensioned wires, the maximum steel stress can normally be assumed as the ultimate tensile strength t_{ult} and, with post-tensioned bonded wires, as $0.75\,t_{ult}$ to t_{ult}, depending on the efficiency of bond. For bonded untensioned reinforcement, $0.85t_{ult}$ to t_{ult} can be assumed, depending on the efficiency of bond, the stress-strain characteristics and surface conditions of the wire, and the strength of the concrete. If the wire employed has a definite yield point, this yield point should be substituted for t_{ult} in all such cases. . . .

* * *

(c) *Loss of prestress.* The prestress in the steel at transfer is obtained:—

(i) *In post-tensioning* (where the steel is tensioned against the hardened concrete), from the initial tensioning stress, less loss due to friction and strain of anchorages.

(ii) *In pre-tensioning* (where the steel is tensioned against independent anchorages before casting the concrete, and the prestress is transferred after the concrete has hardened), from the initial tensioning stress, less losses due to the following:—

(1) Creep of steel between tensioning and transfer.
(2) Shrinkage of the concrete between casting and transfer.
(3) Shortening of the concrete at transfer, whence the steel loses tension corresponding to a strain equal to that in the adjacent concrete.

* * *

(d) *Effective prestress.* The minimum effective prestress in the steel at working load is obtained from the prestress at transfer, by deducting losses due to shrinkage and creep in the concrete, and creep in the steel after transfer. If test results are not available the following approximate assumptions may be made:—

(1) For cases of pre-tensioning, the creep in the concrete may be assumed to be 0.4×10^{-6} per lb./sq. in. stress in the fibres adjacent to the steel concerned; when post-tensioning at about 2–3 weeks, this figure may be reduced to 0.3×10^{-6} per lb./sq. in.

7(d) cont'd.

(2) The ultimate shrinkage of the concrete may be assumed to be 0.03 per cent for cases of pre-tensioning. Where post-tensioning is adopted, the only shrinkage to be considered is that occurring after transfer, which will depend on the age of the concrete at transfer; for transfer at 2–3 weeks, a subsequent shrinkage of 0.02 per cent may be assumed.

Whenever possible, reliable test data should be used for estimating the losses in prestress.

Where there is doubt as to the exact value of the losses to be assumed, the most unfavourable stresses at working load are obtained by assuming the highest estimate for the losses.

(e) *Flexure.* Plane cross sections of the beam are assumed to remain plane after bending; the total compression, minus the total tension in all steel and concrete considered as forming the beam, must be equal to the external thrust; and the moments resulting from these forces must be equal to the applied external moments.

(f) *Shear.* Shear stresses as such are not normally a source of weakness, the main danger resulting from the principal tensile stresses to which they contribute. These should be calculated at points of maximum shear, at points where there is a material change of shear or change of section, and at points of maximum bending moment at all the stages given in clause 7 (a).

At stage 4, the principal tensile stress at an uncracked section may be calculated according to the usual theory for homogeneous members, and this stress should not exceed half of the modulus of rupture of the concrete unless suitable shear reinforcement has been provided.

In post-tensioned systems the steel must be gripped by the concrete in order that it may be structurally connected to the shear reinforcement when the concrete has cracked, or the main steel may be turned up at appropriate intervals and grouted in order that it may effectively truss the compression flange.

For cracked sections, and particularly at sections under maximum bending moment combined with maximum shear, special consideration is necessary; in view of the few experimental data available no specific recommendations can be made.

* * *

8. Pre-tensioning systems

In connection with pre-tensioning, attention should be given to the following:—

(1) The wires should be thoroughly clean when the concrete is placed.
(2) If two or more wires are tensioned simultaneously, a slight initial tension should be applied to each wire prior to anchoring it to the tensioning head, or suitable means be employed to ensure equal tension in each wire.
(3) The magnitude of the tensioning force should be ascertained by gauges and the corresponding extension of the wire due to the stress over the length checked by measurements; yield of the gripping devices should be taken into account.
(4) Between tensioning and release (i.e., during setting and hardening of the concrete) the tension should be maintained by external anchorages.
(5) Release of all wires should be carried out gradually and large differences of tension between the wires should be avoided. If the tension is released from one end only or if there are several moulds, provision should be made for the

moulds to slide and thus to allow a transfer of the force to the concrete all along the tension line.

* * *

PROF. A. D. ROSS' CONCRETE CREEP PRESTRESS LOSS GUIDE[D]

Concrete		Magnitude of Long-Time Unit Creep Strain, δ_t, in millionths per psi of concrete compressive stress								
English Standard Portland Cement and Good Natural Stone Aggregates. 70° Mean Relative Humidity.		Age when loaded								
		7 Days			28 Days			91 Days		
Volumetric W/C	Weight C/W	Area/Perimeter Ratio of Specimen, in inches								
		1.0	2.0	2.5	1.0	2.0	2.5	1.0	2.0	2.5
0.50	3.02	0.50	0.36	0.26	0.39	0.30	0.20	0.24	0.16	0.10
0.54	2.80						0.22†			
0.60	2.52	0.67	0.50	0.38‡	0.49	0.38	0.28	0.37	0.27	0.19
0.70	2.16	0.86	0.67	0.50	0.64	0.50	0.38	0.51	0.38	0.28
0.80	1.89	1.06	0.84	0.64	0.80	0.64	0.50	0.69	0.52	0.40
0.90	1.68	1.35	1.05	0.82	1.08	0.84	0.65	0.92	0.70	0.54
1.00	1.51	1.65	1.25	1.00	1.43*	1.11	0.83	1.22	0.91	0.71
Sources		Deduced from test data from hand-placed ordinary strength concretes by projecting the effect of W/C upon creep, and confirmed by Dr. Magnel's tests on beams of high strength concrete.								

[D] See corresponding item of the Bibliography at the end of Chapter 13.

* Compare with 1.23 obtainable after 5 years of loading by Shank's Formula 10–2 of Chapter 10, deduced from 4 by 4 in. hand-placed compression specimens.

† Dr. Magnel's beams placed by vibration. Ref. *Proc. of ACI*, Vol. 44 (1948), p. 485.

‡ Close to the commonly used value of 0.4.

APPENDIX J

Building Code Requirements for Reinforced Concrete

The 1956 ACI Code

The following articles of the *1956 Building Code Requirements for Reinforced Concrete* have been included by kind permission of the *American Concrete Institute*. This code is subject to revision whenever the studies of the committee responsible indicate that developments in concrete design and construction warrant a change. Inquiries concerning revision should be made periodically. The complete Code can be obtained from the American Concrete Institute, 18263 W. McNichols Road, Detroit 19, Michigan, at $1.00 per copy (50 cents to ACI members).

The original numbering of the sections has been preserved.

General

* * *

103 Special systems of reinforced concrete

(a) The sponsors of any system of design or construction of reinforced concrete which has been in successful use, or the adequacy of which has been shown by test, and the design of which is either in conflict with, or not covered by this code shall have the right to present the data on which their design is based to a "Board of Examiners for Special Construction" appointed by the Building Official. This Board shall be composed of competent engineers, architects, and builders, and shall have the authority to investigate the data so submitted and to formulate rules governing the design and construction of such systems. These rules when approved by the Building Official shall be of the same force and effect as the provisions of this code.

* * *

Materials and Tests

200 Notation

D = deflection, produced by a test load, of a member relative to the ends of the span

L = span of member under load test (the shorter span of flat slabs and of floors supported on four sides)

t = total thickness or depth of a member under load test

201 Tests

(a) The Building Official, or his authorized representative, shall have the right to order the test of any material entering into concrete or reinforced concrete to determine its suitability for the purpose; to order reasonable tests of the concrete from time to time to determine whether the materials and methods in use are such as to produce concrete of the necessary quality; and to order the test under load of any portion of a completed structure, when conditions have been such as to leave doubt as to the adequacy of the structure to serve the purpose for which it is intended.

(b) Tests of materials and of concrete shall be made in accordance with the requirements of the American Society for Testing Materials as noted elsewhere in this code. The complete records of such tests shall be available for inspection during the progress of the work and for 2 years thereafter, and shall be preserved for that purpose by the engineer or architect.

(c) Tests for safe load ratings for reinforced concrete structures which are subject to approval under Section 103 shall be made at an age not greater than the minimum age at which the structure is to be put in service or is assumed to have the design strength (usually 28 days).

202   Load tests of existing structures

(a) A load test of an existing structure to determine its adequacy (stiffness and strength) for the intended use shall not be made until the portion subjected to the load is at least 56 days old, unless the owner of the structure agrees to the test being made at an earlier age.

(b) When a load test is required and the whole structure is not to be tested, the portion of the structure thought to provide the least margin of safety shall be selected for loading. Prior to the application of the test load, a load which simulates the effect of that portion of the design dead load which is not already present shall be applied and shall remain in place until after a decision has been made regarding the acceptability of the structure. The test load shall not be applied until the structural members to be tested have borne the full design dead load for at least 48 hr.

(c) Immediately prior to the application of the test load, the necessary initial readings shall be made for the measurements of deflections (and strains, if these are to be determined) caused by the application of the test load. The members selected for loading shall be subjected to a superimposed test load of two times the design live load, but not less than 80 psf for floor construction nor less than 60 psf for roof construction. The superimposed load shall be applied without shock to the structure and in a manner to avoid arching of the loading materials. Unless otherwise directed by the Building Official, the load shall be distributed to simulate the distribution of the load assumed in the design.

203   Loading and criteria of acceptability

The test load shall be left in position for 24 hr., when readings of the deflections shall again be made. The test load shall be removed and additional readings of deflections shall then be made 24 hr. after the removal of the test load. The following criteria shall be used in determining conformity with the load test requirements.

(a) If the structure shows evident failure, the changes or modifications needed to make the structure adequate for the rated capacity shall be made; or a lower rating may be established.

(b) Floor and roof construction shall be considered to conform to the load test requirements if there is no evidence of failure and the maximum deflection does not exceed:

$$D = \frac{L^2}{12,000\,t} \tag{1}$$

in which all terms are in the same units. Constructions with greater deflections shall meet the requirements of subsections (c), (d), and (e).

(c) The maximum deflection of a floor or roof construction shall not exceed the limit in Table 203(c) considered by the Building Official to be appropriate for the construction.

TABLE 203(c)—MAXIMUM ALLOWABLE DEFLECTION

Construction	Deflection
1. Cantilever beams and slabs	$L^2/1800\,t$
2. Simple beams and slabs	$L^2/4000\,t$
3. Beams continuous at one support and slabs continuous at one support for the direction of the principal reinforcement	$L^2/9000\,t$
4. Flat slabs (L = the longer span)	$L^2/10,000\,t$
5. Beams and slabs continuous at the supports for the direction of the principal reinforcement	$L^2/10,000\,t$

(d) The maximum deflection shall not exceed $L/180$ for a floor construction intended to support or to be attached to partitions or other construction likely to be damaged by large deflections of the floor.

(e) Within 24 hr. after the removal of the test load the recovery of deflection caused by the application of the test load shall be at least 75 per cent of the maximum deflection if this exceeds $L^2/12,000t$. However, constructions failing to show 75 per cent recovery of the deflection may be retested. The second test loading shall not be made until at least 72 hr. after the removal of the test load for the first test. The maximum deflection in the retest shall conform to the requirements of Sections 203(c) and (d) and the recovery of deflection shall be at least 75 per cent.

* * *

Concrete Quality and Allowable Stresses

* * *

305 Allowable unit stresses in concrete

(a) The unit stresses in pounds per square inch on concrete to be used when designs are made in accordance with Section 601(a) shall not exceed the values of Table 305(a) where f'_c equals the minimum specified compressive strength at 28 days, or at the earlier age at which the concrete may be expected to receive its full load.

306 Allowable unit stresses in reinforcement

Unless otherwise provided in this code, steel for concrete reinforcement shall not be stressed in excess of the following limits:

(a) *Tension*

(f_s = tensile unit stress in longitudinal reinforcement)
and (f_v = tensile unit stress in web reinforcement)

20,000 psi for rail-steel concrete reinforcing bars, billet-steel concrete reinforcing bars of intermediate and hard grades, axle-steel concrete reinforcing bars of intermediate and hard grades, and cold-drawn steel wire for concrete reinforcement.

18,000 psi for billet-steel concrete reinforcing bars of structural grade, and axle-steel concrete reinforcing bars of structural grade.

TABLE 305(a)—ALLOWABLE UNIT STRESSES IN CONCRETE

Description		For any strength of concrete in accordance with Section 302 $n = \dfrac{30{,}000}{f'_c}$	Maximum value, psi	For strength of concrete shown below				
				$f'_c = 2000$ psi $n = 15$	$f'_c = 2500$ psi $n = 12$	$f'_c = 3000$ psi $n = 10$	$f'_c = 3750$ psi $n = 8$	$f'_c = 5000$ psi $n = 6$
Flexure: f_c								
Extreme fiber stress in compression	f_c	$0.45f'_c$		900	1125	1350	1688	2250
Extreme fiber stress in tension in plain concrete footings........	f_c	$0.03f'_c$		60	75	90	113	150
Shear: v (as a measure of diagonal tension)								
Beams with no web reinforcement	v_c	$0.03f'_c$	90	60	75	90	90	90
Beams with longitudinal bars and with either stirrups or properly located bent bars.............	v	$0.08f'_c$	240	160	200	240	240	240
Beams with longitudinal bars and a combination of stirrups and bent bars (the latter bent up suitably to carry at least $0.04f'_c$)	v	$0.12f'_c$	360	240	300	360	360	360
Footings*.....................	v_c	$0.03f'_c$	75	60	75	75	75	75
(For flat slabs, see Chapter 10)								
Bond: u								
Deformed bars (as defined in Section 104)								
Top bars†...................	u	$0.07f'_c$	245	140	175	210	245	245
In two-way footings (except top bars).....................	u	$0.08f'_c$	280	160	200	240	280	280
All others..................	u	$0.10f'_c$	350	200	250	300	350	350
Plain bars (as defined in Section 104) (must be hooked)								
Top bars....................	u	$0.03f'_c$	105	60	75	90	105	105
In two-way footings (except top bars).....................	u	$0.036f'_c$	126	72	90	108	126	126
All others..................	u	$0.045f'_c$	158	90	113	135	158	158
Bearing: f_c								
On full area....................	f_c	$0.25f'_c$		500	625	750	938	1250
On one-third area or less ‡.......	f_c	$0.375f'_c$		750	938	1125	1405	1875

* See Sections 905 and 809.

† Top bars, in reference to bond, are horizontal bars so placed that more than 12 in. of concrete is cast in the member below the bar.

‡ This increase shall be permitted only when the least distance between the edges of the loaded and unloaded areas is a minimum of one-fourth of the parallel side dimension of the loaded area. The allowable bearing stress on a reasonably concentric area greater than one-third but less than the full area shall be interpolated between the values given.

(b) *Tension in one-way slabs of not more than 12-ft. span*

(f_s = tensile unit stress in main reinforcement)

For the main reinforcement, ⅜ in. or less in diameter, in one-way slabs, 50 per cent of the minimum yield point specified in the specifications of the American Society for Testing Materials for the particular kind and grade of reinforcement used, but in no case to exceed 30,000 psi.

(c) *Compression, vertical column reinforcement*

(f_s = nominal allowable stress in vertical column reinforcement)

Forty per cent of the minimum yield point specified in the specifications of the American Society for Testing Materials for the particular kind and grade of reinforcement used, but in no case to exceed 30,000 psi.

(f_r = allowable unit stress in the metal core of composite and combination columns)

Structural steel sections..16,000 psi
Cast iron sections..10,000 psi
Steel pipe...............................See limitations of Section 1106(b)

(d) *Compression, flexural members*

For compression reinforcement in flexural members see Section 706(b).

* * *

Forms and Details of Construction

* * *

505 Placing reinforcement

(a) Metal reinforcement shall be accurately placed and adequately secured in position by concrete or metal chairs or spacers. The clear distance between parallel bars, except in columns, shall be not less than the nominal diameter of the bars, $1\frac{1}{3}$ times the maximum size of the coarse aggregate, nor 1 in. Where reinforcement in beams or girders is placed in two or more layers, the clear distance between layers shall not be less than 1 in., and the bars in the upper layers shall be placed directly above those in the bottom layer.

(b) When wire or other reinforcement, not exceeding $\frac{1}{4}$ in. in diameter is used as reinforcement for slabs not exceeding 10 ft. in span, the reinforcement may be curved from a point near the top of the slab over the support to a point near the bottom of the slab at midspan; provided such reinforcement is either continuous over, or securely anchored to, the support.

506 Splices in reinforcement

(a) In slabs, beams and girders, splices of reinforcement at points of maximum stress shall be avoided wherever possible. Such splices where used shall be welded, lapped, or otherwise fully developed, but, in any case, shall transfer the entire stress from bar to bar without exceeding the allowable bond and shear stresses listed in Table 305(a). The minimum overlap for a lapped splice shall be 24 diameters, but not less than 12 in. for bars; for welded wire fabric the overlap of edge bars shall be $\frac{1}{2}$ the distance to the next parallel wire. The clear distance between bars shall also apply to the clear distance between a contact splice and adjacent contact splices or bars.

507 Concrete protection for reinforcement

(a) The reinforcement of footings and other principal structural members in which the concrete is deposited against the ground shall have not less than 3 in. of concrete between it and the ground contact surface. If concrete surfaces after removal of the forms are to be exposed to the weather or be in contact with the ground, the reinforcement shall be protected with not less than 2 in. of concrete for bars larger than #5, and $1\frac{1}{2}$ in. for #5 bars or smaller.

(b) The concrete protective covering for reinforcement at surfaces not exposed directly to the ground or weather shall be not less than $\frac{3}{4}$ in. for slabs and walls; and not less than $1\frac{1}{2}$ in. for beams, girders, and columns. In concrete joist floors in which the clear distance between joists is not more than 30 in., the protection of reinforcement shall be at least $\frac{3}{4}$ in.

(c) If the general code of which this code forms a part specifies, as fire-protective covering of the reinforcement, thicknesses of concrete greater than those given in this section, then such greater thicknesses shall be used.

(d) Concrete protection for reinforcement shall in all cases be at least equal to the diameter of bars.

(e) Exposed reinforcing bars intended for bonding with future extensions shall be protected from corrosion by concrete or other adequate covering.

* * *

Design—General Considerations

601 Design methods

(a) The design of reinforced concrete members shall be made with reference to allowable stresses, working loads, and the accepted straightline theory of flexure except as permitted by Section 601 (b). In determining the ratio n for design purposes, the modulus of elasticity for the concrete shall be assumed as $1000f'_c$, and that for steel as 30,000,000 psi. It is assumed that the steel takes all the tension stresses in flexural computations.

(b) The ultimate strength method of design may be used for the design of reinforced concrete members.*

602 Design loads

(a) The provisions for design herein specified are based on the assumption that all structures shall be designed for all dead and live loads coming upon them, the live loads to be in accordance with the general requirements of the building code of which this forms a part, with such reductions for girders and lower story columns as are permitted therein.

603 Resistance to wind and earthquake forces

(a) The resisting elements in structures required to resist wind and earthquake forces shall be limited to the integral structural parts.

(b) The moments, shears, and direct stresses resulting from wind or earthquake forces determined in accordance with recognized methods shall be added to the maximum stresses which exist at any section for dead and live loads.

(c) Members subject to stresses produced by wind or earthquake forces combined with other loads may be proportioned for unit stresses $33\frac{1}{3}$ per cent greater than those specified in Sections 305 and 306, provided that the section thus required is not less than that required for the combination of dead and live load.

Flexural Computations

700 Notation

b = width of rectangular flexural member or width of flanges for T- and I-sections

b' = width of web in T and I flexural members

d = depth from compression face of beam or slab to centroid of longitudinal tensile reinforcement; the diameter of a round bar

E = modulus of elasticity

---

* For ready reference see the Appendix to this code for an abstract of the report of the ACI–ASCE joint committee on ultimate strength design.

I = moment of inertia of a section about the neutral axis for bending

l = span length of slab or beam

l' = clear span for positive moment and shear and the average of the two adjacent clear spans for negative moment (see Section 701)

t = minimum total thickness of slab

w = uniformly distributed load per unit of length of beam or per unit area of slab

701 General requirements

(a) All members of frames or continuous construction shall be designed to resist at all sections the maximum moments and shears produced by dead load, live load, earthquake and wind load, as determined by the theory of elastic frames in which the simplified assumptions of Section 702 may be used.

(b) Approximate methods of frame analysis are satisfactory for buildings of usual types of construction, spans, and story heights.

(c) In the case of two or more approximately equal spans (the larger of two adjacent spans not exceeding the shorter by more than 20 per cent) with loads uniformly distributed, where the unit live load does not exceed three times the unit dead load, design for the following moments and shears is satisfactory:

Positive moment
End spans

If discontinuous end is unrestrained............................... $\dfrac{1}{11} wl'^2$

If discontinuous end is integral with the support.................... $\dfrac{1}{14} wl'^2$

Interior spans... $\dfrac{1}{16} wl'^2$

Negative moment at exterior face of first interior support

Two spans.. $\dfrac{1}{9} wl'^2$

More than two spans... $\dfrac{1}{10} wl'^2$

Negative moment at other faces of interior supports.................. $\dfrac{1}{11} wl'^2$

Negative moment at face of all supports for (a) slabs with spans not exceeding 10 ft., and (b) beams and girders where ratio of sum of column stiffnesses to beam stiffness exceeds eight at each end of the span............................ $\dfrac{1}{12} wl'^2$

Negative moment at interior faces of exterior supports for members built integrally with their supports

Where the support is a spandrel beam or girder................... $\dfrac{1}{24} wl'^2$

Where the support is a column............................... $\dfrac{1}{16} wl'^2$

Shear in end members at first interior support...................... $1.15 \dfrac{wl'}{2}$

Shear at all other supports....................................... $\dfrac{wl'}{2}$

702   Conditions of design*

(a) *Arrangement of live load*

1. The live load may be considered to be applied only to the floor under consideration, and the far ends of the columns may be assumed as fixed.

2. Consideration may be limited to combinations of dead load on all spans with
full live load on two adjacent spans and with full live load on alternate spans.

(b) *Span length*

1. The span length, l, of members that are not built integrally with their supports
shall be the clear span plus the depth of the slab or beam but shall not exceed the
distance between centers of supports.

2. In analysis of continuous frames, center to center distances, l and h, may be
used in the determination of moments.   Moments at faces of supports may be used
for design of beams and girders.

3. Solid or ribbed slabs with clear spans of not more than 10 ft. that are built
integrally with their supports may be designed as continuous slabs on knife edge
supports with spans equal to the clear spans of the slab and the width of beams
otherwise neglected.

(c) *Stiffness*

1. Any reasonable assumption may be adopted for computing the relative stiffness
of columns and of floor systems.   The assumption made shall be consistent throughout
the analysis.

2. In computing the value of I for relative stiffness of slabs, beams, girders, and
columns, the reinforcement may be neglected.   In T-shaped sections allowance shall
be made for the effect of flange.

(d) *Haunched floor members*

1. The effect of haunches shall be considered both in determining bending
moments and in computing unit stresses.

(e) *Limitations*

1. Wherever at any section positive reinforcement is indicated by analysis, the
amount provided shall be not less than $0.005b'd$ except in slabs of uniform thickness.
(Use b instead of b' for rectangular flexural members.)

2. In structural slabs of uniform thickness the minimum amount of reinforcement
in the direction of the span shall be:

For structural, intermediate, and hard grades and rail steel. . . . . $0.0025bd$
For steel having a minimum yield point of 56,000 psi. . . . . $0.0020bd$

3. In slabs other than concrete joist construction or flat slabs, the principal
reinforcement shall be centered not farther apart than three times the slab thickness
nor more than 18 in.

703   Depth of beam or slab

(a) The depth of the beam or slab shall be taken as the distance from the centroid
of the tensile reinforcement to the compression face of the structural members.   Any
floor finish not placed monolithically with the floor slab shall not be included as a part
of the structural member.   When the finish is placed monolithically with the structural

* For moments in columns see Section 1108 [of this specification].

slab in buildings of the warehouse or industrial class, there shall be placed an additional depth of $\frac{1}{2}$ in. over that required by the design of the member.

704 Distance between lateral supports

(a) The clear distance between lateral supports of a beam shall not exceed 32 times the least width of compression flange.

705 Requirements for T-beams

(a) In T-beam construction the slab and beam shall be built integrally or otherwise effectively bonded together. The effective flange width to be used in the design of symmetrical T-beams shall not exceed one-fourth of the span length of the beam, and its overhanging width on either side of the web shall not exceed eight times the thickness of the slab nor one-half the clear distance to the next beam.

(b) For beams having a flange on one side only, the effective overhanging flange width shall not exceed $\frac{1}{12}$ of the span length of the beam, nor six times the thickness of the slab, nor one-half the clear distance to the next beam.

(c) Where the principal reinforcement in a slab which is considered as the flange of a T-beam (not a joist in concrete joist floors) is parallel to the beam, transverse reinforcement shall be provided in the top of the slab. This reinforcement shall be designed to carry the load on the portion of the slab required for the flange of the T-beam. The flange shall be assumed to act as a cantilever. The spacing of the bars shall not exceed five times the thickness of the flange, nor in any case 18 in.

(d) Provision shall be made for the compressive stress at the support in continuous T-beam construction, care being taken that the provisions of Section 505 relating to the spacing of bars, and 404(d) relating to the placing of concrete shall be fully met.

(e) The overhanging portion of the flange of the beam shall not be considered as effective in computing the shear and diagonal tension resistance of T-beams.

(f) Isolated beams in which the T-form is used only for the purpose of providing additional compression area, shall have a flange thickness not less than one-half the width of the web and a total flange width not more than four times the web thickness.

706 Compression steel in flexural members

(a) Compression steel in beams or girders shall be anchored by ties or stirrups not less than $\frac{1}{4}$ in. in diameter spaced not farther apart than 16 bar diameters, or 48 tie diameters. Such stirrups or ties shall be used throughout the distance where the compression steel is required.

(b) To approximate the effect of creep, the stress in compression reinforcement resisting bending may be taken at twice the value indicated by using the straight-line relation between stress and strain, and the modular ratio given in Section 601(a), but not of greater value than the allowable stress in tension.

707 Shrinkage and temperature reinforcement

(a) Reinforcement for shrinkage and temperature stresses normal to the principal reinforcement shall be provided in structural floor and roof slabs where the principal reinforcement extends in one direction only. Such reinforcement shall provide for the following minimum ratios of reinforcement area to concrete area bt, but in no case shall such reinforcing bars be placed farther apart than five times the slab thickness nor more than 18 in.

Slabs where plain bars are used......................................0.0025
Slabs where deformed bars are used........ ....0.0020
Slabs where wire fabric is used, having welded intersections not farther
    apart in the direction of stress than 12 in............................0.0018

708   Concrete joist floor construction

(*a*) In concrete joist floor construction consisting of concrete joists and slabs placed monolithically with or without burned clay or concrete tile fillers, the joists shall not be farther apart than 30 in. face to face. The ribs shall be straight, not less than 4 in. wide, and of a depth not more than three times the width.

* * *

(*g*) Shrinkage reinforcement shall not be required in the slab parallel to the joists.

709   Two-way systems with supports on four sides*

(*a*) This construction, reinforced in two directions, includes solid reinforced concrete slabs; concrete joists with fillers of hollow concre'e units or clay tile, with or without concrete top slabs; and concrete joists with top slabs placed monolithically with the joists. The slab shall be supported by walls or beams on all sides and, if not securely attached to supports, shall be reinforced as specified in Section 709(b).

(*b*) Where the slab is not securely attached to the supporting beams or walls, special reinforcement shall be provided at exterior corners in both the bottom and top of the slab. This reinforcement shall be provided for a distance in each direction from the corner equal to one-fifth the longest span. The reinforcement in the top of the slab shall be parallel to the diagonal from the corner. The reinforcement in the bottom of the slab shall be at right angles to the diagonal or may be of bars in two directions parallel to the sides of the slab. The reinforcement in each band shall be of equivalent size and spacing to that required for the maximum positive moment in the slab.

(*c*) The slab and its supports shall be designed by approved methods which shall take into account the effect of continuity at supports, the ratio of length to width of slab and the effect of two-way action.

(*d*) In no case shall the slab thickness be less than 4 in. nor less than the perimeter of the slab divided by 180. The spacing of reinforcement shall be not more than three times the slab thickness and the ratio of reinforcement shall be at least 0.0025.

* * *

(*Method 1* not taken up by G. E. Large)

Method 2

Notation

C = moment coefficient for two-way slabs as given in Table 3

m = ratio of short span to long span for two-way slabs

S = length of short span for two-way slabs. The span shall be considered as the center-to-center distance between supports or the clear span plus twice the thickness of slab, whichever value is the smaller.

w = total uniform load per sq ft

(*a*) *Limitations*—A two-way slab shall be considered as consisting of strips in each direction as follows:

A middle strip one-half panel in width, symmetrical about panel centerline and extending through the panel in the direction in which moments are considered.

A column strip one-half panel in width, occupying the two quarter-panel areas outside the middle strip.

---

* The requirements of this section are satisfied by either of the methods of design which follow this section.

TABLE 3—MOMENT COEFFICIENTS

Moments	Short span						Long span, all values of m
	Values of m						
	1.0	0.9	0.8	0.7	0.6	0.5 and less	
Case 1—Interior panels							
Negative moment at—							
Continuous edge	0.033	0.040	0.048	0.055	0.063	0.083	0.033
Discontinuous edge	——	——	——	——	——	——	——
Positive moment at midspan	0.025	0.030	0.036	0.041	0.047	0.062	0.025
Case 2—One edge discontinuous							
Negative moment at—							
Continuous edge	0.041	0.048	0.055	0.062	0.069	0.085	0.041
Discontinuous edge	0.021	0.024	0.027	0.031	0.035	0.042	0.021
Positive moment at midspan	0.031	0.036	0.041	0.047	0.052	0.064	0.031
Case 3—Two edges discontinuous							
Negative moment at—							
Continuous edge	0.049	0.057	0.064	0.071	0.078	0.090	0.049
Discontinuous edge	0.025	0.028	0.032	0.036	0.039	0.045	0.025
Positive moment at midspan	0.037	0.043	0.048	0.054	0.059	0.068	0.037
Case 4—Three edges discontinuous							
Negative moment at—							
Continuous edge	0.058	0.066	0.074	0.082	0.090	0.098	0.058
Discontinuous edge	0.029	0.033	0.037	0.041	0.045	0.049	0.029
Positive moment at midspan	0.044	0.050	0.056	0.062	0.068	0.074	0.044
Case 5—Four edges discontinuous							
Negative moment at—							
Continuous edge	——	——	——	——	——	——	——
Discontinuous edge	0.033	0.038	0.043	0.047	0.053	0.055	0.033
Positive moment at midspan	0.050	0.057	0.064	0.072	0.080	0.083	0.050

Where the ratio of short to long span is less than 0.5, the middle strip in the short direction shall be considered as having a width equal to the difference between the long and short span, the remaining area representing the two column strips.

The critical sections for moment calculations are referred to as principal design sections and are located as follows:

For negative moment, along the edges of the panel at the faces of the supporting beams.

For positive moment, along the centerlines of the panels.

(b) *Bending moments*—The bending moments for the middle strips shall be computed from the formula

$$M = CwS^2$$

The average moments per foot of width in the column strip shall be two-thirds of the corresponding moments in the middle strip. In determining the spacing of the reinforcement in the column strip, the moment may be assumed to vary from a maximum at the edge of the middle strip to a minimum at the edge of the panel.

Where the negative moment on one side of a support is less than 80 per cent of that on the other side, two-thirds of the difference shall be distributed in proportion to the relative stiffnesses of the slabs.

(c) *Shear*—The shearing stresses in the slab may be computed on the assumption that the load is distributed to the supports in accordance with (d).

(d) *Supporting beams*—The loads on the supporting beams for a two-way rectangular panel may be assumed as the load within the tributary areas of the panel bounded by the intersection of 45-deg lines from the corners with the median line of the panel parallel to the long side.

The bending moments may be determined approximately by using an equivalent uniform load per lineal foot of beam for each panel supported as follows:

For the short span: $\dfrac{wS}{3}$

For the long span: $\dfrac{wS}{3} \dfrac{(3 - m^2)}{2}$

Shear and Diagonal Tension

800   Notation

A_v = total area of web reinforcement in tension within a distance of s (measured in a direction parallel to that of the main reinforcement), or the total area of all bars bent up in any one plane

α = angle between inclined web bars and axis of beam

b = width of rectangular flexural member or width of flange for T- and I-sections

b' = width of web in T and I flexural members

d = depth from compression face of beam or slab to centroid of longitudinal tensile reinforcement

f'_c = compressive strength of concrete at age of 28 days unless otherwise specified

f_v = tensile unit stress in web reinforcement

j = ratio of distance between centroid of compression and centroid of tension to the depth d

s = spacing of stirrups or of bent bars in a direction parallel to that of the main reinforcement

v = shearing unit stress

V = total shear

V' = total shear carried by the web reinforcement

801   Shearing unit stress

(a) The shearing unit stress v, as a measure of diagonal tension, in reinforced concrete flexural members shall be computed by formula (2):

$$v = \frac{V}{bjd} \tag{2}$$

(b) For beams of I- or T-section, b' shall be substituted for b in formula (2).

(c) In concrete joist floor construction, where burned clay or concrete tile are used, b' may be taken as a width equal to the thickness of the concrete web plus the thickness of the vertical shells of the concrete or burned clay tile in contact with the joist as in Section 708(b).

(d) Wherever the value of the shearing unit stress computed by formula (2) exceeds the shearing unit stress v_c permitted on the concrete of an unreinforced web (see Section 305), web reinforcement shall be provided to carry the excess. Such reinforcement shall also be provided for a distance equal to the depth, d, of the member beyond the point theoretically required.

(e) Where continuous or restrained beams or frames do not have a slab so cast as to provide T-beam action, the following provisions shall apply. Web reinforcement shall be provided from the support to a point beyond the extreme position of the point of inflection a distance equal to either $\frac{1}{16}$ of the clear span or the depth of the member, whichever is greater, even though the shearing unit stress does not exceed v_c. Such reinforcement shall be designed to carry at least two-thirds of the total shear at the section. Web reinforcement shall be provided sufficient to carry at least two-thirds of the total shear at a section in which there is negative reinforcement.

802   Types of web reinforcement

(a) Web reinforcement may consist of:

1. Stirrups or web reinforcing bars perpendicular to the longitudinal steel.

2. Stirrups or web reinforcing bars welded or otherwise rigidly attached to the longitudinal steel and making an angle of 30 deg or more thereto.

3. Longitudinal bars bent so that the axis of the inclined portion of the bar makes an angle of 15 deg or more with the axis of the longitudinal portion of the bar.

4. Special arrangements of bars with adequate provisions to prevent slip of bars or splitting of the concrete by the reinforcement [see Section 804(f)].

(b) Stirrups or other bars to be considered effective as web reinforcement shall be anchored at both ends, according to the provisions of Section 904.

803   Stirrups

(a) The area of steel required in stirrups placed perpendicular to the longitudinal reinforcement shall be computed by formula (3).

$$A_v = \frac{V's}{f_v jd} \tag{3}$$

(b) Inclined stirrups shall be proportioned by formula (5) [Section 804(d)].

(c) Stirrups placed perpendicular to the longitudinal reinforcement shall not be used alone as web reinforcement when the shearing unit stress, v, exceeds $0.08f'_c$ or 240 psi.

804   Bent bars

(a) Only the center three-fourths of the inclined portion of any longitudinal bar that is bent up for web reinforcement shall be considered effective for that purpose, and such bars shall be bent around a pin having a diameter not less than six times the bar size.

(b) When the web reinforcement consists of a single bent bar or of a single group of parallel bars all bent up at the same distance from the support, the required area of such bars shall be computed by formula (4).

$$A_v = \frac{V'}{f_v \sin \alpha} \tag{4}$$

(c) In formula (4), V' shall not exceed $0.04f'_c bjd$, or $120bjd$.

(d) Where there is a series of parallel bars or groups of bars bent up at different distances from the support, the required area shall be determined by formula (5).

$$A_v = \frac{V's}{f_v jd (\sin \alpha + \cos \alpha)} \tag{5}$$

(e) When bent bars, having a radius of bend of at least six bar diameters are used alone as web reinforcement, they shall be so spaced that the effective inclined portion described in Section 804(a) meets the requirements of Section 806, and the allowable shearing unit stress shall not exceed $0.08f'_c$ nor 240 psi.

(*f*) The shearing unit stress permitted when special arrangements of bars are employed shall be that determined by making comparative tests, to destruction, of specimens of the proposed system and of similar specimens reinforced in conformity with the provisions of this code, the same factor of safety being applied in both cases.

805   Combined web reinforcement

(*a*) Where more than one type of reinforcement is used to reinforce the same portion of the web, the total shearing resistance of this portion of the web shall be assumed as the sum of the shearing resistances computed for the various types separately.   In such computations the shearing resistance of the concrete shall be included only once, and no one type of reinforcement shall be assumed to resist more than $2V'/3$.

806   Maximum spacing of web reinforcement

(*a*) Where web reinforcement is required it shall be so spaced that every 45-deg line (representing a potential crack) extending from the mid-depth of the beam to the longitudinal tension bars shall be crossed by at least one line of web reinfo cement. If a shearing unit stress in excess of $0.06f'_c$ is used, every such line shall be crossed by at least two such lines of web reinforcement.

807   Minimum web reinforcement

Where web reinforcement is required, the amount used shall be not less than 0.15 per cent of the area computed as the product of the width of the member at mid-depth and the horizontal spacing of the web reinforcement.

808   Shearing stresses in flat slabs [see Section 1002(c)]

809   Shear and diagonal tension in footings

(*a*) In isolated footings the shearing unit stress computed by formula (2) on the critical section [see Section 1205(a)] shall not exceed $0.03f'_c$ nor in any case shall it exceed 75 psi.

Bond and Anchorage

900   Notation

d = depth from compression face of beam or slab to centroid of longitudinal tensile reinforcement

f'_c = compressive strength of concrete at age of 28 days unless otherwise specified

j = ratio of distance between centroid of compression and centroid of tension to the depth d

Σ_o = sum of perimeters of bars in one set

u = bond stress per unit of surface area of bar

V = total shear

901   Computation of bond stress in beams

(*a*) In flexural members in which the tensile reinforcement is parallel to the compression face, the bond stress at any cross section shall be computed by formula (6).

$$u = \frac{V}{\Sigma_o jd} \tag{6}$$

in which V is the shear at that section and Σ_o is taken as the perimeter of all effective bars crossing the section on the tension side. Bent-up bars that are not more than $d/3$ from the level of the main longitudinal reinforcement may be included. Critical sections occur at the face of the support, at each point where tension bars terminate within a span, and at the point of inflection.

(b) Bond shall be similarly computed on compressive reinforcement, but the shear used in computing the bond shall be reduced in the ratio of the compressive force assumed in the bars to the total compressive force at the section. Anchorage shall be provided by embedment past the section to develop the assumed compressive force in the bars at the bond stress in Table 305(a).

(c) Adequate end anchorage shall be provided for the tensile reinforcement in all flexural members to which formula (6) does not apply, such as sloped, stepped or tapered footings, brackets or beams in which the tensile reinforcement is not parallel to the compression face.

902   Anchorage requirements

(a) Tensile negative reinforcement in any span of a continuous, restrained or cantilever beam, or in any member of a rigid frame shall be adequately anchored by bond, hooks, or mechanical anchors in or through the supporting member. Within any such span every reinforcing bar, except in a lapped splice, whether required for positive or negative reinforcement, shall be extended at least 12 diameters beyond the point at which it is no longer needed to resist stress. At least one-third of the total reinforcement provided for negative moment at the support shall be extended beyond the extreme position of the point of inflection a distance sufficient to develop by bond one-half the allowable stress in such bars, not less than $\frac{1}{16}$ of the clear span length, or not less than the depth of the member, whichever is greater. The tension in any bar at any section must be properly developed on each side of the section by hook, lap, or embedment (see Section 906). If preferred, the bar may be bent across the web at an angle of not less than 15 deg with the longitudinal portion of the bar and be made continuous with the reinforcement which resists moment of opposite sign.

(b) Of the positive reinforcement in continuous beams not less than one-fourth the area shall extend along the same face of the beam into the support a distance of 6 in.

(c) In simple beams, or at the freely supported end of continuous beams, at least one-third the required positive reinforcement shall extend along the same face of the beam into the support a distance of 6 in.

903   Plain bars in tension

Plain bars in tension shall terminate in standard hooks except that hooks shall not be required on the positive reinforcement at interior supports of continuous members.

904   Anchorage of web reinforcement

(a) The ends of bars forming simple U- or multiple stirrups shall be anchored by one of the following methods:

1. By a standard hook, considered as developing 10,000 psi, plus embedment sufficient to develop by bond the remaining stress in the bar at the unit stress specified in Table 305(a). The effective embedded length of a stirrup leg shall be taken as the distance between the mid-depth of the beam and the tangent of the hook.

2. Welding to longitudinal reinforcement.

3. Bending tightly around the longitudinal reinforcement through at least 180 deg.

4. Embedment above or below the mid-depth of the beam on the compression side, a distance sufficient to develop the stress to which the bar will be subjected at a bond stress not to exceed $0.045f'_c$ on plain bars nor $0.10f'_c$ on deformed bars, but, in any case, a minimum of 24 bar diameters.

(b) Between the anchored ends, each bend in the continuous portion of a U- or multiple U-stirrup shall be made around a longitudinal bar.

(c) Hooking or bending stirrups around the longitudinal reinforcement shall be considered effective only when these bars are perpendicular to the longitudinal reinforcement.

(d) Longitudinal bars bent to act as web reinforcement shall, in a region of tension, be continuous with the longitudinal reinforcement. The tensile stress in each bar shall be fully developed in both the upper and the lower half of the beam as specified in Section 904(a)1 or 904(a)4.

(e) In all cases web reinforcement shall be carried as close to the compression surface of the beam as fireproofing regulations and the proximity of other steel will permit.

905 Anchorage of bars in footing slabs

(a) Plain bars in footing slabs shall be anchored by means of standard hooks. The outer faces of these hooks and the ends of deformed bars shall be not less than 3 in. nor more than 6 in. from the face of the footing.

906 Hooks

(a) The terms "hook" or "standard hook" as used herein shall mean either

1. A complete semicircular turn with a radius of bend on the axis of the bar of not less than three and not more than six bar diameters plus an extension of at least four bar diameters at the free end of the bar, or

2. A 90-deg bend having a radius of not less than four bar diameters plus an extension of 12 bar diameters, or

3. For stirrup anchorage only, a 135-deg turn with a radius on the axis of the bar of three diameters plus an extension of at least six bar diameters at the free end of the bar.

Hooks having a radius of bend of more than six bar diameters shall be considered merely as extensions to the bars.

(b) No hook shall be assumed to carry a load which would produce a tensile stress in the bar greater than 10,000 psi.

(c) Hooks shall not be considered effective in adding to the compressive resistance of bars.

(d) Any mechanical device capable of developing the strength of the bar without damage to the concrete may be used in lieu of a hook. Tests must be presented to show the adequacy of such devices.

Flat Slabs

1000 Notation

A = distance in the direction of span from center of support to the intersection of the centerline of the slab thickness with the extreme 45-deg diagonal line lying wholly within the concrete section of slab and column or other support, including drop panel, capital and bracket

b = width of section

c = effective support size [see Section 1004(c)]

d = depth from compression face of beam or slab to centroid of tensile reinforcement

f'_c = compressive strength of concrete at age of 28 days unless otherwise specified

H = story height in feet of the column or support of a flat slab center to center of slabs

j = ratio of distance between centroids of compression and tension to depth d

L = span length of a flat slab panel center to center of supports

M_o = numerical sum of assumed positive and average negative moments at the critical design sections of a flat slab panel [see Section 1004(f)1]

t = thickness of slab in inches

t_1 = thickness in inches of slabs without drop panels, or through drop panel, if any

t_2 = thickness in inches of slabs with drop panels at points beyond the drop panel

v = shearing unit stress

V = total shear

w' = uniformly distributed unit dead and live load

W = total dead and live load on panel

W_D = total dead load on panel

W_L = total live load on panel, uniformly distributed

1001 Definitions and scope

(a) *Flat slab*—A concrete slab reinforced in two or more directions, generally without beams or girders to transfer the loads to supporting members. Slabs with recesses or pockets made by permanent or removable fillers between reinforcing bars may be considered flat slabs. Slabs with paneled ceilings may be considered as flat slabs provided the panel of reduced thickness lies entirely within the area of intersecting middle strips, and is at least two-thirds the thickness of the remainder of the slab, exclusive of the drop panel, and is not less than 4 in. thick.

(b) *Column capital*—An enlargement of the end of a column designed and built to act as an integral unit with the column and flat slab. No portion of the column capital shall be considered for structural purposes which lies outside of the largest right circular cone with 90-deg vertex angle that can be included wit in the outlines of the column capital. Where no capital is used, the face of the column shall be considered as the edge of the capital.

(c) *Drop panel*—The structural portion of a flat slab which is thickened throughout an area surrounding the column, column capital, or bracket.

(d) *Panel strips*—A flat slab shall be considered as consisting of strips in each direction as follows:

A middle strip one-half panel in width, symmetrical about panel centerline.

A column strip consisting of the two adjacent quarter-panels either side of the column centerline.

1002 Design procedures

(a) *Methods of analysis*—All flat slab structures shall be designed in accordance with a recognized elastic analysis subject to the limitations of Sections 1002 and 1003, except that the empirical method of design given in Section 1004 may be used for the design of flat slabs conforming with the limitations given therein. Flat slabs within the limitations of Section 1004, when designed by elastic analysis, may have resulting analytical moments reduced in such proportion that the numerical sum of the positive and average negative bending moments used in design procedure need not exceed M_o as specified under Section 1004(f).

(b) *Critical sections*—The slab shall be proportioned for the bending moments prevailing at every section except that the slab need not be proportioned for a greater negative moment than that prevailing at a distance A from the support centerline.

(c) *Size and thickness of slabs and drop panels*

1. Subject to limitations of Section 1002(c)3, the thickness of a flat slab and the size and thickness of the drop panel, where used, shall be such that the compressive stress due to bending at any section, and the shear about the column, column capital, and drop panel shall not exceed the unit stresses allowed in concrete of the quality used. When designed under Section 1004, three-fourths of the width of the strip shall be used as the width of the section in computing compression due to bending, except that on a section through a drop panel, three-fourths of the width of the drop panel shall be used. Account shall be taken of any recesses which reduce the compressive area.

2. The shearing unit stress on vertical sections which follow a periphery, b, at distance, d, beyond the edges of the column or column capital and parallel or concentric with it, shall not exceed the following values for the concrete when computed by the formula

$$v = \frac{V}{bjd}$$

  a. $0.03f'_c$ but not more than 100 psi when at least 50 per cent of the total negative reinforcement required for bending in the column strip passes through the periphery.

  b. $0.025f'_c$ but not more than 85 psi when 25 per cent, which is the least value permitted, of the total negative reinforcement required for bending in the column strip passes through the periphery.

  c. Proportionate values of the shearing unit stress for intermediate percentages of reinforcement.

3. Where drop panels are used, the shearing unit stress on vertical sections which lie at a distance, d, beyond the edges of the drop panel, and parallel with them, shall not exceed $0.03f'_c$ nor 100 psi. At least 50 per cent of the total negative reinforcement required for bending in the column strip shall be within the width of strip directly above the drop panel.

4. Slabs with drop panels whose length is at least one-third the parallel span length and whose projection below the slab is at least one-fourth the slab thickness shall be not less than $L/40$ nor 4 in. in thickness.

Slabs without drop panels as described above shall be not less than $L/36$ nor 5 in. in thickness.

5. For determining reinforcement, the thickness of the drop panel below the slab shall not be assumed to be more than one-fourth of the distance from the edge of the drop panel to the edge of the column capital.

(d) *Arrangement of slab reinforcement*

1. The spacing of the bars at critical sections shall not exceed two times the slab thickness, except for those portions of the slab area which may be of cellular or ribbed construction. In the slab over the cellular spaces, reinforcement shall be provided as required by Section 707.

2. In exterior panels, except for bottom bars adequately anchored in the drop panel, all positive reinforcement perpendicular to the discontinuous edge shall extend to the edge of the slab and have embedment, straight or hooked, of at least 6 in. in spandrel beams, walls, or columns where provided. All negative reinforcement perpendicular to the discontinuous edge shall be bent, hooked, or otherwise anchored in spandrel beams, walls, or columns.

3. The area of reinforcement shall be determined from the bending moments at the critical sections but shall not be less than $0.0025bd$ at any section.

4. Required splices in bars may be made wherever convenient, but preferably away from points of maximum stress. The length of any such splice shall be at least 36 bar diameters.

(e) *Openings in flat slabs*—Openings of any size may be provided in flat slabs if provision is made for the total positive and negative moments and for shear without exceeding the allowable stresses except that when design is based on Section 1004, the limitations given therein shall not be exceeded.

(f) *Design of columns*

1. All columns supporting flat slabs shall be designed as provided in Chapter 11 with the additional requirements of this chapter.

1003 Design by elastic analysis (Not taken up by G. E. Large.)

* * *

1004 Design by the empirical method

(a) *General limitations*—Flat slab construction may be designed by the empirical provisions of this section when they conform to all of the limitations on continuity and dimensions given herein.

1. The construction shall consist of at least three continuous panels in each direction.

2. The ratio of length to width of panels shall not exceed 1.33.

3. The grid pattern shall consist of approximately rectangular panels. The successive span lengths in each direction shall differ by not more than 20 per cent of the longer span. Within these limitations, columns may be offset a maximum of 10 per cent of the span, in direction of the offset, from either axis between center-lines of successive columns.

4. The calculated lateral force moments from wind or earthquake may be combined with the critical moments as determined by the empirical method, and the lateral force moments shall be distributed between the column and middle strips in the same proportions as specified for the negative moments in the strips for structures not exceeding 125 ft. high with maximum story height not exceeding 12 ft. 6 in.

(b) *Columns*

1. The minimum dimension of any column shall be 10 in. For columns or other supports of a flat slab, the required minimum average moment of inertia, I_c, of the gross concrete section of the columns above and below the slab shall be determined from the following formula, and shall be not less than 1000 in.[4]

If there is no column above the slab, the I_c of the column below shall be twice that given by the formula with a minimum of 1000 in.[4]

$$I_c = \frac{t^3 H}{0.5 + \dfrac{W_D}{W_L}} \tag{7}$$

Where t need not be taken greater than t_1 or t_2 as determined in Section 1004(d), H is the average story height of the columns above and below the slab, and W_L is the greater value of any two adjacent spans under consideration.

2. Columns supporting flat slabs designed by the empirical method shall be proportioned for the bending moments developed by unequally loaded panels, or uneven spacing of columns. Such bending moment shall be the maximum value derived from

$$(WL_1 - W_D L_2)\,\frac{1}{f}$$

L_1 and L_2 being lengths of the adjacent spans ($L_2 = 0$ when considering an exterior column) and f is 30 for exterior and 40 for interior columns.

This moment shall be divided between the columns immediately above and below the floor or roof line under consideration in direct proportion to their stiffness and shall be applied without further reduction to the critical sections of the columns.

(c) Determination of "c" (effective support size)

1. Where column capitals are used, the value of c shall be taken as the diameter of the cone described in Section 1001(b) measured at the bottom of the slab or drop panel.

2. Where a column is without a concrete capital, the dimension c shall be taken as that of the column in the direction considered.

3. Brackets capable of transmitting the negative bending and the shear in the column strips to the columns without excessive unit stress may be substituted for column capitals at exterior columns. The value of c for the span where a bracket is used shall be taken as twice the distance from the center of the column to a point where the bracket is $1\frac{1}{2}$ in. thick, but not more than the thickness of the column plus twice the depth of the bracket.

4. Where a reinforced concrete beam frames into a column without capital or bracket on the same side with the beam, for computing bending for strips parallel to the beam, the value of c for the span considered may be taken as the width of the column plus twice the projection of the beam above or below the slab or drop panel.

5. The average of the values of c at the two supports at the ends of a column strip shall be used to evaluate the slab thickness t_1 or t_2 as prescribed in Section 1004(d).

(d) Slab thickness

1. The slab thickness, span L being the longest side of the panel, shall be at least:

$L/36$ for slab without drop panels conforming with Section 1004(e), or where a drop panel is omitted at any corner of the panel, but not less than 5 in. nor t_1 as given below.

$L/40$ for slabs with drop panels conforming to Section 1004(e) at all supports, but not less than 4 in. nor t_2 as given below.

2. The total thickness, t_1, in inches, of slabs without drop panels, or through the drop panel if any, shall be at least

$$t_1 = 0.028L\left(1 - \frac{2c}{3L}\right)\sqrt{\frac{w'}{f'_c/2000}} + 1\frac{1}{2}{}^* \qquad (8)$$

Table 1004(f)—Moments in Flat Slab Panels in Percentages of M_o

Strip	Column Head	Side Support Type	End Support Type	Exterior Panel			Interior Panel	
				Exterior Negative Moment	Positive Moment	Interior Negative Moment	Positive Moment	Negative Moment
Column strip	With drop		A	44				
			B	36	24	56	20	50
			C	6	36	72		
	Without drop		A	40				
			B	32	28	50	22	46
			C	6	40	66		
Middle strip	With drop		A	10				
			B	20	20	17*	15	15*
			C	6	26	22*		
	Without drop		A	10				
			B	20	20	18*	16	16*
			C	6	28	24*		
Half-column strip adjacent to marginal beam or wall	With drop	1	A	22				
			B	18	12	28	10	25
			C	3	18	36		
		2	A	17				
			B	14	9	21	8	19
			C	3	14	27		
		3	A	11				
			B	9	6	14	5	13
			C	3	9	18		
	Without drop	1	A	20				
			B	16	14	25	11	23
			C	3	20	33		
		2	A	15				
			B	12	11	19	9	18
			C	3	15	25		
		3	A	10				
			B	8	7	13	6	12
			C	3	10	17		

Percentage of panel load to be carried by marginal beam or wall in addition to loads directly superimposed thereon	Type of support listed in Table 1004(f)		
	Side support parallel to strip	Side or end edge condition of slabs of depth t	End support at right angles to strip
0	1	Columns with no beams	
20	2	Columns with beams of total depth 1¼t	A
40	3	Columns with beams of total depth 3t or more	B
		Reinforced concrete bearing walls integral with slab	
		Masonry or other walls providing negligible restraint	C

* Increase negative moments 30 per cent of tabulated values when middle strip is continuous across support of type B or C. No other values need be increased.

Note: For intermediate proportions of total beam depth to slab thickness, values for loads and moments may be obtained by interpolation. See also Fig. 1004 (f)a and b.

TABLE 1004(g)1—MINIMUM LENGTH OF NEGATIVE REINFORCEMENT

Strip	Percentage of required reinforcing steel area to be extended at least as indicated	Minimum distance beyond centerline of support to end of straight bar or to bend point of bent bar*			
		Flat slabs without drop panels		Flat slabs with drop panels	
		Straight	Bend point where bars bend down and continue as positive reinforcement	Straight	Bend point where bars bend down and continue as positive reinforcement
Column strip reinforcement	Not less than 33 percent	0.30L†		0.33L‡	
	Not less than an additional 34 percent	0.27L†		0.30L‡	
	Remainder §	0.25L or 0.20L		0.25L or	To edge of drop but at least 0.20L
Middle strip reinforcement	Not less than 50 percent	0.25L		0.25L	
	Remainder §	0.25L or 0.15L		0.25L or 0.15L	

* At exterior supports where masonry walls or other construction provide only negligible restraint to the slab, the negative reinforcement need not be carried further than 0.20L beyond the centerline of such support.

† Where no bent bars are used, the 0.27L bars may be omitted, provided the 0.30L bars are at least 50 percent of total required.

‡ Where no bent bars are used, the 0.30L bars may be omitted provided the 0.33L bars provide at least 50 percent of the total required.

§ Bars may be straight, bent, or any combination of straight and bent bars. All bars are to be considered straight bars for the end under consideration unless bent at that end and continued as positive reinforcement.

Note: See also Fig. 1004 (g).

3. The total thickness, t_2, in inches, of slabs with drop panels, at points beyond the drop panel shall be at least

$$t_2 = 0.024L \left(1 - \frac{2c}{3L} \right) \sqrt{\frac{w'}{f'_c/2000}} + 1*$$ (9)

4. Where the exterior supports provide only negligible restraint to the slab, the values of t_1 and t_2 for the exterior panel shall be increased by at least 15 per cent.

(e) *Drop panels*

1. The maximum total thickness at the drop panel used in computing the negative steel area for the column strip shall be $1.5t_2$.

2. The side or diameter of the drop panel shall be at least 0.33 times the span in the parallel direction.

3. The minimum thickness of slabs where drop panels at wall columns are omitted shall equal $(t_1 + t_2)/2$ provided the value of c used in the computations complies with Section 1004(c).

---

* In the above formulas, t_1 and t_2 are in inches and L and c are in feet.

TABLE 1004(g)2—MINIMUM LENGTH OF POSITIVE REINFORCEMENT

Strip	Percentage of required reinforcing steel area to be extended at least as indicated	Maximum distance from centerline of support to end of straight bar or bend point of bent bar			
		Flat slabs without drop panels		Flat slabs with drop panels	
		Straight	Bend point where bars bend up and continue as negative reinforcement	Straight	Bend point where bars bend up and continue as negative reinforcement
Column strip reinforcement	Not less than 33 percent	0.125L		Minimum embedment in drop panel of 16 bar diameters but at least 10 in.	
	Not less than 50 percent*	3 in. or 0.25L			
	Remainder*	0.125L or 0.25L		Minimum embedment in drop panel of 16 bar diameters but at least 10 in. or 0.25L	
Middle strip reinforcement	50 percent	0.15L		0.15L	
	50 percent*	3 in. or 0.25L		3 in. or 0.25L	

* Bars may be straight, bent, or any combination of straight and bent bars. All bars are to be considered straight bars for the end under consideration unless bent at that end and continued as negative reinforcement.

Note: See also Fig. 1004(g).

(f) Bending moment coefficients

1. The numerical sum of the positive and negative bending moments in the direction of either side of a rectangular panel shall be assumed as not less than

$$M_o = 0.09WLF\left(1 - \frac{2c}{3L}\right)^2 \tag{10}$$

in which $F = 1.15 - c/L$ but not less than 1.

2. Unless otherwise provided, the bending moments at the critical sections of the column and middle strips shall be at least those given in Table 1004(f).

3. The average of the values of c at the two supports at the ends of a column strip shall be used to evaluate M_o in determining bending in the strip. The average of the values of M_o, as determined for the two parallel half-column strips in a panel, shall be used in determining bending in the middle strip.

4. Bending in the middle strips parallel to a discontinuous edge shall be assumed the same as in an interior panel.

5. For design purposes, any of the moments determined from Table 1004(f) may be varied by not more than 10 per cent, but the numerical sum of the positive and negative moments in a panel shall be not less than the amount specified.

(g) Length of reinforcement—In addition to the requirements of Section 1002(d), reinforcement shall have the minimum lengths given in Tables 1004(g)1 and 1004(g)2.

Where adjacent spans are unequal, the extension of negative reinforcement on each side of the column centerline as prescribed in Table 1004(g)1 shall be based on the requirements of the longer span.

(h) Openings in flat slabs

1. Openings of any size may be provided in a flat slab in the area common to two intersecting middle strips provided the total positive and negative steel areas required in Section 1004(f) are maintained.

2. In the area common to two column strips, not more than one-eighth of the width of strip in any span shall be interrupted by openings. The equivalent of all bars interrupted shall be provided by extra steel on all sides of the openings. The shearing unit stresses given in Section 1002(c)2 shall not be exceeded.

3. In any area common to one column strip and one middle strip, openings may interrupt one-quarter of the bars in either strip. The equivalent of the bars so interrupted shall be provided by extra steel on all sides of the opening.

4. Any opening larger than described above shall be analyzed by accepted engineering principles and shall be completely framed as required to carry the loads to the columns.

Reinforced Concrete Columns and Walls

1100   Notation

A_c = area of core of a spirally reinforced column measured to the outside diameter of the spiral; net area of concrete section of a composite column

A_g = over-all or gross area of spirally reinforced or tied columns; the total area of the concrete encasement of combination columns

A_r = area of the steel or cast-iron core of a composite column; the area of the steel core in a combination column

A_s = effective cross-sectional area of reinforcement in compression in columns

B = trial factor [see Section 1109(c) and footnote thereto]

e = eccentricity of the resultant load on a column, measured from the gravity axis

F_a = nominal allowable axial unit stress $(0.225f'_c + f_s p_g)$ for spiral columns and 0.8 of this value for tied columns

F_b = allowable bending unit stress that would be permitted if bending stress only existed

f_a = nominal axial unit stress = axial load divided by area of member, A_g

f_b = bending unit stress (actual) = bending moment divided by section modulus of member

f_c = computed concrete fiber stress in an eccentrically loaded column where the ratio of e/t is greater than $\frac{2}{3}$

f'_c = compressive strength of concrete at age of 28 days, unless otherwise specified

f_r = allowable unit stress in the metal core of a composite column

f'_r = allowable unit stress on unencased steel columns and pipe columns

f_s = nominal allowable stress in vertical column reinforcement

f'_s = useful limit stress of spiral reinforcement

h = unsupported length of column

K_c = radius of gyration of concrete in pipe columns

K_s = radius of gyration of a metal pipe section (in pipe columns)

N = axial load applied to reinforced concrete column

p' = ratio of volume of spiral reinforcement to the volume of the concrete core (out to out of spirals) of a spirally reinforced concrete column

p_g = ratio of the effective cross-sectional area of vertical reinforcement to the gross area A_g

P = total allowable axial load on a column whose length does not exceed ten times its least cross-sectional dimension

P' = total allowable axial load on a long column

t = over-all depth of rectangular column section, or the diameter of a round column

1101 Limiting dimensions

(a) The following sections on reinforced concrete and composite columns, except Section 1107(a), apply to a short column for which the unsupported length is not greater than ten times the least dimension. When the unsupported length exceeds this value, the design shall be modified as shown in Section 1107(a). Principal columns in buildings shall have a minimum diameter of 12 in., or in the case of rectangular columns, a minimum thickness of 8 in., and a minimum gross area of 120 sq. in. Posts that are not continuous from story to story shall have a minimum diameter or thickness of 6 in.

1102 Unsupported length of columns

(a) For purposes of determining the limiting dimensions of columns, the unsupported length of reinforced concrete columns shall be taken as the clear distance between floor slabs, except that

1. In flat slab construction, it shall be the clear distance between the floor and the lower extremity of the capital, the drop panel or the slab, whichever is least.

2. In beam and slab construction, it shall be the clear distance between the floor and the under side of the deeper beam framing into the column in each direction at the next higher floor level.

3. In columns restrained laterally by struts, it shall be the clear distance between consecutive struts in each vertical plane; provided that to be an adequate support, two such struts shall meet the column at approximately the same level, and the angle between vertical planes through the struts shall not vary more than 15 degrees from a right angle. Such struts shall be of adequate dimensions and anchorage to restrain the column against lateral deflection.

4. In columns restrained laterally by struts or beams, with brackets used at the junction, it shall be the clear distance between the floor and the lower edge of the bracket, provided that the bracket width equals that of the beam or strut and is at least half that of the column.

(b) For rectangular columns, that length shall be considered which produces the greatest ratio of length to depth of section.

1103 Spirally reinforced columns

(a) *Allowable load*—The maximum allowable axial load, P, on columns with closely spaced spirals enclosing a circular concrete core reinforced with vertical bars shall be that given by formula (11).

$$P = A_g \ (0.225f'_c + f_s p_g) \tag{11}$$

Wherein f_s = nominal allowable stress in vertical column reinforcement, to be taken at 40 per cent of the minimum specification value of the yield point; *viz.*, 16,000 psi for intermediate grade steel and 20,000 psi for rail or hard grade steel.*

---

* Nominal allowable stresses for reinforcement of higher yield point may be established at 40 per cent of the yield point stress, but not more than 30,000 psi, when the properties of such reinforcing steels have been definitely specified by standards of ASTM designation. If this is done, the lengths of splice required by Section 1103(c) shall be increased accordingly.

(b) *Vertical reinforcement*—The ratio p_g shall not be less than 0.01 nor more than 0.08. The minimum number of bars shall be six, and the minimum bar size shall be #5. The center to center spacing of bars within the periphery of the column core shall not be less than $2\frac{1}{2}$ times the diameter for round bars or three times the side dimension for square bars. The clear spacing between individual bars or between pairs of bars at lapped splices shall not be less than $1\frac{1}{2}$ in. or $1\frac{1}{2}$ times the maximum size of the coarse aggregate used. These spacing rules also apply to adjacent pairs of bars at a lapped splice; each pair of lapped bars forming a splice may be in contact, but the minimum clear spacing between one splice and the adjacent splice should be that specified for adjacent single bars.

(c) *Splices in vertical reinforcement*—Where lapped splices in the column verticals are used, the minimum amount of lap shall be as follows:

    1. For deformed bars with concrete having a strength of 3000 psi or above, 20 diameters of bar of intermediate or hard grade steel. For bars of higher yield point, the amount of lap shall be increased one diameter for each 1000 psi by which the allowable stress exceeds 20,000 psi. When the concrete strengths are less than 3000 psi, the amount of lap shall be one-third greater than the values given above.

    2. For plain bars, the minimum amount of lap shall be twice that specified for deformed bars.

    3. Welded splices or other positive connections may be used instead of lapped splices. Welded splices shall preferably be used in cases where the bar size exceeds #11. An approved welded splice shall be defined as one in which the bars are butted and welded and that will develop in tension at least the yield point stress of the reinforcing steel used.

*   *   *

(d) *Spiral reinforcement*—The ratio of spiral reinforcement, p', shall not be less than the value given by formula (12).

$$p' = 0.45 \left(\frac{A_g}{A_c} - 1 \right) \frac{f'_c}{f'_s} \tag{12}$$

Wherein f'_s = useful limit stress of spiral reinforcement, to be taken as 40,000 psi for hot rolled rods of intermediate grade, 50,000 psi for rods of hard grade, and 60,000 psi for cold drawn wire.

The spiral reinforcement shall consist of evenly spaced continuous spirals held firmly in place and true to line by vertical spacers. . . The center to center spacing of the spirals shall not exceed one-sixth of the core diameter. The clear spacing between spirals shall not exceed 3 in. nor be less than $1\frac{3}{8}$ in. or $1\frac{1}{2}$ times the maximum size of coarse aggregate used. The reinforcing spiral shall extend from the floor level in any story or from the top of the footing in the basement, to the level of the lowest horizontal reinforcement in the slab, drop panel or beam above. In a column with a capital, it shall extend to a plane at which the diameter or width of the capital is twice that of the column.

(e) *Protection of reinforcement*—The column spiral reinforcement shall be protected everywhere by a covering of concrete cast monolithically with the core, for which the thickness shall not be less than $1\frac{1}{2}$ in. nor less than $1\frac{1}{2}$ times the maximum size of the coarse aggregate, nor shall it be less than required by the fire protection and weathering provisions of Section 507.

*   *   *

(g) *Limits of section of column built monolithically with wall*—For a spiral column built monolithically with a concrete wall or pier, the outer boundary of the column section shall be taken either as a circle at least $1\frac{1}{2}$ in. outside the column spiral or as a square or rectangle of which the sides are at least $1\frac{1}{2}$ in. outside the spiral or spirals.

(h) *Equivalent circular columns*—As an exception to the general procedure of utilizing the full gross area of the column section, it shall be permissible to design a circular column and to build it with a square, octagonal, or other shaped section of the same least lateral dimension. In such case, the allowable load, the gross area considered, and the required percentages of reinforcement shall be taken as those of the circular column.

1104 Tied columns

(a) *Allowable load*—The maximum allowable axial load on columns reinforced with longitudinal bars and separate lateral ties shall be 80 per cent of that given by formula (11). The ratio, p_g, to be considered in tied columns shall not be less than 0.01 nor more than 0.04. The longitudinal reinforcement shall consist of at least four bars, of minimum bar size of #5. Splices in reinforcing bars shall be made as described in Section 1103(c). The spacing requirements for vertical reinforcement in Section 1103(b) shall also apply for all tied columns.

(b) *Combined axial and bending load*—For tied columns which are designed to withstand combined axial and bending stresses, the limiting steel ratio of 0.04 may be increased to 0.08. The amount of steel spliced by lapping shall not exceed a steel ratio of 0.04 in any 3-ft. length of column. The size of the column designed under this provision shall in no case be less than that required to withstand the axial load alone with a steel ratio of 0.04.

(c) *Lateral ties*—Lateral ties shall be at least $\frac{1}{4}$ in. in diameter and shall be spaced apart not over 16 bar diameters, 48 tie diameters, or the least dimension of the column. When there are more than four vertical bars, additional ties shall be provided so that every longitudinal bar is held firmly in its designed position and has lateral support equivalent to that provided by a 90-deg. corner of a tie.

(d) *Limits of column section*—In a tied column which for architectural reasons has a larger cross section than required by considerations of loading, a reduced effective area, A_g, not less than one-half of the total area may be used in applying the provisions of Section 1104(a).

* * *

1107 Long columns

(a) The maximum allowable load, P', on axially loaded reinforced concrete or composite columns having an unsupported length, h, greater than ten times the least lateral dimension, t, shall be given by formula (17).

$$P' = P[1.3 - 0.03h/t] \tag{17}$$

where P is the allowable axial load on a short column as given by Sections 1103, 1104, and 1105.

The maximum allowable load, P', on eccentrically loaded columns in which h/t exceeds 10 shall also be given by formula (17), in which P is the allowable eccentrically applied load on a short column as determined by the provisions of Section 1109. In long columns subjected to definite bending stresses, as determined in Section 1108, the ratio h/t shall not exceed 20.

1108 Bending moments in columns

(a) The bending moments in the columns of all reinforced concrete structures shall be determined on the basis of loading conditions and restraint and shall be provided

for in the design. When the stiffness and strength of the columns are utilized to reduce moments in beams, girders, or slabs, as in the case of rigid frames, or in other
forms of continuous construction wherein column m ments are unavoidable, they
shall be provided for in the design. In building frames, particular attention shall be
given to the effect of unbalanced floor loads on both exterior and interior columns and
of eccentric loading due to other causes. In computing moments in columns, the far
ends may be considered fixed. Columns shall be designed to resist the axial forces
from loads on all floors. plus the maximum bending due to loads on a single adjacent
span of the floor under consideration.

Resistance to bending moments at any floor level shall be provided by distributing
the moment between the columns immediately above and below the given floor in
proportion to their relative stiffnesses and conditions of restraint.

1109 Columns subjected to axial load and bending

(a) Members subject to an axial load and bending in one principal plane, but with
the ratio of eccentricity to depth e/t no greater than $\tfrac{2}{3}$, shall be so proportioned that

$$\frac{f_a}{F_a} + \frac{f_b}{F_b} \text{ does not exceed unity} \tag{18}$$

(b) When bending exists on both of the principal axes, formula (18) becomes

$$\frac{f_a}{F_a} + \frac{f_{bx}}{F_b} + \frac{f_{by}}{F_b} \text{ does not exceed unity} \tag{19}$$

where f_{bx} and f_{by} are the bending moment components about the x and y principal
axes divided by the section modulus of the transformed section relative to the respective axes, provided that the ratio e/t is no greater than $\tfrac{2}{3}$ in either direction.

(c) In designing a column subject to both axial load and bending, the preliminary
selection of the column may be made by use of an equivalent axial load given by
formula (20).

$$P = N\left(1 + \frac{Be}{t}\right)^* \tag{20}$$

When bending exists on both of the principal axes, the quantity Be/t is the numerical
sum of the Be/t quantities in the two directions.

(d) For columns in which the load, N, has an eccentricity, e, greater than $\tfrac{2}{3}$ the
column depth, t, the determination of the fiber stress f_c shall be made by use of recognized theory for cracked sections, based on the assumption that the concrete does not
resist tension. In such cases the modular ratio for the compressive reinforcement
shall be assumed as double the value given in Section 601; but the stress in the compressive reinforcement when calculated on this basis shall not be greater than the
allowable stress in tension. The maximum combined compressive stress in the concrete shall not exceed $0.45f'_c$. For such cases the tensile steel stress shall also be
investigated.

1110 Wind and earthquake stresses

(a) When the allowable stress in columns is modified to provide for combined
axial load and bending, and the stress due to wind or earthquake loads is also added,
the total shall still come within the allowable values specified for wind or earthquake
loads in Section 603(c).

---

*For trial computations B may be taken from 3 to $3\tfrac{1}{2}$ for rectangular tied columns, the lower value
being used for columns with the minimum amount of reinforcement. Similarly for circular spiral
columns, the value of B from 5 to 6 may be used.

1111   Reinforced concrete walls

(a) The allowable stresses in reinforced concrete bearing walls with minimum reinforcement as required by Section 1111(h), shall be $0.25f'_c$ for walls having a ratio of height to thickness of ten or less, and shall be reduced proportionally to $0.15f'_c$ for walls having a ratio of height to thickness of 25.   When the reinforcement in bearing walls is designed, placed, and anchored in position as for tied columns, the allowable stresses shall be on the basis of Section 1104, as for columns.   In the case of concentrated loads, the length of the wall to be considered as effective for each shall not exceed the center to center distance between loads, nor shall it exceed the width of the bearing plus four times the wall thickness.   The ratio p_g shall not exceed 0.04.

(b) Walls shall be designed for any lateral or other pressure to which they are subjected.   Proper provision shall be made for eccentric loads and wind stresses.   In such designs the allowable stresses shall be as given in Section 305(a) and 603(c).

*   *   *

(h) The area of the horizontal reinforcement of reinforced concrete walls shall be not less than 0.0025 and that of the vertical reinforcement not less than 0.0015 times the area of the reinforced section of the wall if of bars, and not less than three-fourths as much if of welded wire fabric.   The wire of the welded fabric shall be of not less than No. 10 AS&W gage.   Walls more than 10 in. thick, except for basement walls, shall have the reinforcement for each direction placed in two layers parallel with the faces of the wall.   One layer consisting of not less than one-half and not more than two-thirds the total required shall be placed not less than 2 in. nor more than one-third the thickness of the wall from the exterior surface.   The other layer, comprising the balance of the required reinforcement, shall be placed not less than ¾ in. and not more than one-third the thickness of the wall from the interior surface.   Bars, if used, shall not be less than #3 bars, nor shall they be spaced more than 18 in. on centers.   Welded wire reinforcement for walls shall be in flat sheet form.

*   *   *

Footings

1201   Scope

(a) The requirements prescribed in Sections 1202 to 1209 apply only to isolated footings.*

1202   Loads and reactions

(a) Footings shall be proportioned to sustain the applied loads and induced reactions without exceeding the allowable stresses as prescribed in Sections 305 and 306, and as further provided in Sections 1205, 1206, and 1207.

(b) In cases where the footing is concentrically loaded and the member being supported does not transmit any moment to the footing, computations for moments and shears shall be based on an upward reaction assumed to be uniformly distributed per unit area or per pile and a downward applied load assumed to be uniformly distributed over the area of the footing covered by the column, pedestal, wall, or metallic column base.

(c) In cases where the footing is eccentrically loaded and/or the member being supported transmits a moment to the footing, proper allowance shall be made for

---

* The committee is not prepared at this time to make recommendations for combined footings—those supporting more than one column or wall.

any variation that may exist in the intensities of reaction and applied load consistent with the magnitude of the applied load and the amount of its actual or virtual eccentricity.

(*d*) In the case of footings on piles, computations for moments and shears may be based on the assumption that the reaction from any pile is concentrated at the center of the pile.

1203   Sloped or stepped footings

(*a*) In sloped or stepped footings, the angle of slope or depth and location of steps shall be such that the allowable stresses are not exceeded at any section.

(*b*) In sloped or stepped footings, the effective cross section in compression shall be limited by the area above the neutral plane.

(*c*) Sloped or stepped footings shall be cast as a unit.

1204   Bending moment

(*a*) The external moment on any section shall be determined by passing through the section a vertical plane which extends completely across the footing, and computing the moment of the forces acting over the entire area of the footing on one side of said plane.

(*b*) The greatest bending moment to be used in the design of an isolated footing shall be the moment computed in the manner prescribed in Section 1204(a) at sections located as follows:

1. At the face of the column, pedestal or wall, for footings supporting a concrete column, pedestal or wall.

2. Halfway between the middle and the edge of the wall, for footings under masonry walls.

3. Halfway between the face of the column or pedestal and the edge of the metallic base, for footings under metallic bases.

(*c*) The width resisting compression at any section shall be assumed as the entire width of the top of the footing at the section under consideration.

(*d*) In one-way reinforced footings, the total tensile reinforcement at any section shall provide a moment of resistance at least equal to the moment computed in the manner prescribed in Section 1204(a); and the reinforcement thus determined shall be distributed uniformly across the full width of the section.

(*e*) In two-way reinforced footings, the total tensile reinforcement at any section shall provide a moment of resistance at least equal to 85 per cent of the moment computed in the manner prescribed in Section 1204(a); and the total reinforcement thus determined shall be distributed across the corresponding resisting section in the manner prescribed for the square footings in Section 1204(f), and for rectangular footings in Section 1204(g).

(*f*) In two-way square footings, the reinforcement extending in each direction shall be distributed uniformly across the full width of the footing.

(*g*) In two-way rectangular footings, the reinforcement in the long direction shall be distributed uniformly across the full width of the footing. In the case of the reinforcement in the short direction, that portion determined by formula (21) shall be uniformly distributed across a band-width (*B*) centered with respect to the centerline of the column or pedestal and having a width equal to the length of the short side of the footing. The remainder of the reinforcement shall be uniformly distributed in the outer portions of the footing.

$$\frac{\text{Reinforcement in band-width } (B)}{\text{Total reinforcement in short direction}} = \frac{2}{(S+1)} \tag{21}$$

In formula (21), S is the ratio of the long side to the short side of the footing.

1205   Shear and bond

(a) The critical section for shear to be used as a measure of diagonal tension shall be assumed as a vertical section obtained by passing a series of vertical planes through the footing, each of which is parallel to a corresponding face of the column, pedestal, or wall and located a distance therefrom equal to the depth d for footings on soil, and one-half the depth d for footings on piles.

(b) Each face of the critical section as defined in Section 1205(a) shall be considered as resisting an external shear equal to the load on an area bounded by said face of the critical section for shear, two diagonal lines drawn from the column or pedestal corners and making 45-deg angles with the principal axes of the footing, and that portion of the corresponding edge or edges of the footing intercepted between the two diagonals.

(c) Critical sections for bond shall be assumed at the same planes as those prescribed for bending moment in Section 1204(b); also at all other vertical planes where changes of section or of reinforcement occur.

(d) Computation for shear to be used as a measure of bond shall be based on the same section and loading as prescribed for bending moment in Section 1204(a).

(e) The total tensile reinforcement at any section shall provide a bond resistance at least equal to the bond requirement as computed from the following percentages of the external share at the section:

    1. In one-way reinforced footings, 100 per cent.

    2. In two-way reinforced footings, 85 per cent.

(f) In computing the external shear on any section through a footing supported on piles, the entire reaction from any pile whose center is located 6 in. or more outside the section shall be assumed as producing shear on the section; the reaction from any pile whose center is located 6 in. or more inside the section shall be assumed as producing no shear on the section.   For intermediate positions of the pile center, the portion of the pile reaction to be assumed as producing shear on the section shall be based on straight-line interpolation between full value at 6 in. outside the section and zero value at 6 in. inside the section.

(g) For allowable shearing stresses, see Sections 305 and 809.

(h) For allowable bond stresses, see Sections 305 and 901 to 905.

1206   Transfer of stress at base of column

(a) The stress in the longitudinal reinforcement of a column or pedestal shall be transferred to its supporting pedestal or footing either by extending the longitudinal bars into the supporting member, or by dowels.

(b) In case the transfer of stress in the reinforcement is accomplished by extension of the longitudinal bars, they shall extend into the supporting member the distance required to transfer to the concrete, by allowable bond stress, their full working value.

(c) In cases where dowels are used, their total sectional area shall be not less than the sectional area of the longitudinal reinforcement in the member from which the stress is being transferred.   In no case shall the number of dowels per member be less than four and the diameter of the dowels shall not exceed the diameter of the column bars by more than $\frac{1}{8}$ in.

(d) Dowels shall extend up into the column or pedestal a distance at least equal to that required for lap of longitudinal column bars (see Section 1103) and down into the supporting pedestal or footing the distance required to transfer to the concrete, by allowable bond stress, the full working value of the dowel [see Section 906(c)].

(e) The compressive stress in the concrete at the base of a column or pedestal shall be considered as being transferred by bearing to the top of the supporting pedestal or footing. The unit compressive stress on the loaded area shall not exceed the bearing stress allowable for the quality of concrete in the supporting member as limited by the ratio of the loaded area to the supporting area.

(*f*) For allowable bearing stresses see Table 305(a), Section 305.

(*g*) In sloped or stepped footings, the supporting area for bearing may be taken as the top horizontal surface of the footing, or assumed as the area of the lower base of the largest frustum of a pyramid or cone contained wholly within the footing and having for its upper base the area actually loaded, and having side slopes of one vertical to two horizontal.

1207   Pedestals and footings (plain concrete)

(*a*) The allowable compressive unit stress on the gross area of a concentrically loaded pedestal shall not exceed $0.25f'_c$. Where this stress is exceeded, reinforcement shall be provided and the member designed as a reinforced concrete column.

(*b*) The depth and width of a pedestal or footing of plain concrete shall be such that the tension in the concrete shall not exceed $0.03f'_c$, and the average shearing stress shall not exceed $0.02f'_c$ taken on sections as prescribed in Section 1204 and 1205 for reinforced concrete footings.

1208   Footings supporting round columns

(*a*) In computing the stresses in footings which support a round or octagonal concrete column or pedestal, the "face" of the column or pedestal shall be taken as the side of a square having an area equal to the area enclosed within the perimeter of the column or pedestal.

1209   Minimum edge-thickness

(*a*) In reinforced concrete footings, the thickness above the reinforcement at the edge shall be not less than 6 in. for footings on soil, nor less than 12 in. for footings on piles.

(*b*) In plain concrete footings, the thickness at the edge shall be not less than 8 in. for footings on soil, nor less than 14 in. above the tops of the piles for footings on piles.

* * *

Appendix of the ACI Code

ABSTRACT OF REPORT OF ACI–ASCE JOINT COMMITTEE ON ULTIMATE STRENGTH DESIGN*

A600   Notation

(*a*) *Loads and load factors*

U = ultimate strength capacity of section

B = effect of basic load consisting of dead load plus volume change due to creep, elastic action, shrinkage, and temperature

L = effect of live load plus impact

W = effect of wind load

E = effect of earthquake forces

K = load factor

M_u = ultimate resisting moment

P_b = load defined by Eq. (A8)

P_o = ultimate strength of concentrically loaded member given by Eq. (A6)

P_u = ultimate strength of eccentrically loaded member

P'_u = maximum axial load on long member given by Eq. (A14)

(b) *Cross-sectional constants*

A_g = gross area of section

A_s = area of tensile reinforcement

A'_s = area of compressive reinforcement

A_{sf} = steel area to develop compressive strength of overhanging flange in T-sections, defined by Eq. (A5)

A_{st} = total area of longitudinal reinforcement

b = width of a rectangular section or over-all width of flange in T-sections

b' = width of web in T-sections

D = total diameter of circular section

D_s = diameter of circle circumscribing the longitudinal reinforcement in circular section

d = distance from extreme compressive fiber to centroid of tensile reinforcement

d' = distance from extreme compressive fiber to centroid of compressive reinforcement

e = eccentricity of axial load measured from the centroid of tensile reinforcement

e' = eccentricity of axial load measured from plastic centroid of section

e'_b = eccentricity of load P_b measured from plastic centroid of section

f'_c = 28-day cylinder strength

f_s = stress in tensile reinforcement at ultimate strength

f_y = yield point of reinforcement, not to be taken greater than 60,000 psi

k_u = defined by $k_u d$ = distance from extreme compressive fiber to neutral axis at ultimate strength

k_1 = ratio of average compressive stress to $0.85f'_c$

k_2 = ratio of distance between extreme compressive fiber and resultant of compressive stresses to distance between extreme fiber and neutral axis

$m = f_y/0.85f'_c$

$m' = m - 1$

$p = A_s/bd$

$p' = A'_s/bd$

$p_f = A_{sf}/b'd$

$p_t = A_{st}/A_g$

$p_w = A_s/b'd$

$q = pf_y/f'_c$

t = flange thickness in T-sections, also total depth of rectangular section

* For full report see *Proceedings*, ASCE, V. 81, Paper No. 809, Oct., 1955. Also see ACI *Journal*, Jan., 1956; *Proc.* V, 52, pp. 505–524.

A601 Definitions and scope

(a) This appendix presents recommendations for design of reinforced concrete structures by ultimate strength theories. The term "ultimate strength design" indicates a method of design based on the ultimate strength of a reinforced concrete cross section in simple bending, combined bending and axial load on the basis of inelastic action.

(b) These recommendations are confined to design of sections. It is assumed that external moments and forces acting in a structure will be determined by the theory of elastic frames. With the specified load factors, stresses under service loads will remain within safe limits.

A602 General requirements

(a) The American Concrete Institute "Building Code Requirements for Reinforced Concrete" shall apply to the design of members by ultimate strength theory except where otherwise provided in this appendix.

(b) Analysis of indeterminate structures, such as continuous girders and arches, shall be based on the theory of elastic frames. For buildings of usual types of construction, spans, and story heights, approximate methods such as the use of coefficients recommended in the ACI Building Code are acceptable for determination of moments and shears.

(c) Bending moments in compression members shall be taken into account in the calculation of their required strength.

(d) In arches the effect of shortening of the arch axis, temperature, shrinkage, and secondary moments due to deflection shall be considered.

(e) Attention shall be given to the deflection of members, including the effect of creep, especially whenever the net ratio of reinforcement, which is defined as $(p - p')$ or $(p_w - p_f)$, in any section of a flexural member exceeds $0.18 f'_c / f_y$.

(f) Controlled concrete should be used and shall meet the following requirements. The quality of concrete shall be such that not more than one test in ten shall have an average strength less than the strength assumed in the design, and the average of any three consecutive tests shall not be less than the assumed design strength. Each test shall consist of not less than three standard cylinders.

A603   Assumptions

Ultimate strength design of reinforced concrete members shall be based on the following assumptions:

(a) Plane sections normal to the axis remain plane after bending.

(b) Tensile strength in concrete is neglected in sections subject to bending.

(c) At ultimate strength, stresses and strains are not proportional. The diagram of compressive concrete stress distribution may be assumed a rectangle, trapezoid, parabola, or any other shape which results in ultimate strength in reasonable agreement with comprehensive tests.

(d) Maximum fiber stress in concrete does not exceed $0.85 f'_c$.

(e) Stress in tensile and compressive reinforcement at ultimate load shall not be assumed greater than the yield point or 60,000 psi, whichever is smaller.

A604   Load factors

(a) Members shall be so proportioned that an ample factor of safety is provided against an increase in live load beyond that assumed in design; and strains under service loads should not be so large as to cause excessive cracking. These criteria are satisfied by the following formulas:

1. For structures in which, due to location or proportions, the effects of wind and earthquake loading can be properly neglected:

$$U = 1.2B + 2.4L \tag{I}$$

$$U = K(B + L) \tag{II}$$

2. For structures in which wind loading must be considered:

$$U = 1.2B + 2.4L + 0.6W \tag{Ia}$$

$$U = 1.2B + 0.6L + 2.4W \tag{Ib}$$

$$U = K(B + L + \tfrac{1}{2}W) \tag{IIa}$$

$$U = K(B + \tfrac{1}{2}L + W) \tag{IIb}$$

3. For those structures in which earthquake loading must be considered, substitute E for W in the preceding equations.

(b) The load factor, K, shall be taken equal to 2 for columns and members subjected to combined bending and axial load, and equal to 1.8 for beams and girders subject to bending only.

A605   Rectangular beams with tensile reinforcement only

(a) The ultimate capacity of an under-reinforced section is approached when the tensile steel begins to yield. The steel shall then be assumed to elongate plastically at its yield point stress, thereby reducing the concrete area in compression until crushing takes place. The ultimate strength so obtained is controlled by tension.

(b) The computed ultimate moment shall not exceed that given by:

$$M_u = bd^2 f'_c q(1 - 0.59q) \tag{A1}$$

in which $q = pf_y/f'_c$.

(c) In Eq. (A1), the maximum ratio of reinforcement shall be so limited that p does not exceed:

$$p = 0.40 f'_c / f_y \tag{A2}$$

The coefficient 0.40 is to be reduced at the rate of 0.025 per 1000 psi concrete strength in excess of 5000 psi.

A606   Rectangular beams with compressive reinforcement

(a) The ultimate moment shall not exceed that computed by:

$$M_u = (A_s - A'_s)f_y d[1 - 0.59(p - p')f_y/f'_c] + A'_s f_y *(d - d') \tag{A3}$$

(b) In Eq. (A3), the maximum ratio of reinforcement shall be so limited that $(p - p')$ does not exceed the values given by Eq. (A2).

A607   T-sections

(a) When the flange thickness equals or exceeds the depth to the neutral axis given by $k_u d = 1.30 q d$ or the depth of the equivalent stress block ($1.18\ qd$), the section may be designed by Eq. (A1), with q computed as for a rectangular beam with a width equal to the over-all flange width.

(b) When the flange thickness is less than $k_u d$ or less than the depth of the equivalent stress block, the ultimate moment shall not exceed that computed by:

$$M_u = (A_s - A_{sf})f_y d[1 - 0.59(p_w - p_f)f_y/f'_c] + A_{sf}f_y(d - 0.5t) \tag{A4}$$

in which A_{sf}, the steel area necessary to develop the compressive strength of the overhanging portions of the flange, is:

$$A_{sf} = 0.85(b - b')tf'_c/f_y \tag{A5}$$

(c) In Eq. (A4), the maximum ratio of reinforcement shall be so limited that $(p_u - p_f)$ does not exceed the values given by Eq. (A2).

A608   Concentrically loaded short columns

(a) All members subject to axial loads shall be designed for at least a minimum eccentricity:

For spirally reinforced columns, the minimum eccentricity measured from the centroidal axis of column shall be 0.05 times the depth of the column section,

For tied columns, the minimum eccentricity shall be 0.10 times the depth.

(b) The maximum load capacity for concentric loads for use in Eq. (A10) is given by the formula:

$$P_o = 0.85 f'_c(A_g - A_{st}) + A_{st} f_y \tag{A6}$$

---

* Correction for concrete area displaced by compressive reinforcement may be made by subtracting 0.85 f'_c from f_y in this term only.

A609   Bending and axial load : Rectangular section

(a) The ultimate strength of members subject to combined bending and axial load shall be computed from the equations of equilibrium, which when k_u is less than unity may be expressed as follows:

$$P_u = 0.85f'_c bd k_u k_1 + A'_s f_y{}^* - A_s f_s \tag{A7a}$$

$$P_u e = 0.85f'_c bd^2 k_u k_1 (1 - k_2 k_u) + A'_s f_y{}^*(d - d') \tag{A7b}$$

In Eqs. (A7a) and (A7b), k_2/k_1 shall not be taken as less than 0.5, and k_1 shall not be taken greater than 0.85 for $f'_c \leqq 5000$ psi. The coefficient 0.85 is to be reduced at the rate of 0.05 per 1000 psi concrete strength in excess of 5000 psi.

(b) It shall be assumed that the maximum concrete strain is limited to 0.003 so that the section is controlled by tension when:

$$P_u \leqq P_b = 0.85k_1 \left(\frac{90,000}{90,000 + f_y} \right) f'_c bd + A'_s f_y\dagger - A_s f_y \tag{A8}$$

k_1 being limited as for Eqs. (A7a) and (A7b). The section is controlled by compression when P_u exceeds P_b.

(c) When the section is controlled by tension, the ultimate strength shall not exceed that computed by:

$$P_u = 0.85f'_c bd \Big\{ p'm' - pm + (1 - e/d)$$
$$+ \sqrt{(1 - e/d)^2 + 2[(e/d)(pm - p'm') + p'm'(1 - d'/d)]} \Big\} \tag{A9}$$

(d) When the section is controlled by compression, a linear relationship between axial load and moment may be assumed for values of P_u between that given as P_b by Eq. (A8) and the concentric ultimate strength P_o given by Eq. (A6). For this range the ultimate strength may be computed by either Eq. (A10) or (A11):

$$P_u = \frac{P_o}{1 + [(P_o/P_b) - 1]e'/e'_b} \tag{A10}$$

$$P_u = \frac{A'_s f_y}{e'/(d - d') + \frac{1}{2}} + \frac{btf'_c}{(3te'/d^2) + 1.18} \tag{A11}$$

A610   Bending and axial load : Circular sections

(a) The ultimate strength of circular sections subject to combined bending and axial load may be computed on the basis of the equations of equilibrium taking into account inelastic deformations, or by the empirical formulas Eqs. (A12) and (A13):

When tension controls:

$$P_u = 0.85f'_c D^2 \left[\sqrt{\left(\frac{0.85e'}{D} - 0.38 \right)^2 + \frac{p_t m D_s}{2.5D}} - \left(\frac{0.85e'}{D} - 0.38 \right) \right] \tag{A12}$$

When compression controls:

$$P_u = \frac{A_{st} f_y}{\frac{3e'}{D_s} + 1} + \frac{A_g f'_c}{\frac{9.6De'}{(0.8D + 0.67D_s)^2} + 1.18} \tag{A13}$$

---

* Correction for concrete area displaced by compressive reinforcement may be made by subtracting $0.85f'_c$ from f_y in this term only.

† Correction for concrete area displaced by compressive reinforcement may be made by subtracting $0.85f'_c$ from f_y in this term only.

A611 Long members

(a) When the unsupported length, L, of an axially loaded member is greater than 15 times its least lateral dimension, the maximum axial load, P'_u, shall be determined by one of the following methods:

$$1. \qquad\qquad P'_u = P_o(1.6 - 0.04L/t_u) \qquad\qquad (A14)$$

2. A stability determination for P'_u may be made with an apparent reduced modulus of elasticity used for sustained loads, such as the method recommended in the report of ACI Committee 312, "Plain and Reinforced Concrete Arches" (*ACI Journal*, May 1951, *Proc.* V. 47, p. 681).

APPENDIX K

MINIMUM DESIGN LIVE LOADS
FOR BUILDINGS AND OTHER STRUCTURES

Principally from American Standard Building Code Requirements A 58 1–1945
National Bureau of Standards, Sponsor
United States Department of Commerce

UNIFORMLY DISTRIBUTED FLOOR LOADS†

Occupancy or Use	Pounds per Sq. Ft.	Occupancy or Use	Pounds per Sq. Ft.
Apartment houses:		Hotels.	
Private apartments	40	Guest rooms	40
Public stairways	100	Corridors serving public	
*Armories	150	rooms	100
Assembly halls·		Public rooms	100
Fixed seats	60	Loft buildings	125
Movable seats	100	Manufacturing, light	125
Corridors, upper floors	100	Office buildings:	
Corridors:		Offices	80
First floor	100	Lobbies	100
Other floors, same as oc-		*Public rooms	100
cupancy served except		Schools:	
as indicated		Classrooms	40
Courtrooms	80	Corridors	100
Dance halls	100	Stores	
Dining rooms, public	100	Light merchandise	125
Dwellings	40	Heavy merchandise	*250
*Garages	100	*Storage	
*Grandstands	100	Light	125
Hospitals and asylums:		Heavy	250 min.
Operating rooms	60	Theatres:	
Private rooms	40	Aisles, corridors, and	
Wards	40	lobbies	100
Public space	80	Orchestra floor	60
		Balconies	60
		Stage floor	150

* From other sources.

† For loading specifications and additional information see the 1947 American Institute of Steel Construction manual, *Steel Construction*, p. 343 *et seq.*

WEIGHTS OF BUILDING MATERIALS†
AND STRUCTURAL ELEMENTS
(Dead Load)

Item	Pounds per Cubic Foot	Pounds per Sq. Ft. of Surface
ALUMINUM		
Structural	165	
BRICK MASONRY		
Common brick	120	
Pressed brick	140	
CEILINGS		
Plaster, on tile or concrete		5
Lath and plaster, ¾ in.		8
Suspended, plaster and metal lath		10
CONCRETE		
Reinforced, stone aggregate	150	
Unreinforced, stone aggregate	145	
slag "	130–140	
Haydite "	95–100	
cinder "	85–90	
CONCRETE BLOCK, 8 by 16 in. including mortar		
All per square foot of wall		
Stone aggregate		
12 in. wall		78
8 in. wall		54
Haydite aggregate		
8 in. partition or wall		35
4 in. " "		24
Cinder aggregate		
- 8 in. partition		32
4 in. "		20
EARTH		
Clay, damp and plastic	110	
Sand and/or gravel, dry and packed	100–120	
FLOORS		
Hardwood, ⅞ in.		4
Sheathing, 1-in. yellow pine		4
Terrazzo, tile, or mastic, per inch of thickness		12
Wood block, 3-in., creosoted		15
PARTITIONS, nonload-bearing		
Clay tile, hollow, 4 in.		18
6 in.		25
8 in.		31
Gypsum block, hollow, 3 in.		10
4 in.		13
6 in.		17

WEIGHTS OF BUILDING MATERIALS AND
STRUCTURAL ELEMENTS—*Continued*

Item	Pounds per Cubic Foot	Pounds per Sq. Ft. of Surface
PARTITIONS, nonload-bearing		
Glass block masonry, 4-in.		18
Plaster surface only, ½ in. on block or tile (one side only)		4
Steel, removable		4
Studs, 2 by 4 in., lath, ¾ in. plaster, both sides		18
ROOFING		
All per square foot of roof surface		
Asbestos shingles		4
Copper		1
Corrugated iron, 20 gage		2
Roll roofing, per ply		1
Slate, ¼ in.		10
Tar and gravel, 5-ply		6
STEEL	490	
STONE MASONRY		
Granite	165	
Limestone or marble	160	
Sandstone	140	
TIMBER, seasoned		
Cedar	22	
Cypress	30	
Fir, Douglas	32	
Maple, hard	43	
Oak, white	46	
Pine, yellow, long leaf	44	
Redwood	26	
WALLS, load bearing		
Brick, per inch of thickness		9½
Brick, 4 in., tile backup 4 in.		60
4 in., tile backup 8 in.		75
9 in., tile backup 4 in.		100
Limestone, 4 in., brick 9 in.		140
4 in., tile 8 in.		90

INDEX